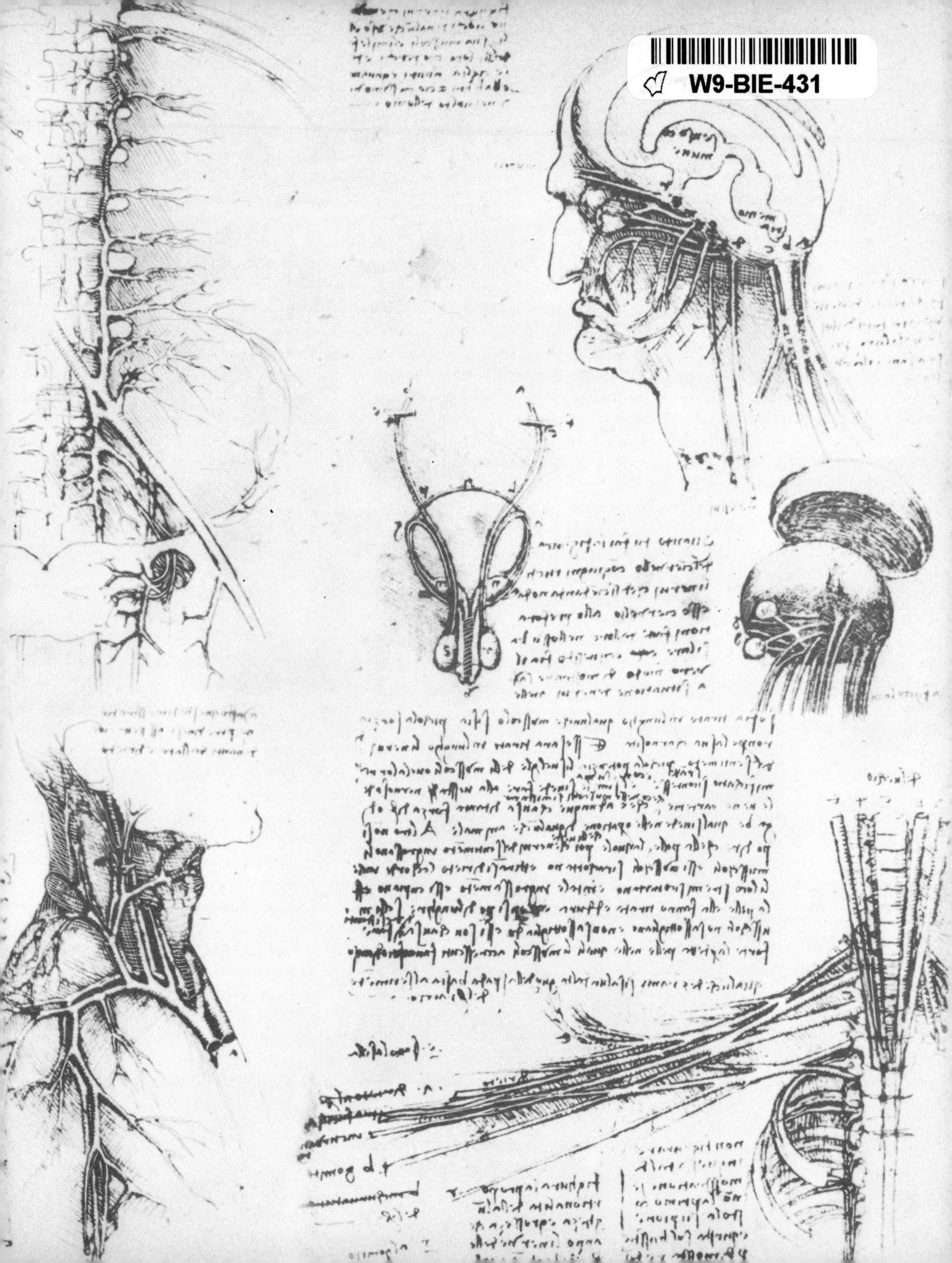

SOBOTTA-FIGGE

# ATLAS OF HUMAN ANATOMY

VOL. III

PART II

# ATLAS OF HUMAN ANATOMY

BY

DR. MED. JOHANNES SOBOTTA †

LATE PROFESSOR OF ANATOMY AND DIRECTOR OF THE ANATOMICAL INSTITUTE
UNIVERSITY OF BONN, GERMANY

8TH ENGLISH EDITION

BY

FRANK H. J. FIGGE, PH.D.

PROFESSOR OF ANATOMY
CHAIRMAN OF THE DEPARTMENT OF ANATOMY
SCHOOL OF MEDICINE, UNIVERSITY OF MARYLAND

BASED UPON THE 16TH GERMAN EDITION
EDITED BY PROF. DR. MED. ET PHIL. H. BECHER

VOL. I

ATLAS OF BONES, JOINTS AND MUSCLES

(OSTEOLOGY, SYNDESMOLOGY AND MYOLOGY)

VOL. II

ATLAS OF VISCERAL ANATOMY

DIGESTIVE, RESPIRATORY, AND UROGENITAL SYSTEMS

VOL. III

PART I. ATLAS FOR DISSECTION

HEART, BLOOD VESSELS, NERVES, AND LYMPHATICS

PART II. ATLAS OF NEUROANATOMY

CENTRAL NERVOUS SYSTEM, AUTONOMIC NERVOUS SYSTEM
EYE, EAR, AND SKIN

1963

---

HAFNER PUBLISHING COMPANY, INC., NEW YORK

# ATLAS OF HUMAN ANATOMY

BY

DR. MED. JOHANNES SOBOTTA †

LATE PROFESSOR OF ANATOMY AND DIRECTOR OF THE ANATOMICAL INSTITUTE
UNIVERSITY OF BONN, GERMANY

8TH ENGLISH EDITION

BY

FRANK H. J. FIGGE, PH.D.

PROFESSOR OF ANATOMY
CHAIRMAN OF THE DEPARTMENT OF ANATOMY
SCHOOL OF MEDICINE, UNIVERSITY OF MARYLAND

BASED UPON THE 16TH GERMAN EDITION
EDITED BY PROF. DR. MED. ET PHIL. H. BECHER

VOL. III

PART II: ATLAS OF NEUROANATOMY

CENTRAL NERVOUS SYSTEM, AUTONOMIC NERVOUS SYSTEM

EYE, EAR, AND SKIN

With 75 Colored and 146 Black and White Illustrations on Full-Page Plates
and, in addition, 33 Colored and 53 Black and White Figures in the Text.

1963

---

HAFNER PUBLISHING COMPANY, INC., NEW YORK

The pictures on the inside covers are reprints of some of the anatomical illustrations of Leonardo da Vinci (1452–1519). They present some of the anatomical subject matter depicted in this volume and illustrate how far the great artist and scholar of the Renaissance Period had progressed as a result of his own first hand investigations of the anatomy of the human body.

Printed and Published by
Hafner Publishing Company, Inc.
31 East 10th Street
New York 3, N. Y.

Library of Congress Catalogue Card Number 63–21261

Based upon the 16th German Edition
Published by Urban & Schwarzenberg, Munich 1962

Printed in Germany

# American Editor's Preface to the 8th Edition in English

The primary goal of this revision was to introduce material to enhance the value of the illustrations which are the heart and soul of the work. On the page opposite or with the illustrations, brief notes call the student's attention to important structures or relationships. These notes are not intended to be a substitute for a textbook of descriptive anatomy. There are excellent anatomical texts which the student should use in conjunction with this ATLAS.

Since many of the illustrations in the Sobotta ATLAS are more completely labeled than those in other atlases, a label-finding key based on clock number positions, was devised. It was felt that this would be of service, especially to beginning students, to enable them to find the labels more quickly and thus save untold hours which they would otherwise spend searching for labels. The clock key numbers were also incorporated in the index. Opposite the figures, the Latin terms were arranged in the same order as on the illustration, beginning with clock position "1". The term, commonly used in this and other English-speaking countries, appears in heavy type above each italicized Latin term. The student, thus exposed to both English and Latin equivalents, will automatically develop the ability to easily transpose Latin to English terms. The value of retaining the bilingual approach is self-evident. In this shrinking world, it is becoming more necessary for students of medicine and students of anatomy in every country to know the International or Latin terminology, as well as the translation into their own language. The English-Latin sets of corresponding terms will also make the ATLAS useful to foreign students who want to become acquainted with the English terms. Those who read or write medical or anatomical papers, that involve international circulation, will also find it useful.

At the bottom of some of the pages, appropriate etymology has been added to give meaning to some of the anatomical terms and to foster an appreciation of the significance of anatomical terminology. A more complete etymology will be found in alphabetical order in the first part of the book.

In the past, Volume III was found to be the most useful in the dissecting room. In this new edition, the part of Volume III dealing with the nervous system and sense organs has been bound separately. Some of the illustrations in Sobotta's ATLAS have been used for many years in reduced size in the popular textbooks of neuroanatomy. It was felt that this division would not only make available the excellent and complete set of illustrations in Part II of Volume III as an **Atlas of Neuroanatomy,** but would also lighten the load of books that need to be carried by the student to the dissecting room.

The Anatomical Nomenclature (Nomina Anatomica, Paris, 1955) was the revision of the Basle Nomina Anatomica (B.N.A., Basle, 1895). This N.A. revision was used in this and the last edition of the ATLAS. The recent minor revision of this, which was adopted in 1960 at the meeting in New York, has also been included in this (the 8th) edition in brackets [ ]. It appeared desirable to occasionally include some of the older B.N.A. terms in parentheses, especially the ones which are radically different from those in the N.A. This was done because there are many older physicians who learned the B.N.A. terminology. In order to pass examinations given by some of these older physicians, and even some of the older anatomists, it will be necessary for the younger students to learn both the N.A. and the few equivalent B.N.A. terms that were dropped in recent revisions.

I am indebted to many people who have been involved in this revision: To Mr. Robert E. Krieger of the Hafner Publishing Company, for his cooperation and effort to make this type of revision feasible. To the staff of the Anatomy Department; to all the students in Anatomy in the Class of 1964 at the University of Maryland for their participation in this effort. To the technical staff and secretaries, especially Mrs. Eleanore Derbil, who have given valuable assistance and deserve commendation for their willing and painstaking efforts. To my daughters, Rosalie Ann Figge Beasley and Barbara Figge Fox, who have assisted in the preparation of the clock label-finding key, proofreading, and compiling the index. For all of this, I express my gratitude and deep appreciation. It is impossible to adequately express the special indebtedness to my wife, Rosalie Yerkes Figge, who was responsible for the major share of all phases of the revision, particularly the tedious and technical problems in connection with the preparation of the manuscript and index. The revision could not have been completed without this loyal and conscientious effort.

It is my hope and expectation that all this concerted and time-consuming work will make Sobotta's unsurpassed illustrations even more useful to future students of anatomy.

Frank H. J. Figge

Department of Anatomy
University of Maryland School of Medicine
Baltimore, Maryland
1962

# Abstract of Preface to the 16th German Edition of Volume III

Since the 13th edition (1956), at which time I undertook the continuation of this work, many changes and additions have been made in the book..... In this new edition, 43 illustrations of the earlier edition were eliminated, 10 figures were transferred from Volume II and 140 new illustrations were introduced..... Through the transfer of the material on the Heart from Volume II to Volume III, the unity of the circulatory system was achieved. The addition of the lymphatic system to this part brings together the entire vascular system. In recognition of the usefulness of the ATLAS in the dissecting room, the plan to illustrate nerves, arteries, and veins on the same plate was retained.....

The new colored illustrations were made by the medical artist Professor Erich Lepier of Vienna..... His signature may be observed on the illustrations he contributed to this volume of Sobotta. The extensive experience of Professor Lepier in the depiction of anatomical preparations has been demonstrated in other medical books, such as "The Topographic Anatomy of Man" by E. Pernkopf. Most of these new illustrations were based on preparations in the Anatomical Institute of Münster and often more than one preparation was used for one illustration. Some of the pictures were modifications of illustrations in Pernkopf's Atlas..... Some of the photographic reproductions of preparations (for example: the heart and heart-lung preparations) were lightly retouched by Prof. Lepier. The new schematic diagrams, especially in the section on the central nervous system and nerve tracts, were converted to engravings from my sketches.....

I wish to express my appreciation to colleagues in my Institute for their help in the completion of this volume. My student, medical assistant Meinhard Köhler, rendered careful and reliable assistance in the reorganization and introduction of new text material. I am also grateful for the part played by the students through their suggestions of desired changes in the book. My special thanks go again to the publisher..... Dr. Heinz Urban, gave the book his personal interest so that my wishes were liberally and obligingly met. The unified goal gave rise to a harmonious working relationship reflected in the expeditious completion of the book.....

H. Becher

Münster (Westf.) December 1961.

# Preface to the First German Edition

Experience with the work in the student anatomical laboratory, extending over a period of many years, has convinced the author of the advisability of presenting illustrations of the peripheral nervous system and of the blood vessels as they are seen by the student in his dissections, that is, nerves and vessels of any region in the same figure. For this reason in the majority of the figures, arteries and nerves, or arteries, veins and nerves, or arteries and veins were illustrated side by side in the same figure. Only occasionally a departure from this plan was necessary, when for the sake of clearness supplementary figures had to be added showing only the arteries or the nerves (as for instance in the case of the cranial nerves).

This method of illustrating anatomical dissections has the advantage that the student finds in a single illustration all the structures which he actually encounters in any particular stratum of the region which he dissects; otherwise the student must waste too much precious time in searching for each type of structure on different pages of the volume or even in different volumes. Moreover as the structures are pictured in their natural relationship, this set of illustrations represents at the same time an atlas of topographical anatomy.

The simultaneous illustration of blood vessels and nerves made the use of colored illustrations an indispensable necessity. The arteries are shown in red, the veins in blue, and the nerves in yellow. The three color-plates employed in depicting the arteries, veins, and nerves, were used at the same time to reproduce in color, by means of the three-color process, the parts of the body in their natural colors; the object was to obtain illustrations in which individual types of structures could be readily distinguished from other types by their color.

In this volume of the atlas, as in Volumes I and II, text pages alternate with full-page plates. The text pages contain the explanations of these plates, some helpful diagrams, and brief descriptions of the essential structures; the descriptions, however, are sufficiently complete to serve the student as a convenient guide and means of quick orientation while he is working in the laboratory.

Würzburg, May 1906

The Author
[Johannes Sobotta]

# Volume III, Part II
# ATLAS of NEUROANATOMY
## Central and Autonomic Nervous Systems
Eye, Ear, and Skin

CONTENTS


| | Figures | |
|---|---|---|
| PREFACE . . . . . . . . . . . . . . . . . . . . . . . . . | | V |
| INTRODUCTION . . . . . . . . . . . . . . . . . . . . . . | | X |
| Historical Sketch . . . . . . . . . . . . . . . . . . . | | X |
| Abbreviations Used in This Volume . . . . . . . . | | XIV |
| Etymology of Anatomical Terms . . . . . . . . . . | | XVI |
| Clock Label-Finding Key . . . . . . . . . . . . . . | | XIX |
| THE NERVOUS SYSTEM, GENERAL CONSIDERATIONS | 176–179 | |
| **SPINAL CORD AND MENINGES** . . . . . . . . . . | 179–194 | |
| Cerebrospinal Fluid, Circulation of . . . . . . . . . | 197 198, 199 | |
| Cranial Cavity and Meninges . . . . . . . . . . . . | 232, 233, 239, 240 | |
| Blood Supply of Brain . . . . . . . . . . . . . . . . | 195, 196, 200–205, 234–238, 241, 242 | |
| Arteriograms and Venograms . . . . . . . . . . . . | 243–246 | |
| Ventricles and Ventriculograms . . . . . . . . . . . | 218–220, 263–264 | |
| **BRAIN** (ENCEPHALON) . . . . . . . . . . . . . . | 239–242, 247, 248, 272, 277, 279 | |
| Brain Sections . . . . . . . . . . . . . . . . . . . | 277–288 | |
| Cerebral Hemispheres (Telencephalon) . . . . . | 206–217, 221, 222, 249–262, 265–271 | |
| Diencephalon, Hypothalamus . . . . . . . . | 223–226, 274, 275 | |
| Midbrain (Mesencephalon) . . . . . . . . . . | 272–274, 276, 289, 290 | |
| Cerebellum . . . . . . . . . . . . . . . . . . . | 227, 228, 291–296, 343 | |
| Medulla Oblongata (Rhombencephalon) . . . . | 229–231, 276, 289, 290 | |
| Brain Stem . . . . . . . . . . . . . . . . . . . | 299–231, 274, 276, 289, 290 | |
| Brain Stem Sections and Tracts . . . . . . . | 324–342 | |
| Brain Tract Dissections . . . . . . . . . . . . | 320–323, 343 | |
| **FUNCTIONAL DIAGRAMS AND TRACTS** . . . . . . . . . | 297–319 | |
| **AUTONOMIC NERVOUS SYSTEM** . . . . . . . . . . . | 344–355 | |
| **THE SENSE ORGANS** | | |
| The Eye . . . . . . . . . . . . . . . . . . . . . . . | 356–408 | |
| The Ear . . . . . . . . . . . . . . . . . . . . . . . | 409–465 | |
| The Skin and Its Derivatives . . . . . . . . . . . | 466–481 | |
| OLD AND NEW TERMINOLOGY . . . . . . . . . . . | | |
| INDEX, English and Latin . . . . . . . . . . . . . . | | |

# INTRODUCTION

## Historical Sketch*

Johannes Sobotta was born in Berlin, Germany, January 31, 1869. He studied medicine at the University of Berlin. He showed such a great aptitude for anatomical research, that he was accepted for guidance by the famous anatomist, Waldeyer. At the age of 26, he went to Würzburg as prosector to work with Kölliker, another outstanding anatomist of that period. He stayed in Würzburg 21 years, where he conducted some of his most important research. The idea of the ATLAS was conceived there and its early editions were published while Sobotta was in Würzburg where, at the age of 34, he was made Professor of Anatomy. Sobotta became Director of the Anatomical Institute of the University of Königsberg from 1916 to 1919 when he was made Director of the Anatomical Institute at Bonn. He worked there until the end of his 75th year of life, April, 1945.

Sobotta was not only an investigator; he excelled also as a teacher. The experience which he had gained through intimate contact with his students and his sympathetic understanding of the problems which confront the medical student led to the publication of his ATLAS. It was the custom among German authors of anatomical atlases of that period to illustrate arteries, veins, and nerves of the same region in separate illustrations. Sobotta had observed that this procedure had several great disadvantages. For this reason he decided to prepare an atlas in which the student could find all these structures in one single illustration just as the student sees them in his dissection (see author's Preface).

The excellence of Sobotta's ATLAS of HUMAN ANATOMY and value as a visual aid for anatomical studies has been recognized from the time it was first published over fifty years ago. It has been one of the most popular atlases with medical students. Physicians use it as a convenient and rapid way to review anatomy. Nine editions appeared during the first thirty-five years, and seven since that time. During and after World War II, conditions were such that the ATLAS disappeared from the market. It was valued so highly that even though other new atlases had been published, students paid as high as $125.00 for a second-hand set of Sobotta's ATLAS.

---

* Information obtained from the preface of the 5th Ed. in English by the late Professor Eduard Uhlenhuth of the University of Maryland Medical School (1925–1961).

Prof. Dr. Sobotta.

In the ATLAS, the accurate and adequately labeled color plates are arranged in sequence, wherever possible, to illustrate the various stages of dissection, beginning with the superficial and displaying deeper structures in the order encountered in the dissecting room. Since the structures of the human body are the same today, the essential facts depicted by the illustrations do not require modification. The changes that have occurred in the ATLAS, over the half-century of its development, have involved the addition of new plates and changes in the labels to keep the ATLAS up-to-date with respect to anatomical terminology.

Another very valuable feature of Sobotta's ATLAS of HUMAN ANATOMY, is its completeness with respect to coverage of the human body and all its systems. In particular, the anatomy of the special sensory organs and the central, as well as the peripheral nervous system, are extensively covered by Sobotta's ATLAS. These are omitted or inadequately treated in most atlases. The oral or dental anatomy and the development of teeth have also been depicted in a complete and detailed way. The ATLAS has, therefore, been useful not only for the medical, clinical, and dental specialities, but also for courses involving neuroanatomy, radiological anatomy, and anatomy for physical therapists and nurses.

# Abbreviations Used in Volume III

ant. or anter. = anterior, anteriores
a. or art. (aa.) = arteria, arteriae
caud. = caudalis
cran. = cranialis
dist. or distal. = distalis
dors. = dorsalis
ext. = externus, externa
fasc. = fasciculus
gangl. = ganglion
gland. = glandula, glandulae
int. = internus, interna
lat., lateral. = lateralis, laterales
longit. = longitudinalis
med., medial. = medialis, mediales
n. = nervus
nn. = nervi
nu. or nucl. = nucleus
post., poster. = posterior, posteriores
prof. = profundus, profunda
proxim. = proximalis
r., ram. (rr.) = ramus (rami)
superf. = superficialis, superficiales
tr. = truncus, trunci
tract. = tractus
v., vv. = vena, venae
ventr. = ventralis

× behind a name denotes that a part of the structure so named has been divided or cut away entirely.

Other abbreviations which have been used in places, will be understood from the context in which they occur. If a structure is not named in one illustration, its name will be found in one of the preceding illustrations.

# ETYMOLOGY
# ANATOMICAL EQUIVALENTS
# ENGLISH-LATIN-GREEK

| *English* | *Latin* | *Greek* | *Stem (Greek)* |
|---|---|---|---|
| arm | brachium | brachion | (brachi-) |
| bile | bilis | cholē | (chol-) |
| blood | sanguis | haema | (haemat-) |
| body | corpus | sōma | (somat-) |
| bone | os | osteon | (oste-) |
| brain | cerebrum | encephalon | (encephal-) |
| breast | mamma | mastos | (mast-) |
| buttocks | nates | gloutoi | (glout-) |
| cartilage | cartilago | chondros | (chondr-) |
| chest | thorax | thorax | (thorac-) |
| chin | mentum | geneion | (genei-) |
| cornea | cornu | keras | (kerat-) |
| ear | auris | ous | (ōt-) |
| elbow | cubitus | angkon | (ancon-) |
| eye | oculus | ophthalmos | (ophthalm-) |
| fat | adeps | lipos | (lip-) |
| finger | digitus | dactylos | (dactyl-) |
| flesh | caro (carnis) | sarx | (sarc-) |
| foot | pes | pous | (pod-) |
| hair | capillus | thrix | (trich-) |
| hand | manus | cheir | (cheir-) |
| head | caput | cephalē | (cephal-) |
| heart | cor | cardia | (cardi-) |
| intestine | intestinum | enteron | (enter-) |
| joint | artus | arthron | (arthr-) |
| kidney | ren | nephros | (nephr-) |
| knee | genu | gonu | (gonat-) |
| ligament | ligamentum | syndesmos | (syndesm-) |
| liver | jecur (gen. jecoris) | hepar | (hepat-) |
| loin | lumbus | lapara | (lapar-) |
| lung | pulmo | pneumon | (pneumon-) |
| mouth | os | stoma | (stomat-) |
| muscle | musculus | mys | (my-) |
| navel | umbilicus | omphalos | (ompha-) |
| neck | collum | trachelos | (trachel-) |
| nerve | nervus | neuron | (neur-) |
| nose | nasus | rhis | (rhin-) |
| omentum | omentum | epiploon | (epiplo-) |
| pubic bone | os pubis | pecten | (pecten-) |
| shoulder | humerus | ōmos | (ōm-) |
| skin | cutis | derma | (dermat-) |
| skull | cranium | cranion | (crani-) |
| stomach | stomachus | gastēr | (gastr-) |
| sweat | sudor | idros | (idro(t)-) |
| tendon | tendo | tenon | (tenon-) |
| testicle | testis | orchis | (orch-) |
| throat | fauces | pharynx | (pharyng-) |
| tongue | lingua | glossa | (gloss-) |
| tooth | dens | odous | (odont-) |
| vagina | vagina | colpos | (colp-) |
| vein | vena | phleps | (phleb-) |
| vertebra | vertebra | spondylos | (spondyl-) |
| womb | uterus | hystera | (hyster-) |
| wrist | carpus | carpos | (carp-) |

# ETYMOLOGY AND MEANING OF ANATOMICAL TERMS OF VOL. III

**accessory** ...... L. *accedere; nervus accessorius* so called because it is accessory to the vagus nerve
**acetabulum** .... L. *acetabulum* = small vessel to hold vinegar; cup-shaped socket of hipjoint
**amygdaloid** .... Gr. *amygdalē* = almond
**aqueduct** ...... L. water conduit
**arachnoid** ...... Gr. *arachnoidēs* from *ho arachnos* = the spider; spider web membrane covering brain and spinal cord
**artery** ......... Latinized Gr., etymology uncertain. Probably from *aggeia ta aera terenta* = air-containing vessels. The ancients thought that the arteries contained air.
**auricle** ........ L. diminutive of *auris* = ear; outer ear and also the ear of the heart
**bulbus** ......... L. from the Gr. *ho bolbos* = onion
**calcar avis** ..... L. = the spur of the rooster
**calcarine** ...... Part of spur (from calcar)
**callosum** ....... L. *callum* = horny skin
**capillary** ....... L. *capillus*, hair of the scalp
**cauda equina** ... horse's tail (L. *cauda* = tail; *equina*, adj. from *equus* = horse); name applied to the roots of the lumbar and sacral spinal nerves which are arranged around the caudal end of the spinal cord like the hair of a horse's tail
**cava** .......... L. *cavus* = hollow *(venae cavae)*
**cephalic** ....... Gr. = *kephalikos* from *kephalē* = head
**cerebellum** ..... L. diminutive of *cerebrum*, the small brain
**cerebrum**....... L. brain; cerebral hemispheres
**chiasma** ....... Gr. crossing or intersecting in the manner of an X
**chorda tympani**. Cord of the middle ear cavity. Only nerve which is not called "*nervus*"; it received its name at a time when its nervous nature was not known.
**chorioid** ....... Gr. *chorion* = a skin, membrane
**ciliary** ......... L. *cilium* = eyelash
**cingulum** ...... L. belt (from *cingere* = to gird or surround)
**claustrum** ...... L. *claudere* = to close, bar
**cluneal** ........ L. *clunis*, buttock
**cochlea** ........ shell of a snail (Lat., but perhaps originally Gr.)
**celiac** ......... Gr. *koilos* = hollow, referring to abdominal cavity
**commissure** .... L. *committere* = to connect
**concha** ........ Gr. *conchē*, shell of a mussel
**conjunctiva** .... L. *conjungere* = to connect
**cor** ........... L. *cor*, genitive, *cordis* = heart
**corium** ........ L., but originally Gr. = skin
**cornea** ........ L. *cornu* = horn
**coronary** ....... L. *corona* = wreath, crown
**corpus** ......... L. a body, mass or structure
**crus** ........... L. leg (adj. *cruralis*)
**culmen** ........ L. summit
**cuneus** ........ L. a wedge (adj. *cuneatus*)
**cutaneous** ...... L. *cutis* = skin
**decussation** .... L. *decussare* = to cross each other in the form of an X
**dentate** ........ L. *dens* = tooth
**diencephalon** ... Gr. *dia* = between + encephalon
**ductus deferens** . L. from *de* = away and *ferre* = to carry
**dura mater** .... L. *durus* = hard; *mater* = mother, protection
**emboliform** .... L. from the Gr. *ho embolos* = plug
**encephalon** ..... Gr. from *hē kephalē* = the head, and *en* = in
**epidermis** ...... Gr. *epi* = on top, and *derma* = skin
**epigastric** ..... Gr. *epi* = above; *gaster* = stomach or belly
**fasciculus** ...... L. diminutive of *fascis* = a bundle or bunch
**fasciolar** ...... L. *fasciola* = a small band, diminutive of *fascia* = band
**fastigial** ....... L. *fastigium*, gable
**flaccid** ......... L. *flaccus*, flabby
**flocculus** ....... L. diminutive of *floccus* = a flock or tuft (of wool)
**fornix** ......... L. arch of a vault
**fossa** .......... L. a ditch; in anatomy, a depressed area
**fovea** .......... L. a pit; in anatomy, a depression of small diameter
**ganglion** ....... Gr. swelling, node
**gastroepiploic** .. Gr. *gaster* = stomach; Gr. *epiploon* = greater omentum
**geniculate** ..... L. *geniculum* = a small knee
**glomus** ........ L. a ball of thread
**gluteus** ........ Gr. *gloutos* = buttocks
**griseus** ........ L. gray
**gyrus** ......... Gr. *gyros* = a convolution
**habenula** ...... L. diminutive of *habena* = bridle, strap
**helicotrema** .... Gr. *helix* = snail, and *trema* = hole
**hippocampus** ... Gr. from *hippos* = horse; and *kamptein* = to bend. Refers to the shape of the foot (*pes hippocampi*) of a legendary animal and is one of the fantastic names of the old nomenclature.

At an earlier period the same structure was compared with Ammon's horns (amonites) and called cornu Ammonis.

**hirci** ........ L. *hircus* = buck or he-goat. Hair of the axilla.

**hyaloid** ........ Gr. *hyaloeidēs* = like glass

**hypoglossus** .... Gr. *hypo* = beneath, and *glossa* = tongue

**hypothalamus** .. Gr. *hypo* = beneath. The part of the brain located beneath the thalamus

**incus** .......... L. *cudere* = to beat; anvil, one of the ossicles of the ear

**infundibulum** ... L. funnel

**integument** .... L. *integere* = to cover, clothe

**iris** .......... Gr. *iris*. Gen. *iridis* = rainbow

**lacuna** ........ L. *lacus* = lake

**lanugo** ........ L. *lana* = wool; the fine primary hair

**lenticular** ...... L. from *lens*, Gen. *lentis* = lentil

**leptomeninx** .... Gr. *leptos* = soft, delicate

**luteus** ......... L. yellow

**lymph** ......... L. *lympha* = a clear liquid

**mamilla** ....... L. diminutive from *mamma* = female breast, nipple

**medulla** ........ L. marrow

**meninges** ...... Gr. (sing. *meninx*) = membrane

**myenteric** ...... Gr. *mys* = muscle, *enteron* = gut. Nerve plexus in muscle layer of gut

**nerve** ......... Latinized Gr. from *to neyron* = (at first) tendon; later, nerve

**nucleus** ........ L. *nux* = nut, literally a kernel, designates an aggregation of nerve cells.

**obturator** ...... L. *obturare* = to stop up

**operculum** ..... L. *operire* = to cover; lid or cover

**pachymeninx** ... Gr. *pachys* = thick, firm; *meninx* = membrane

**pallidus** ........ L. pale

**palpebral** ...... L. *palpebra* = eyelid

**pampiniform** ... L. *pampinus* = shoot of a vine, as in connection with plexus pampiniformis in spermatic cord

**peduncle** ...... L. diminutive of *pes* = foot

**pellucidus** ...... L. *pellucere* = to shine through

**petrosal** ....... Gr. *petra* = rock; as applied to pars petrosa (hardest portion) of temporal bone

**phrenic** ........ Gr. *phrenes* = diaphragm

**pia mater** ...... L. *pius* = soft; *mater* = mother, in the sense of protection

**pineal** ......... L. *pinus* = pine tree

**plexus** ......... L. *plectere* = to interweave

**pons** .......... L. bridge

**pterygoid** ...... Gr. *pteryx* = wing *eidos* = resemblance

**pupil** .......... L. a little girl, a small doll; this name for the pupil is very ancient and refers to the diminutive mirror image which the observer sees of himself in the cornea of a (female) person confronting him. The pupil of the eye.

**quadrigeminal** .. L. *quadri* = combining form of *quattuor*, four, and *geminus* = twin or alike

**ramus** ......... L. branch

**raphe** ......... Gr. *rhaphe* = a seamlike junction or suture

**rete** ........... L. network

**rostral** ......... L. *rostrum* = beak; located towards the front end of the body

**ruga** .......... L. wrinkle

**sacculus** ....... L. a small sack, diminutive from *saccus* = a sack or bag

**saphenous** ...... Hebrew or Aramaic, hidden; *vena saphena*, the hidden vein of lower extremity, so called because it does not show through the skin

**scala** .......... L. staircase

**scapha** ........ Gr. *scaphē* = boat; a boat-shaped depression

**sclera** ......... Gr. *skleros* = hard

**serratus** ....... L. *serra* = saw

**sinus** .......... L. a cavity, a hollow, roundish recess

**spinalis** ........ L. *spina* = thorn; used in the sense of belonging to the spinal column

**splenius** ....... Gr. *splenion* = a bandage

**stapes** ......... A late L. word from *stare* = to stand, and *pes* = foot; stirrup, one of the ossicles of the ear

**striatus** ........ L. *stria* = stripe

**suralis** ......... L. *sura* = calf; of the leg

**sympathetic** .... A division of the autonomic nervous system. Gr. *syn* = with and *pathos* = suffering, compassion

**taenia** ......... L. band, stripe

**tapetum** ....... L. carpet, curtain

**tarsus** ......... Gr. *tarsos* = a wickerwork frame. In the anatomy of the eye, it designates the cartilage of the eyelid; in the skeleton, the anklebones of the foot

**tegmen** ........ L. cover or roof

**telencephalon** .. Gr. *telos* = end + encephalon, endbrain or cerebral hemispheres

**tentorium** ...... L. tent, sheet stretched across, from *tendere* = to stretch

**thalamus** ...... Gr. chamber; does not designate a cavity as the word would suggest, but two massive bodies forming the walls of the third ventricle.

**tractus** ........ L. *trahere* = to drag or conduct; in neuroanatomy a large bundle of nerve fibers (larger than a fasciculus).

**tragus** ......... Gr. *tragos* = a buck or he-goat; so named from the longer and thicker hair growing on that part of the outer ear and carrying the same name

**tympanum** ..... Gr. *tympanon* = drum; the cavity of the middle ear

**vagus** ......... L. wandering, roving; *nervus vagus*, so called because its branches extend as far as the abdomen although the nerve takes origin from the brain

**vallecula** ....... L. diminutive of *valles* = valley

**vas** ........... L. a vessel (pl. = *vasa*; gen. pl. = *vasorum*)

**ventricle** ....... L. ventriculus = the belly; used to designate the cavities of the brain, and also the two great chambers of the heart

**vesicalis** ....... L. *vesica* = bladder

**vibrissa** ........ L. *vibrare* = to tremble or vibrate; hair of the nostril

**vitreus** ........ L. *vitrum* = glass; translucent like glass

**vorticose** ....... L. *vortex* = whirl

# THE ANATOMICAL LABEL-FINDING KEY

(see Preface)

The **anatomical label-finding key** based on clock numbers was designed to:

1. Save the student's time, and facilitate the use of the ATLAS with textbooks of anatomy.
2. Expose the student to corresponding English and Latin anatomical terms.

The clock is divided into twelve 30° arcs or segments of a circle. Experience has shown that it is easy to estimate the position of the arc for any given clock number. "One" has been used to indicate that the label will be found in the segment of a circle between 12:30 and 1:30 on the imaginary clock, and so on, around to the number 12, which indicates that the labels are located between 11:30 and 12:30. The clock number for any given term arbitrarily refers to the position of the **first few letters of the term.**

On the page opposite each illustration, the names of the structures are listed in the same order as they occur on the illustration in a clockwise direction beginning with clock position "1". When the student looks at a Latin term on the figure, its approximate clock position may be estimated and the same Latin term quickly and easily found on the opposite page with the English term. This method may also be used in reverse, going from English to Latin to expedite locating the Latin label and the structures on the figure.

When any given term is referred to in the text, the anatomical label-finding key number is preceded by a hyphen to distinguish it from any anatomical enumeration system. In the INDEX, there will be two numbers, the figure number and the clock location number. This should enable the student to find the illustration of the structure and its label in the minimum time.

Not all the illustrations are the same size and shape, but most of them can, however, be classified to correspond to one of the following clock face shapes: circular, square, or rectangular. In assigning clock numbers, a transparent plastic circle with clock hour divisions has been meticulously used. The center was carefully placed in the **center** of the illustration. It must be realized, however, that the clock-key number gives only the approximate position of the label, but a more precise system would be unduly complicated and unnecessary.

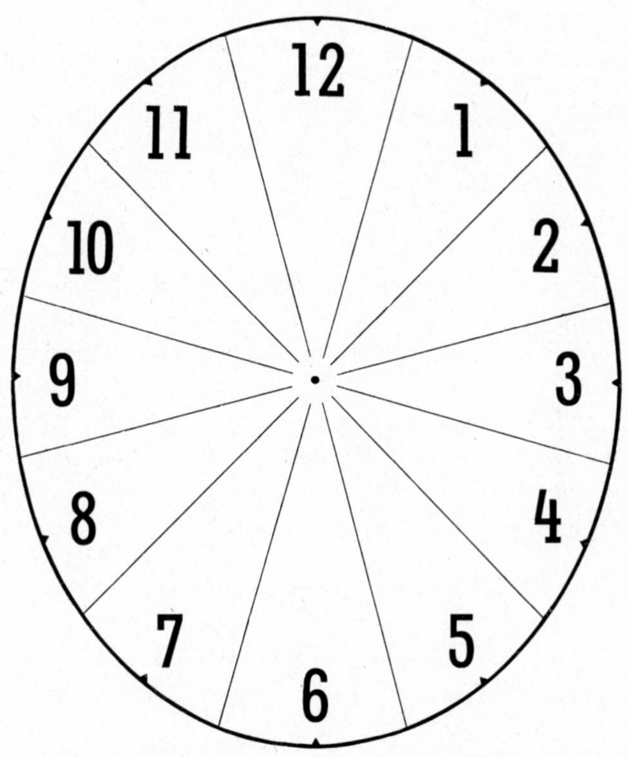

12
1
2
3
4
5
6
7
8
9
10
11


**Basis for Anatomical Label-Finding Key.**

(See preceding page for explanation)

# THE NERVOUS SYSTEM

## General Considerations

## The Relationship to Other Systems and the Names of its Parts

The nervous system is composed of cells that have specialized to establish rapid intercommunication between various tissues and cells of the body and the outside environment. It enables the organism to adapt to the environment in the most appropriate and advantageous manner. It functions by converting certain physical and chemical stimuli that are received from all areas (internal and external) into impulses that pass with relatively great rapidity from the place where the stimulus is applied to the central nervous system and back to the proper effector organ.

The human nervous system also has "memory" associated with it. This is the capacity to store experience or knowledge (with some considerable individual variation). The imagination or capacity to utilize this stored knowledge and experience for creative and abstract thought, results in the continuous modification of our concepts and the progressive advancement of knowledge. The nervous system thus has a major responsibility for the ontogenetic-memory-system of the individual, and this supplements and integrates with the phylogenetic-memory-system or "know-how regulatory system" which resides in the chromosomes of every cell. There can be little doubt that man's position in the phylogenetic scale is primarily related to the superior development of his efficient nervous system with the resulting increased capacity for creativity. It also made possible the elaborate intercommunication which takes place between individuals and groups in our society. This development of the forebrain of man and the associated mechanisms of intercommunication, coupled with the assumption of the upright state and the development of dexterity and manual skill, has been responsible for man's dominance in the vertebrate scale of animals.

In considering the various cellular intercommunication mechanisms within the living human body, the nervous system may be compared to the very rapid intercommunication mechanisms of our society – the telephone and television. The endocrine system may be compared to the postal system, in which the messages are carried in a less direct manner. The diffusion mechanisms, utilized by cells that communicate over very small distances, may be compared to conversations between individuals in our society close enough to each other to be heard. This comparison of the methods of communication in our society and in the human body could be carried much further, but it is significant that our body is made up of a "society" of a large number ($10^{14}$, more than the number of people on the earth) of differentiated cells. The activities of the cells require coordination by means of intercommunication.

The nervous system is usually studied as a separate system, but it is apparent that the activity of every part of the nervous system is intimately involved in the function of all the other cells and parts of the body, particularly the muscular system. The nervous system itself, however, is divided for the purpose of study and description. It was divided very early into the central nervous system and the peripheral nervous system. This division is arbitrary, the parts are intimately interconnected and one cannot function without the other. The division was practical, however, because different methods and techniques are required for the study of each. The central nervous system consists of the brain and spinal cord. It is an extremely complicated network which requires special methods to ascertain the connections and pathways of the various functional types of neurons. These important structures are within the skull and spinal column and cushioned with spinal fluid to protect them from injury or even slight trauma.

The neurons and groups of nerve processes outside the central nervous system, connecting it with all parts of the body, constitute the peripheral nervous system. This has been divided into two parts, on an anatomical and functional basis: The somatic part of the nervous system controls the voluntary muscles and functions. The autonomic portion controls the involuntary or autonomic activities primarily associated with smooth muscle, cardiac muscle, and glands. The names for these two separate parts of the peripheral nervous system evolved gradually. "Somatic" (which comes from the Greek term *soma* = body) was applied to the voluntary part of the nervous system and indicates that the somatic nerves supply the muscles (and other structures) which are derived from an embryological somite or body segment. These somatic nerves are concerned with the various types of general sensation, and with reflexes involving somatic (voluntary striated) muscles, where a fast specific response is desirable. In the somatic motor system the impulses are carried to the peripheral voluntary muscle by a single neuron, whose cell body is located in the central nervous system.

The autonomic or involuntary portion of the peripheral nervous system was a difficult one to name. Today it is called the autonomic nervous system because it supplies, primarily, the viscera, glands, smooth and cardiac muscle. These are structures that function somewhat automatically, in that they are not primarily under voluntary control. In the autonomic nervous system the impulses are relayed to the peripheral effector structure by a two-neuron chain in contrast to the single neuron in the somatic outflow (see Fig. 344). Thus, there is the possibility of a single neuron in the central nervous system sending an axon to 30 or 40 secondary neurons, located outside the central nervous system, which then distribute the impulse to more than one effector structure. This is a type of amplification or spreading system which has the possibility of stimulating widespread response of a large number of units which may be located in different parts of the body.

The basic unit of the nervous system is the neuron or nerve cell. In order for such cells to carry messages for a relatively great distance, at least one of the processes must extend over this distance. The nerve cell bodies in the central nervous system tend to form aggregates according to their sizes, their shapes, and their functions. Such aggregates of nerve cells in the central nervous system are called nuclei. The neuroglia that surround and infiltrate the nuclei were so named because they were thought to hold the neurons together (*glia* = glue) or to function as a connective tissue element of the nervous system. It is now thought that they have more than a packing or adhesive function. The part of the nervous system in which there is a high proportion of neuron cell bodies is called gray matter; that which is made up predominantly of nerve fibers (myelinated) is called white matter. Outside the central nervous system, aggregations of nerve cell bodies give the appearance of swellings on nerve trunks, and are called ganglia (Gr. *ganglion* = a swelling).

The nervous system is one of the earliest systems to develop. Nerve processes from the neural crest ganglia and from the central nervous system grow out and establish connections with the somatic and branchial segments during pre-natal development. The nerve fibers remain connected and thus follow the structures which they initially innervated and this is responsible for nerve plexuses, loops, and other unusual nerve pathways. The large nerve plexuses seen in the adult are thus a representation of the developmental migrations and fusions of parts of somites initially supplied by the nerves. They provide us with an indelible record of some of the complicated events that occurred during the early development of the individual.

The autonomic or visceral motor nervous system (in contrast to the cerebrospinal, somatic, or voluntary nervous system) is relatively involuntary. It is divided into two parts, a sympathetic and a parasympathetic. The name parasympathetic indicates that this portion is beside the sympathetic nervous system. Both of these divisions have in common a two-neuron chain in the peripheral pathway. The cell body of the presynaptic neuron is within the central nervous system, while the postsynaptic neuron cell body is located either in a ganglion outside the central nervous system, or in nerve plexuses within the organ innervated. In general, the presynaptic neurons give off fibers which are myelinated or white, while the postsynaptic neurons have unmyelinated or gray fibers that end in contact with the smooth muscle or gland cell. For some reason, not yet understood, the outflow of the sympathetic presynaptic neurons from the central nervous system is limited to the thoracic and upper lumbar segments. The outflow of parasympathetic presynaptic neurons is limited to four of the cranial nerves (III, VII, IX and X) and two or three of the sacral nerves ($S_2$, $S_3$). The parasympathetic portion of the autonomic nervous system is sometimes called the craniosacral division, while the sympathetic division is called the thoracolumbar division of the autonomic nervous system.

# 176. Origin and Branching of Nerves from Two Spinal Cord Segments Showing Connections to the Ganglionated Sympathetic Trunk.

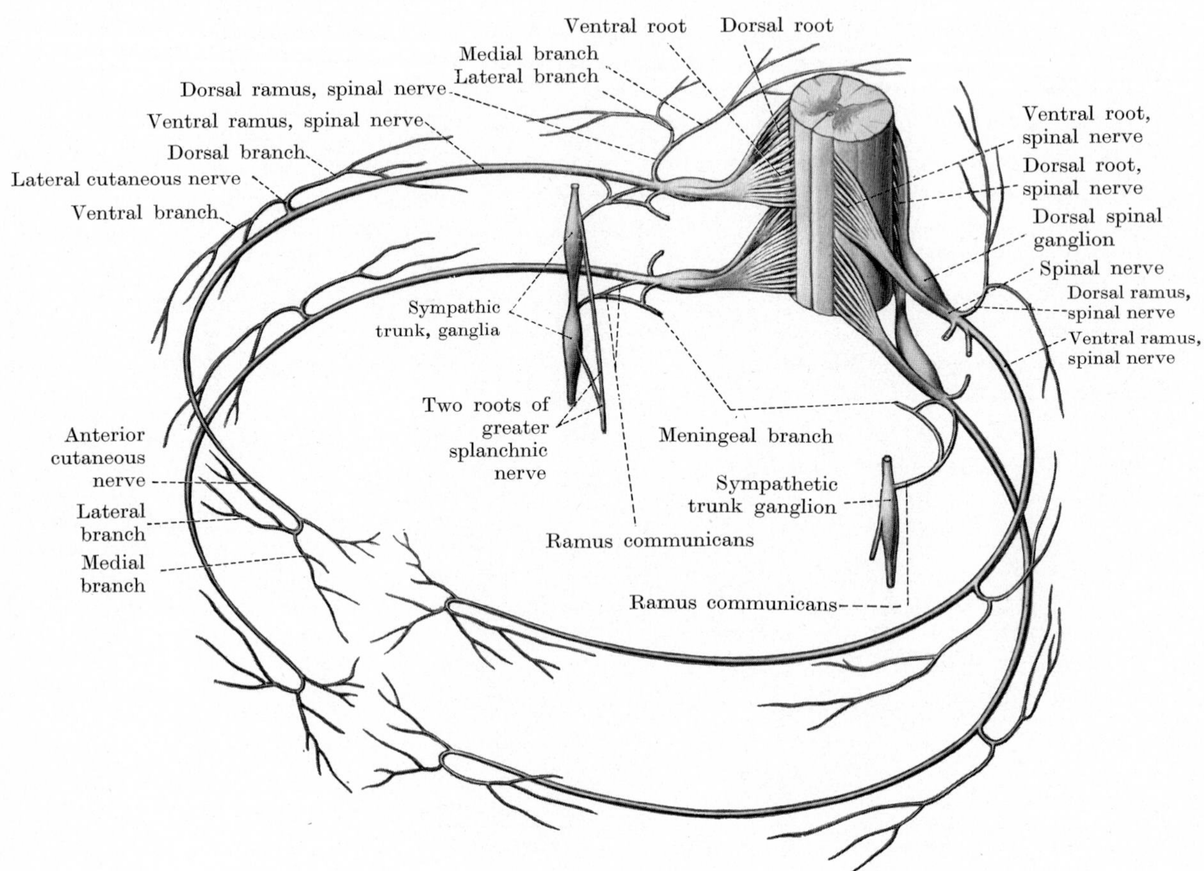
Ventral root
Dorsal root
Medial branch
Lateral branch
Dorsal ramus, spinal nerve
Ventral ramus, spinal nerve
Dorsal branch
Lateral cutaneous nerve
Ventral branch
Ventral root, spinal nerve
Dorsal root, spinal nerve
Dorsal spinal ganglion
Spinal nerve
Dorsal ramus, spinal nerve
Ventral ramus, spinal nerve
Sympathic trunk, ganglia
Two roots of greater splanchnic nerve
Meningeal branch
Anterior cutaneous nerve
Lateral branch
Medial branch
Sympathetic trunk ganglion
Ramus communicans
Ramus communicans

Fig. 176.

# 176. Origin and Branching of Nerves from Two Spinal Cord Segments Showing Connections to the Ganglionated Sympathetic Trunk.

**Note:** 1. Ventral and dorsal roots are not single nerve strands near spinal cord, but are composed of a number of small rootlets or filaments (fila radicularia).

2. Ganglion on dorsal root is very close to the point of junction with the ventral rootlets where the spinal nerve is formed.

3. Spinal nerves divide almost immediately into dorsal and ventral rami. These continue branching to supply both somatic and autonomic peripheral structures.

4. In thoracic and upper lumbar segments, spinal nerves send small "white" communicating rami to ganglionated sympathetic chain. These connections transmit presynaptic nerve fibers of neurons in intermediolateral nucleus of lateral gray column to secondary neurons in sympathetic ganglia.

5. To send presynaptic fibers to cervical and sacral segments, fibers of neurons in thoracic and upper lumbar cord segments must pass cranially and caudally in the sympathetic chain to reach neurons in ganglia of segments where there is no sympathetic outflow ($C_1$—$C_8$, $L_3$—$L_5$, $S_1$—$S_5$).

6. Each spinal nerve receives a gray ramus communicans from its corresponding ganglion. This gray ramus communicans transmits "unmyelinated" fibers from ganglionic neurons (post synaptic fibers) to the spinal nerve for distribution peripherally to autonomic structures. (Arrector pili muscles, smooth muscles on blood vessels, sweat glands, etc.)

# 177. Formation of a Nerve Plexus by Spinal Nerves.

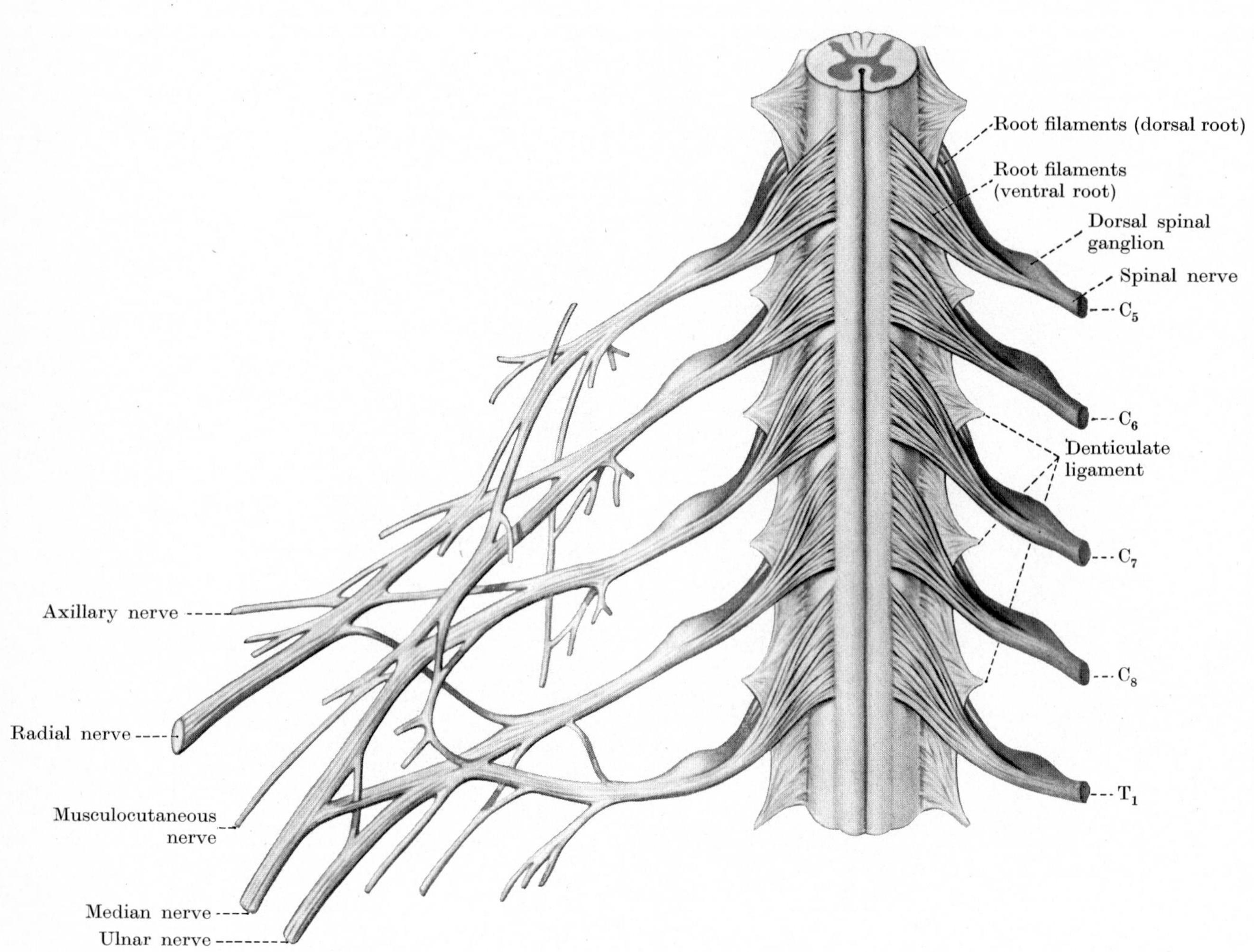
Root filaments (dorsal root)
Root filaments (ventral root)
Dorsal spinal ganglion
Spinal nerve
$C_5$
$C_6$
Denticulate ligament
$C_7$
$C_8$
$T_1$
Axillary nerve
Radial nerve
Musculocutaneous nerve
Median nerve
Ulnar nerve

Fig. 177.

## 177. Formation of a Nerve Plexus by Spinal Nerves.

Illustration based on brachial plexus, formed from ventral rami of $C_5$ to $T_1$, ventral view. C = cervical segment, T = Thoracic.

**Note:** 1. The major plexuses are formed from the ventral rami of spinal nerves because most of the muscle masses and dermal contributions to an extremity are derived from the ventrolateral parts of body segments.

2. The pattern of the plexus in the adult is the result of the fusions and separations of the muscle masses as development proceeds. The plexus is thus the result; and makes possible the complicated muscle arrangements necessary for the fine control of movement of parts of extremity.

3. The dorsal rami of spinal nerves form minor connections with each other but do not form complicated plexuses.

**Etymology:**

*ganglion* = Gr. a swelling. Originally referred to a subcutaneous swelling, such as on tendons. Galen used it exclusively for a swelling on a nerve, hence a group or knot of nerve cell bodies.

denticulate = L. *dens (dentis)*, tooth.

axillary = L. *axilla*, armpit.

## 178. Side View of Index Finger. (slightly enlarged).

Dissection shows ramification of digital nerves and the associated lamellated (Pacinian) corpuscles in the subcutaneous tissues.

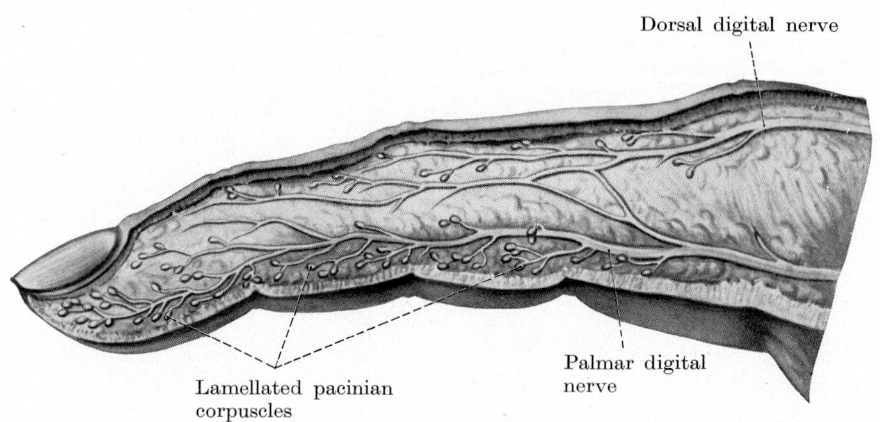
Dorsal digital nerve
Lamellated pacinian corpuscles
Palmar digital nerve

Fig. 178.

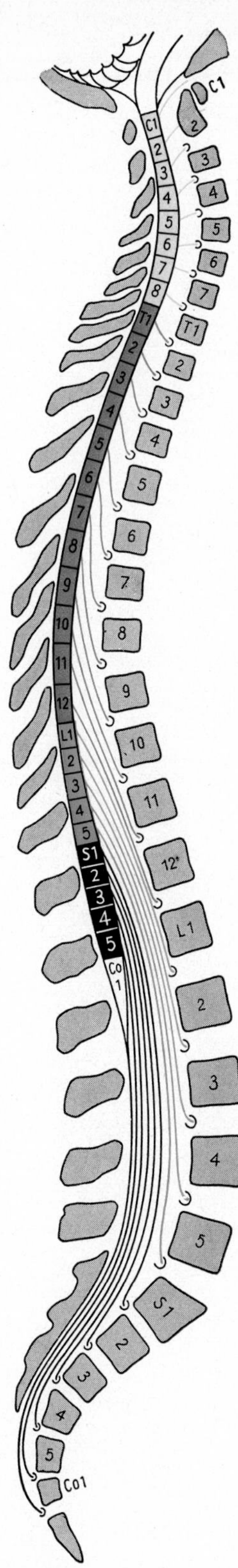

## 179. Vertebral Level of Spinal Cord Segments in the Vertebral Canal and the Exit Sites of the Spinal Nerve Roots.

**Note:** 1. Individual spinal cord segments have been indicated; the cord regions by colors.

**Yellow,** cervical segments 1–8
**Red,** thoracic segments 1–12
**Blue,** lumbar segments 1–5
**Black,** sacral segments 1–5
**White,** coccygeal segments 1, 2

2. Differential rates of growth give rise to a spinal cord which is much shorter than the vertebral canal.

3. **Roots of spinal nerves** traverse variable distances to the dural canal exit at the appropriate intervertebral foramen.

4. **Cervical nerve roots** pass almost transversely to the exits. The lumbosacral nerve roots pass caudally in an almost longitudinal direction for a considerable distance (4–8 vertebral segments) to the appropriate exit.

5. **Cauda equina** is composed of the caudal end of the spinal cord and the ventral and dorsal roots of the spinal nerves which, in these segments, pass caudally in the dural canal.

**Fig. 179.**

# 180. Dorsal View of the Central Nervous System of Newborn Infant. (3/4)

The nervous system has been exposed from the dorsal side. The skin, musculature, and vertebral arches were removed from the sacral to the cranial region. Portions of the scalp and neurocranium were also removed and the dura was resected to expose the spinal cord and brain.

1 **Cerebral Hemisphere**
*hemispherium telencephali*

**Cerebellum**
*cerebellum*

**Medulla Oblongata**
*medulla oblongata*

**Spinal Ganglion II**
*ganglion spinale II*

**Spinal Cord, Cervical Enlargement**
*medulla spinalis (intumescentia cervicalis)*

**Spinal Ganglia**
*ganglia spinalia*

3 **Intercostal Nerves**
*nervi intercostales*

**Thoracic Spinal Nerve Ventral Rami, Dorsal Rami**
*n. spinalis thoracic.*
*rami ventr., rami dorsales*

**Cutaneous Branches**
*rami cutanei*

4 **Lumbar Ganglia**
*ganglia spinalia lumbalia*

**Right Kidney**
*ren dexter*

5 **Ala of Ilium**
*ala ossis ilii*

7 **Sacral Spinal Ganglia**
*ganglia spinalia sacralia*

**Cauda Equina**
*cauda equina*

**Conus Medullaris**
*conus medullaris*

8 **Lumbar Enlargement of Spinal Cord**
*intumescentia lumbalis medullae spinalis*

**Ribs**
*costae*

**Spinal Cord**
*medulla spinalis*

9 **Thoracic Nerves, Dorsal Roots**
*radices dorsales nervorum thoracicorum*

11 **Occipital Bone**
*os occipitale*

**Brain**
*encephalon*

**Note:** 1. **Spinal ganglion**-1 on second cervical nerve is large and conspicuous; but on the first cervical nerve, the ganglion is very small or the whole dorsal root is absent. This condition is observed frequently.

2. **Spinal ganglia** are large in the brachial-1 and lumbosacral-4 regions in order to supply the large skin areas on the extremities.

3. **Spinal ganglia**-1, -4, -7 are outside dural canal in the intervertebral foramina, but **enclosed in a dural sleeve** or sheath.

4. **Dorsal roots** of the cervical region are almost perpendicular to neuraxis. More caudally, the angle between the inferior side of the root becomes more and more acute. At the sacral enlargement, the nerve roots are almost parallel to the spinal cord, are very long, and thus form the **cauda equina**-7.

5. **Spinal cord**-8, not as long as the vertebral column or the dural canal, ends as the **conus medullaris**-7 **near lower border of first lumbar vertebra.**

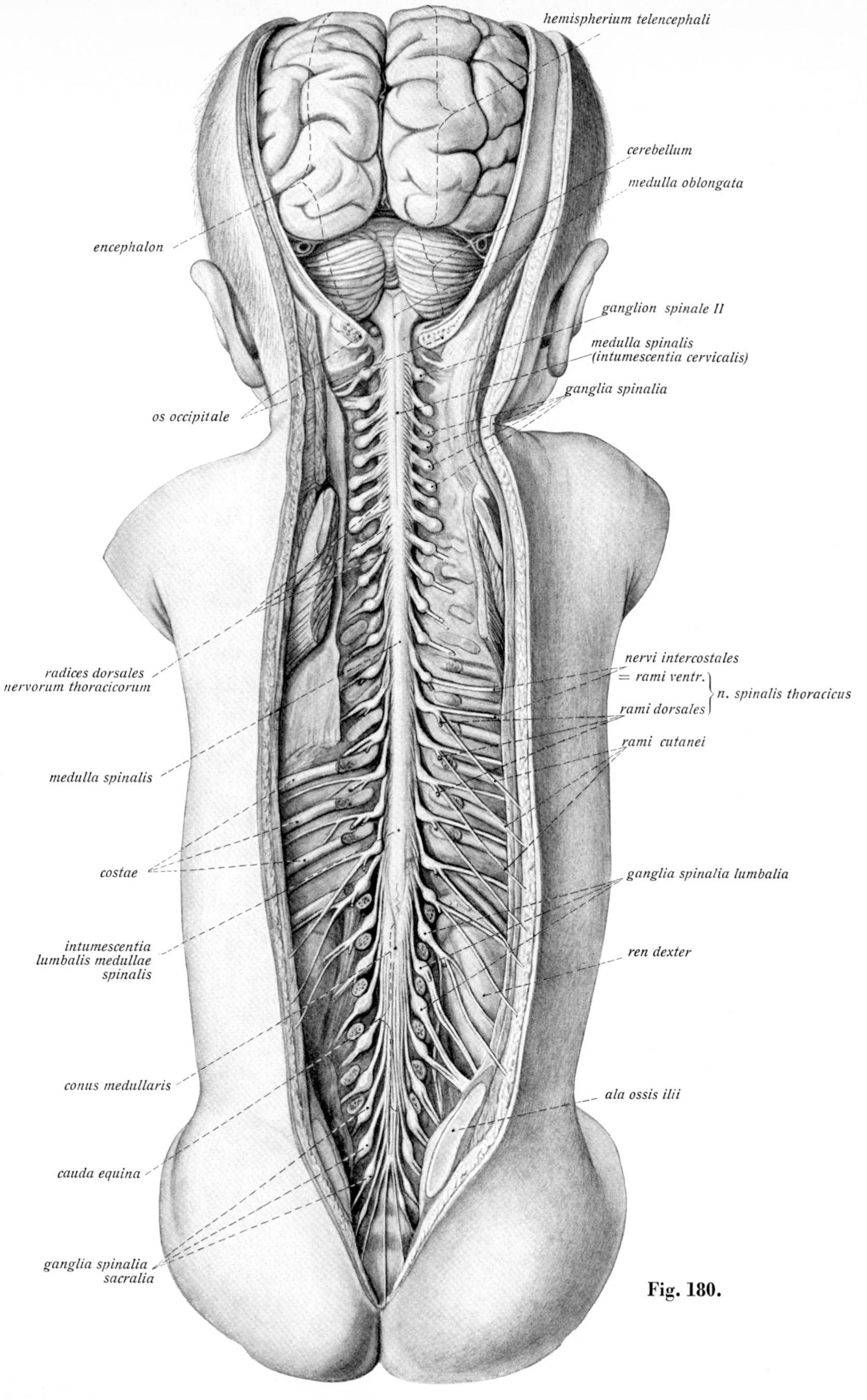
hemispherium telencephali
cerebellum
medulla oblongata
encephalon
ganglion spinale II
medulla spinalis
(intumescentia cervicalis)
ganglia spinalia
os occipitale
radices dorsales
nervorum thoracicorum
nervi intercostales
= rami ventr.
rami dorsales
n. spinalis thoracicus
rami cutanei
medulla spinalis
costae
ganglia spinalia lumbalia
intumescentia
lumbalis medullae
spinalis
ren dexter
conus medullaris
ala ossis ilii
cauda equina
ganglia spinalia
sacralia

**Fig. 180.**

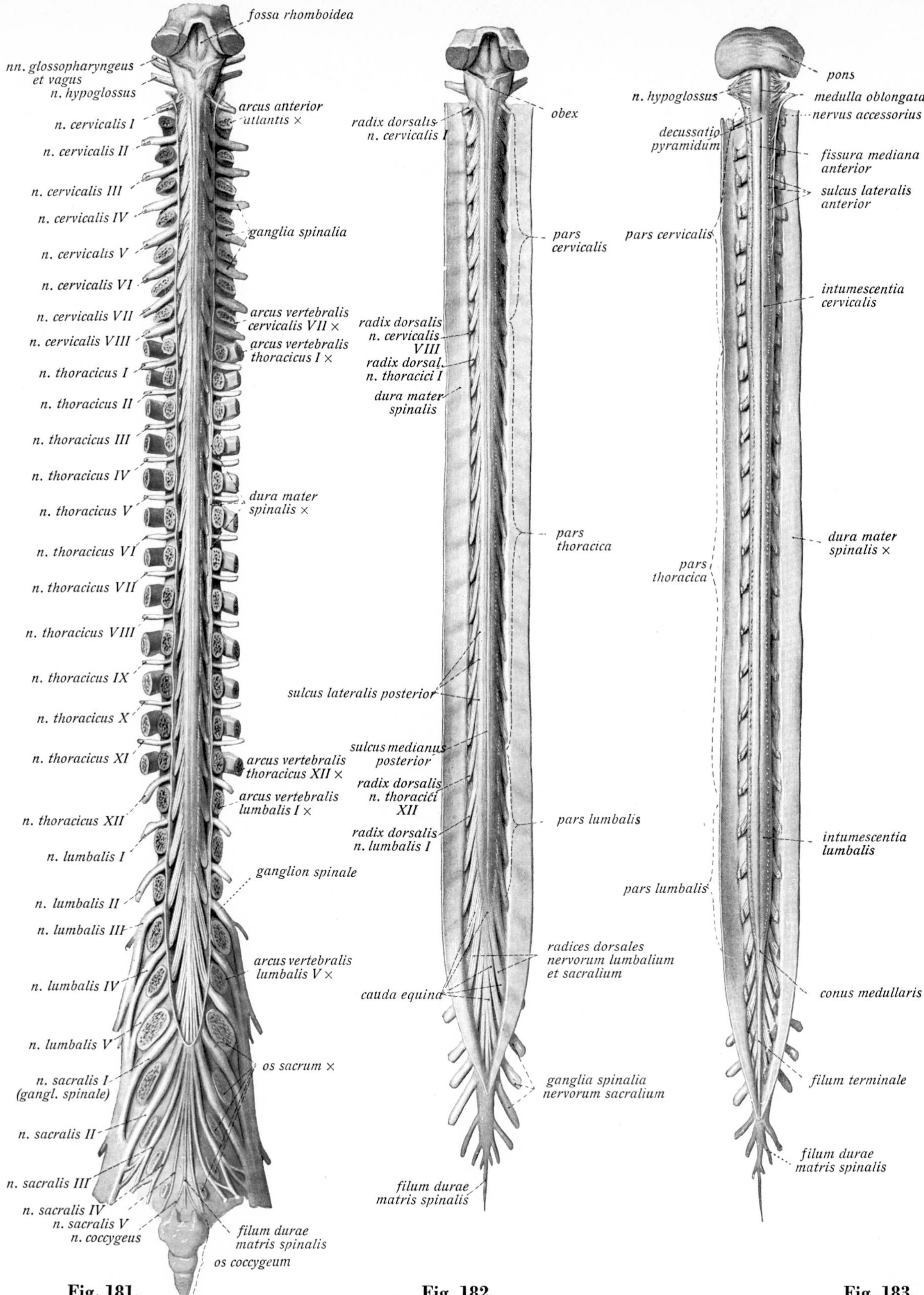

fossa rhomboidea
nn. glossopharyngeus et vagus
n. hypoglossus
arcus anterior atlantis ×
n. cervicalis I
n. cervicalis II
n. cervicalis III
n. cervicalis IV
ganglia spinalia
n. cervicalis V
n. cervicalis VI
n. cervicalis VII
arcus vertebralis cervicalis VII ×
n. cervicalis VIII
arcus vertebralis thoracicus I ×
n. thoracicus I
n. thoracicus II
n. thoracicus III
n. thoracicus IV
dura mater spinalis ×
n. thoracicus V
n. thoracicus VI
n. thoracicus VII
n. thoracicus VIII
n. thoracicus IX
n. thoracicus X
n. thoracicus XI
arcus vertebralis thoracicus XII ×
arcus vertebralis lumbalis I ×
n. thoracicus XII
n. lumbalis I
ganglion spinale
n. lumbalis II
n. lumbalis III
arcus vertebralis lumbalis V ×
n. lumbalis IV
n. lumbalis V
os sacrum ×
n. sacralis I (gangl. spinale)
n. sacralis II
n. sacralis III
n. sacralis IV
n. sacralis V
n. coccygeus
filum durae matris spinalis
os coccygeum
obex
radix dorsalis n. cervicalis I
pars cervicalis
radix dorsalis n. cervicalis VIII
radix dorsal. n. thoracici I
dura mater spinalis
pars thoracica
sulcus lateralis posterior
sulcus medianus posterior
radix dorsalis n. thoracici XII
pars lumbalis
radix dorsalis n. lumbalis I
radices dorsales nervorum lumbalium et sacralium
cauda equina
ganglia spinalia nervorum sacralium
filum durae matris spinalis
pons
n. hypoglossus
medulla oblongata
nervus accessorius
decussatio pyramidum
fissura mediana anterior
sulcus lateralis anterior
pars cervicalis
intumescentia cervicalis
dura mater spinalis ×
pars thoracica
intumescentia lumbalis
pars lumbalis
conus medullaris
filum terminale
filum durae matris spinalis


**Fig. 181.** **Fig. 182.** **Fig. 183.**

## 181. Dorsal View of Spinal Cord in the Vertebral Canal. (1/4)

1 **Anterior Arch of the Atlas**
*arcus anterior atlantis*
**Spinal Ganglia**
*ganglia spinalia*
**Spinal Nerves**
*nervi spinales*

2 **Vertebral Arch $C_7$**
*arcus vertebralis cervicalis VII [vertebrae]*
**Vertebral Arch $T_1$**
*arcus vertebralis thoracicus I [vertebrae]*

3 **Spinal Dura Mater**
*dura mater spinalis*

4 **Vertebral Arch $T_{12}$**
*arcus vertebralis thoracicus XII [vertebrae]*
**Vertebral Arch $L_1$**
*arcus vertebralis lumbalis I [vertebrae]*
**Spinal Ganglion**
*ganglion spinale*

5 **Vertebral Arch $L_5$**
*arcus vertebralis lumbalis V [vertebrae]*
**Sacrum**
*os sacrum*

6 **Filum of Dura Mater**
*filum durae matris spinalis*
**Coccyx**
*os coccygeum*
**Coccygeal Nerve**
*n. coccygeus*

7 **Sacral Nerves ($S_1$–$S_5$)**
*n. sacralis I–V*

8 **Lumbar Nerves $L_1$–$L_5$**
*n. lumbalis I–V*

9, 10 **Thoracic Nerves ($T_1$–$T_{12}$)**
*n. thoracicus I–XII*

11 **Cervical Nerves $C_1$–$C_8$**
*n. cervicalis I–VIII*

12 **Hypoglossal Nerve**
*n. hypoglossus*
**Glossopharyngeal and Vagus Nerves**
*nn. glossopharyngeus + vagus*
**Rhomboid Fossa**
*fossa rhomboidea*

**Note:** 1. **Spinal cord** (tip of conus medullaris) extends only to **lower border of first lumbar** vertebra. A needle may be introduced through the space between the lumbar vertebrae below this point and into the dural and subarachnoid space, without injuring the spinal cord.

## 182. Dorsal View of Spinal Cord and Roots of Spinal Nerves. (1/4)

1 **Obex**
*obex*
**Cervical Portion**
*pars cervicalis*

3 **Thoracic Portion**
*pars thoracica*

4 **Lumbar Portion**
*pars lumbalis*

5 **Lumbar and Sacral Nerves, Dorsal Root**
*radices dorsales nervorum lumbalium et sacralium*
**Sacral Nerves, Spinal ganglia**
*ganglia spinalia nervorum sacralium*

6 **Filum of Dura Mater**
*filum durae matris spinalis*

7 **Cauda Equina**
*cauda equina*

8 **First Lumbar Nerve, Dorsal Root**
*radix dorsalis n. lumbalis I*
**12th Thoracic Nerve, Dorsal Root**
*radix dorsalis n. thoracici XII*
**Posterior Median Sulcus**
*sulcus medianus posterior*

9 **Posterior Lateral Sulcus**
*sulcus lateralis posterior*

10 **Spinal Dura Mater**
*dura mater spinalis*

11 **1st Thoracic Nerve, Dorsal Root**
*radix dorsal. n. thoracici I*
**1st Cervical Nerve, Dorsal Root**
*radix dorsalis n. cervicalis I*

**Note:** 1. Dorsal root of first cervical nerve-12. (Frequently absent or small).

## 183. Ventral View of the Spinal Cord. (1/4) (Ventral rootlets removed)

1 **Medulla Oblongata**
*medulla oblongata*
**Accessory Nerve**
*nervus accessorius*
**Anterior Median Fissure**
*fissura mediana anterior*

2 **Anterior Lateral Sulcus**
*sulcus lateralis anterior*
**Cervical Enlargement**
*intumescentia cervicalis*

3 **Spinal Dura Mater**
*dura mater spinalis*

4 **Lumbar Enlargement**
*intumescentia lumbalis*

5 **Conus Medullaris**
*conus medullaris*
**Filum Terminale**
*filum terminale*

6 **Filum of Dura Mater**
*filum durae matris spinalis*

7 **Lumbar Portion**
*pars lumbalis*

9 **Thoracic Portion**
*pars thoracica*

11 **Cervical Portion**
*pars cervicalis*
**Decussation of Pyramids**
*decussatio pyramidum*

12 **Hypoglossal Nerve**
*n. hypoglossus*
**Pons**
*pons*

**Note:** 1. Origin of accessory nerve-1, between ventral and dorsal rootlets, $C_1$ to $C_6$.

2. Ventral rootlets are in a direct line with rootlets of the **hypoglossal nerve**-12, indicating that the hypoglossal nerve is similar to a ventral root or motor portion of a spinal nerve. The transient ganglion, which appears embryologically on the hypoglossal nerve, is known as Froriep's ganglion. The hypoglossal appears to be a spinal nerve that has gained entrance into skull by the fusion of several vertebral segments to form the occipital bone (during phylogeny).

# 184. Ventral Exposure of Mid-Thoracic Spinal Cord and Its Membranes.

1 **Spinal Dura Mater**
*dura mater spinalis*
**Spinal Arachnoid**
*arachnoidea spinalis*
**Anterior Spinal Artery and Vein**
*a. v. spinalis anterior*
**Radicular Branch, Anterior Spinal Artery**
*r. radicularis a. spinalis anterioris*
**Spinal Nerve, Dorsal and Ventral Rami**
*r. posterior [dorsalis]* } *n. spinalis*
*r. anterior [ventralis]* }
**Spinal Ganglion and Ventral Root of Spinal Nerve**
*ganglion spinale et radix ventralis n. spinalis*

2 **Subarachnoid Space**
*cavum subarachnoidale*
**Subdural Space**
*cavum subdurale*
**Spinal Nerve, Posterior Meningeal Branch**
*r. meningeus posterior n. spinalis*
**Spinal Ganglion with Sheath of Dura Mater**
*ganglion spinale cum vagina dura matris*
**Spinal Nerve, Anterior Meningeal Branch**
*r. meningeus anterior n. spinalis*
**Internal Vertebral Venous Plexus**
*plexus venosi vertebrales interni*
**Intercostal Artery, Spinal Branches**
*rr. spinales a. intercostalis*
**Fat in Epidural Space**
*corpus adiposum spatii interduralis (epiduralis)*

3 **Posterior Longitudinal Ligament**
*lig. longitudinale posterius*
**Body of Vertebra, Superior Surface**
*facies superior corporis vertebrae*
**Anterior Longitudinal Ligament**
*lig. longitudinale anterius*
**Hemiazygos Vein**
*v. hemiazygos*

4 **Endothoracic Fascia**
*fascia endothoracica*
**Costal Pleura**
*pleura costalis*
**Thoracic Aorta and Aortic Plexus**
*aorta thoracica et plexus aorticus*
**Posterior Esophageal Cords (Vagus)**
*chordae esophageae posteriores (n. vagus dexter)*
**Branches of Esophageal Arteries and Veins**
*[rr. aa. et vv. esophageae]*
*rr. esophagei et vv. esophageae*
**Esophagus**
*esophagus*
**Anterior Esophageal Cord (Vagus Nerve)**
*chordae esophageae anteriores (n. vagus sinister)*

5 **Diaphragmatic Portion of Pericardium**
*planum inclinatum et pars diaphragmatica pericardii*
**Thoracic Duct**
*ductus thoracicus*

6 **Inferior Vena Cava**
*v. cava inferior*
**Hepatic Veins (joining Inferior Vena Cava)**
*vv. hepaticae confluentes*
**Azygos Vein**
*v. azygos*

7 **Pericardiacophrenic Artery and Vein** (between mediastinal pleura and parietal pericardium)
*a. v. pericardiacophrenica (interpleuram mediastinalem et pericardium parietale)*
**Phrenic Nerve**
*n. phrenicus*

8 **Central Tendon of Diaphragm and Diaphragmatic Pleura**
*centrum tendineum diaphragmatis et pleura diaphragmatica*
**Greater Splanchnic Nerve**
*n. splanchnicus major*
**Sympathetic Trunk**
*truncus sympathicus*
**Costal Pleura**
*pleura costalis*
**Internal Intercostal Muscle**
*m. intercostalis internum (translucens)*
**Endothoracic Fascia**
*fascia endothoracica*

9 **Intercostal Vein, Artery, and Nerve**
*v., a. et n. intercostalis*
**Body of Rib**
*corpus costae*
**External Intercostal Muscle**
*m. intercostalis externus*
**Fovea Costalis for Head of Rib**
*fovea costalis capituli costae*
**Rami Communicantes and Sympathetic Trunk Ganglia**
*ganglia trunci sympathici et rr. communicantes*

10 **Fovea Costalis of Transverse Process**
*fovea costalis transversalis*
**Pedicle of Vertebral Arch**
*pediculus arcus vertebralis*
**Spinal Ganglion, Dural Sheath** resected
*ganglion spinale, vagina durae matris resecta*

11 **Denticulate Ligament**
*lig. denticulatum*
**Superior Articular Process of Vertebra**
*processus articularis superior vertebrae*
**Root Filaments, Dorsal and Ventral, of Spinal Nerve**
*fila radicularia radicis dorsalis et ventralis n. spinalis*

**Note:** 1. Denticulate ligament-11, which extends from pia mater to dura mater-1, stabilizes the spinal cord in the subarachnoid space-2.

2. Arachnoid is closely applied to dura. The subdural space is, therefore, a narrow slit.

3. Epidural space-2 is occupied by a venous plexus, small arteries, and fat.

4. Spinal ganglia and nerve roots are enclosed in sheaths of dura in the intervertebral foramina.

5. In the thoracic region, each ventral ramus of a spinal nerve (intercostal nerve) has at least 2 connections with the ganglionated sympathetic trunk, the rami communicantes-9 (gray and white).

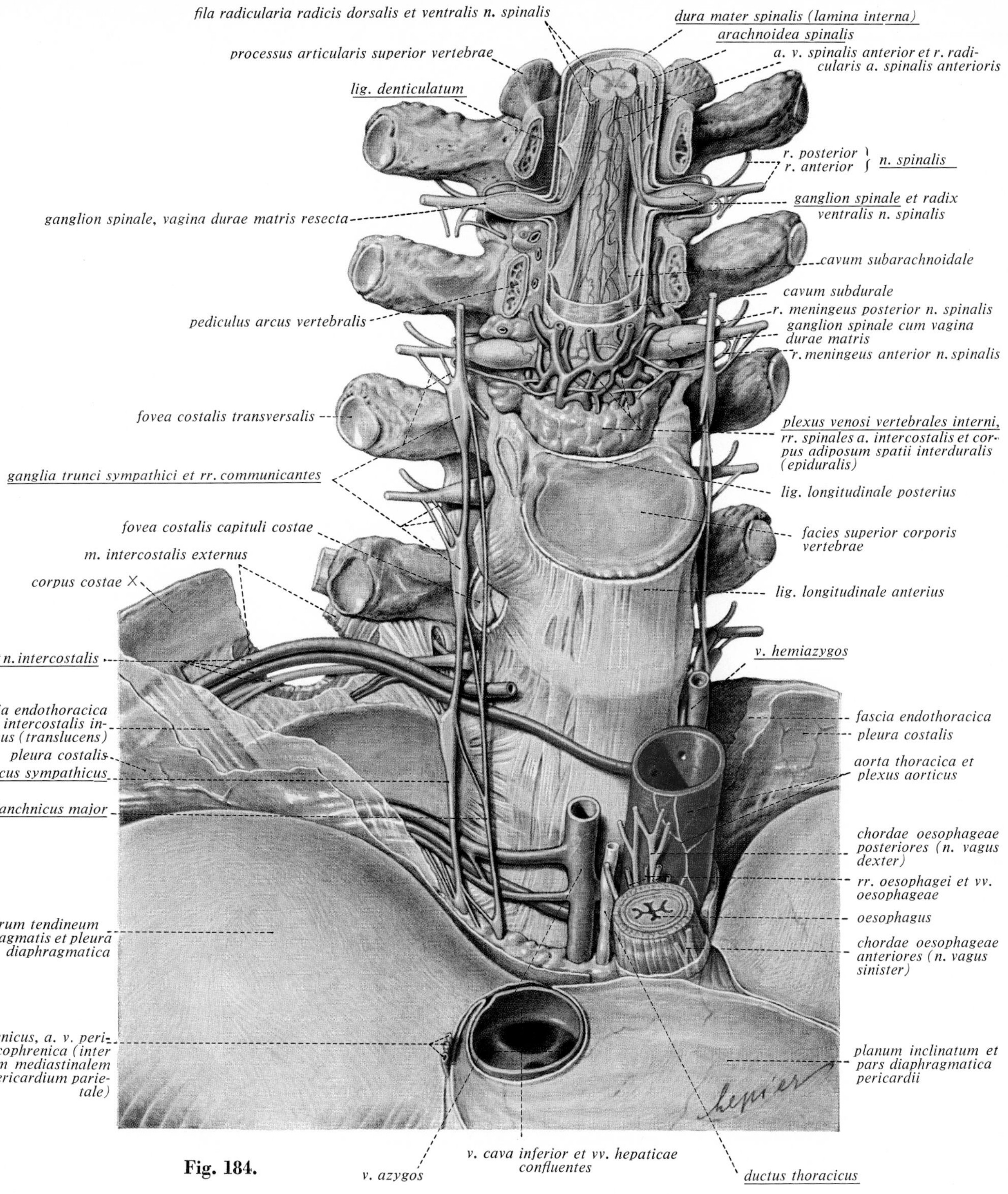
fila radicularia radicis dorsalis et ventralis n. spinalis
processus articularis superior vertebrae
lig. denticulatum
ganglion spinale, vagina durae matris resecta
pediculus arcus vertebralis
fovea costalis transversalis
ganglia trunci sympathici et rr. communicantes
fovea costalis capituli costae
m. intercostalis externus
corpus costae X
. et n. intercostalis
scia endothoracica
m. intercostalis in-
ernus (translucens)
pleura costalis
uncus sympathicus
splanchnicus major
entrum tendineum
hragmatis et pleura
diaphragmatica
hrenicus, a. v. peri-
iacophrenica (inter
ram mediastinalem
pericardium parie-
tale)
v. azygos
v. cava inferior et vv. hepaticae
confluentes
ductus thoracicus
dura mater spinalis (lamina interna)
arachnoidea spinalis
a. v. spinalis anterior et r. radicularis a. spinalis anterioris
r. posterior
r. anterior
n. spinalis
ganglion spinale et radix
ventralis n. spinalis
cavum subarachnoidale
cavum subdurale
r. meningeus posterior n. spinalis
ganglion spinale cum vagina
durae matris
r. meningeus anterior n. spinalis
plexus venosi vertebrales interni,
rr. spinales a. intercostalis et corpus adiposum spatii interduralis
(epiduralis)
lig. longitudinale posterius
facies superior corporis
vertebrae
lig. longitudinale anterius
v. hemiazygos
fascia endothoracica
pleura costalis
aorta thoracica et
plexus aorticus
chordae oesophageae
posteriores (n. vagus
dexter)
rr. oesophagei et vv.
oesophageae
oesophagus
chordae oesophageae
anteriores (n. vagus
sinister)
planum inclinatum et
pars diaphragmatica
pericardii

**Fig. 184.**

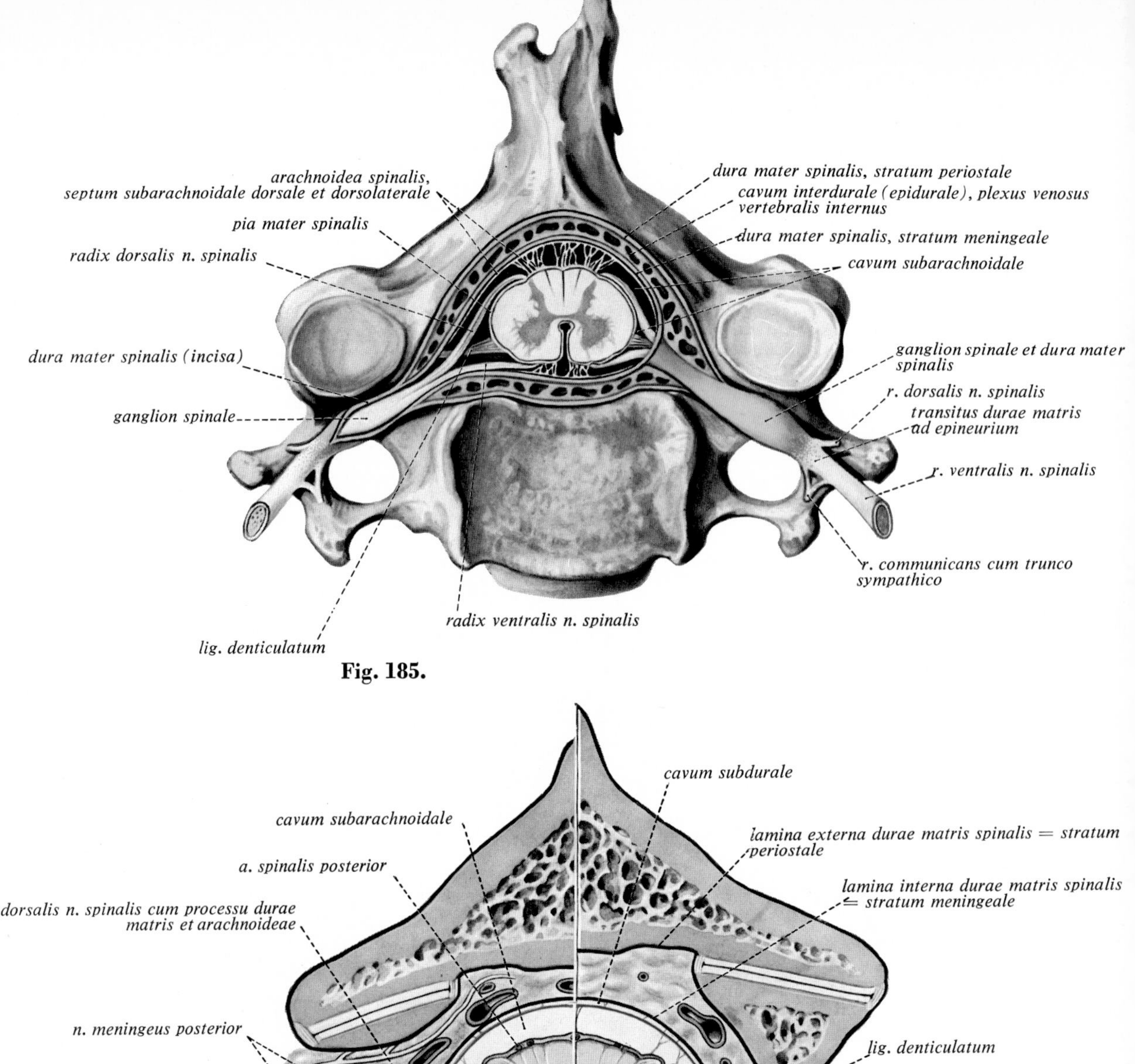
arachnoidea spinalis,
septum subarachnoidale dorsale et dorsolaterale
pia mater spinalis
radix dorsalis n. spinalis
dura mater spinalis (incisa)
ganglion spinale
dura mater spinalis, stratum periostale
cavum interdurale (epidurale), plexus venosus vertebralis internus
dura mater spinalis, stratum meningeale
cavum subarachnoidale
ganglion spinale et dura mater spinalis
r. dorsalis n. spinalis
transitus durae matris ad epineurium
r. ventralis n. spinalis
r. communicans cum trunco sympathico
radix ventralis n. spinalis
lig. denticulatum

**Fig. 185.**

cavum subarachnoidale
a. spinalis posterior
radix dorsalis n. spinalis cum processu durae matris et arachnoideae
n. meningeus posterior
ganglion spinale
n. spinalis { r. ventralis
r. dorsalis
r. spinalis a. et v. intercostalis
radix ventralis n. spinalis cum processu durae matris et arachnoideae
n. meningeus anterior
vv. basivertebrales et ostium plexus venosi vertebralis interni
cavum subdurale
lamina externa durae matris spinalis = stratum periostale
lamina interna durae matris spinalis = stratum meningeale
lig. denticulatum
corpus adiposum spatii interdur (epiduralis) et plexus venosi ve bralis interni, rr. a. spinalis
anulus fibrosus disci intervertebralis
fissura mediana anterior, pia mater spinalis et a. spinalis anterior
ig. longitudinale posterius

**Fig. 186.**

## 185. Investing Membranes of Spinal Cord at Cervical Level.

Periosteum of cervical vertebra, shown in yellow and labeled "dura mater spinalis, stratum periostale"-2, is usually regarded as periosteum lining the vertebral canal.

2 **Periosteum of Vertebra**
*dura mater spinalis, stratum periostale*

**Epidural Venous Plexus and Space**
*cavum interdurale (epidurale) plexus venosus vertebralis internus*

**Spinal Dura Mater**
*dura mater spinalis, stratum meningeale*

3 **Subarachnoid Space**
*cavum subarachnoidale*

**Spinal Ganglion within Dural Sheath**
*ganglion spinale et dura mater spinalis*

**Spinal Nerve, Dorsal Ramus**
*r. dorsalis n. spinalis*

**Transition of Dura Mater to Epineurium**
*transitus durae matris ad epineurium*

4 **Spinal Nerve, Ventral Ramus**
*r. ventralis n. spinalis*

**Communicating Ramus with Sympathetic Trunk**
*r. communicans cum trunco sympathico*

7 **Spinal Nerve, Ventral Root**
*radix ventralis n. spinalis*

8 **Denticulate Ligament**
*lig. denticulatum*

9 **Spinal Ganglion**
*ganglion spinale*

**Sleeve of Dura Mater** (opened)
*dura mater spinalis (incisa)*

**Spinal Nerve, Dorsal Root**
*radix dorsalis n. spinalis*

10 **Pia Mater**
*pia mater spinalis*

**Arachnoidal Membrane; Dorsal and Dorsolateral Septa**
*arachnoidea spinalis, septum subarachnoidale dorsale et dorsolaterale*

**Note:** 1. Outer **investing membrane** of spinal cord is the **dura mater** (stratum meningeal-2) (yellow). It is sometimes called the **pachymeninx** because it is thick and tough. It almost fills the bony cavity. The narrow **epidural space**-2 contains fat and blood vessels which pass to and from the spinal cord and its meninges. Spinal nerves pierce and carry with them a sleeve of dura mater-3, -9 as they pass through the intervertebral foramina. Smooth deep surface of the dura is in contact with the arachnoid membrane-10.

## 186. Investing Membranes of Spinal Cord at Thoracic Level.

(Modified from Pernkopf's Topographische Anatomie des Menschen I)

1 **Subdural Space**
*cavum subdurale*

**Periosteum of Vertebra**
*lamina externa dura matris spinalis = stratum periostale*

2 **Spinal Dura Mater**
*lamina interna durae matris spinalis = stratum meningeale*

3 **Denticulate Ligament**
*lig. denticulatum*

**Fat,** and **Venous Plexus in Epidural Space**
*corpus adiposum spatii interduralis (epiduralis) et plexus venosi vertebralis interni*

**Branches** of **Spinal Artery**
*rr. a. spinalis*

**Intervertebral Disc, Anulus Fibrosus**
*anulus fibrosus disci intervertebralis*

4 **Spinal Pia Mater** and **Anterior Spinal Artery**
*pia mater spinalis et a. spinalis anterior*

5 **Anterior Median Fissure**
*fissura mediana anterior*

6 **Posterior Longitudinal Ligament**
*lig. longitudinale posterius*

8 **Basivertebral Veins and Communication with Internal Vertebral Venous Plexus**
*v. v. basivertebrales et ostium plexus venosi vertebralis interni*

**Anterior Meningeal Nerve**
*n. meningeus anterior*

**Ventral Root of Spinal Nerve within Sleeve of Dura Mater** and **Arachnoid**
*radix ventralis n. spinalis cum processu durae matris et arachnoideae*

9 **Intercostal Artery** and **Vein, Spinal Branch**
*r. spinalis a. et v. intercostalis*

**Spinal Nerve, Ventral** and **Dorsal Rami**
*n. spinalis* { *r. ventralis* / *r. dorsalis* }

**Spinal Ganglion**
*ganglion spinale*

**Posterior Meningeal Nerve**
*n. meningeus posterior*

10 **Dorsal Root** of **Spinal Nerve** within Sleeve of **Dura** and **Arachnoid**
*radix dorsalis n. spinalis cum processu durae matris et arachnoideae*

**Posterior Spinal Artery**
*a. spinalis posterior*

11 **Subarachnoid Space**
*cavum subarachnoidale*

**Note:** 1. The **arachnoid** (red) and **pia mater** (blue) **(leptomeninx)** form a double-walled jacket which is in direct contact with the central nervous system. Space between arachnoidal and pial membranes is the **subarachnoid space**-11, and is distended by the **cerebrospinal fluid** to such a degree that it fills the space between the dura and spinal cord. Very delicate filaments that connect the two membranes resemble spider webs but, in some areas, have a septal-like character. Outer wall of the space is the **arachnoidal membrane.** Inner wall is the pia mater-4 which is firmly attached to spinal cord and, in some areas, penetrates it.

## 187. Part of Spinal Cord with Meninges Dissected. (Dorsal View) (1/1)

At top, dura mater-1 was reflected and arachnoid-8 removed.

1 **Denticulate Ligament**
*ligamentum denticulatum*

**Spinal Dura Mater**
*dura mater spinalis*

5 **Spinal Ganglia**
*ganglia spinalia*

7 **Spinal Dura Mater (Pachymeninx)**
*dura mater spinalis (pachymeninx)*

8 **Spinal Arachnoid**
*arachnoidea spinalis*

10 **Dorsal Root Filaments**
*fila radicularia dorsalia*

11 **Posterior Lateral Sulcus**
*sulcus lateralis posterior*

12 **Posterior Median Sulcus**
*sulcus medianus posterior*

**Anterior Median Fissure**
*fissura mediana anterior*

**Note:** 1. **Dorsal roots of spinal nerves** are not single nerve trunks but multiple strands called the **dorsal root filaments**-10.

2. **Spinal arachnoidal membrane**-8 in life and in some cadavers is a thin transparent membrane. It is connected to the pia by fine spider-web like filaments. The **pia mater** also sends wing-like extensions to the dura attached intermittently between the openings for nerves. Since they have the appearance of teeth, the pial extension is called the **denticulate ligament**-1.

## 188. Part of Spinal Cord, with its Nerve Roots. (Ventral View) (1/1)

1 **Dorsal Root Filaments**
*fila radicularia radicis dorsalis*

**Ventral Root Filaments**
*fila radicularia radicis ventralis*

2 **Spinal Ganglion**
*ganglion spinale*

3, 10 **Spinal Nerve**
*nervus spinalis*

10 **Anterior Lateral Sulcus**
*sulcus lateralis anterior*

11 **Anterior Median Fissure**
*fissura mediana anterior*

**Note:** 1. **Dorsal spinal ganglion**-2 located near junction of dorsal and ventral roots. At this point, rootlets have united to form a common trunk.

## 189. Segment of Spinal Cord with Roots and Ganglia. (1/1)

1 **Posterior Lateral Sulcus**
*sulcus lateralis posterior*

2 **Posterior Column**
*columna posterior*

3 **Spinal Ganglion**
*ganglion spinale*
**Spinal Nerve, Dorsal Ramus**
*ramus dorsalis n. spinalis*

**Spinal Nerve, Ventral Ramus**
*ramus ventralis nervi spinalis*

5 **Anterior Column**
*columna anterior*

6 **Anterior Median Fissure**
*fissura mediana anterior*

7 **Anterior Column**
*columna anterior*

8 **Ventral Root**
*radix ventralis*

9 **Spinal Nerve**
*nervus spinalis*

11 **Dorsal Root**
*radix dorsalis*

12 **Posterior Median Septum**
*septum medianum posterius*

**Note:** 1. **Dorsal root fibers**-11 **enter the cord at posterior lateral sulcus**-1.

2. Right and left halves of spinal cord separated dorsally by **posterior median septum**-12 and, on ventral side, by the **anterior median fissure**-6.

3. Near dorsal spinal ganglion-3, the spinal nerve divides into a small **dorsal ramus**-3 and a large **ventral ramus**-3.

## 190. Display of Conus Medullaris and Cauda Equina. (Vent. View) (1/1)

1 **Spinal Ganglia**
*ganglia spinalia*

**Anterior Median Fissure**
*fissura mediana anterior*

2 **Spinal Nerves, Lumbar**
*nervi spinales (lumbales)*

3 **Conus Medullaris**
*conus medullaris*

4 **Filum Terminale**
*filum terminale*

**Spinal Dura Mater**
*dura mater spinalis*

6 **Coccygeal Nerve**
*nervus coccygeus*

7 **Filum Terminale**
*filum terminale*
**Cauda Equina**
*cauda equina*

8 **Spinal Dura Mater**
*dura mater spinalis*

**Note:** 1. Resemblance of **cauda equina**-7 to a horse's tail; the sudden tapering of spinal cord to form **conus medullaris**-3; and continuation of pia as the **filum terminale**-4.

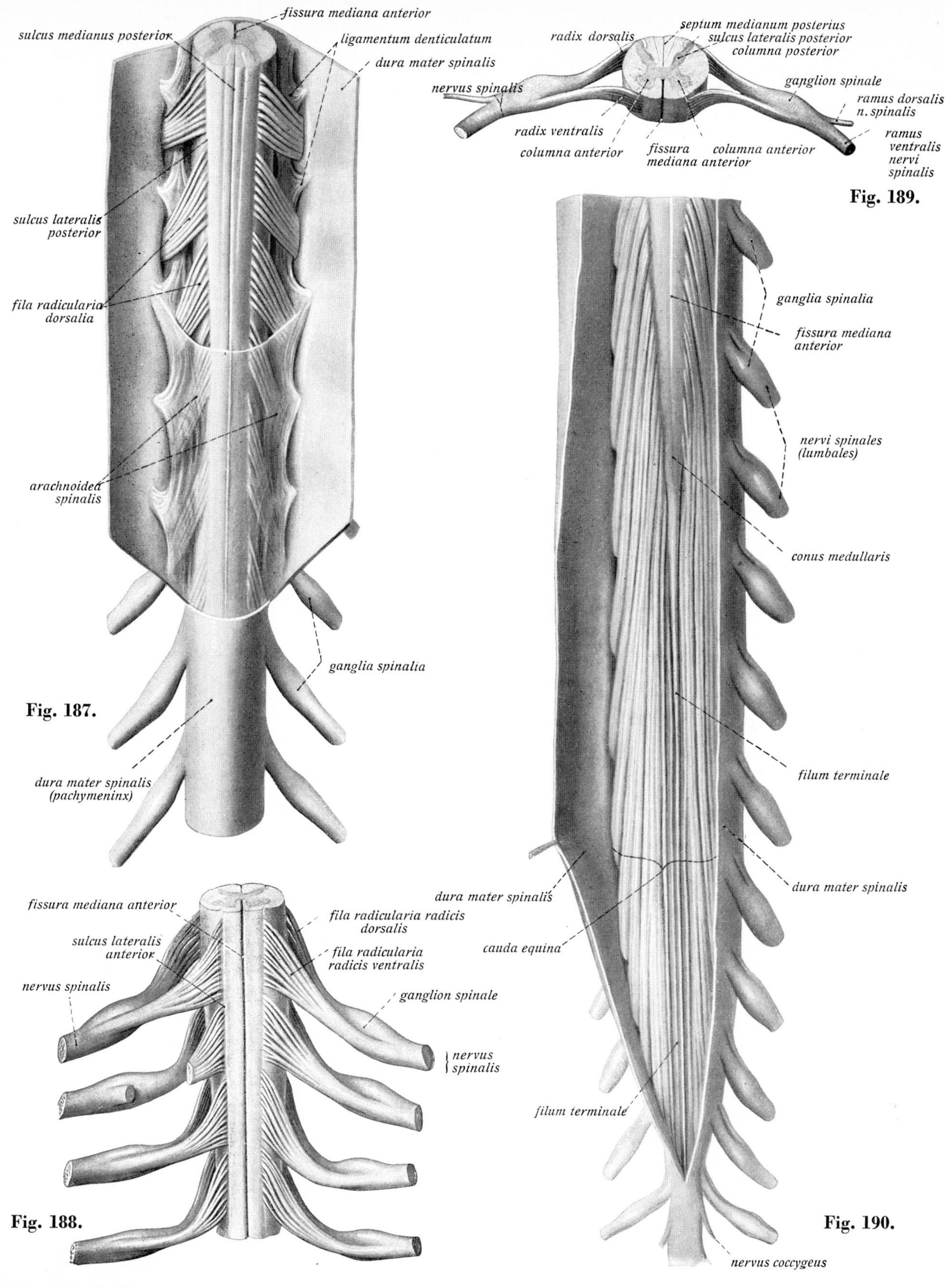
fissura mediana anterior
sulcus medianus posterior
ligamentum denticulatum
dura mater spinalis
sulcus lateralis posterior
fila radicularia dorsalia
arachnoidea spinalis
ganglia spinalia
dura mater spinalis (pachymeninx)
radix dorsalis
septum medianum posterius
sulcus lateralis posterior
columna posterior
ganglion spinale
nervus spinalis
ramus dorsalis n. spinalis
radix ventralis
columna anterior
fissura mediana anterior
columna anterior
ramus ventralis nervi spinalis
ganglia spinalia
fissura mediana anterior
nervi spinales (lumbales)
conus medullaris
filum terminale
dura mater spinalis
dura mater spinalis
cauda equina
filum terminale
nervus coccygeus
fissura mediana anterior
fila radicularia radicis dorsalis
sulcus lateralis anterior
fila radicularia radicis ventralis
nervus spinalis
ganglion spinale
nervus spinalis

Fig. 187.

Fig. 188.

Fig. 189.

Fig. 190.

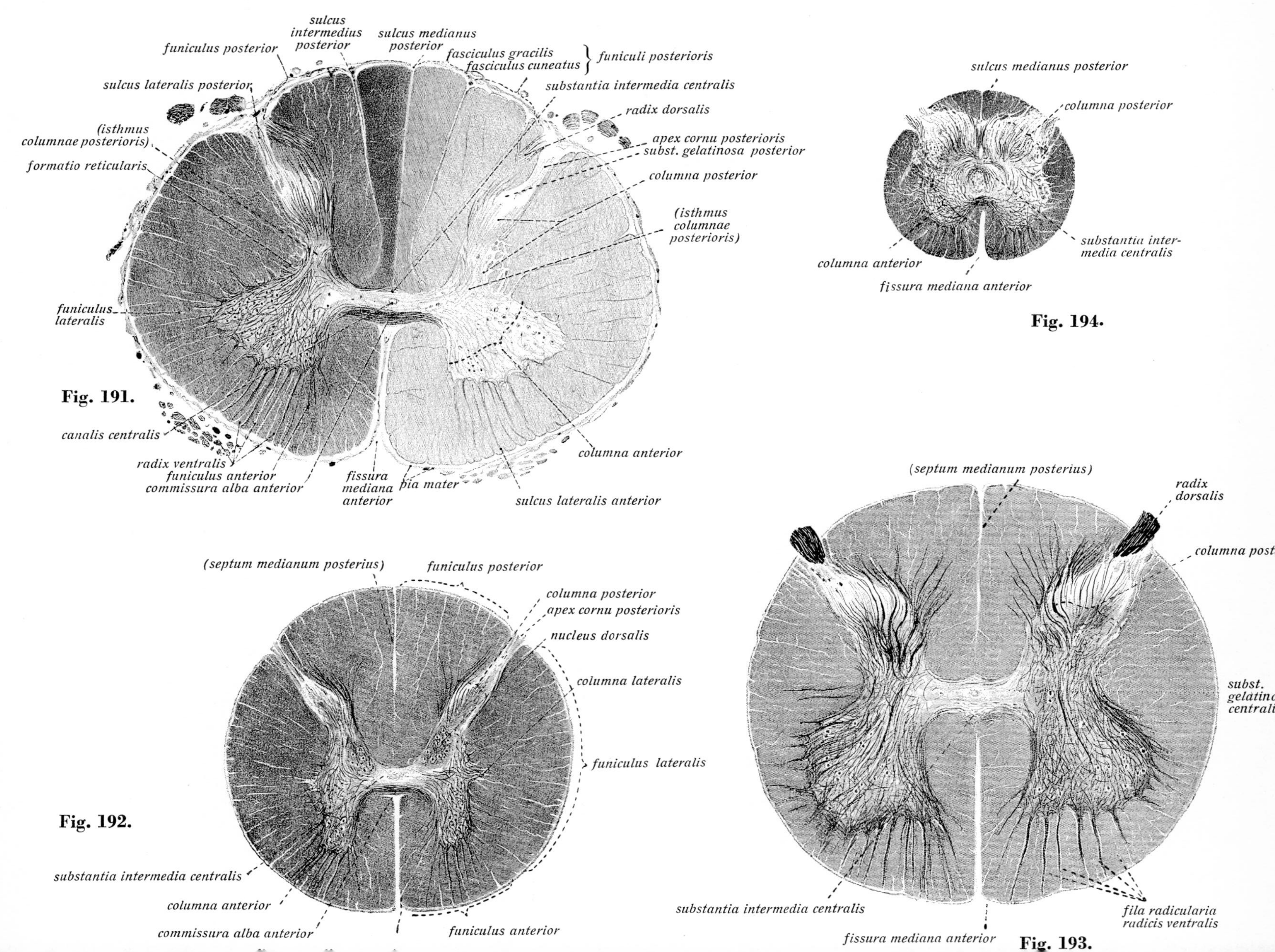

sulcus intermedius posterior
sulcus medianus posterior
funiculus posterior
fasciculus gracilis
fasciculus cuneatus
funiculi posterioris
sulcus lateralis posterior
substantia intermedia centralis
radix dorsalis
(isthmus columnae posterioris)
apex cornu posterioris
subst. gelatinosa posterior
formatio reticularis
columna posterior
(isthmus columnae posterioris)
funiculus lateralis
canalis centralis
columna anterior
radix ventralis
funiculus anterior
commissura alba anterior
fissura mediana anterior
pia mater
sulcus lateralis anterior
sulcus medianus posterior
columna posterior
substantia intermedia centralis
columna anterior
fissura mediana anterior
(septum medianum posterius)
funiculus posterior
columna posterior
apex cornu posterioris
nucleus dorsalis
columna lateralis
funiculus lateralis
substantia intermedia centralis
columna anterior
commissura alba anterior
funiculus anterior
(septum medianum posterius)
radix dorsalis
columna posterior
subst. gelatinosa centralis
substantia intermedia centralis
fila radicularia radicis ventralis
fissura mediana anterior


Fig. 191.

Fig. 192.

Fig. 193.

Fig. 194.

# CROSS SECTIONS OF SPINAL CORD. (9/1)

## 191. Through the Cervical Enlargement.

1 **Posterior Funiculus:**
**Fasciculus Gracilis**
**Fasciculus Cuneatus**
*funiculi posterioris:*
*fasciculus gracilis*
*fasciculus cuneatus*
**Substantia Intermedia Centralis**
*substantia intermedia centralis*
2 **Dorsal Root**
*radix dorsalis*
**Apex of the Dorsal Horn**
*apex cornus posterioris*
**Substantia Gelatinosa**
*subst. gelatinosa posterior*
**Posterior Column**
*columna posterior*
**(Isthmus of Posterior Column)**
*(isthmus columnae posterioris)*
4 **Anterior Column**
*columna anterior*
5 **Anteriolateral Sulcus**
*sulcus lateralis anterior*
6 **Pia Mater**
*pia mater*
**Anterior Median Fissure**
*fissura mediana anterior*
8 **(Anterior White Commissure)**
*(commissura alba anterior)*
**Anterior Funiculus**
*funiculus anterior*
**Ventral Root**
*radix ventralis*
**Central Canal**
*canalis centralis*
9 **Lateral Funiculus**
*funiculus lateralis*
10 **Reticular Formation**
*formatio reticularis*
**(Isthmus of Posterior Column)**
*(isthmus columnae posterioris)*
**Posteriolateral Sulcus**
*sulcus lateralis posterior*
11 **Posterior Funiculus**
*funiculus posterior*
**Posterior Intermediate Sulcus**
*sulcus intermedius posterior*
12 **Posterior Median Sulcus**
*sulcus medianus posterior*

**Note:** 1. Massive **anterior column** (motor fibers to sup. ext.)
2. Division of white matter of **posterior funiculus**-1 into strap-like **fasciculus gracilis**-1 and wedge-shaped **fasciculus cuneatus**-1 near posterior column-2.
3. Relatively conspicuous area, the **substantia gelatinosa**-2, near apex of posterior horn.

## 192. Through Thoracic Spinal Cord.

1 **Posterior Column**
*columna posterior*
2 **Apex of Posterior Horn**
*apex cornu[s] posterioris*
**Dorsal Nucleus**
*nucleus dorsalis*
**Lateral Column**
*columna lateralis*
3 **Lateral Funiculus**
*funiculus lateralis*
5 **Anterior Funiculus**
*funiculus anterior*
7 **Anterior Median Fissure**
*fissura mediana anterior*
8 **(Anterior White Commissure)**
*(commissura alba anterior)*
**Anterior Column**
*columna anterior*
**Substantia Intermedia Centralis**
*substantia intermedia centralis*
12 **(Posterior Median Septum)**
*(septum medianum posterius)*
**Posterior Funiculus**
*funiculus posterior*

**Note:** 1. H-shaped appearance of **gray matter**.
2. Prominent **lateral columns**-2 or **intermediolateral horns**, for **presynaptic sympathetic neuron cell bodies**.
3. Relatively small amount of gray matter in **anterior column**-8 (muscle mass of these segments small.)

## 194. Through Conus Medullaris.

1 **Posterior Column**
*columna posterior*
4 **Substantia Intermedia Centralis**
**(Posterior Commissure)**
*substantia intermedia centralis*
7 **Anterior Median Fissure**
*fissura mediana anterior*
8 **Anterior Column**
*columna anterior*
12 **Posterior Median Sulcus**
*sulcus medianus posterior*

**Note:** Relatively large amount of gray matter as compared to white. Amount of gray is, however, much smaller than at lumbar enlargement. (Compare Fig. 193)

## 193. Through Lumbar Enlargement.

1 **Dorsal Root**
*radix dorsalis*
2 **Posterior Column**
*columna posterior*
5 **Root Filaments of Ventral Root**
*fila radicularia radicis ventralis*
7 **Anterior Median Fissure**
*fissura mediana anterior*
8 **Substantia Intermedia Centralis**
**(Anterior Commissure)**
*substantia intermedia centralis*
12 **(Posterior Median Septum)**
*(septum medianum posterius)*

**Note:** 1. Large **anterior columns** (ventral horns) to supply muscles of inferior extremity and relatively large **posterior columns**-2 (dorsal horns) to receive sensory impulses from skin of inferior extremity.
2. Relatively large amount of gray matter as compared to white or tract areas.

## 195. Diagram of the Arrangement of the Meninges and the Subarachnoid Space.

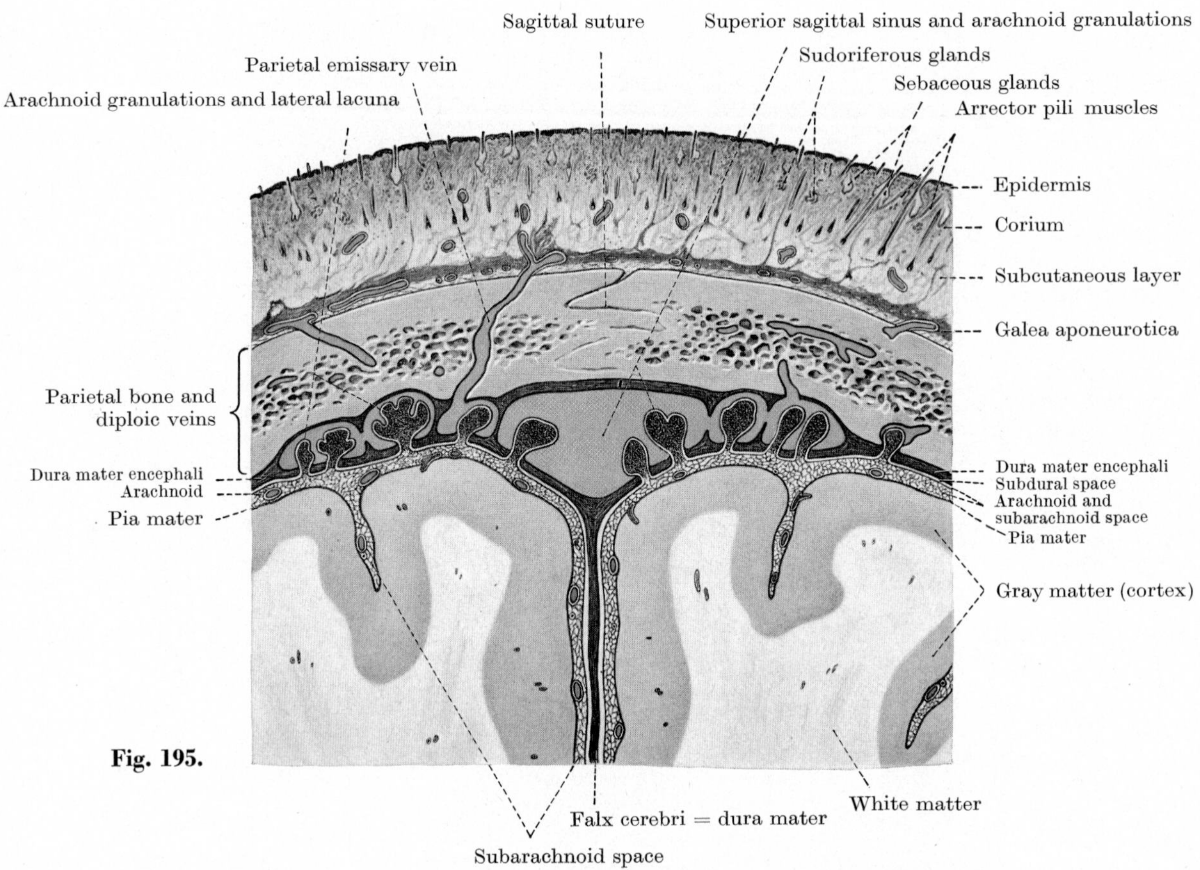
Sagittal suture
Superior sagittal sinus and arachnoid granulations
Sudoriferous glands
Parietal emissary vein
Sebaceous glands
Arachnoid granulations and lateral lacuna
Arrector pili muscles
Epidermis
Corium
Subcutaneous layer
Galea aponeurotica
Parietal bone and diploic veins
Dura mater encephali
Arachnoid
Pia mater
Dura mater encephali
Subdural space
Arachnoid and subarachnoid space
Pia mater
Gray matter (cortex)
White matter
Falx cerebri = dura mater
Subarachnoid space

Fig. 195.

The middle portion of a frontal section through the roof of the cranium and upper part of the cerebral hemispheres is depicted to illustrate the relationship of the meninges. Veins and sinuses are blue.

**Note:** 1. **Arachnoidal granulations** extend through dura into superior sagittal sinus and, further laterally, through dura and inner table of bone into diploë of skull.

2. Arachnoidal granulations assist in circulation of cerebrospinal fluid, which fills the subarachnoid spaces.

## 196. The Diploic Veins in the Roof and Walls of the Cranium.

(Exposed by chiseling off the outer table of the flat cranial bones.) (Viewed from above and the right.)

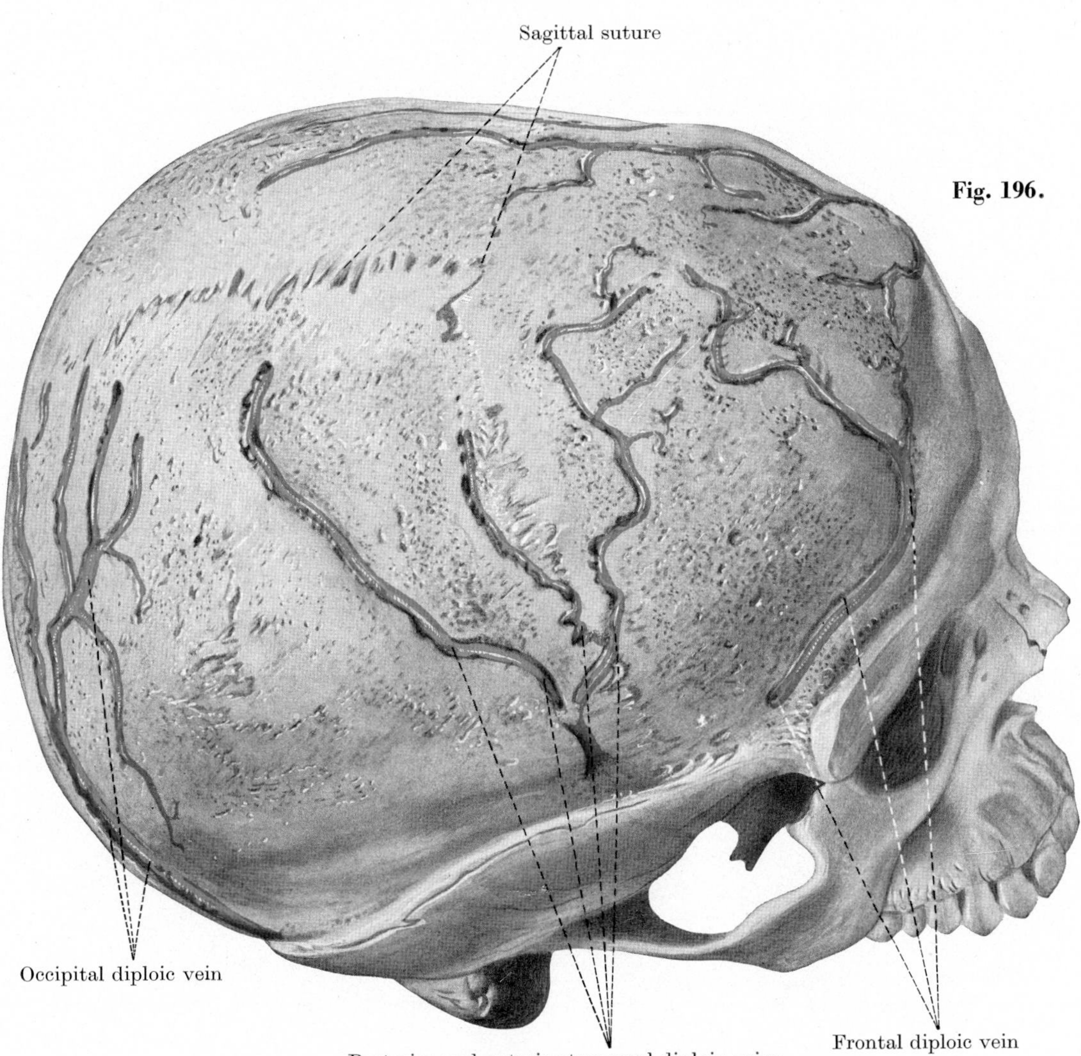
Sagittal suture
Fig. 196.
Occipital diploic vein
Posterior and anterior temporal diploic veins
Frontal diploic vein

**Note:** 1. In the flat bones that form the vault of the skull between inner and outer tables of compact bone, there is spongy bone filled with marrow and venous channels. This is called the "diploë". The venous channels are referred to as **diploic veins.** They communicate with meningeal veins, sinuses of the dura mater, and scalp veins, and are named according to their position.

## 197. Sagittal Section of Head near Median Plane to Illustrate the Circulation Pattern and Outflow Areas of the Cerebrospinal Fluid.

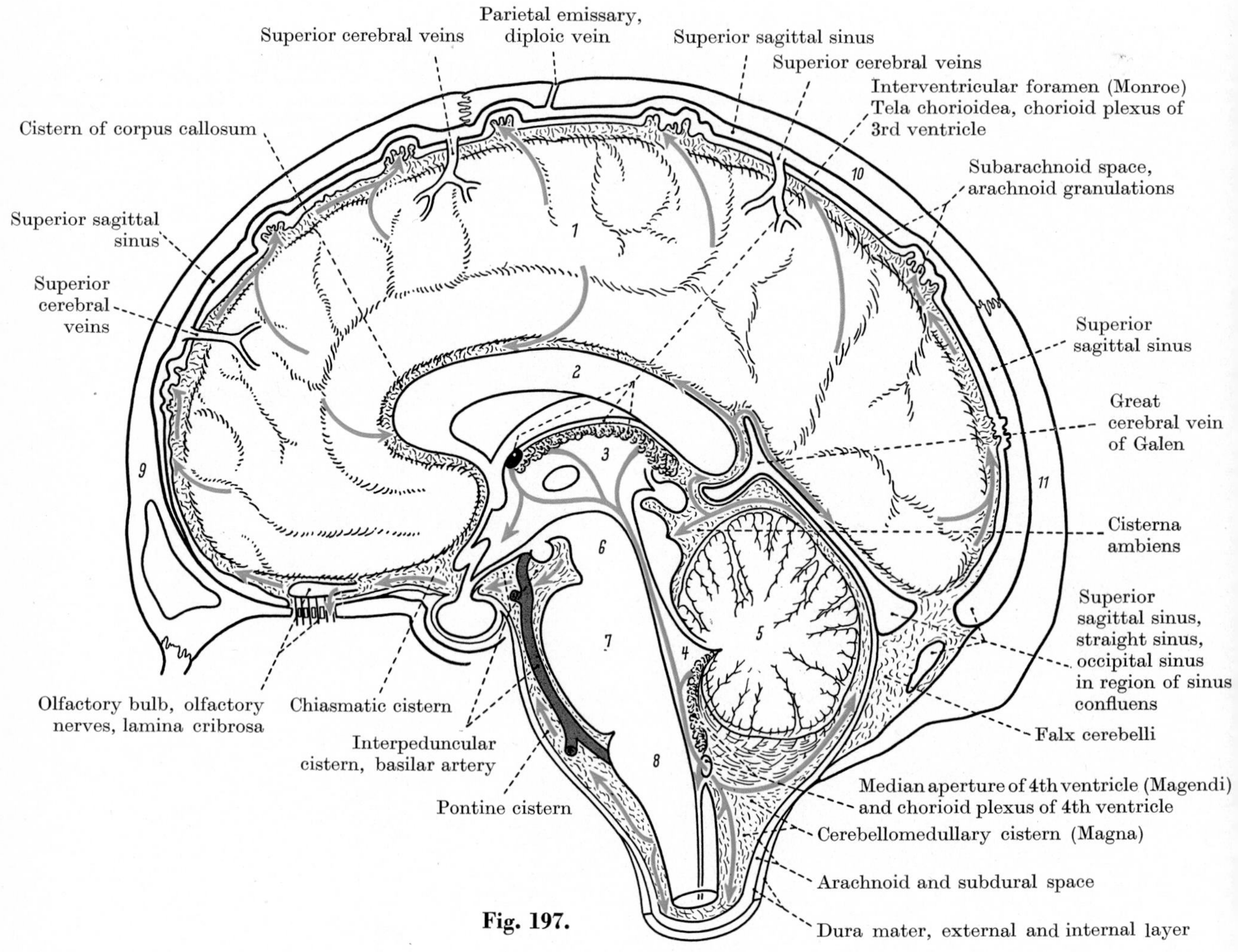

Parietal emissary, diploic vein
Superior cerebral veins
Superior sagittal sinus
Superior cerebral veins
Interventricular foramen (Monroe)
Tela chorioidea, chorioid plexus of 3rd ventricle
Cistern of corpus callosum
Subarachnoid space, arachnoid granulations
Superior sagittal sinus
Superior cerebral veins
Superior sagittal sinus
Great cerebral vein of Galen
Cisterna ambiens
Superior sagittal sinus, straight sinus, occipital sinus in region of sinus confluens
Falx cerebelli
Olfactory bulb, olfactory nerves, lamina cribrosa
Chiasmatic cistern
Interpeduncular cistern, basilar artery
Pontine cistern
Median aperture of 4th ventricle (Magendi) and chorioid plexus of 4th ventricle
Cerebellomedullary cistern (Magna)
Arachnoid and subdural space
Dura mater, external and internal layer
1
2
3
4
5
6
7
8
9
10
11


Fig. 197.

1. Interhemispheric surface of cerebral hemisphere with arachnoid
2. Corpus callosum, septum pellucidum, and fornix
3. Third ventricle
4. Fourth ventricle
5. Cerebellum
6. Mesencephalon, interpeduncular fossa, cerebral aqueduct, and quadrigeminal lamina
7. Pons
8. Medulla oblongata
9. Frontal bone with frontal sinus
10. Parietal bone
11. Occipital bone

**Note:** (for Fig. 197)

1. The 130–150 cc. of cerebrospinal fluid in the subarachnoid spaces is formed in the ventricles of the brain at the chorioid plexuses-1, -4, and circulates through the central aqueducts and ventricles. It flows out of these spaces to the subarachnoid space through the medial (foramen of Magendi) and lateral apertures of the fourth ventricle.

2. In the subarachnoid space, the cerebrospinal fluid bathes the surface of the central nervous system, filling in all the irregularities and clefts. The large depressions in the brain, which are filled by this fluid, are called cisternae and are named according to their positions: cerebellomedullary cistern (cisterna magna); interpeduncular cistern; basilar cistern; chiasmatic cistern, etc. The fluid thus suspends and protects the central nervous system from mechanical trauma.

3. Much of the cerebrospinal fluid leaves the subarachnoid space at the arachnoidal granulations where it enters the venous blood in the dural sinuses. Small amounts of the fluid (see Figs. 198–199) may leave through the perineural channels of the cranial and spinal nerves to flow into the lymphatic capillaries.

## 198. Frontal Section through Caudal End of Spinal Cord and its Membranes.

Blue arrows indicate the flow pattern of the cerebrospinal fluid.

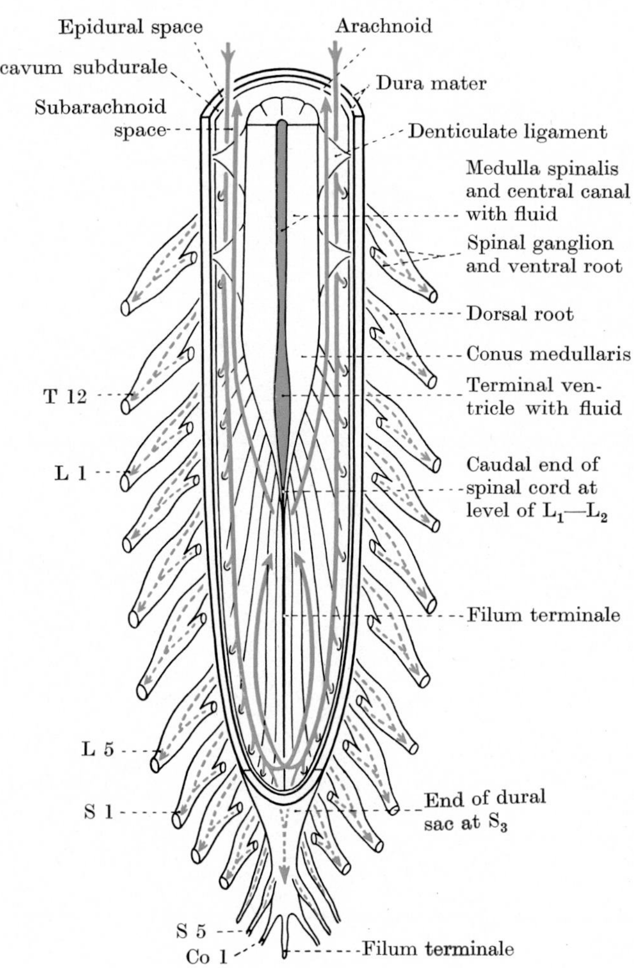
Epidural space
Arachnoid
cavum subdurale
Dura mater
Subarachnoid space
Denticulate ligament
Medulla spinalis and central canal with fluid
Spinal ganglion and ventral root
Dorsal root
Conus medullaris
T 12
Terminal ventricle with fluid
L 1
Caudal end of spinal cord at level of $L_1$—$L_2$
Filum terminale
L 5
S 1
End of dural sac at $S_3$
S 5
Co 1
Filum terminale

**Fig. 198.**

Fig. 199

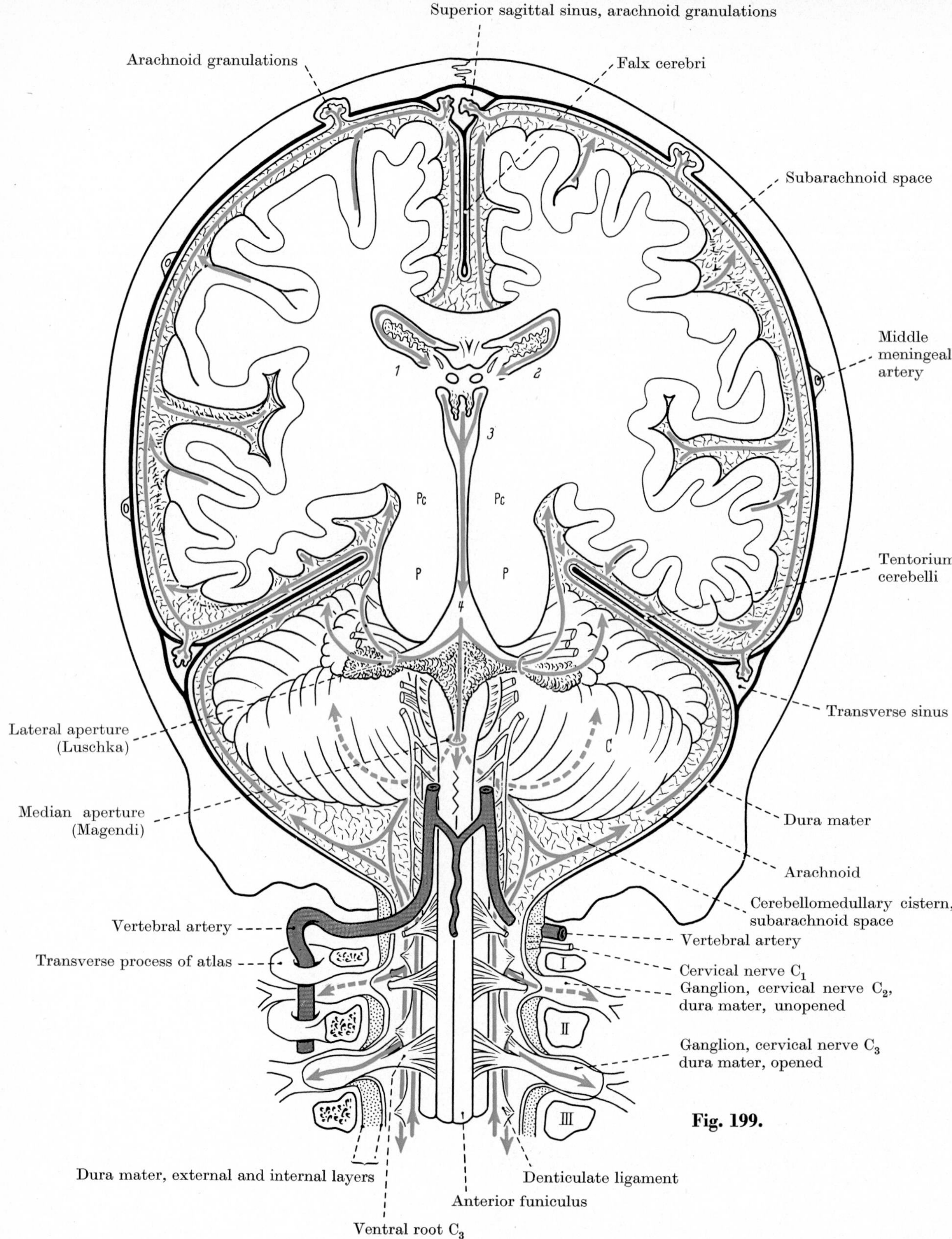

Superior sagittal sinus, arachnoid granulations
Arachnoid granulations
Falx cerebri
Subarachnoid space
Middle meningeal artery
1
2
3
4
Pc
Pc
P
P
C
Tentorium cerebelli
Transverse sinus
Lateral aperture (Luschka)
Median aperture (Magendi)
Dura mater
Arachnoid
Cerebellomedullary cistern, subarachnoid space
Vertebral artery
Transverse process of atlas
Vertebral artery
Cervical nerve $C_1$
Ganglion, cervical nerve $C_2$, dura mater, unopened
Ganglion, cervical nerve $C_3$ dura mater, opened
I
II
III
Dura mater, external and internal layers
Denticulate ligament
Anterior funiculus
Ventral root $C_3$


Fig. 199.

## 199. Frontal Section of Head to Illustrate Flow Pattern of Cerebrospinal Fluid.

The section passes through the cerebral peduncles and the pons, but the cerebellum, medulla oblongata, and spinal cord were not cut.

## 200. The Relation of the Arteries of the Brain and the Circulus Arteriosus (Arterial Circle of Willis) to the Bones of the Cranial Cavity.

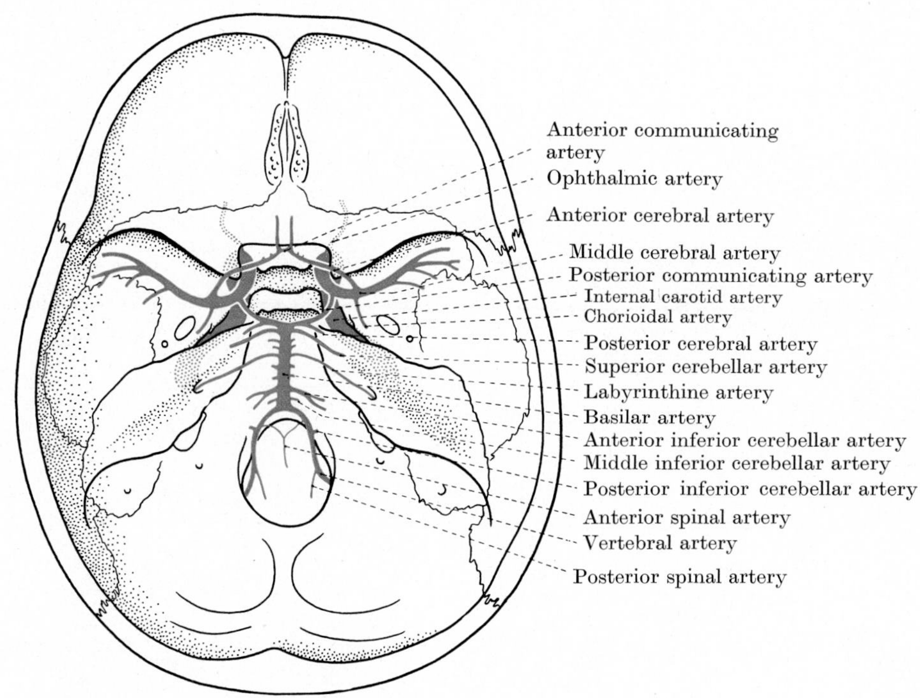
Anterior communicating artery
Ophthalmic artery
Anterior cerebral artery
Middle cerebral artery
Posterior communicating artery
Internal carotid artery
Chorioidal artery
Posterior cerebral artery
Superior cerebellar artery
Labyrinthine artery
Basilar artery
Anterior inferior cerebellar artery
Middle inferior cerebellar artery
Posterior inferior cerebellar artery
Anterior spinal artery
Vertebral artery
Posterior spinal artery

**Note:** 1. Four large arteries (two internal carotid and two vertebral) enter the cranial cavity.

2. These vessels communicate with each other through relatively large anastomotic channels at the base of the brain. The anastomoses, which connect the branches of these vessels, form a circle around the infundibulum above the hypophyseal fossa. This circle of anastomotic channels is called the circulus arteriosus (Circle of Willis).

## 201. Distribution Areas of Cerebral Arteries. (Basal Surface of Brain)

(After Töndury: Angewandte und topographische Anatomie.)

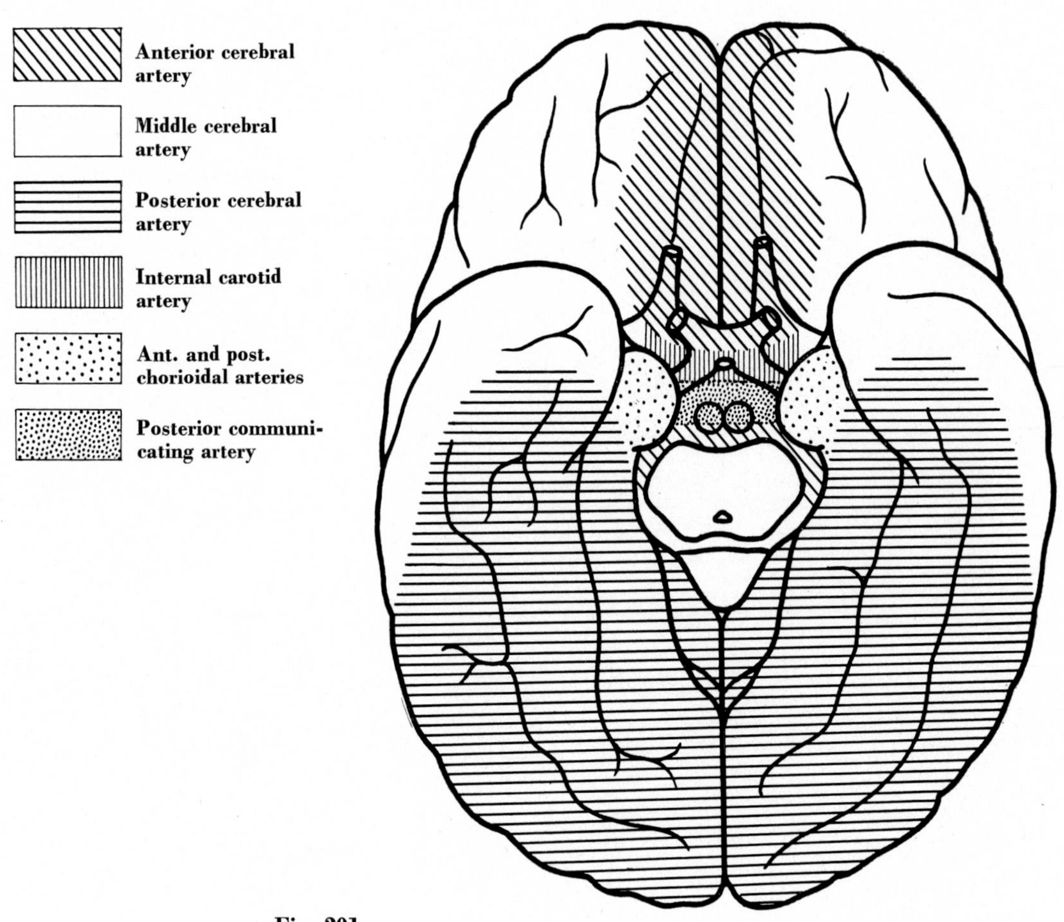
Anterior cerebral artery
Middle cerebral artery
Posterior cerebral artery
Internal carotid artery
Ant. and post. chorioidal arteries
Posterior communicating artery

Fig. 201.

## 202. Distribution Areas of Cerebral Arteries. (Lateral surface)

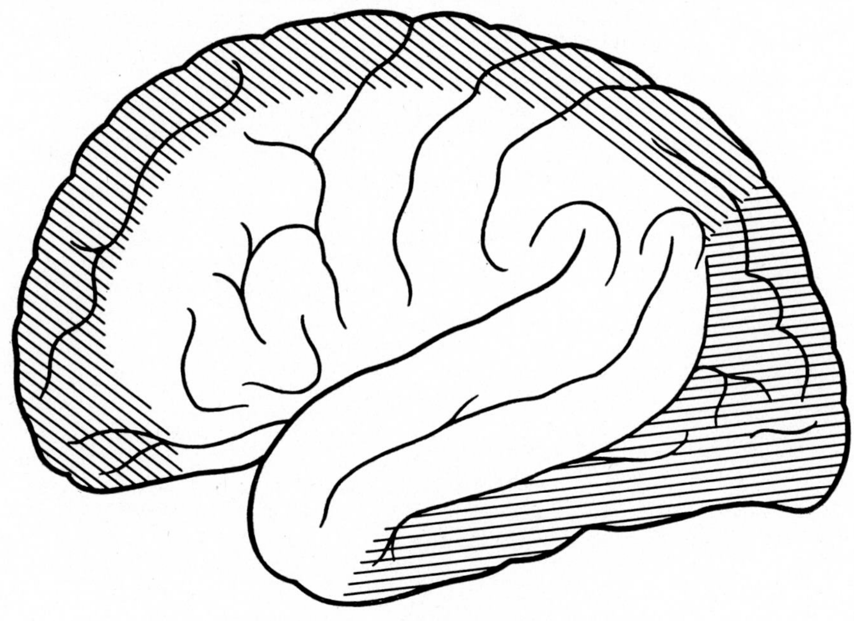

Fig. 202.

## 203. Distribution Areas of Cerebral Arteries. (Medial surface)

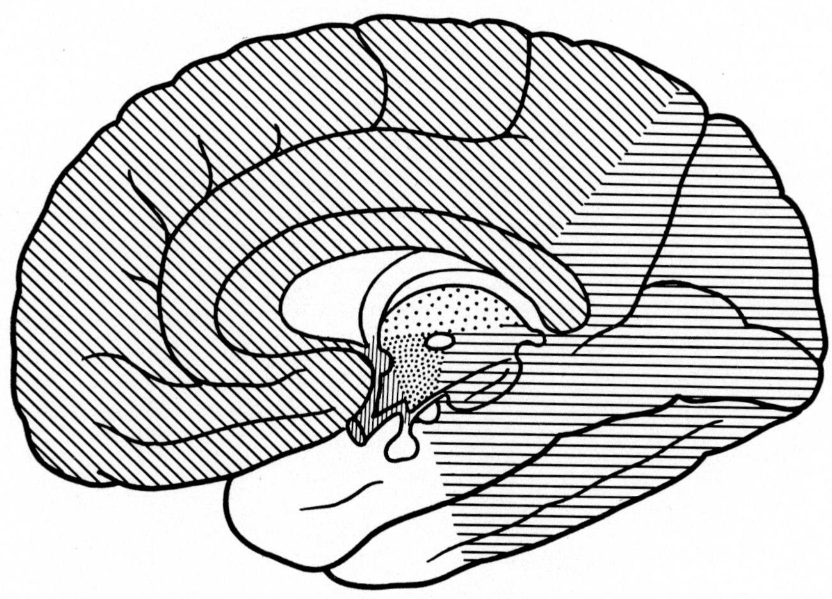

Fig. 203.

## 204. Branches of Middle Cerebral Artery to the Basal Ganglia.

**Diagonal Lines:** anterior cerebral artery (area supplied by)
**Horizontal Lines:** posterior cerebral artery (area supplied by)

1. Thalamic artery
2. Pallidostriate arteries
3. Lenticulostriate "arteries of cerebral hemorrhage" (stroke)
4. Area supplied by the anterior striate artery (Heubner's artery) (recurrent branch of the anterior cerebral artery to the rostral portion of the caudate nucleus and the anterior portion of the internal capsule).
5. Insular arteries.

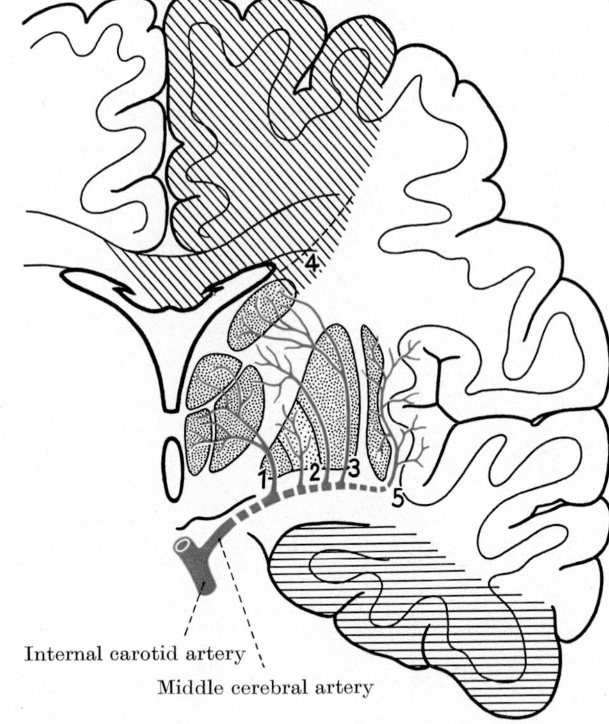
4
1
2
3
5
Internal carotid artery
Middle cerebral artery

Fig. 204.

## 205. The Internal Veins of the Cerebrum. (After Ferner: Z. Anat.-Entw.-Gesch. 120, 1958)

**Broken blue line:** Delineates the collecting areas of the internal and external cerebral veins.

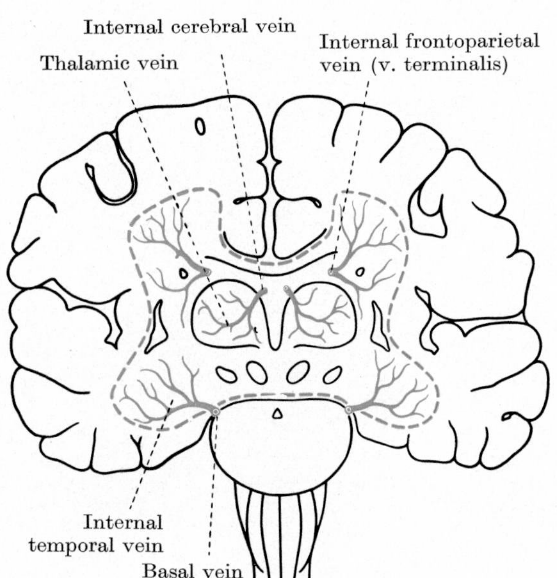
Internal cerebral vein
Thalamic vein
Internal frontoparietal vein (v. terminalis)
Internal temporal vein
Basal vein

Fig. 205.

## 206. Dissection of Left Hemisphere to Expose Insula.

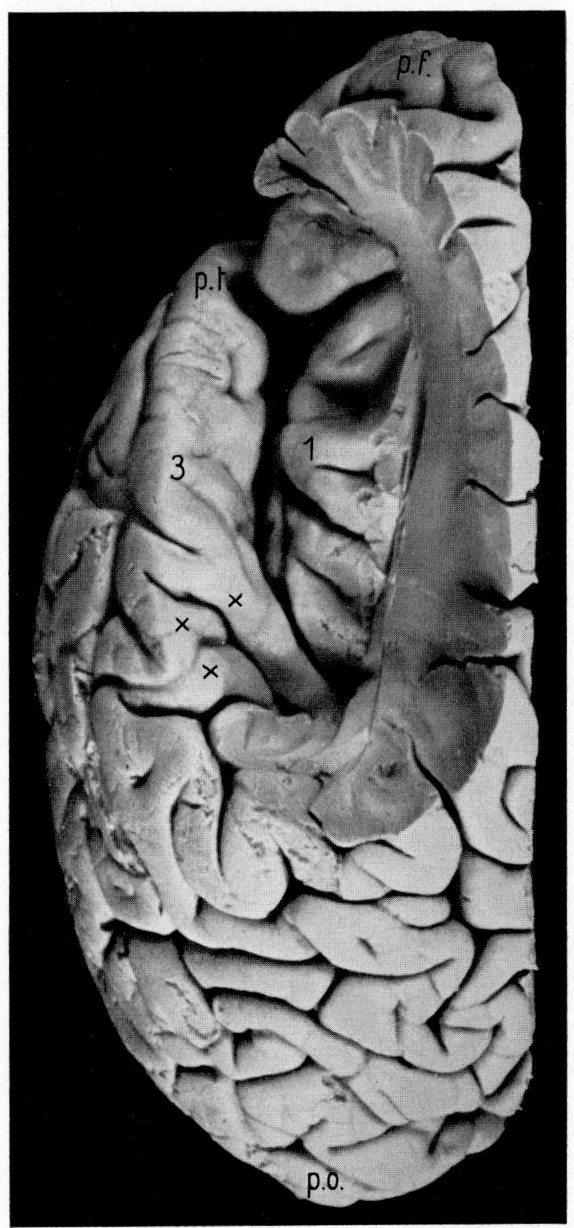
p.f.
p.t.
1
3
×
×
×
p.o.

Fig. 206.

| | | | |
|---|---|---|---|
| 1 | Insula | p. f. | Frontal pole |
| ××× | Transverse temporal gyri | p. t. | Temporal pole |
| 3 | Superior temporal gyrus | p. o. | Occipital pole |

# 207. Sulci and Gyri of Lateral Aspect of Left Cerebral Hemisphere. (See Fig. 249)

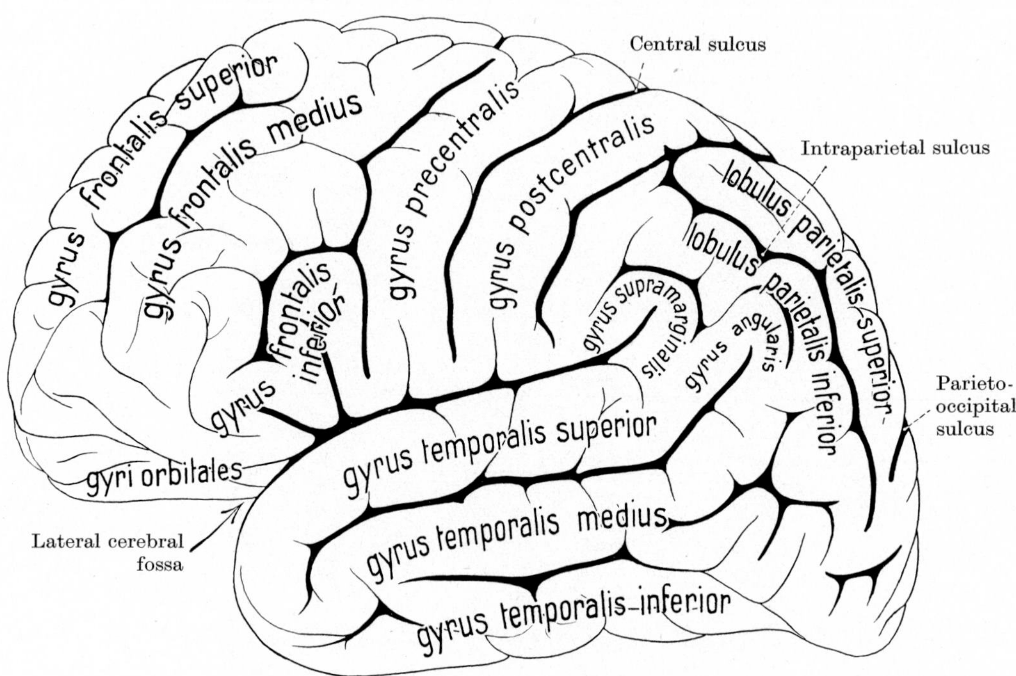
Central sulcus
Intraparietal sulcus
Parieto-occipital sulcus
Lateral cerebral fossa
gyrus frontalis superior
gyrus frontalis medius
gyrus frontalis inferior
gyrus precentralis
gyrus postcentralis
lobulus parietalis superior
lobulus parietalis inferior
gyrus supramarginalis
gyrus angularis
gyri orbitales
gyrus temporalis superior
gyrus temporalis medius
gyrus temporalis inferior

Fig. 207.

## 208. Sulci and Gyri of Cerebral Cortex. (Viewed from above)
(See Fig. 253)

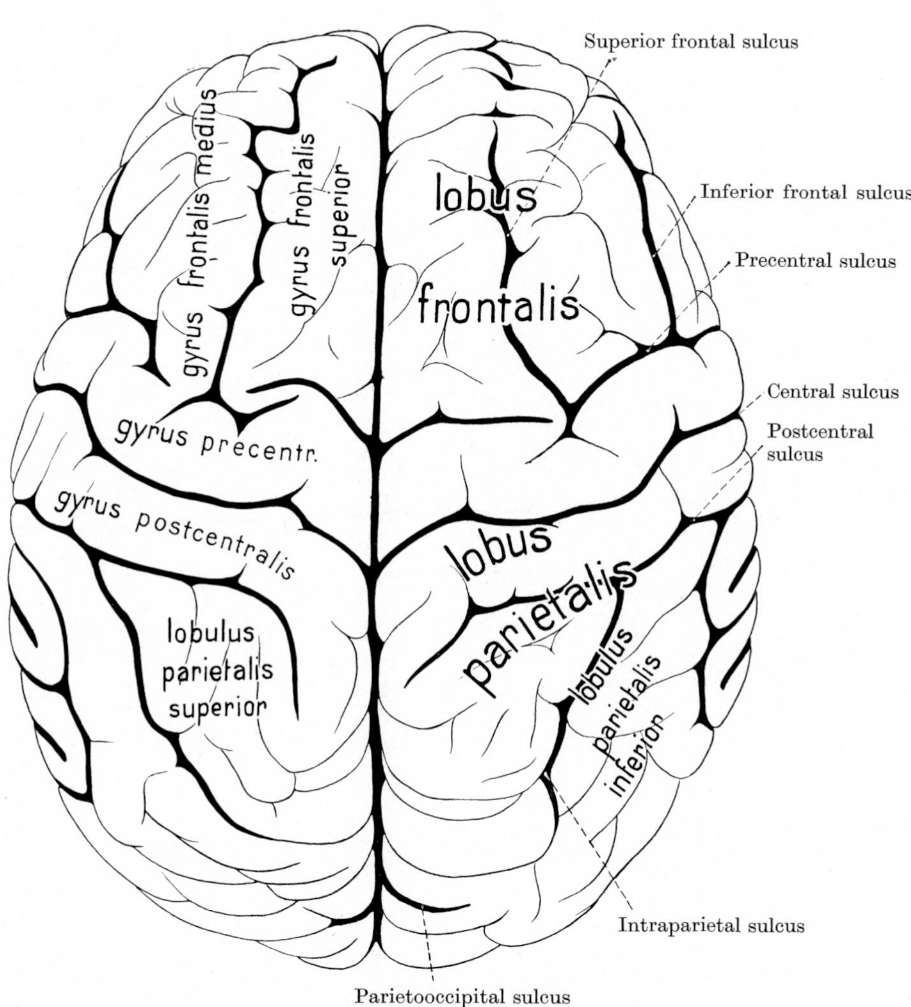
Superior frontal sulcus
Inferior frontal sulcus
Precentral sulcus
Central sulcus
Postcentral sulcus
Intraparietal sulcus
Parietooccipital sulcus
gyrus frontalis medius
gyrus frontalis superior
lobus frontalis
gyrus precentr.
gyrus postcentralis
lobus parietalis
lobulus parietalis superior
lobulus parietalis inferior

Fig. 208.

## 209. Sulci and Gyri of Basal Aspect of Cerebral Hemispheres.

(Forebrain) (See Fig. 255)

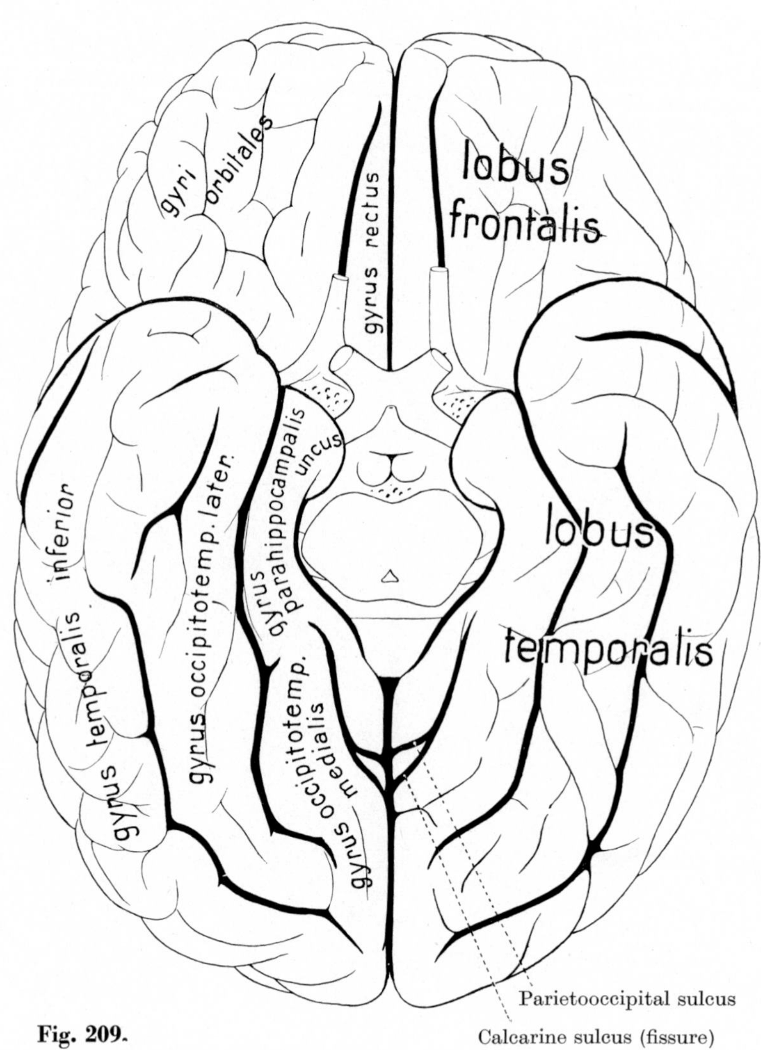
gyri
orbitales
gyrus rectus
lobus
frontalis
uncus
gyrus
parahippocampalis
gyrus occipitotemp. later.
inferior
gyrus temporalis
gyrus
lobus
temporalis
gyrus occipitotemp.
medialis
gyrus
Parietooccipital sulcus
Calcarine sulcus (fissure)

Fig. 209.

The brain stem and cerebellum were removed. The hypophysis, olfactory tracts, and optic nerves were cut off.

## 210. Gyri and Sulci of the Cerebral Hemisphere.

(Viewed from the medial surface) (See Fig. 251)

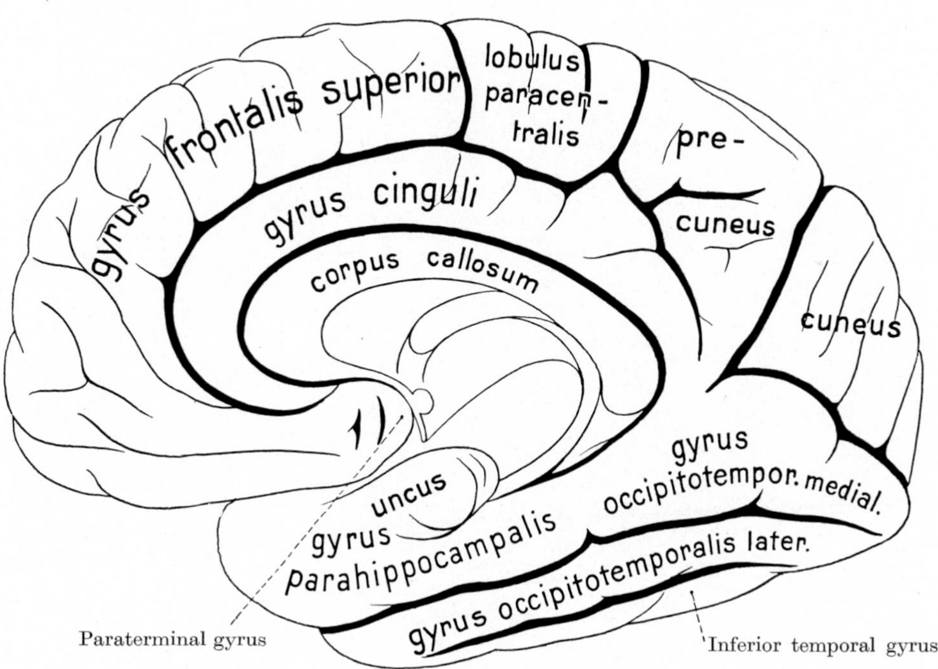
gyrus
frontalis superior
lobulus
paracen-
tralis
pre-
cuneus
gyrus cinguli
corpus callosum
cuneus
gyrus
occipitotempor. medial.
uncus
gyrus
parahippocampalis
gyrus occipitotemporalis later.
Paraterminal gyrus
Inferior temporal gyrus

Fig. 210.

The brain was divided in the median sagittal plane. The brain stem and the cerebellum were removed by a diagonal cut through the region of the thalamus.

## 211 and 212. Cytoarchitectural Maps of Cerebral Cortex.

(After K. Brodmann)

The fields are numbered and delimited by various markings.

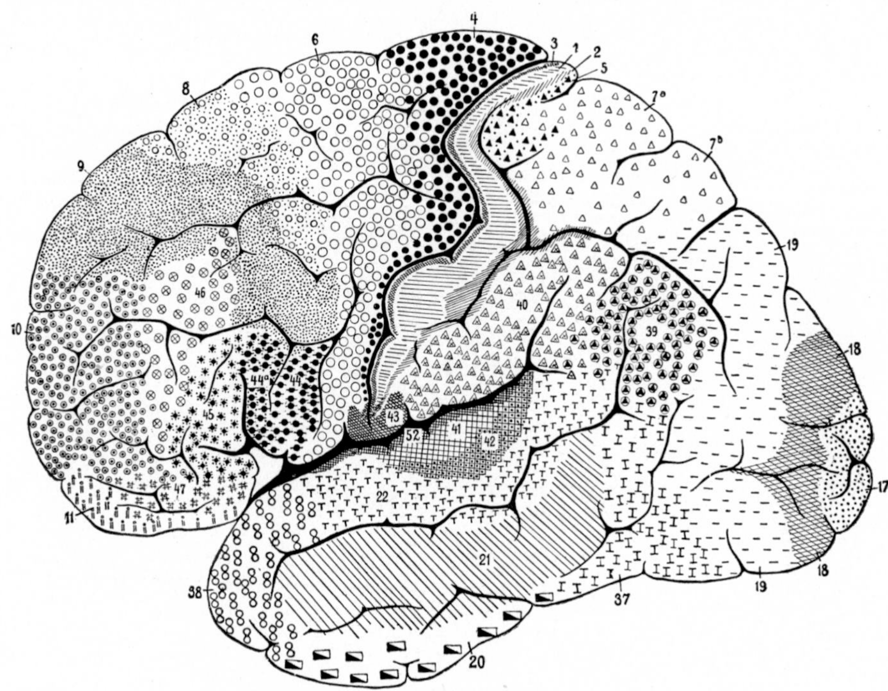
4
6
3
1
2
5
8
7a
7b
9
19
46
40
10
39
18
44
43
52
41
42
45
22
17
47
11
21
38
37
18
19
20

**Fig. 211.**

**211.** Lateral surface of hemisphere.

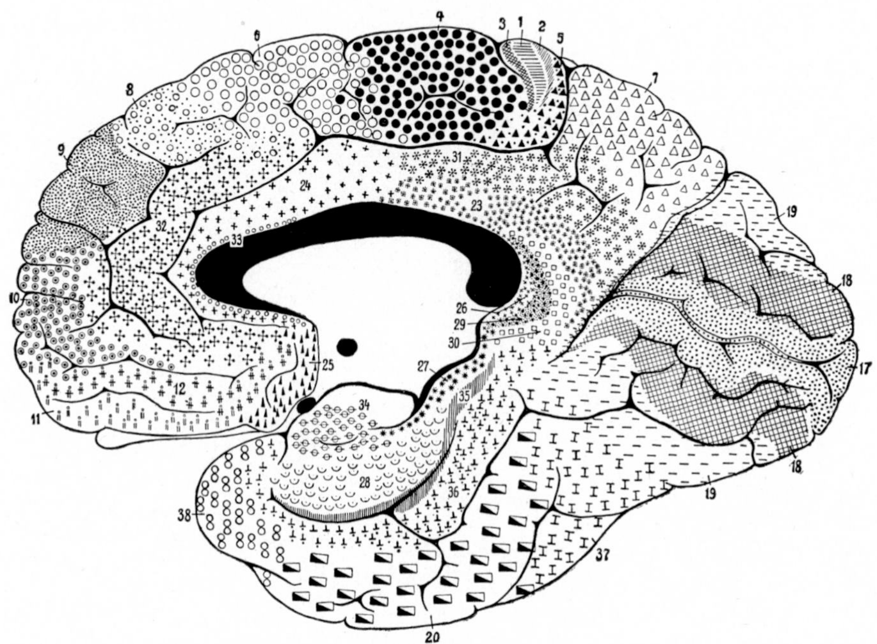
4
3
1
2
5
6
8
7
9
31
24
23
19
32
33
18
10
26
29
30
25
27
17
35
34
12
11
28
36
18
19
38
37
20

**Fig. 212.**

**212.** Medial surface of hemisphere.

# 213 and 214. Motor Areas of the Cerebral Cortex.

(After Förster, Handbuch d. Neurologie, Vol. VI)

**Black** = pyramidal area
**Lines** = extrapyramidal area
**Dotted** = visual areas

SR = central sulcus (Rolandi)
SPO = parietooccipital sulcus
SF = sulcus cinguli

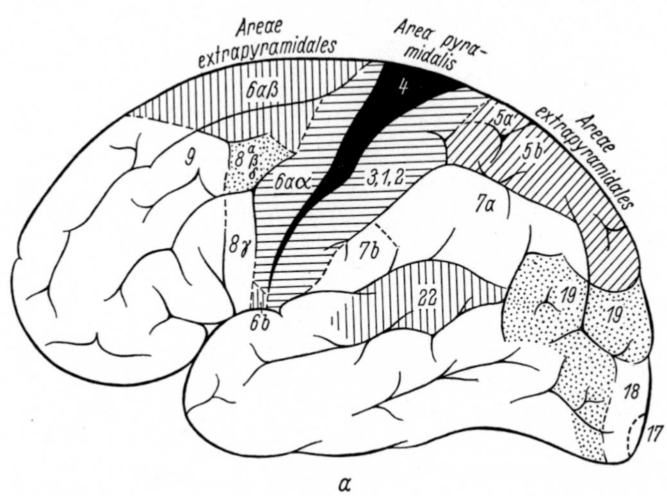
Areae extrapyramidales
Area pyramidalis
6aβ
4
5a
Areae extrapyramidales
5b
9
8 α β δ
6aα
3,1,2
7a
8γ
7b
22
19
19
6b
18
17
a

Fig. 213.

**213.** Lateral surface.

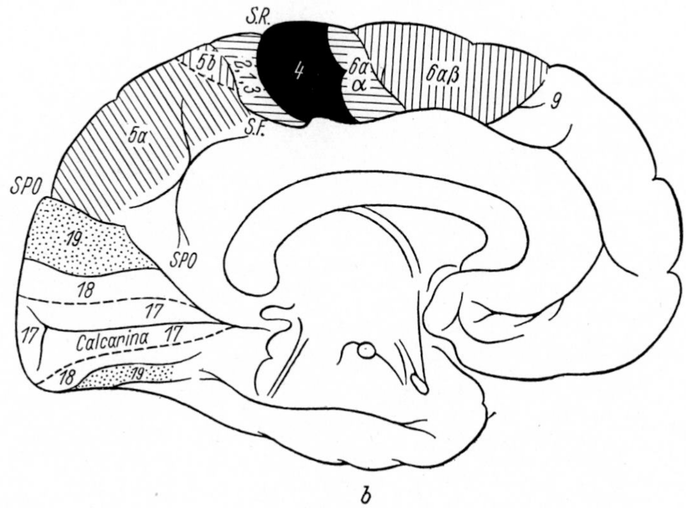
S.R.
5b
2,1,3
4
6a α
6aβ
9
S.F.
5a
SPO
19
SPO
18
17
17
Calcarina
17
18
19
b

Fig. 214.

**214.** Medial surface.

**Figs. 215–216**

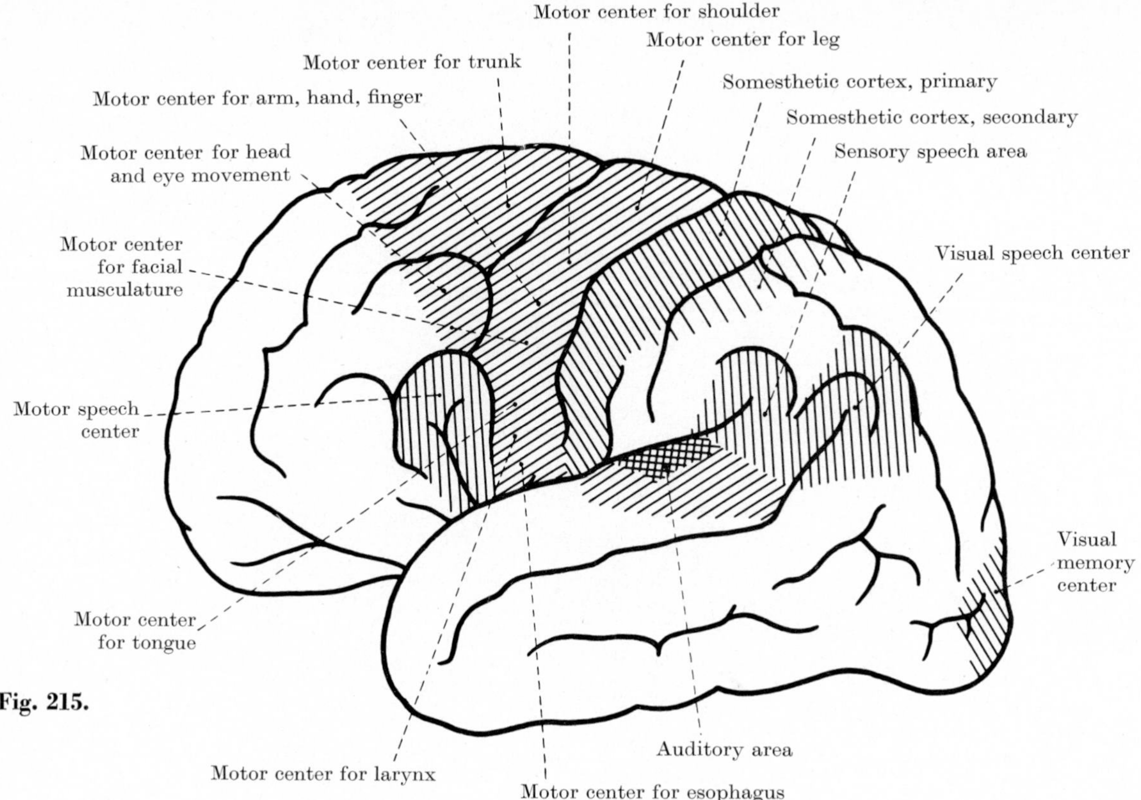
Motor center for shoulder
Motor center for leg
Motor center for trunk
Somesthetic cortex, primary
Motor center for arm, hand, finger
Somesthetic cortex, secondary
Sensory speech area
Motor center for head
and eye movement
Motor center
for facial
musculature
Visual speech center
Motor speech
center
Visual
memory
center
Motor center
for tongue
Auditory area
Motor center for larynx
Motor center for esophagus

**Fig. 215.**

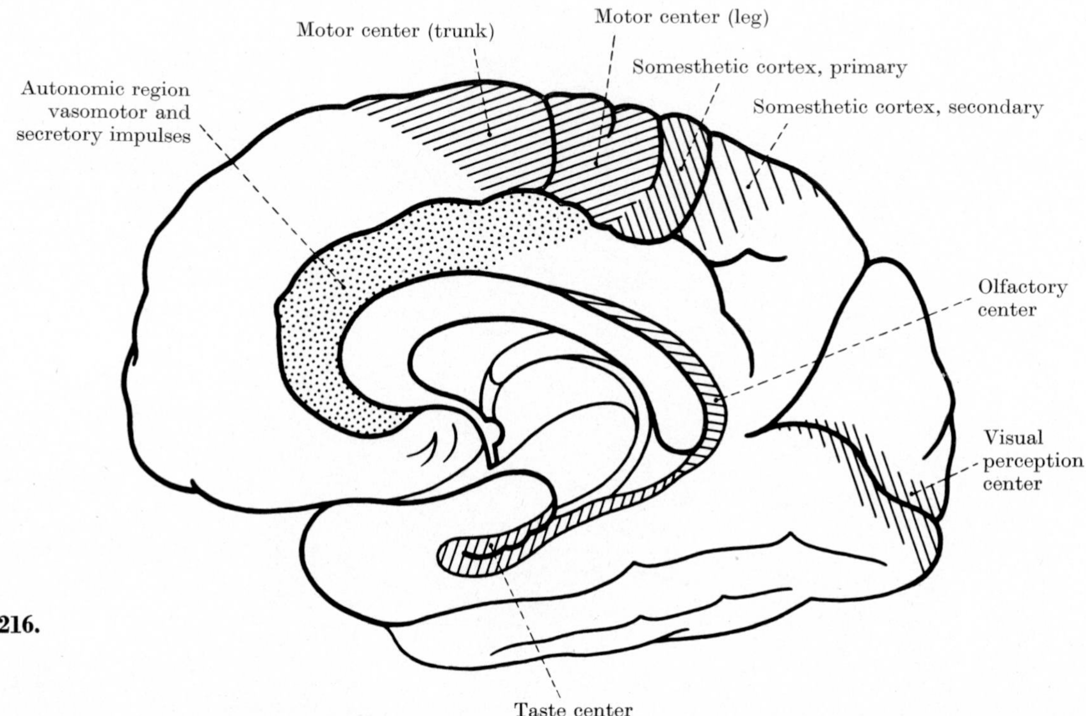
Motor center (leg)
Motor center (trunk)
Somesthetic cortex, primary
Autonomic region
vasomotor and
secretory impulses
Somesthetic cortex, secondary
Olfactory
center
Visual
perception
center
Taste center

**Fig. 216.**

## 215 and 216. Diagrams of Functional Areas on Lateral and Medial Surfaces of Cerebral Hemisphere.

(After Villiger and Ludwig: Gehirn und Rückenmark, Basel, 1946) (See Figs. 207 and 210)

A precise delimitation of the boundaries and size of the fields is not possible because overlapping gradients exist.

## 217. Schematic Representation of the Body Superimposed on the Motor Cortex of the Precentral Gyrus.

(After Penfield and Rasmussen, "The Cerebral Cortex of Man," 1950)

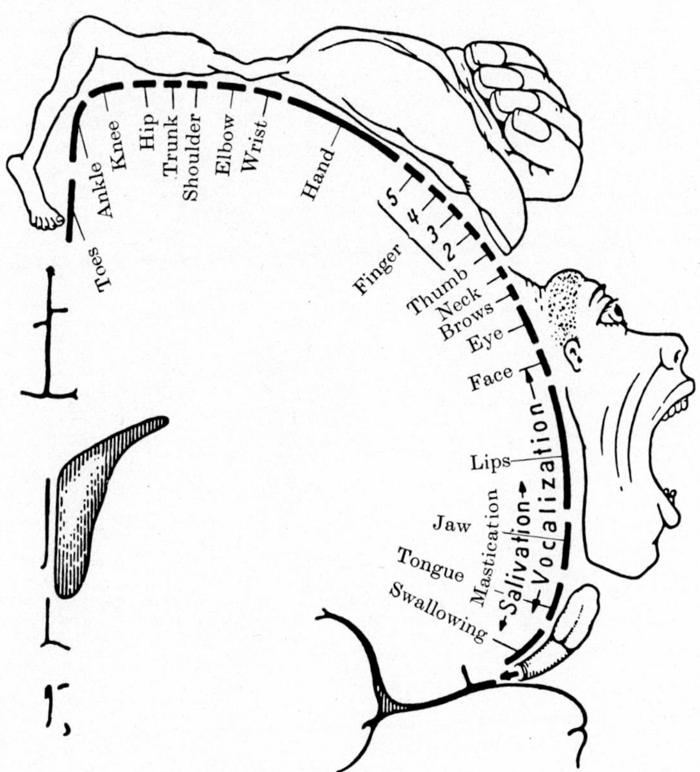
Toes
Ankle
Knee
Hip
Trunk
Shoulder
Elbow
Wrist
Hand
5
4
3
2
Finger
Thumb
Neck
Brows
Eye
Face
Lips
Jaw
Tongue
Swallowing
Mastication
Salivation
Vocalization

**Note:** 1. The extraordinary size of the motor area for the hand and structures involved in speech.

## 218. Cast of Ventricle System of Brain of Adult. (Viewed from left side)

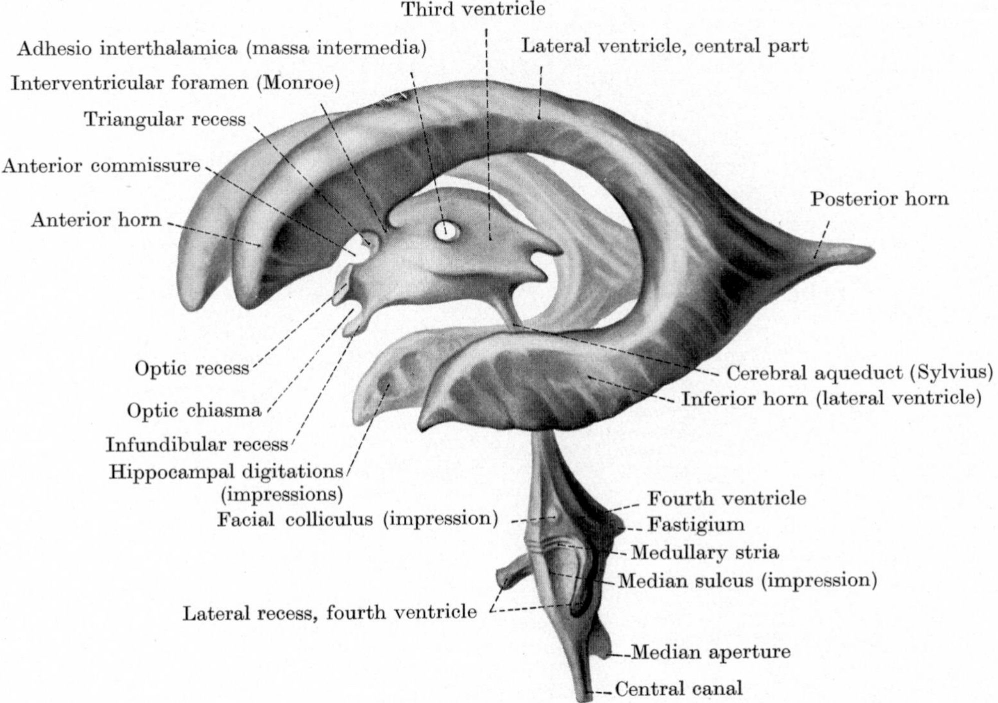
Third ventricle
Adhesio interthalamica (massa intermedia)
Lateral ventricle, central part
Interventricular foramen (Monroe)
Triangular recess
Anterior commissure
Anterior horn
Posterior horn
Optic recess
Optic chiasma
Infundibular recess
Hippocampal digitations (impressions)
Cerebral aqueduct (Sylvius)
Inferior horn (lateral ventricle)
Fourth ventricle
Facial colliculus (impression)
Fastigium
Medullary stria
Median sulcus (impression)
Lateral recess, fourth ventricle
Median aperture
Central canal

**Fig. 218.**

## 219. Diagram of Roof and Tela Chorioidea of Third Ventricle and Central Part of Lateral Ventricle.

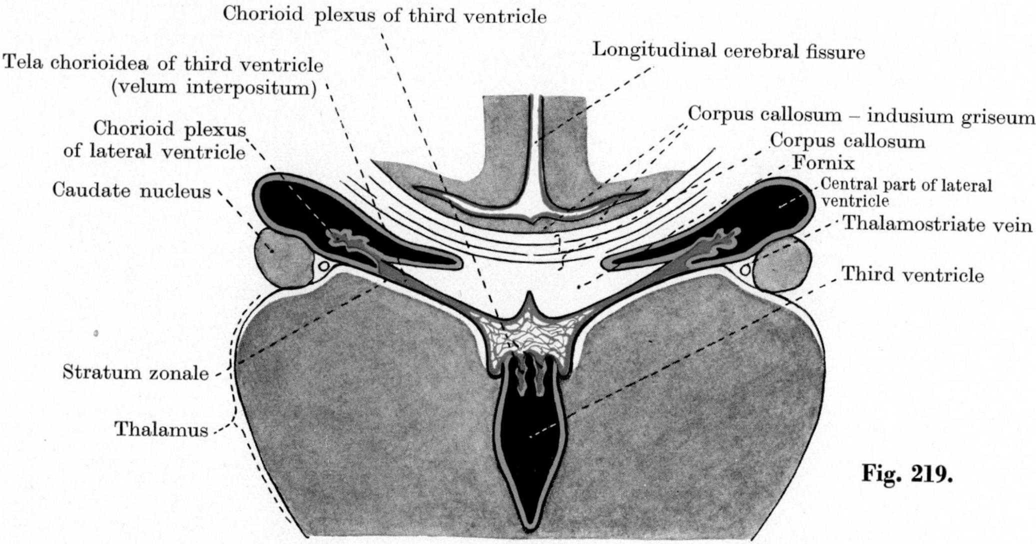

Chorioid plexus of third ventricle
Longitudinal cerebral fissure
Tela chorioidea of third ventricle (velum interpositum)
Corpus callosum – indusium griseum
Chorioid plexus of lateral ventricle
Corpus callosum
Fornix
Caudate nucleus
Central part of lateral ventricle
Thalamostriate vein
Third ventricle
Stratum zonale
Thalamus


Fig. 219.

**Red:** Pia mater and arachnoid. **Blue:** Ependyma.

**Note:** 1. The pia and arachnoid, which contain the vascular structures, invaginate the ependymal linings of the ventricles to form the chorioid plexuses.

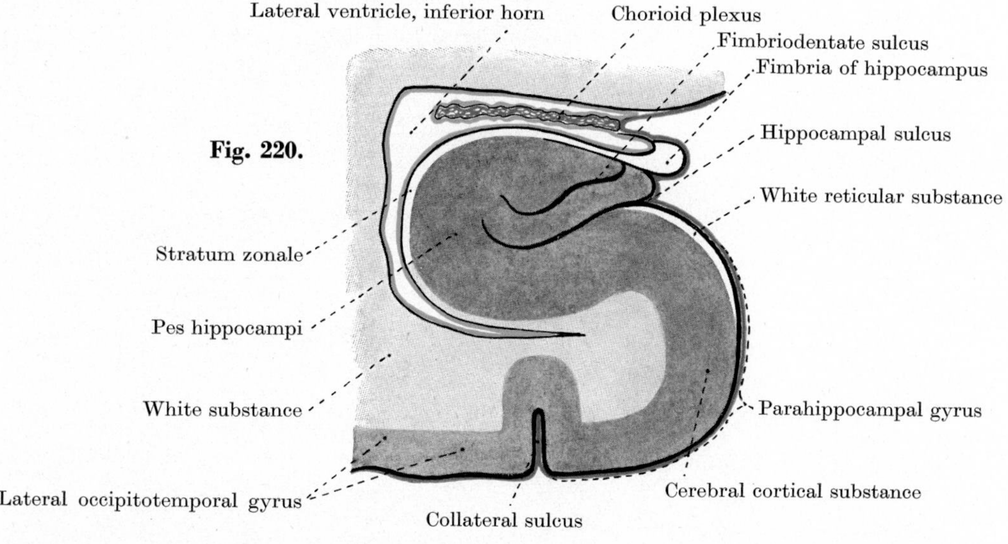

Lateral ventricle, inferior horn
Chorioid plexus
Fimbriodentate sulcus
Fimbria of hippocampus
Hippocampal sulcus
White reticular substance
Stratum zonale
Pes hippocampi
White substance
Parahippocampal gyrus
Lateral occipitotemporal gyrus
Cerebral cortical substance
Collateral sulcus


Fig. 220.

## 220. Diagram of Frontal Section: Inferior Horn of Lateral Ventricle.

# 221. Dissection of Basal Ganglia and Other Nuclear Masses in a Right Cerebral Hemisphere. (Photos not retouched)

a. View of medial aspect:

1. Thalamus medial surface
2. Head of caudate nucleus
3. Body of caudate nucleus
4. Red nucleus
5. Substantia nigra
6. Amygdaloid body
7. Anterior commissure
8. Tuber cinereum
9. Mammillary body and mammillothalamic fasciculus
10. Cortex of dentate gyrus
11. Cortex of parahippocampal gyrus

b. Lateral view:

1. Putamen, lateral surface
2. Head of caudate nucleus
3. Connections between 1 and 2
4. Tail of caudate nucleus
5. Claustrum (not complete)
6. Thalamus
7. Uncinate fasciculus

c. Viewed from above:

1. Putamen
2. Head of caudate nucleus
3. Connections between 1 and 2
4. Tail of caudate nucleus
5. Claustrum (not complete)
6. Thalamus
7. Anterior commissure

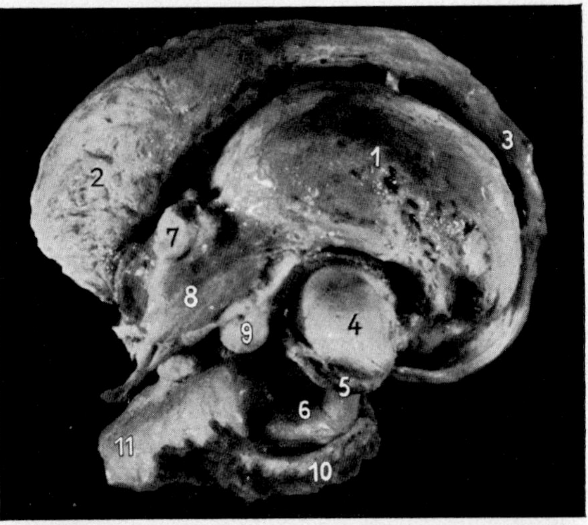
2
3
1
7
8
9
4
5
6
11
10
a

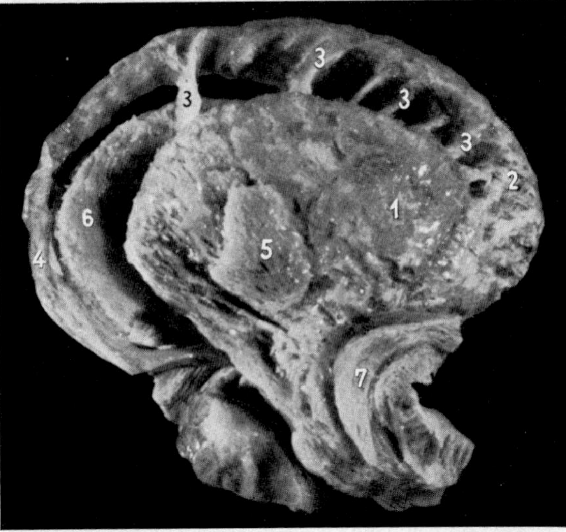
3
3
3
3
2
1
6
4
5
7
b

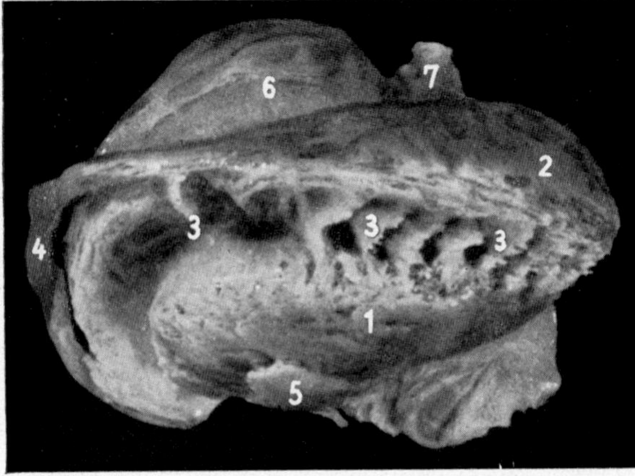
6
7
2
4
3
3
3
1
5
c

## 222. Corona Radiata, Thalamic Radiations.

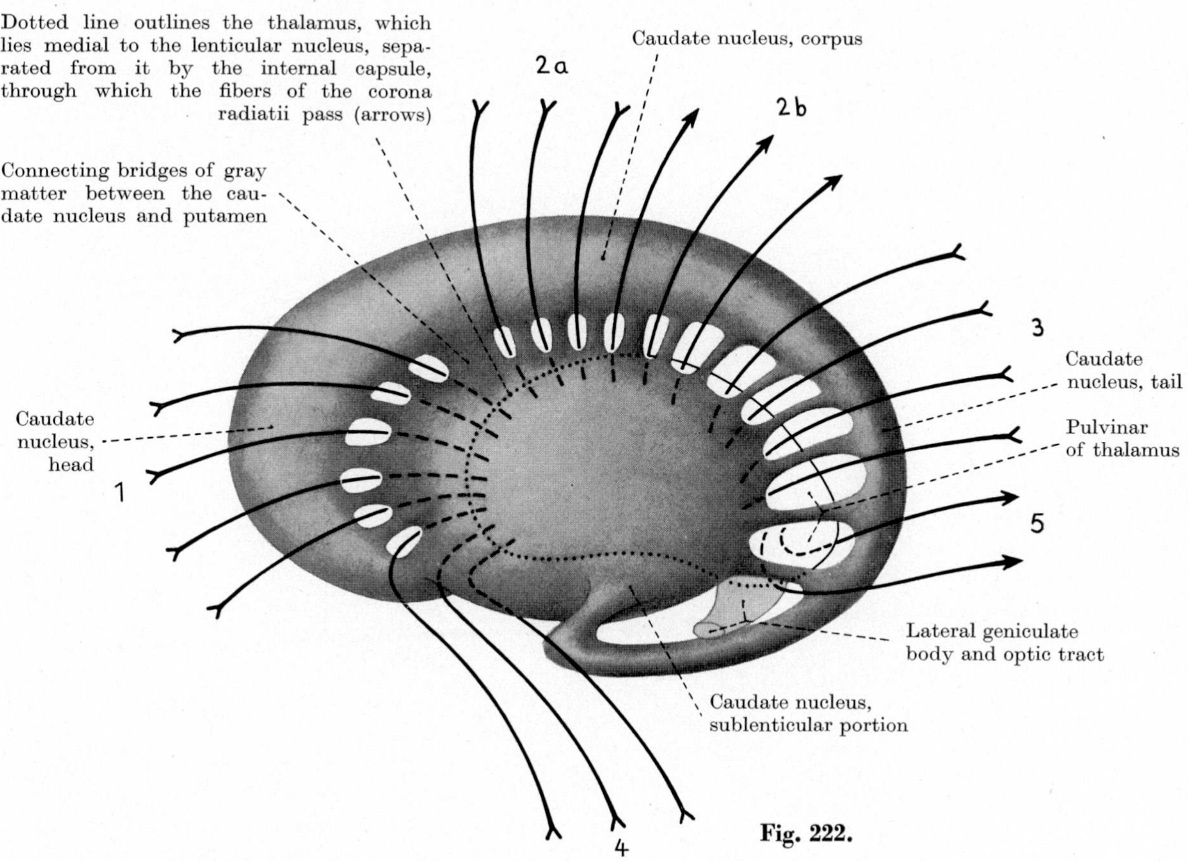
Dotted line outlines the thalamus, which lies medial to the lenticular nucleus, separated from it by the internal capsule, through which the fibers of the corona radiatii pass (arrows)
Connecting bridges of gray matter between the caudate nucleus and putamen
Caudate nucleus, corpus
2a
2b
3
Caudate nucleus, tail
Pulvinar of thalamus
5
Caudate nucleus, head
1
Lateral geniculate body and optic tract
Caudate nucleus, sublenticular portion
4

Fig. 222.

Caudate nucleus and putamen seen from lateral side. Position of the more medial thalamus is indicated by dotted line.

1. Frontal peduncle.
2. a, b } Parietal peduncle.
3. Occipital peduncle.
4. Inferior peduncle (not actually a part of the corona radiata).
5. Optic radiations.

## 223. Hypothalamic Nuclei. (Outlined on median sagittal section of brain stem).

Nuclei boundaries are less definite than indicated, because the borders are not sharply defined and they overlap each other. The physiological experiments involving stimulation of hypothalamic areas in the cat (W. R. Hess) tended to indicate that the posterior part of the hypothalamus is involved in sympathetic functions, while stimulation of the more rostral parts gave parasympathetic responses. In view of the multiplicity of the nuclei and functions assigned to the hypothalamus, it may be undesirable to generalize with respect to these somewhat arbitrary divisions of the autonomic nervous system.

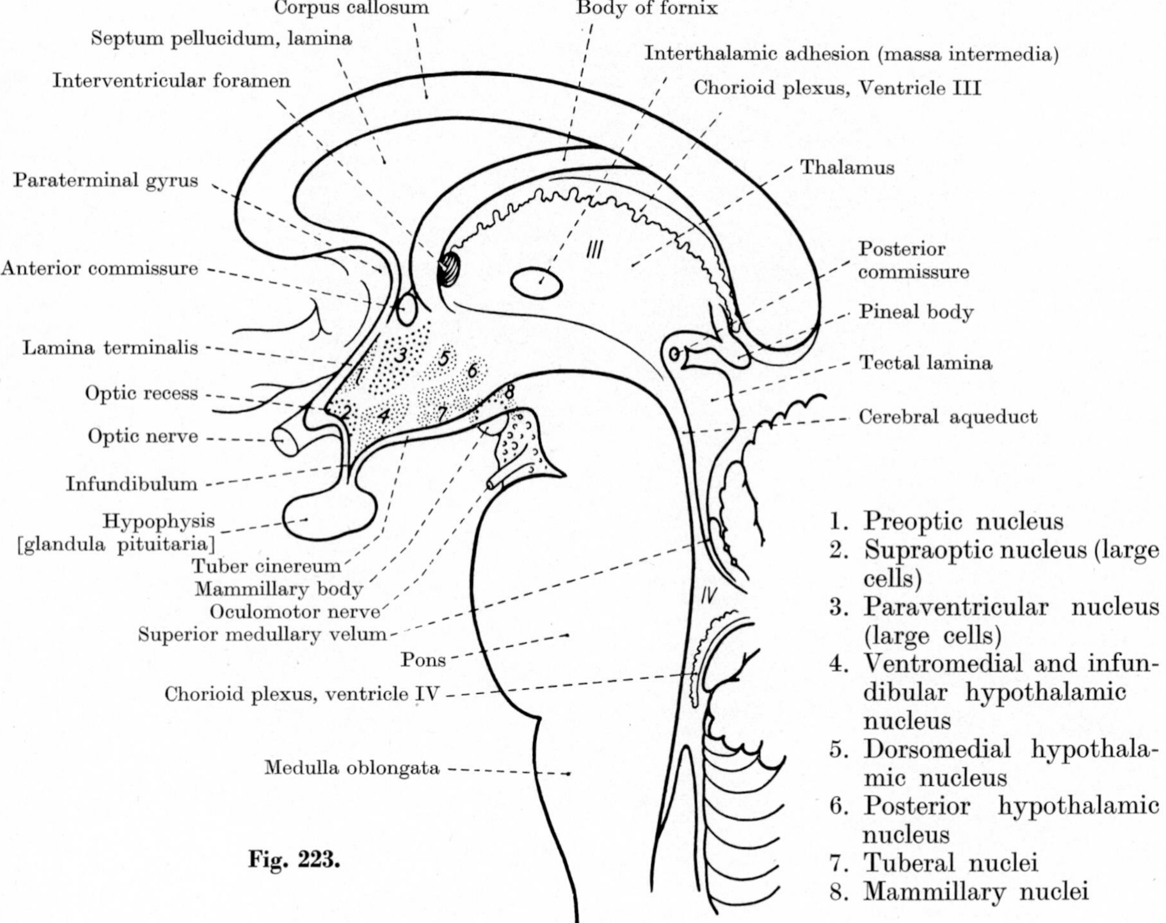
Corpus callosum
Body of fornix
Septum pellucidum, lamina
Interthalamic adhesion (massa intermedia)
Interventricular foramen
Chorioid plexus, Ventricle III
Thalamus
Paraterminal gyrus
III
Anterior commissure
Posterior commissure
Pineal body
Lamina terminalis
Tectal lamina
Optic recess
Cerebral aqueduct
Optic nerve
Infundibulum
Hypophysis [glandula pituitaria]
Tuber cinereum
Mammillary body
Oculomotor nerve
Superior medullary velum
IV
Pons
Chorioid plexus, ventricle IV
Medulla oblongata
1. Preoptic nucleus
2. Supraoptic nucleus (large cells)
3. Paraventricular nucleus (large cells)
4. Ventromedial and infundibular hypothalamic nucleus
5. Dorsomedial hypothalamic nucleus
6. Posterior hypothalamic nucleus
7. Tuberal nuclei
8. Mammillary nuclei

Fig. 223.

## 224 and 225. Hypothalamic Nuclei in Frontal Section of the Diencephalon.

224. Through the Tuber Cinereum
225. Through the Mammillary Bodies

Nuclei and central gray matter are red stippled (after Villiger-Ludwig, nuclei depicted by M. Clara).

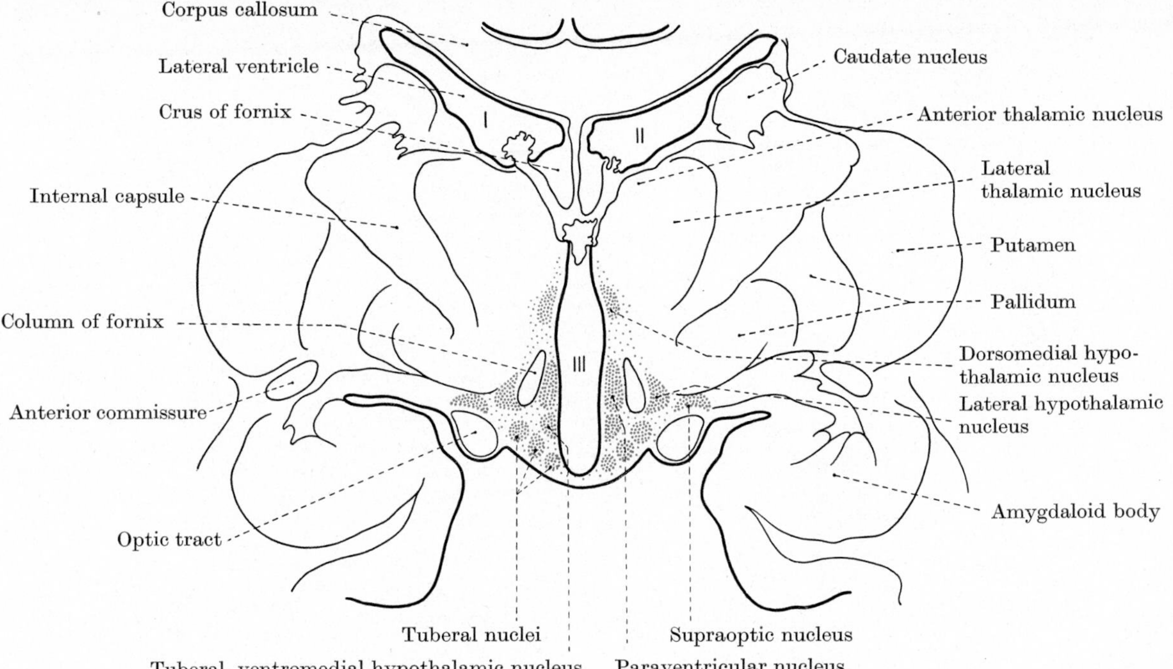
Corpus callosum
Lateral ventricle
Crus of fornix
Internal capsule
Column of fornix
Anterior commissure
Optic tract
I
II
III
Caudate nucleus
Anterior thalamic nucleus
Lateral thalamic nucleus
Putamen
Pallidum
Dorsomedial hypothalamic nucleus
Lateral hypothalamic nucleus
Amygdaloid body
Tuberal nuclei
Supraoptic nucleus
Tuberal, ventromedial hypothalamic nucleus
Paraventricular nucleus

**Fig. 224.**

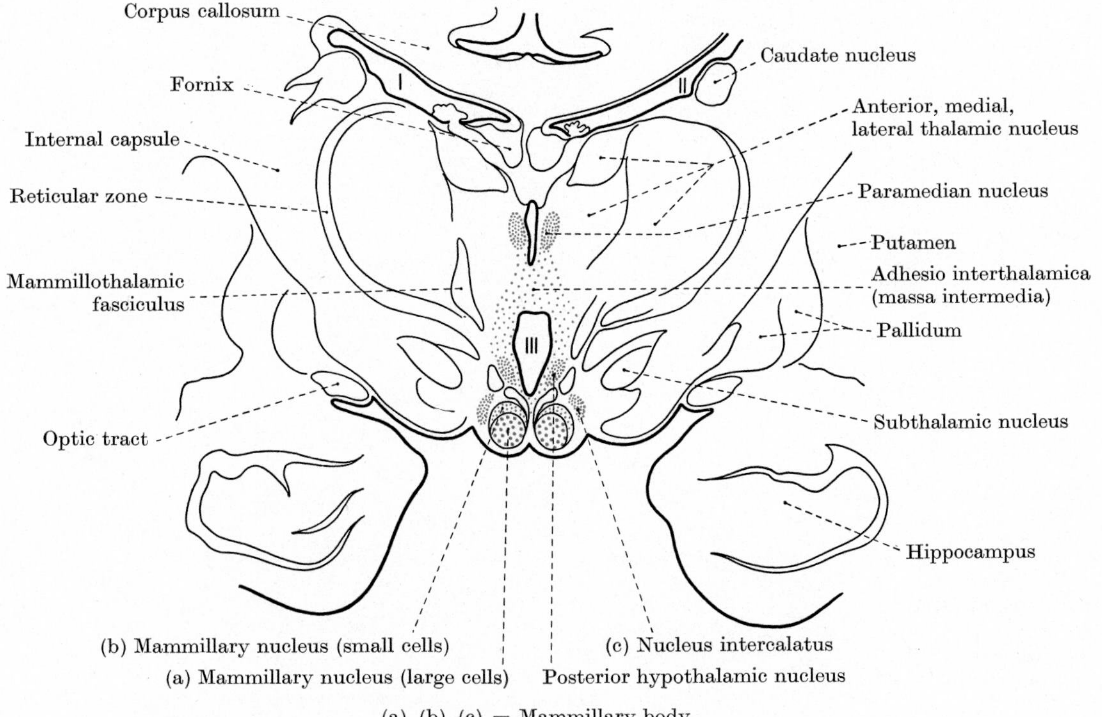
Corpus callosum
Fornix
Internal capsule
Reticular zone
Mammillothalamic fasciculus
Optic tract
I
II
III
Caudate nucleus
Anterior, medial, lateral thalamic nucleus
Paramedian nucleus
Putamen
Adhesio interthalamica (massa intermedia)
Pallidum
Subthalamic nucleus
Hippocampus
(b) Mammillary nucleus (small cells)
(c) Nucleus intercalatus
(a) Mammillary nucleus (large cells)
Posterior hypothalamic nucleus
(a), (b), (c) = Mammillary body

**Fig. 225.**

## 226. **Hypothalamic Nuclei and Hypophyseal Tracts.** (After Diepgen, 1948; Spatz, 1951; from M. Clara: Das Nervensystem des Menschen, 1959)

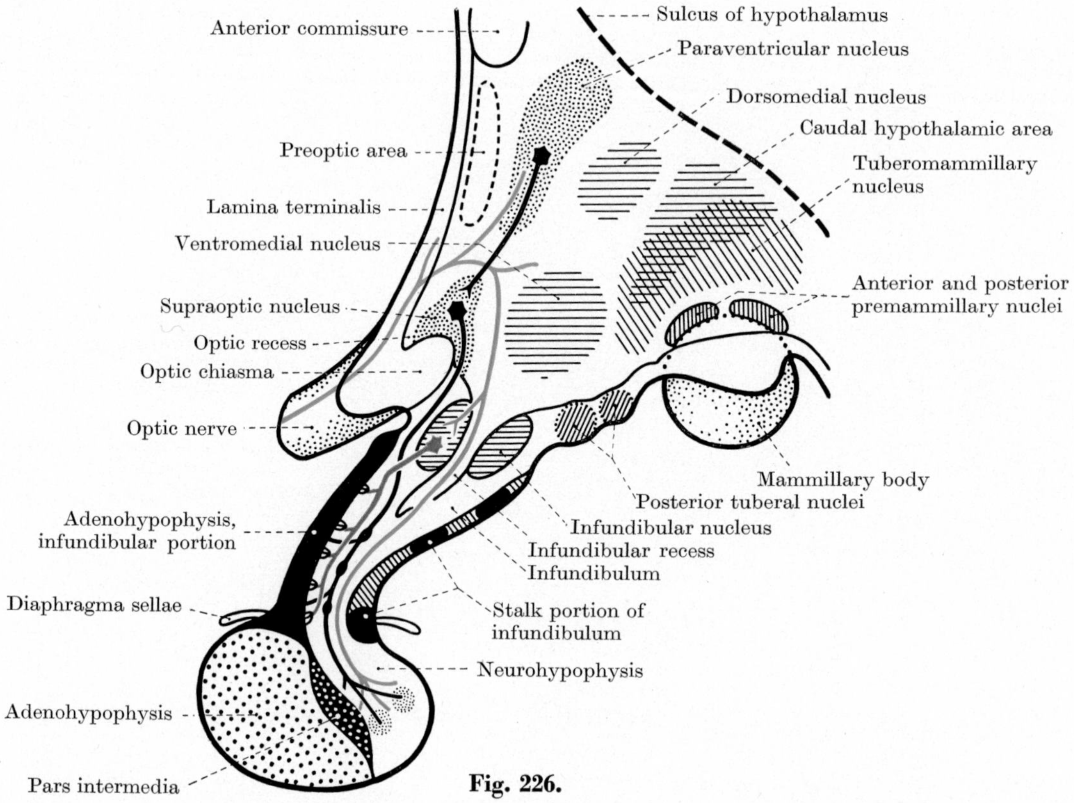

Anterior commissure
Sulcus of hypothalamus
Paraventricular nucleus
Dorsomedial nucleus
Caudal hypothalamic area
Preoptic area
Tuberomammillary nucleus
Lamina terminalis
Ventromedial nucleus
Anterior and posterior premammillary nuclei
Supraoptic nucleus
Optic recess
Optic chiasma
Optic nerve
Mammillary body
Posterior tuberal nuclei
Adenohypophysis, infundibular portion
Infundibular nucleus
Infundibular recess
Infundibulum
Diaphragma sellae
Stalk portion of infundibulum
Neurohypophysis
Adenohypophysis
Pars intermedia

**Fig. 226.**

**Blue:** Retinohypothalamic tract

**Red:** Tubero-infundibular tract

**Black:** Neurosecretory pathway between the paraventricular and supraoptic nuclei and the extension to neurohypophysis and the infundibular portion of the anterior lobe.

## 227 and 228. Simplified Diagrams of Cerebellum and the Subdivisions of the Vermis.

(Median sagittal section through cerebellum)

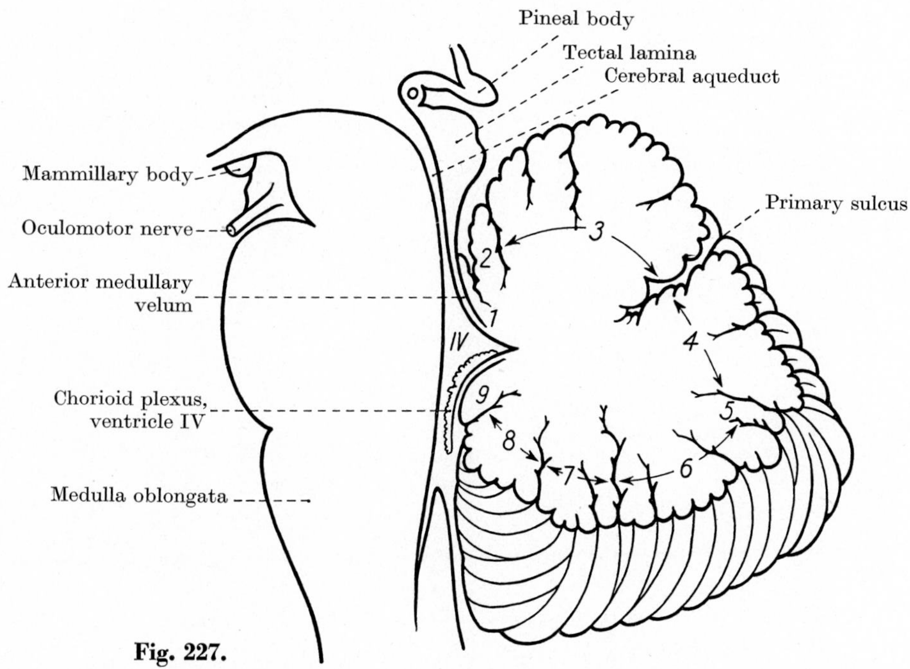
Pineal body
Tectal lamina
Cerebral aqueduct
Mammillary body
Oculomotor nerve
Anterior medullary velum
Primary sulcus
Chorioid plexus, ventricle IV
Medulla oblongata
IV
1
2
3
4
5
6
7
8
9

**Fig. 227.**

**Note:** 1. The posterior lobe (according to Larsell's plan) includes both the middle and posterior lobes that are depicted in Figure 228. He also calls the flocculonodular node, the archicerebellum.

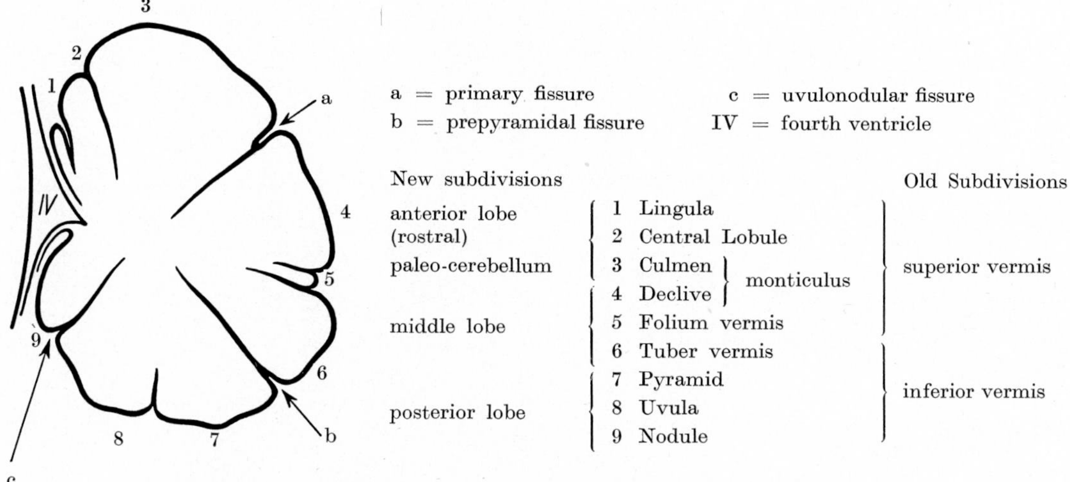
1
2
3
4
5
6
7
8
9
a
b
c
IV
a = primary fissure
c = uvulonodular fissure
b = prepyramidal fissure
IV = fourth ventricle
New subdivisions
Old Subdivisions
anterior lobe (rostral)
paleo-cerebellum
middle lobe
posterior lobe
1 Lingula
2 Central Lobule
3 Culmen
4 Declive
monticulus
5 Folium vermis
6 Tuber vermis
7 Pyramid
8 Uvula
9 Nodule
superior vermis
inferior vermis

**Fig. 228.**

## 229. Nuclei of Cranial Nerves and Primary Optic Centers.

(Diagram drawn into Figure 289).

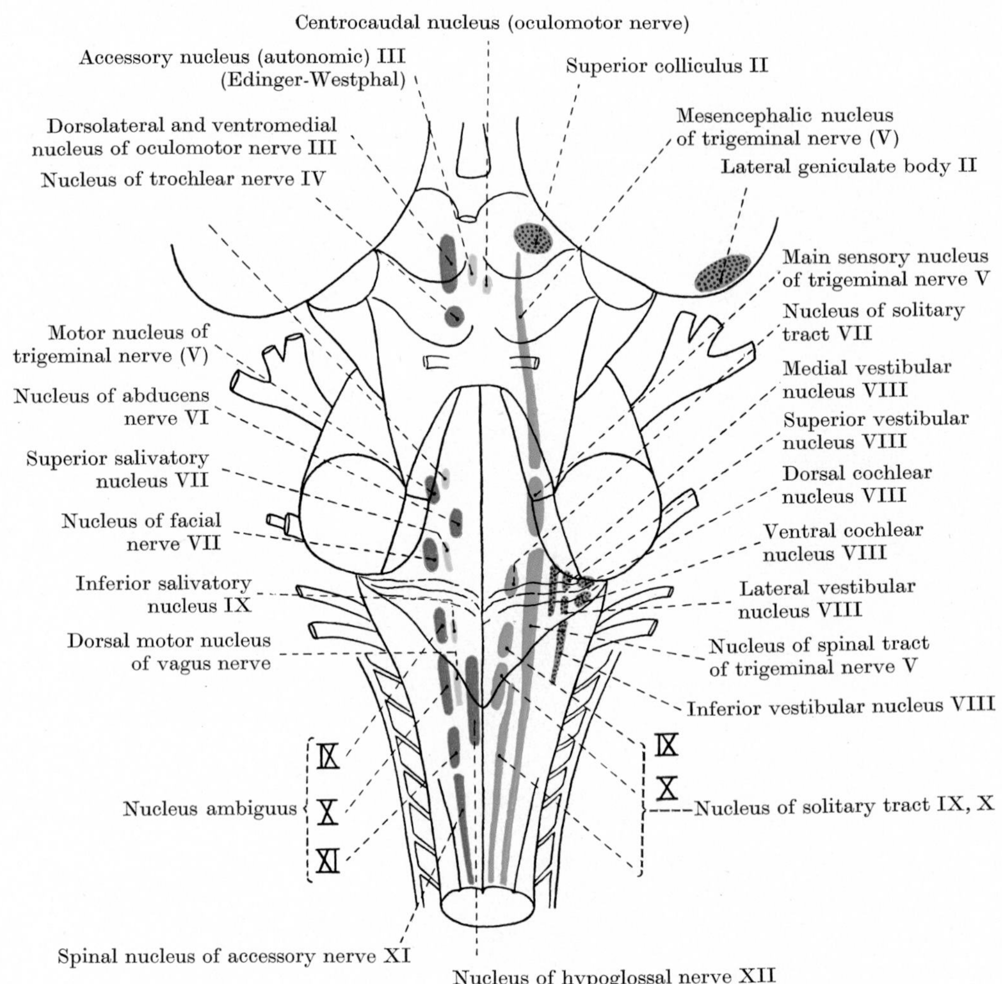
Centrocaudal nucleus (oculomotor nerve)
Accessory nucleus (autonomic) III
(Edinger-Westphal)
Superior colliculus II
Dorsolateral and ventromedial
nucleus of oculomotor nerve III
Mesencephalic nucleus
of trigeminal nerve (V)
Lateral geniculate body II
Nucleus of trochlear nerve IV
Main sensory nucleus
of trigeminal nerve V
Nucleus of solitary
tract VII
Motor nucleus of
trigeminal nerve (V)
Medial vestibular
nucleus VIII
Nucleus of abducens
nerve VI
Superior vestibular
nucleus VIII
Superior salivatory
nucleus VII
Dorsal cochlear
nucleus VIII
Nucleus of facial
nerve VII
Ventral cochlear
nucleus VIII
Inferior salivatory
nucleus IX
Lateral vestibular
nucleus VIII
Dorsal motor nucleus
of vagus nerve
Nucleus of spinal tract
of trigeminal nerve V
Inferior vestibular nucleus VIII
IX
X
XI
Nucleus ambiguus
IX
X
Nucleus of solitary tract IX, X
Spinal nucleus of accessory nerve XI
Nucleus of hypoglossal nerve XII

| | | | |
|---|---|---|---|
| **Left Side:** | Motor and parasympathetic nuclei. | **Right Side:** | Sensory nuclei. |
| **Red:** | Motor nuclei of origin. | **Blue:** | Terminal nuclei of afferent fibers. |
| **Yellow:** | Parasympathetic nuclei of origin. | **Purple:** | Terminal nuclei for vision, hearing, and equilibrium. |

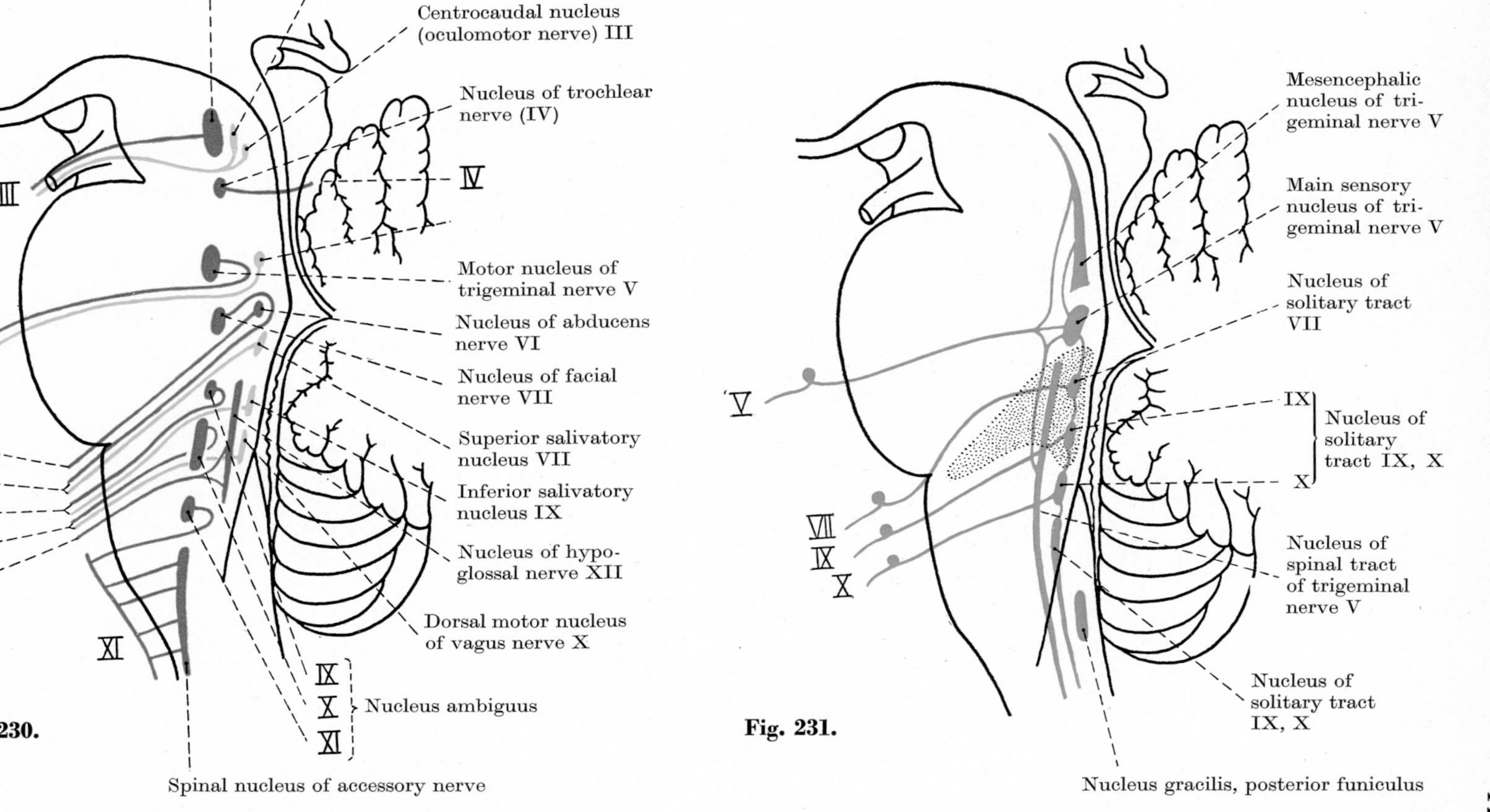
Dorsolateral and ventromedial nuclei of oculomotor nerve III
Accessory oculomotor nucleus (autonomic) (Edinger-Westphal)
Centrocaudal nucleus (oculomotor nerve) III
Nucleus of trochlear nerve (IV)
IV
III
Motor nucleus of trigeminal nerve V
V
Nucleus of abducens nerve VI
Nucleus of facial nerve VII
Superior salivatory nucleus VII
Inferior salivatory nucleus IX
Nucleus of hypoglossal nerve XII
VI
VII
IX
X
XII
XI
Dorsal motor nucleus of vagus nerve X
IX
X
XI
Nucleus ambiguus
Spinal nucleus of accessory nerve
Mesencephalic nucleus of trigeminal nerve V
Main sensory nucleus of trigeminal nerve V
Nucleus of solitary tract VII
V
IX
X
Nucleus of solitary tract IX, X
VII
IX
X
Nucleus of spinal tract of trigeminal nerve V
Nucleus of solitary tract IX, X
Nucleus gracilis, posterior funiculus

**Fig. 230.**

**Fig. 231.**

**230 and 231. Nuclei of Cranial Nerves.** (Lateral views). (Colors same as in Fig. 229) (From illustrations by Clara, 1942)

Figure 230 shows the motor and parasympathetic nuclei and roots.

Figure 231 shows the sensory nuclei and roots. Stippled area designates nuclei of vestibulocochlear nerve.

# 232. Blood Vessels, Cranial Nerves, and Dura on Floor of Cranial Cavity. (1/1)

On **left**, orbital cavity dissected. On **right,** structures in middle cranial fossa displayed. Tentorium cerebelli-8 removed to open sigmoid portion of transverse sinus-5.

1 **Anterior Ethmoidal Artery**
*arteria ethmoidalis anterior*
**Anterior Intercavernous Sinus**
*sinus intercavernosus anterior*
**Optic Nerve**
*nervus opticus*
**Internal Carotid Artery**
*arteria carotis interna*
**Middle Meningeal A., Frontal Br.**
*r. frontalis a. meningeae mediae*
**Ophthalmic Nerve**
*n. ophthalmicus*

2 **Trochlear Nerve**
*n. trochlearis*
**Oculomotor Nerve**
*nervus oculomotorius*
**Maxillary Nerve**
*n. maxillaris*
**Internal Carotid Plexus**
*plexus caroticus internus*
**Mandibular Nerve**
*n. mandibularis*
**Meningeal Branches**
*rr. meningei*
**Middle Meningeal Artery**
*a. meningea media*
**Greater Petrosal Nerve**
*n. petrosus major*
**Superior Tympanic Artery**
*art. tympanica superior*

3 **Lesser Petrosal Nerve**
*n. petrosus minor*
**Middle Meningeal Artery Petrosal Branch**
*r. petrosus a. meningeae mediae*

4 **Trigeminal Nerve**
*nervus trigeminus*
**Superior Petrosal Sinus**
*sinus petrosus superior*
**Facial Nerve**
*nervus facialis*
**Vestibulocochlear Nerve**
*n. vestibulocochlearis*
**Transverse Sinus**
*sinus transversus*

5 **Intermedius Nerve**
*nervus intermedius*
**Arteries of Labyrinth**
*art. labyrinthi*
**Jugular Foramen**
*foramen jugulare*
**Occipital A., Meningeal Br.**
*r. meningeus a. occipitalis*
**Abducens Nerve**
*nervus abducens*
**Accessory Nerve**
*nervus accessorius*

6 **Cut Margins of Tentorium Cerebelli**
*
**Vertebral Art., Meningeal Br.**
*ramus meningeus arteriae vertebralis*
**Medulla Oblongata**
*medulla oblongata*
**Superior Sagittal Sinus**
*sinus sagittalis superior*
**Falx Cerebri**
*falx cerebri*

7 **Straight Sinus**
*sinus rectus*
**Inferior Sagittal Sinus**
*sinus sagittalis inferior*
**Great Cerebral Vein**
*vena cerebri magna*
**Dura Mater Cranial**
*dura mater encephali*
**Vertebral Artery**
*arteria vertebralis*
**Roots of Hypoglossal Nerve**
*radices nervi hypoglossi*
**Accessory Nerve**
*nervus accessorius*
**Vagus Nerve**
*nervus vagus*

8 **Glossopharyngeal Nerve**
*nervus glossopharyngeus*
**Transverse Sinus + (Inferior Cerebral Veins)**
*sinus transversus (+ vv. cerebri inf.)*
**Tentorium Cerebelli**
*tentorium cerebelli*
**Basilar Plexus**
*plexus basilaris*
**Superior Petrosal Sinus**
*sinus petrosus superior*
**Posterior Intercavernous Sinus**
*sinus intercav. posterior*

10 **Cavernous Sinus**
*sinus cavernosus*
**Hypophysis [Pituitary Gland]**
*hypophysis [glandula pituitaria]*
**Sphenoparietal Sinus**
*sinus sphenoparietalis*
**Superior Ophthalmic Vein**
*vena ophthalmica superior*
**Ophthalmic Artery**
*arteria ophthalmica*

11 **Lacrimal Vein**
*vena lacrimalis*
**Vorticose Veins**
*venae vorticosae*
**Vorticose Vein**
*vena vorticosa*
**Levator Palpebrae Superioris Muscle**
*m. levator palpebrae superioris*
**Superior Rectus Muscle**
*m. rectus superior*
**Bulbus Oculi**
*bulbus oculi*
**Optic Nerve**
*nervus opticus*

12 **Nasofrontal Vein**
*vena nasofrontalis*
**Superior Sagittal Sinus**
*sinus sagittalis superior*
**Falx Cerebri**
*falx cerebri*
**Inferior Sagittal Sinus**
*sinus sagittalis inferior*
**Anterior Meningeal Artery**
*a. meningea anterior*

**Note:** 1. The Connection of the **ophthalmic** vein-10 with the **cavernous sinus**-10 through the superior orbital fissure.

2. The **Optic nerve**-1 enters the optic canal at junction of the anterior with the middle cranial fossa.

3. **Oculomotor** III and **trochlear** IV pierce the dura near the border between the posterior and middle cranial fossae. The last 8 cranial nerves pierce the dura in the posterior cranial fossa.

4. Three divisions of the **trigeminal nerve** pass through the middle cranial fossa between the dura and the periosteum of the skull and leave through the openings in the middle cranial fossa.

5. **Oculomotor**-2, **trochlear**-2, **abducens**-5 nerves, and the **ophthalmic division of** the **trigeminal**-2 pass through the **superior orbital fissure.**

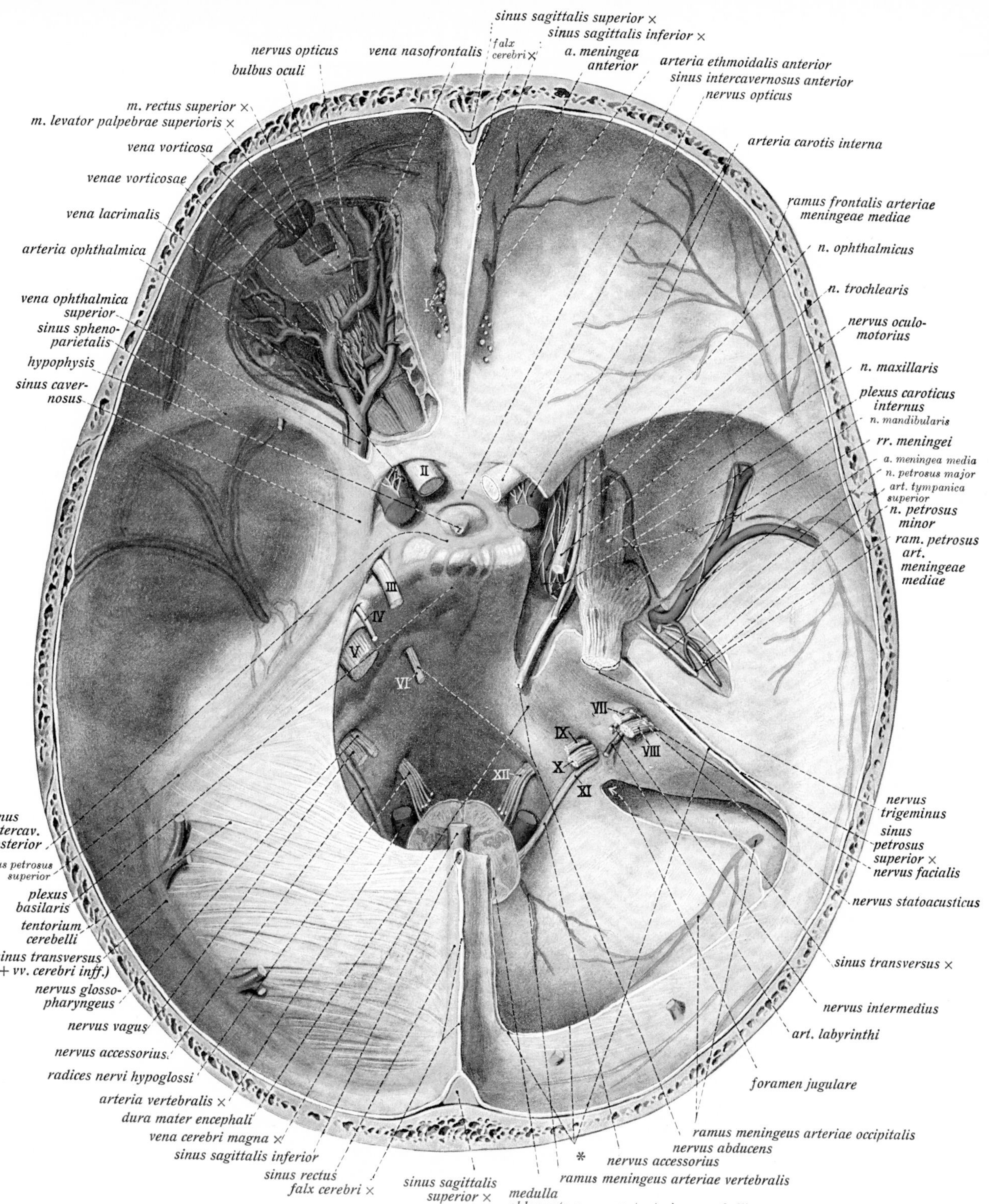

sinus sagittalis superior ×
sinus sagittalis inferior ×
nervus opticus
vena nasofrontalis
falx cerebri ×
a. meningea anterior
arteria ethmoidalis anterior
sinus intercavernosus anterior
nervus opticus
bulbus oculi
m. rectus superior ×
m. levator palpebrae superioris ×
vena vorticosa
arteria carotis interna
venae vorticosae
vena lacrimalis
ramus frontalis arteriae meningeae mediae
arteria ophthalmica
n. ophthalmicus
n. trochlearis
vena ophthalmica superior
sinus spheno-parietalis
nervus oculo-motorius
hypophysis
n. maxillaris
sinus caver-nosus
plexus caroticus internus
n. mandibularis
rr. meningei
a. meningea media
n. petrosus major
art. tympanica superior
n. petrosus minor
ram. petrosus art. meningeae mediae
I
II
III
IV
V
VI
VII
VIII
IX
X
XI
XII
nervus trigeminus
sinus petrosus superior ×
nervus facialis
sinus intercav. posterior
sinus petrosus superior
plexus basilaris
nervus statoacusticus
tentorium cerebelli
sinus transversus (+ vv. cerebri inff.)
sinus transversus ×
nervus glosso-pharyngeus
nervus intermedius
nervus vagus
art. labyrinthi
nervus accessorius
radices nervi hypoglossi
foramen jugulare
arteria vertebralis ×
dura mater encephali
ramus meningeus arteriae occipitalis
vena cerebri magna ×
nervus abducens
sinus sagittalis inferior
*
nervus accessorius
sinus rectus
ramus meningeus arteriae vertebralis
falx cerebri ×
sinus sagittalis superior ×
medulla oblongata ×
* tentorium cerebelli ×


Fig. 232.

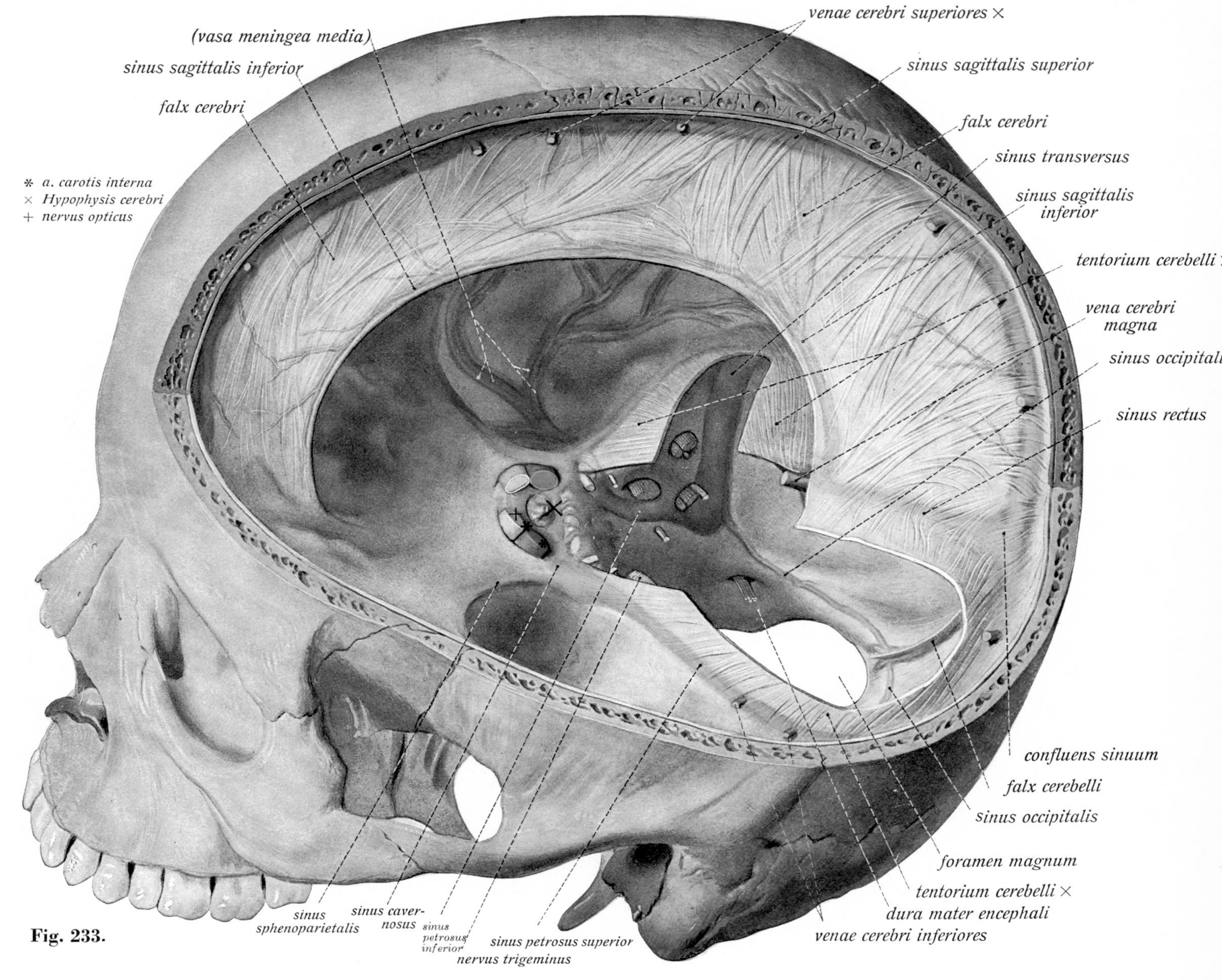

(vasa meningea media)
sinus sagittalis inferior
falx cerebri
* a. carotis interna
× Hypophysis cerebri
+ nervus opticus
venae cerebri superiores ×
sinus sagittalis superior
falx cerebri
sinus transversus
sinus sagittalis inferior
tentorium cerebelli ×
vena cerebri magna
sinus occipitalis
sinus rectus
confluens sinuum
falx cerebelli
sinus occipitalis
foramen magnum
tentorium cerebelli ×
dura mater encephali
venae cerebri inferiores
sinus sphenoparietalis
sinus cavernosus
sinus petrosus inferior
sinus petrosus superior
nervus trigeminus


**Fig. 233.**

## 233. Dura Mater of Cranial Cavity and Its Venous Sinuses. (seen from above and left) (1/1)

Left wall of cranial cavity was cut away and brain removed. Veins and sinuses are blue, arteries red. Most of tentorium cerebelli-5 was removed from right side and a narrow strip on left-2 to display structures in posterior cranial fossa, particularly the transverse sinus-2.

1 **Superior Cerebral Veins** *venae cerebri superiores*
**Superior Sagittal Sinus** *sinus sagittalis superior*
2 **Falx Cerebri** *falx cerebri*
**Transverse Sinus** *sinus transversus*
**Inferior Sagittal Sinus** *sinus sagittalis inferior*
**Tentorium Cerebelli** *tentorium cerebelli*
**Great Cerebral Vein** *vena cerebri magna*
3 **Occipital Sinus** *sinus occipitalis*
**Straight Sinus** *sinus rectus*
4 **Sinus Confluens** *confluens sinuum*
**Falx Cerebelli** *falx cerebelli*
**Occipital Sinus** *sinus occipitalis*
5 **Foramen Magnum** *foramen magnum*
**Tentorium Cerebelli** *tentorium cerebelli*
**Dura Mater of Brain** *dura mater encephali*
**Inferior Cerebral Veins** *venae cerebri inferiores*
6 **Superior Petrosal Sinus** *sinus petrosus superior*
**Trigeminal Nerve** *nervus trigeminus*
7 **Inferior Petrosal Sinus** *sinus petrosus inferior*
**Cavernosus Sinus** *sinus cavernosus*
**Sphenoparietal Sinus** *sinus sphenoparietalis*
10 **Falx Cerebri** *falx cerebri*
**Inferior Sagittal Sinus** *sinus sagittalis inferior*
11 **(Middle Meningeal Vessels)** *(vasa meningea media)*

**Note:** 1. **Inferior sagittal sinus**-2 joins the **straight sinus**-3, which is continuation of the **great cerebral vein**-2 (of Galen). The straight sinus-3 flows into sinus confluens-4 where it meets the superior sagittal sinus-1. Right-2 and left transverse sinuses convey blood from the sinus confluens-4 to jugular foramen where they form the internal jugular vein. Transverse sinuses also collect blood from ophthalmic vein, cavernous sinus-7, sphenoparietal sinus-7 and **superior**-6 **and inferior**-7 **petrosal sinuses**.

2. Most of the arteries that enter the cranial cavity supply the brain and are, therefore, removed with it.

3. Hypophysis (x-in center) located in the hypophyseal fossa of the sphenoid bone, almost covered by a dural sheet and a venous plexus which form the diaphragm of the sella turcica.

4. The middle meningeal artery-11 enters the floor of the middle cranial fossa through the foramen spinosum and is distributed to the dura and walls of the cranium.

# 234. The Superior Sagittal Sinus and Cerebral Blood Vessels.

(from above) (1/1)

1 **Superior Cerebral Vein**
*vena cerebri superior*
**Frontal Lobe**
*lobus frontalis cerebri*

2 **Lateral Lacuna of Superior Sagittal Sinus + Arachnoidal Granulations**
*(lacuna lateralis sin. sagitt. super. + granulationes arachnoideales)*

6 **Superior Sagittal Sinus**
*sinus sagittalis superior*

7 **Superior Cerebral Vein**
*vena cerebri superior*

8 **Parietal Branch of Middle Cerebral Artery**
*ramus parietalis arteriae cerebri mediae*

10 **Lateral Lacuna of Superior Sagittal Sinus**
*(lacuna lat. sinus sagitt. sup.)*
**Root of Superior Cerebral Vein**
*radix v. cerebri superioris*

12 **Superior Sagittal Sinus**
*sinus sagittalis superior*
**Openings of Sup. Cerebral V.**
*ostia venarum cerebri superiorum*

**Note:** 1. Terminal branches of **anterior**, **middle**-8 and **posterior cerebral arteries** depicted in red.

2. **Superior cerebral veins**-1, in blue, usually turn sharply ventrally to enter the superior sagittal sinus at an acute angle.

3. The enlargements or extension of venous spaces which communicate with the superior sagittal sinus-12 are called **lateral lacuni**-2. Tufted processes of the arachnoid that extend into these are called **arachnoidal granulations**-2. (see Figs. 195 and 240)

**Etymology:**

sagittal = L. *sagitta*, arrow
arachnoid = Gr., *ho arachnos*, spider

Arachnoidal granulations formerly called Pacchionian Bodies after an Italian Anatomist of the 17th century.

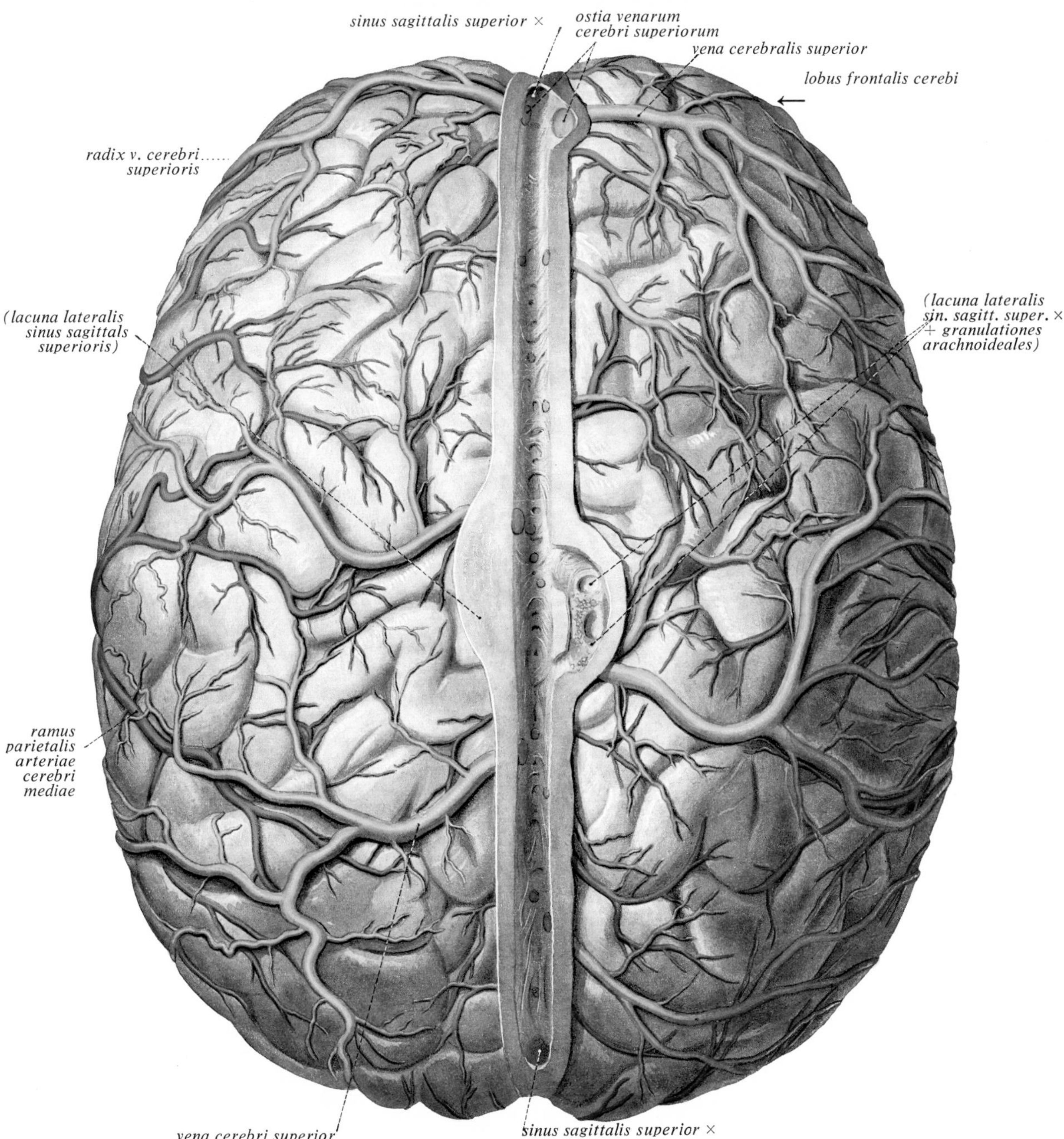
sinus sagittalis superior ×
ostia venarum
cerebri superiorum
vena cerebralis superior
lobus frontalis cerebi
radix v. cerebri
superioris
(lacuna lateralis
sinus sagittals
superioris)
(lacuna lateralis
sin. sagitt. super. ×
+ granulationes
arachnoideales)
ramus
parietalis
arteriae
cerebri
mediae
vena cerebri superior
sinus sagittalis superior ×

**Fig. 234.**

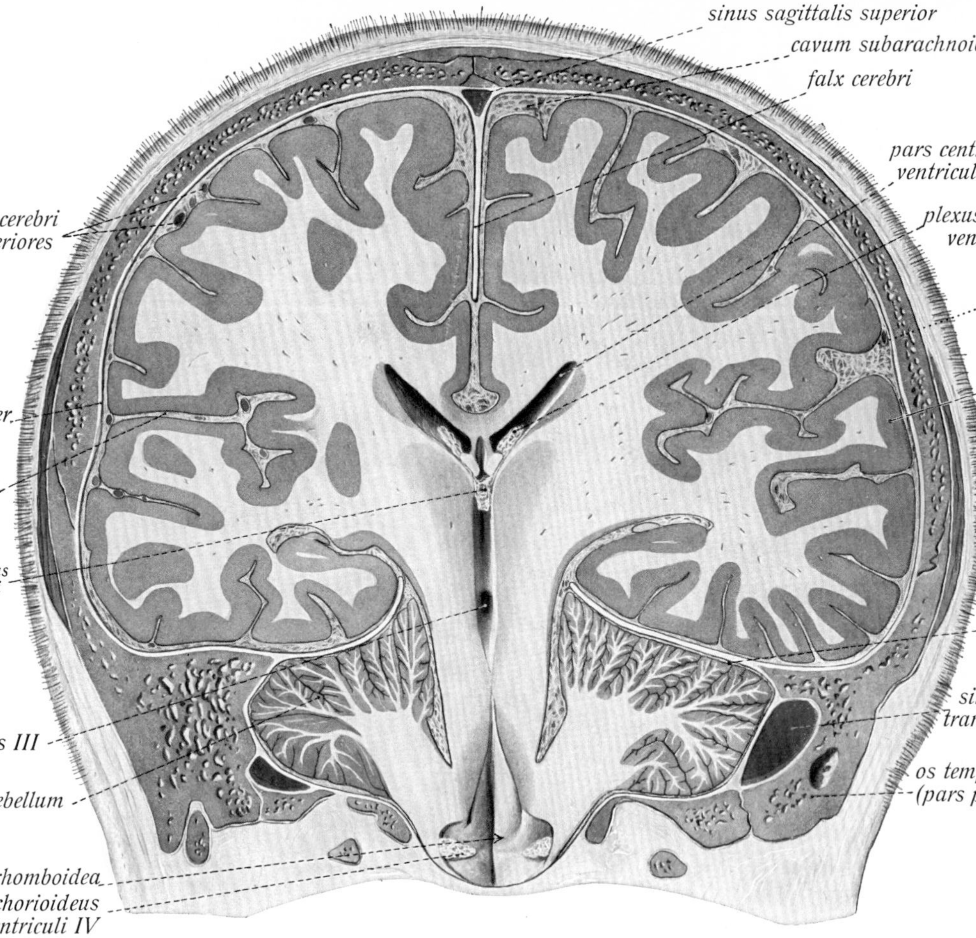

sinus sagittalis superior
cavum subarachnoideale
falx cerebri
pars centralis ventriculi lateralis
plexus chorioideus ventr. lateralis
cavum subarachnoideale
gyrus temporalis superior
tentorium cerebelli
sinus transversus
os temporale (pars petro-mastoidea)
venae cerebri superiores
dura mater
pia mater
plexus chorioideus ventriculi III
ventriculus III
cerebellum
fossa rhomboidea
plexus chorioideus ventriculi IV

**Fig. 235.**

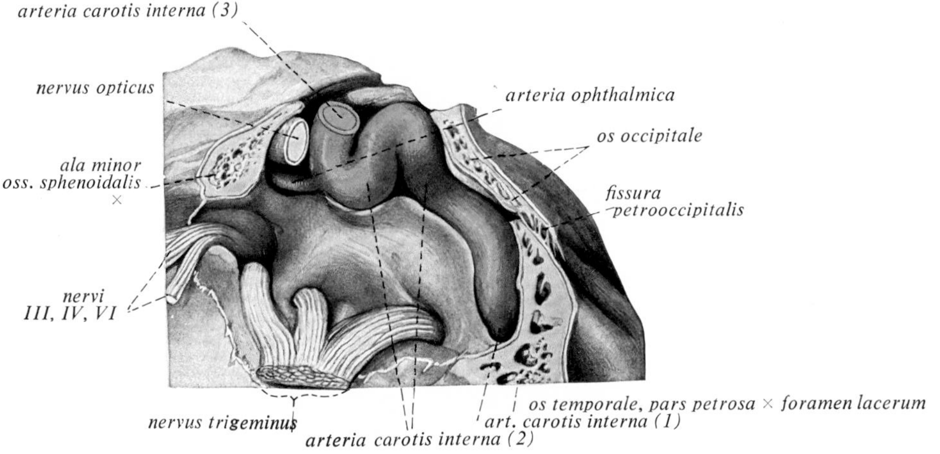

arteria carotis interna (3)
nervus opticus
arteria ophthalmica
os occipitale
ala minor oss. sphenoidalis
×
fissura petrooccipitalis
nervi III, IV, VI
os temporale, pars petrosa × foramen lacerum
art. carotis interna (1)
nervus trigeminus
arteria carotis interna (2)


**Fig. 236.**

## 235. Frontal Section of Head near Ventral Part of Interparietal Sagittal Suture. (2/3)

Dura mater-9 white. Pia mater-9 and arachnoid light red. Blood in the sinuses-4 dark red.

1 **Superior Sagittal Sinus**
*sinus sagittalis superior*
**Subarachnoid Cavity**
*cavum subarachnoideale*
**Falx Cerebri**
*falx cerebri*

2 **Central Portion of Lateral Ventricle**
*pars centralis ventriculi lateralis*
**Chorioid Plexus of Lateral Ventricle**
*plexus chorioideus ventr. lateralis*
**Subarachnoid Cavity**
*cavum subarachnoideale*

3 **Superior Temporal Gyrus**
*gyrus temporalis superior*
**Tentorium Cerebelli**
*tentorium cerebelli*

4 **Transverse Sinus**
*sinus transversus*
**Temporal Bone (Petromastoid Portion)**
*os temporale (pars petromastoidea)*

8 **Chorioid Plexus of 4th Ventricle**
*plexus chorioideus ventriculi IV*
**Rhomboid Fossa**
*fossa rhomboidea*
**Cerebellum**
*cerebellum*
**3rd Ventricle**
*ventriculus III*

9 **Chorioid Plexus of 3rd Ventricle**
*plexus chorioideus ventriculi III*
**Pia Mater**
*pia mater*
**Dura Mater**
*dura mater*

10 **Superior Cerebral Veins**
*venae cerebri superiores*

**Note:** 1. The **pia mater**-9 is closely applied to the brain, even to the extent that it lines the sulci and fissures. The **arachnoid,** on the other hand, forms a continuous outer sac or envelope, so that **subarachnoid spaces**-1, -2 and fissures and cisternae exist for circulation of cerebrospinal fluid.

2. The **chorioid plexuses** are shown protruding into the lateral ventricles-2, the third ventricle-9, and the fourth ventricle-8.

## 236. Course of Left Internal Carotid Artery through Cavernous Sinus Lateral to Sella Turcica. (1/1)

The third, fourth, and sixth cranial nerves and the ophthalmic nerve have been turned laterally where they enter the superior orbital fissure. The trigeminal nerve was reflected laterally and the dura in the region resected. The number following "arteria carotis interna" indicates the landmarks in the course of the **carotid artery.** Number "1" is where it enters the cranial cavity; "2" is the S-shaped coil near sella turcica; "3" where it enters arachnoid.

1 **Ophthalmic Artery**
*arteria ophthalmica*

2 **Occipital Bone**
*os occipitale*
**Petrooccipital Fissure**
*fissura petrooccipitalis*

5 **Petrosal Portion, Temporal Bone at Foramen Lacerum**
*os temporale, pars petrosa, foramen lacerum*
**Internal Carotid Artery 1**
*art. carotis interna 1*

6 **Internal Carotid Artery 2**
*arteria carotis interna 2*

8 **Trigeminal Nerve**
*nervus trigeminus*
**III, IV, VI Nerves**
*nervi III, IV, VI*

9 **Sphenoid Bone, Lesser Wing**
*ala minor oss. sphenoidalis*

10 **Optic Nerve**
*nervus opticus*
**Internal Carotid Artery 3**
*arteria carotis interna 3*

**Note:** 1. **Ophthalmic artery**-2 given off at bend of internal **carotid artery**-6 (caudal to **optic nerve**-10) passes through optic canal with the nerve to enter orbital cavity.

## 237. Frontal Section of Brain at Level of the Dorsal Fourth of the Interparietal Sagittal Suture. (2/3)

Same color scheme as in Figure 253.

1 **Superior Sagittal Sinus**
*sinus sagittalis superior*

2 **Falx Cerebri**
*falx cerebri*

**Superior Cerebral Vein**
*vena cerebri superior*

3 **Sinus Confluens, Superior, Sagittal, and Straight**
*confluens sinuum sagittalis superior et recti*

4 **Tentorium Cerebelli**
*tentorium cerebelli*

**Transverse Sinus**
*sinus transversus*

7 **Cerebellum**
*cerebellum*

9 **Skin**
*integumentum commune*
**Galea Aponeurotica**
*galea aponeurotica*

10 **Parietal Bone**
*os parietale*

**Note:** 1. The venous sinuses-1, -3, -4 are channels between layers of dura.

## 238. Frontal Section Through Left Cavernous Sinus. (3/1)

1 **Optic Nerve**
*nervus opticus*

2 **Hypophysis** [Pituitary Gland]
*hypophysis [glandula pituitaria]*

3 **Internal Carotid Artery**
*art. carotis interna*

**Sphenoidal Sinus Mucous Membrane**
*tunica mucosa sinus sphenoidalis*

5 **Cavernous Sinus Trabeculae**
*(trabeculae sinus cavernosi)*

6 **Body of Sphenoid Bone**
*corpus ossis sphenoidalis*

8 **Dura Mater**
*dura mater*

9 **Maxillary Nerve**
*nervus maxillaris*

**Ophthalmic Nerve**
*n. ophthalmicus*

10 **Abducens Nerve**
*n. abducens*

**Trochlear Nerve**
*n. trochlearis*

**Oculomotor Nerve**
*nervus oculomotorius*

12 **Dura Mater**
*dura mater*

**Internal Carotid Artery**
*art. carotis interna*

**Note:** 1. **Hypophysis**-2 in midline, is unpaired and covered by the dura-12 of **diaphragma sella** over sella turcica.

2. **Optic nerve**-1 is closely related to **internal carotid artery**-12, -3 which has turned back upon itself.

3. **Internal carotid artery**-3 passes through cavernous venous sinus-5, on lateral side of body of sphenoid bone-6. Nerves III, IV, V, and VI are located in a more lateral position, close to the dura mater-8.

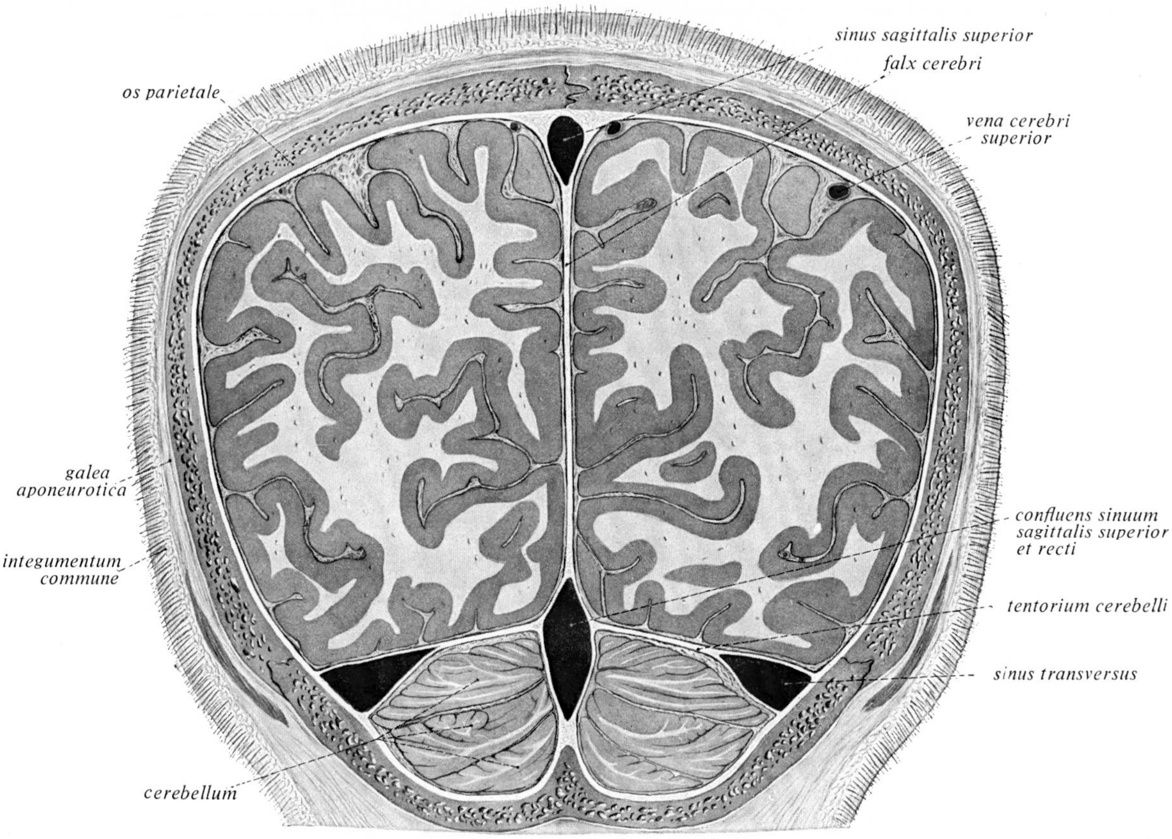

sinus sagittalis superior
falx cerebri
os parietale
vena cerebri superior
galea aponeurotica
integumentum commune
confluens sinuum sagittalis superior et recti
tentorium cerebelli
sinus transversus
cerebellum

**Fig. 237.**

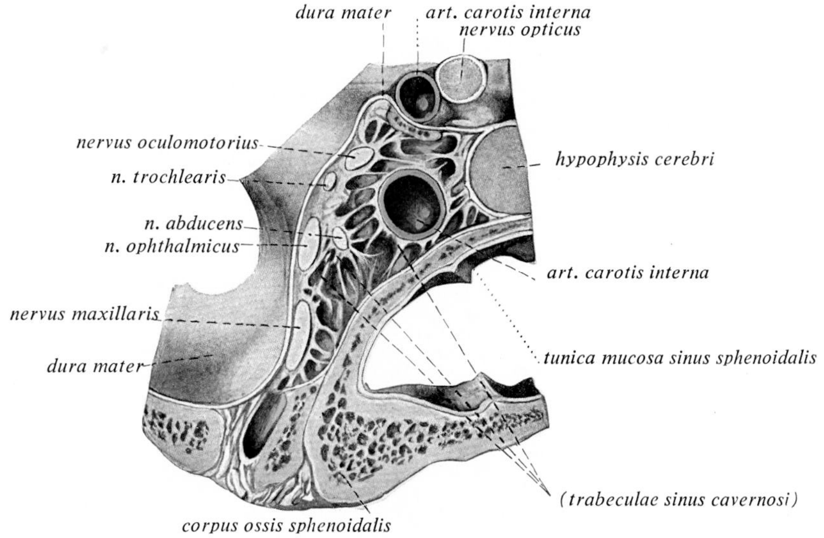
dura mater
art. carotis interna
nervus opticus
nervus oculomotorius
hypophysis cerebri
n. trochlearis
n. abducens
n. ophthalmicus
art. carotis interna
nervus maxillaris
dura mater
tunica mucosa sinus sphenoidalis
(trabeculae sinus cavernosi)
corpus ossis sphenoidalis

**Fig. 238.**

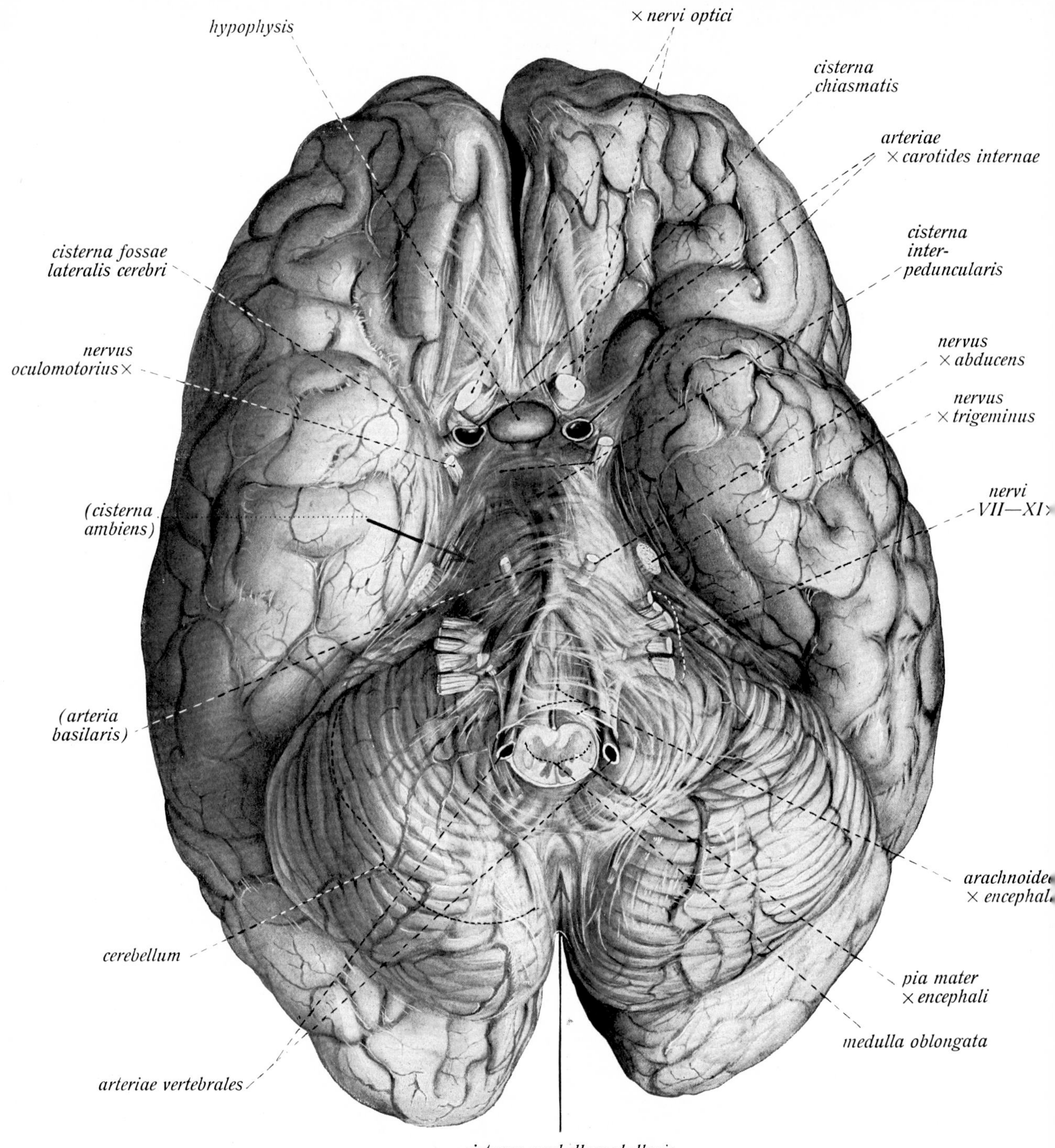
hypophysis
× nervi optici
cisterna chiasmatis
arteriae × carotides internae
cisterna inter-peduncularis
cisterna fossae lateralis cerebri
nervus oculomotorius ×
nervus × abducens
nervus × trigeminus
(cisterna ambiens)
nervi VII—XI
(arteria basilaris)
arachnoidea × encephali
cerebellum
pia mater × encephali
medulla oblongata
arteriae vertebrales
cisterna cerebellomedullaris

**Fig. 239.**

## 239. Base of Brain with its Arachnoidal and Pial Coverings. (4/5)

The caudal part of the medulla oblongata was cut off. Arrows were introduced into some of the subarachnoid spaces to indicate the position of the larger cisternae.

1 **Chiasmatic Cistern**
*cisterna chiasmatis*

**Internal Carotid Arteries**
*arteriae carotides internae*

2 **Interpeduncular Cistern**
*cisterna interpeduncularis*

**Abducens Nerve**
*nervus abducens*

**Trigeminal Nerve**
*nervus trigeminus*

3 **Nerves VII–XI**
*nervi VII–XI*

4 **Arachnoid**
*arachnoidea encephali*

5 **Pia mater**
*pia mater encephali*

**Medulla Oblongata**
*medulla oblongata*

6 **Cerebellomedullary Cistern**
*cisterna cerebellomedullaris*

7 **Vertebral Arteries**
*arteriae vertebrales*

8 **Cerebellum**
*cerebellum*

9 **Basilar Artery**
*(arteria basilaris)*

**Cisterna Ambiens**
*(cisterna ambiens)*

10 **Oculomotor Nerve**
*nervus oculomotorius*

**Lateral Cerebral Cisternal Fossa**
*cisterna fossae lateralis cerebri*

11 **Hypophysis [Pituitary Gland]**
*hypophysis [glandula pituitaria]*

12 **Optic nerves**
*nervi optici*

**Note:** 1. The **subarachnoid cisternae** may be defined as areas where the distance between the pial covering of the nervous system and the arachnoidal membrane are widely separated. This occurs where there are fissures and large depressions on the surface of the brain.

2. The **cerebellomedullary cistern**-6 (cisterna magna) is located between the medulla oblongata and the cerebellar hemispheres. The **chiasmatic cistern**-1 is located in the region of the optic chiasm.

3. Observe where cranial nerves pierce the arachnoidal membrane.

# 240. Brain with the Arachnoid and Pia Mater.

(Leptomeninx) (Viewed from above) (4/5)

**1 Arachnoid**
*arachnoidea*

**5 Arachnoid Granulations**
*granulationes arachnoideales*

**6 Corpus Callosum, Cistern of**
*cisterna corporis callosi*

**7 Superior Cerebral Veins**
*venae cerebri superiores*

**12 Longitudinal Cerebral Fissure**
*fissura longitudinalis cerebri*

**Note:** 1. The **arachnoidal granulations**-5 on either side of the **longitudinal cerebral fissure**-12.

2. The **superior cerebral veins**-7 have been cut as they emerged from the arachnoidal membrane-1 to enter the superior sagittal sinus in the falx cerebri.

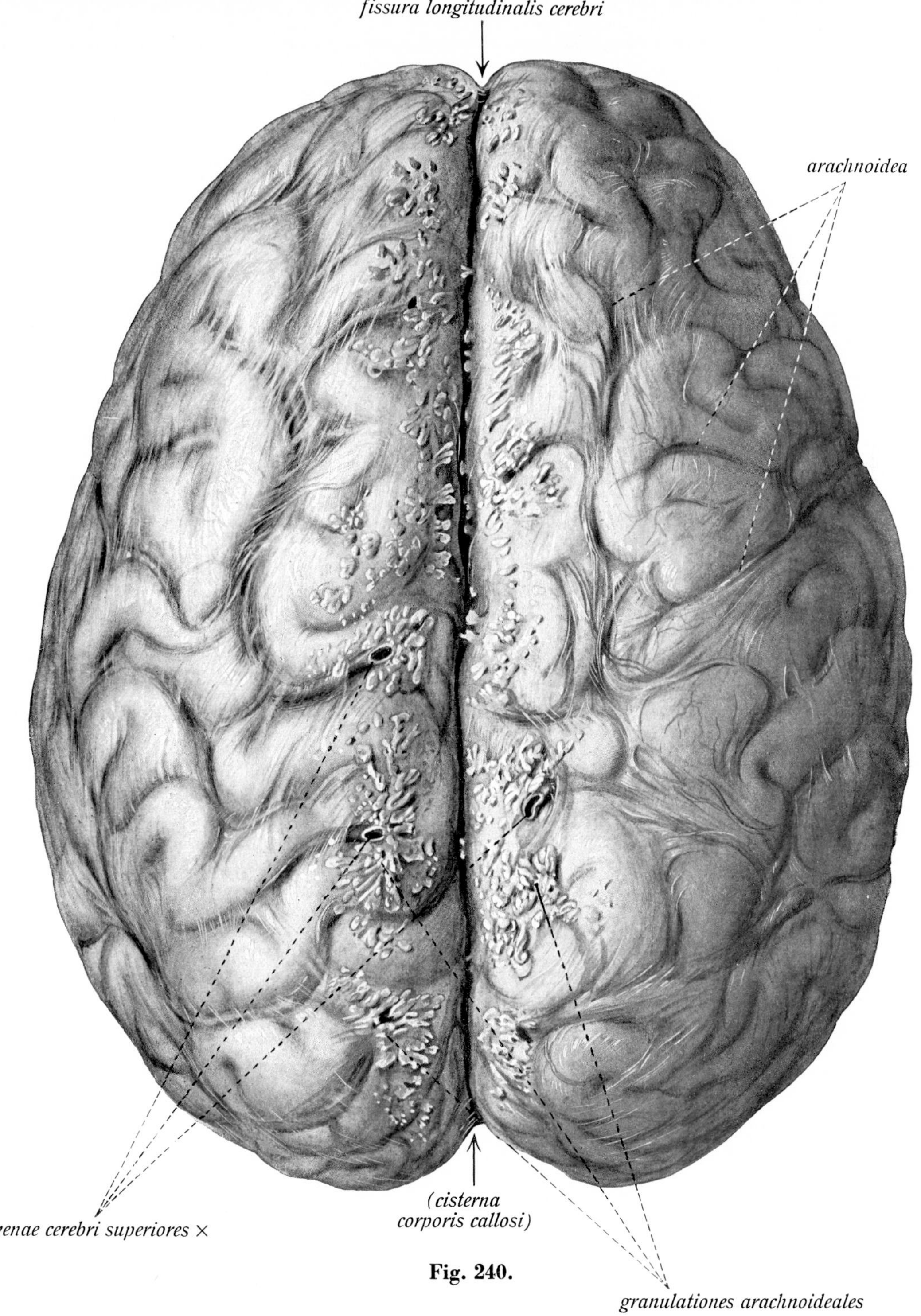
fissura longitudinalis cerebri
arachnoidea
venae cerebri superiores ×
(cisterna
corporis callosi)
granulationes arachnoideales

**Fig. 240.**

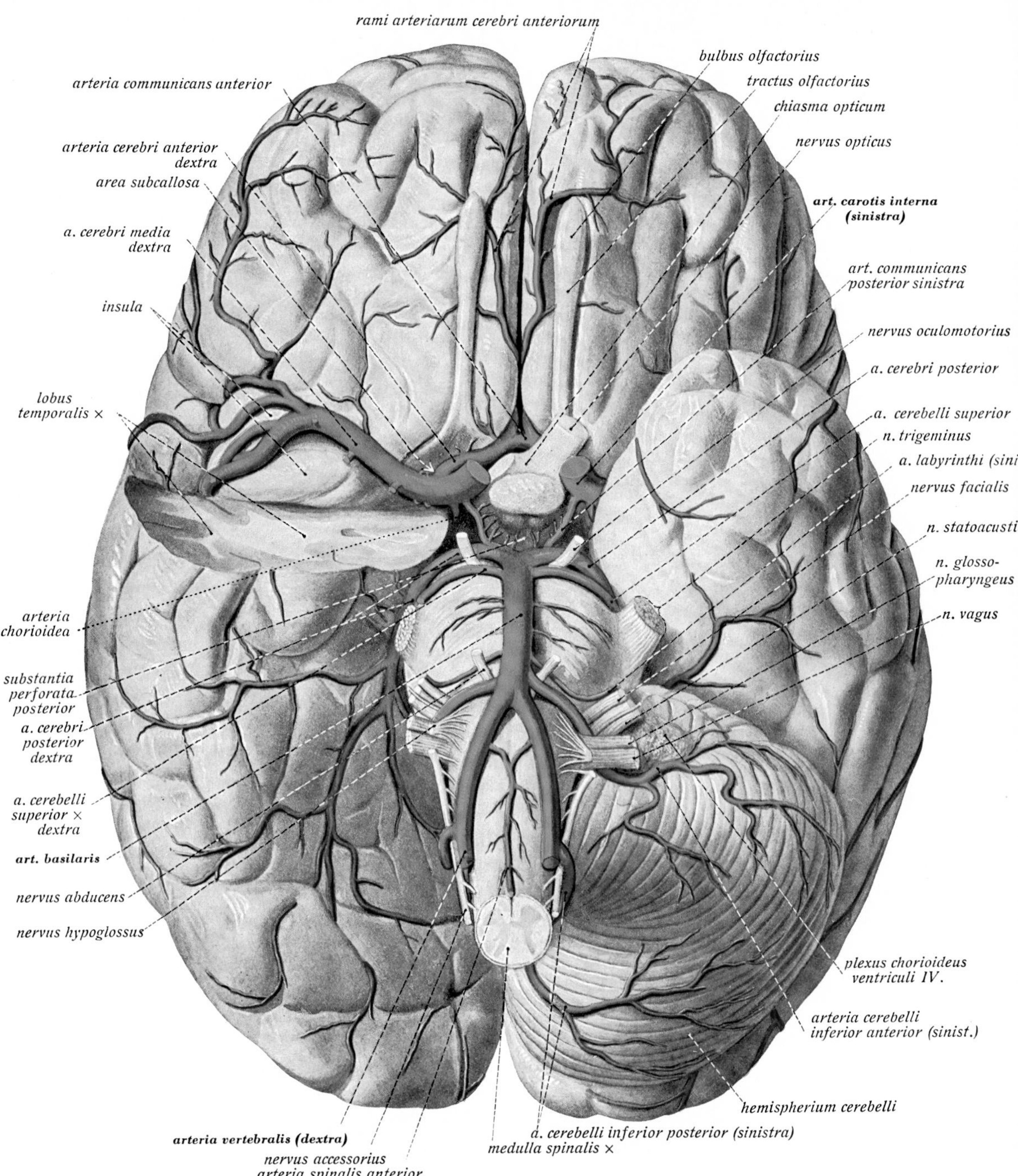
rami arteriarum cerebri anteriorum
bulbus olfactorius
tractus olfactorius
chiasma opticum
nervus opticus
art. carotis interna (sinistra)
art. communicans posterior sinistra
nervus oculomotorius
a. cerebri posterior
a. cerebelli superior
n. trigeminus
a. labyrinthi (sini.
nervus facialis
n. statoacustic
n. glosso-pharyngeus
n. vagus
arteria communicans anterior
arteria cerebri anterior dextra
area subcallosa
a. cerebri media dextra
insula
lobus temporalis ×
arteria chorioidea
substantia perforata posterior
a. cerebri posterior dextra
a. cerebelli superior × dextra
art. basilaris
nervus abducens
nervus hypoglossus
plexus chorioideus ventriculi IV.
arteria cerebelli inferior anterior (sinist.)
hemispherium cerebelli
arteria vertebralis (dextra)
a. cerebelli inferior posterior (sinistra)
medulla spinalis ×
nervus accessorius
arteria spinalis anterior

Fig. 241.

## 241. The Arteries at the Base of the Brain. (4/5)

Tip of right temporal lobe-10 and right cerebellar hemisphere-5 were removed. Right optic nerve was cut off to display the anterior cerebral artery-11.

1 **Olfactory Bulb**
*bulbus olfactorius*
**Olfactory Tract**
*tractus olfactorius*
**Optic Chiasma**
*chiasma opticum*
**Optic nerve**
*nervus opticus*
**Internal Carotid Artery,** Left
*art. carotis interna (sinistra)*

2 **Posterior Communicating A.**
*art. communicans post. sin.*
**Oculomotor Nerve**
*nervus oculomotorius*
**Posterior Cerebral Artery**
*a. cerebri posterior*
**Superior Cerebellar Artery**
*a. cerebelli superior*
**Trigeminal Nerve**
*n. trigeminus*
**Labyrinthine Artery,** Left
*a. labyrinthi (sinistr.)*

3 **Facial Nerve**
*nervus facialis*
**Vestibulocochlear Nerve**
*[n. vestibulocochlearis]*
*n. statoacusticus*
**Glossopharyngeal Nerve**
*n. glossopharyngeus*
**Vagus Nerve**
*n. vagus*

5 **Chorioid Plexus of IV Ventricle**
*plexus chorioideus ventriculi IV*
**Anterior Inferior Cerebellar A.**
*a. cerebelli inferior ant. (sinist.)*
**Cerebellar Hemisphere**
*hemispherium cerebelli*

6 **Posterior Inferior Cerebellar Artery,** Left
*a. cerebelli inferior posterier (sinistra)*
**Spinal Cord**
*medulla spinalis*

7 **Anterior Spinal Artery**
*arteria spinalis anterior*
**Accessory Nerve**
*nervus accessorius*
**Vertebral Artery** (right)
*arteria vertebralis (dextra)*

8 **Hypoglossal Nerve**
*nervus hypoglossus*
**Abducens Nerve**
*nervus abducens*
**Basilar Artery**
*art. basilaris*
**Superior Cerebellar Artery,**
*a. cerebelli superior dextra*
**Posterior Cerebral Artery,** Right
*a. cerebri posterior dextra*

9 **Posterior Perforated Substance**
*substantia perforata posterior*
**Anterior Chorioidal Artery**
*arteria chorioidea [anterior]*

10 **Temporal Lobe**
*lobus temporalis*
**Insula**
*insula*
**Middle Cerebral Artery,** Right
*a. cerebri media dextra*

11 **Subcallosal Area**
*area subcallosa*
**Anterior Cerebral Artery,** Right
*arteria cerebri anterior dextra*
**Anterior Communicating Art.**
*arteria communicans anterior*

12 **Ant. Cerebral Arteries (Branches of)**
*rami arteriarum cerebri anteriorum*

**Note:** 1. **Anterior spinal artery**-7 originating from vertebral arteries-7.

2. **Basilar artery**-8 gives off **inferior cerebellar artery**-5, arteries to the labyrinth-2, **superior cerebellar arteries**-8, and **posterior cerebral arteries**-2. **Posterior communicating arteries**-2 connect **posterior cerebral arteries**-8 to **internal carotid arteries**-1. These each give rise to **anterior cerebral arteries**-12 that have a **communication**-11 just rostral to optic chiasma-1 to form the **circulus arteriosus** (circle of Willis), an arterial circle around the optic chiasma and the hypophysis. This unusually large anastomosis is between branches of the vertebral basilar arteries and the two internal carotid arteries.

3. **Internal carotid artery**-1 communicates with posterior cerebral branch-2 of the basilar arteries-8 and gives off the **anterior cerebral**-12, **middle cerebral**-10, and **chorioidal arteries**-9. **Anterior cerebral arteries** pass to longitudinal fissure and communicate-11 with each other. **Middle cerebral** artery passes through lateral cerebral fissure and ramifies to supply temporal, frontal, and parietal lobes and the insula. In addition to labeled branches, several small branches just distal to anterior chorioidal artery origin, supply the corpus striatum and are called the **striatal arteries.** When these vessels rupture, paralysis frequently follows and they have been called the arteries of cerebral hemorrhage.

## 242. Arteries of Medial Surface of Right Cerebral Hemisphere and of Left Surface of Cerebellum. (4/5)

The left cerebral hemisphere was removed by a midsagittal section through the corpus callosum-8 and an oblique cut through the cerebral peduncle-7 at the midbrain level.

2 **Pineal Body**
*corpus pineale*

**Parietooccipital Sulcus (Fissure)**
*sulcus parietooccipitalis*

**Internal Cerebral Vein,** Left
*vena cerebri interna sinistra*

**Great Cerebral Vein**
*vena cerebri magna*

3 **Posterior Cerebral Artery, Branch of (Calcarine Sulcus)**
*ramus arteriae cerebri posterioris (sulcus calcarinus)*

6 **Anterior Spinal Artery**
*arteria spinalis anterior*

**Posterior Spinal Artery**
*arteria spinalis posterior*

**Posterior Inferior Cerebellar Artery,** Left
*arteria cerebelli inferior posterior sinistra*

**Vertebral Artery,** Left
*arteria vertebralis sinistra*

7 **Anterior Inferior Cerebellar Artery,** Left
*arteria cerebelli inferior anterior sinistra*

**Basilar Artery**
*arteria basilaris*

**Trochlear Nerve**
*nervus trochlearis*

**Superior Cerebellar Artery,** Left
*arteria cerebelli superior sinistra*

**Posterior Cerebral Artery,** Left
*arteria cerebri posterior sinistra*

**Cerebral Peduncle**
*pedunculus cerebri*

**Oculomotor Nerve**
*nervus oculomotorius*

8 **Posterior Communicating Artery,** Left
*art. communicans posterior sinistra*

**Tela Chorioidea of 3rd Ventricle**
*tela chorioidea ventriculi III*

**Column of Fornix**
*columna fornicis*

**Optic Nerve**
*nervus opticus*

**Anterior Communicating Artery**
*art. communicans anter.*

**Anterior Cerebral Artery,** Right
*art. cerebri anterior dextra*

**Corpus Callosum**
*corpus callosum*

10 **Gyrus Cinguli**
*gyrus cinguli*

**Anterior Cerebral Artery,** Right
*art. cerebri anterior dextra*

**Note:** 1. **Vertebral artery** gives rise to **posterior inferior cerebellar artery**-6, **anterior spinal**-6 and **posterior spinal arteries**-6.

2. **Anterior inferior cerebellar**-7 and **superior cerebellar**-7 **arteries** arise from pontine portion of **basilar artery**-7.

3. **Oculomotor nerve**-7 separates **superior cerebellar artery** from **posterior cerebral artery**-7, terminal branch of the basilar artery. Posterior cerebral artery-7 receives posterior communicating artery-8 from internal carotid artery.

4. Distribution of **anterior cerebral artery**-8 on medial surface of cerebral hemisphere in longitudinal fissure.

5. **Great cerebral vein** (of Galen)-2 emerging from cerebral hemisphere to join straight sinus in tentorium cerebelli. (Figs. 232-7; 233-2).

6. **Pineal body**-2 extending over midbrain.

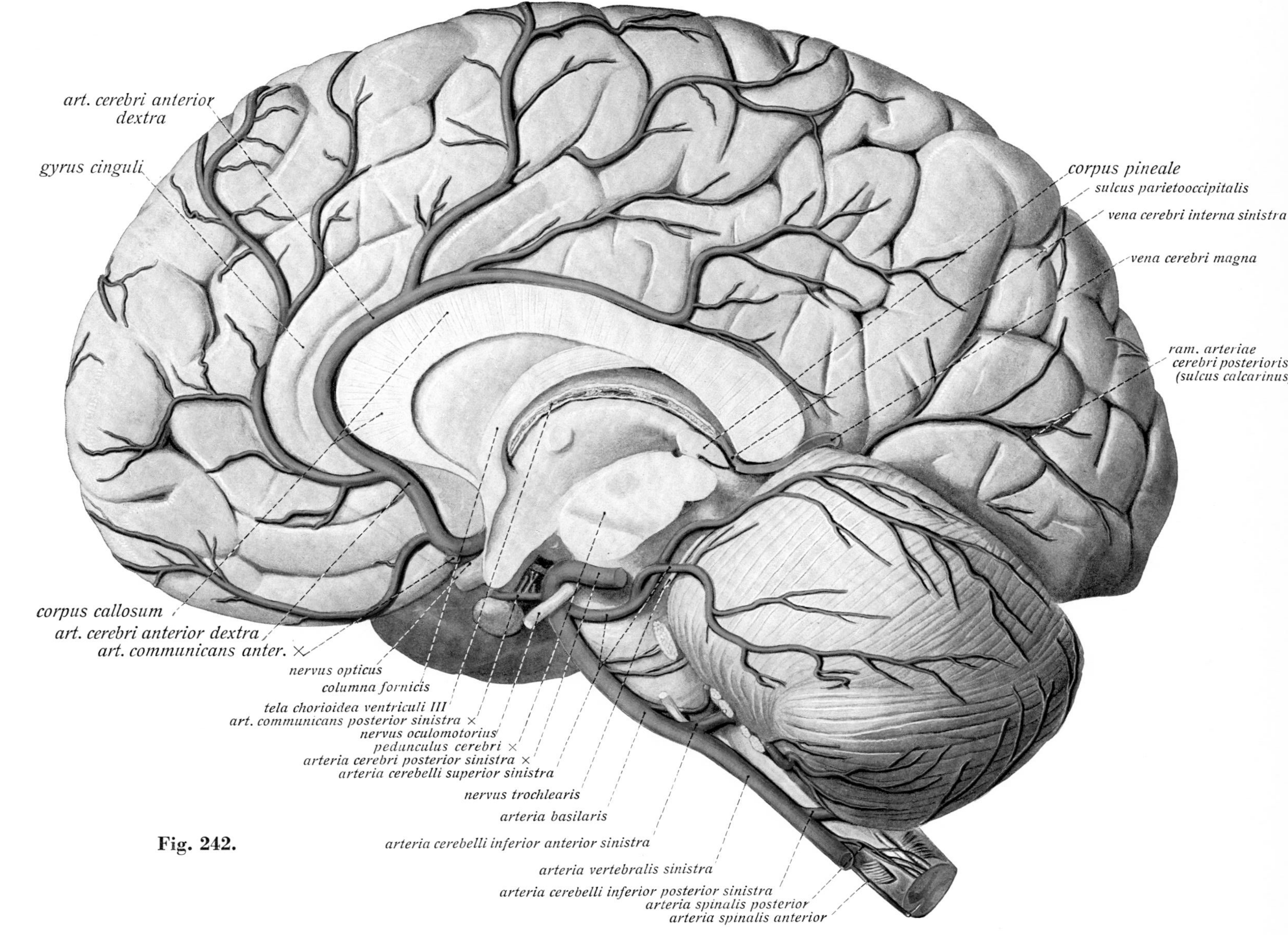
art. cerebri anterior dextra
gyrus cinguli
corpus pineale
sulcus parietooccipitalis
vena cerebri interna sinistra
vena cerebri magna
ram. arteriae cerebri posterioris (sulcus calcarinus)
corpus callosum
art. cerebri anterior dextra
art. communicans anter. ×
nervus opticus
columna fornicis
tela chorioidea ventriculi III
art. communicans posterior sinistra ×
nervus oculomotorius
pedunculus cerebri ×
arteria cerebri posterior sinistra ×
arteria cerebelli superior sinistra
nervus trochlearis
arteria basilaris
arteria cerebelli inferior anterior sinistra
arteria vertebralis sinistra
arteria cerebelli inferior posterior sinistra
arteria spinalis posterior
arteria spinalis anterior

**Fig. 242.**

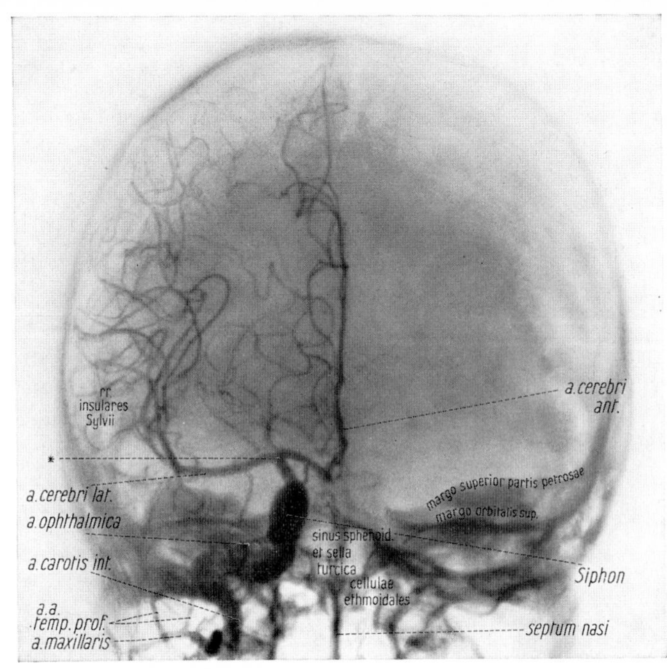
rr.
insulares
Sylvii
a.cerebri
ant.
*
a.cerebri lat.
margo superior partis petrosae
margo orbitalis sup.
a.ophthalmica
sinus sphenoid.
et sella
turcica
a.carotis int.
Siphon
cellulae
ethmoidales
a.a.
temp. prof.
a.maxillaris
septum nasi

**Fig. 243.**

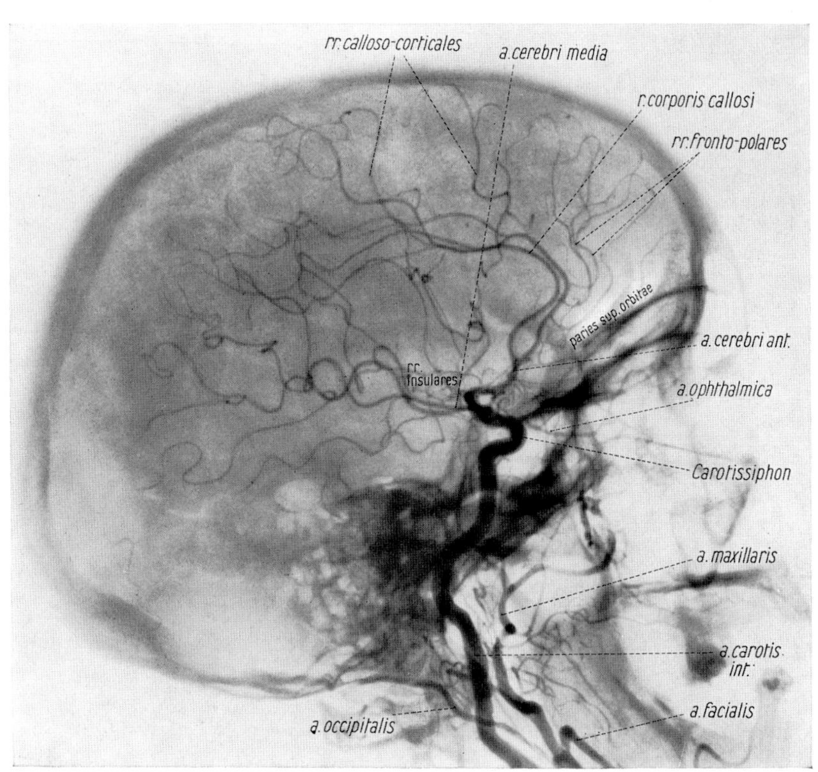
rr.calloso-corticales
a.cerebri media
r.corporis callosi
rr.fronto-polares
paries sup. orbitae
a.cerebri ant.
rr.
insulares
a.ophthalmica
Carotissiphon
a.maxillaris
a.carotis
int.
a.facialis
a.occipitalis

**Fig. 244.**

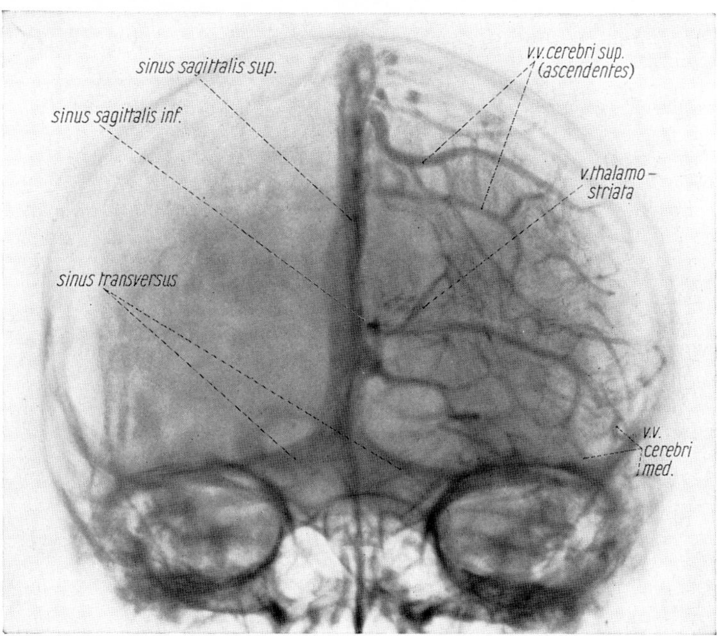
sinus sagittalis sup.
sinus sagittalis inf.
v.v. cerebri sup. (ascendentes)
v. thalamo-striata
sinus transversus
v.v. cerebri med.

**Fig. 245**

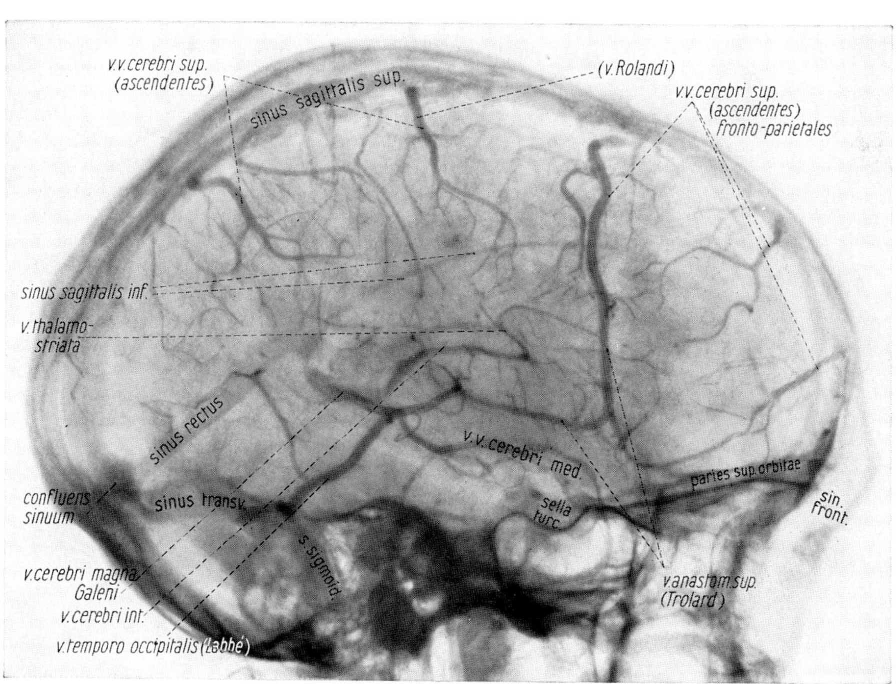
v.v. cerebri sup. (ascendentes)
sinus sagittalis sup.
(v. Rolandi)
v.v. cerebri sup. (ascendentes) fronto-parietales
sinus sagittalis inf.
v. thalamo-striata
sinus rectus
v.v. cerebri med.
paries sup. orbitae
confluens sinuum
sinus transv.
sella turc.
sin. front.
s. sigmoid.
v. cerebri magna Galeni
v. cerebri int.
v. anastom. sup. (Trolard)
v. temporo occipitalis (Labbé)

**Fig. 246.**

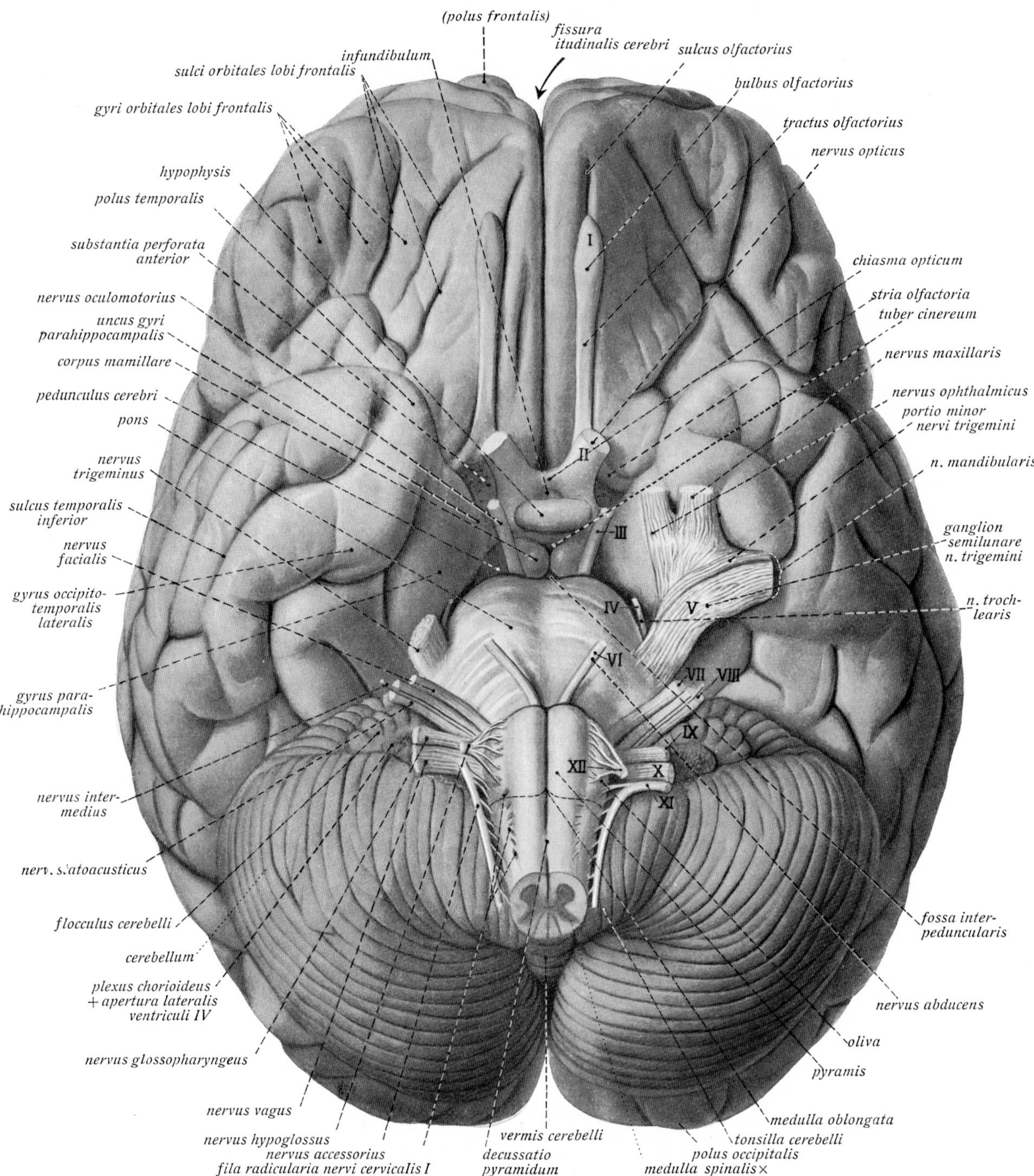
(polus frontalis)
fissura
itudinalis cerebri
sulcus olfactorius
infundibulum
sulci orbitales lobi frontalis
bulbus olfactorius
gyri orbitales lobi frontalis
tractus olfactorius
nervus opticus
hypophysis
polus temporalis
substantia perforata
anterior
I
chiasma opticum
nervus oculomotorius
stria olfactoria
uncus gyri
parahippocampalis
tuber cinereum
corpus mamillare
nervus maxillaris
pedunculus cerebri
nervus ophthalmicus
portio minor
nervi trigemini
pons
II
nervus
trigeminus
n. mandibularis
sulcus temporalis
inferior
III
ganglion
semilunare
n. trigemini
nervus
facialis
gyrus occipito-
temporalis
lateralis
IV
V
n. troch-
learis
VI
VII
VIII
gyrus para-
hippocampalis
IX
XII
X
XI
nervus inter-
medius
nerv. statoacusticus
flocculus cerebelli
fossa inter-
peduncularis
cerebellum
plexus chorioideus
+ apertura lateralis
ventriculi IV
nervus abducens
oliva
nervus glossopharyngeus
pyramis
nervus vagus
medulla oblongata
nervus hypoglossus
vermis cerebelli
tonsilla cerebelli
nervus accessorius
decussatio
polus occipitalis
fila radicularia nervi cervicalis I
pyramidum
medulla spinalis×

**Fig. 247.**

## 243 and 244. Arteriogram of Internal Carotid Artery and Its Branches. (See Fig. 242)

**243.** (anteroposterior projection) **244.** (lateral projection)

## 245 and 246. Carotid Venogram of Cerebral Veins and Sinuses of Dura Mater. (See Figs. 233–234)

**245.** (anteroposterior projection) **246.** (lateral projection)

## 247. Ventral Aspect of Brain Showing Origins of Cranial Nerves. (4/5)

The **left semilunar [trigeminal] ganglion**-3 was left attached to the trigeminal root. The **hypophysis (pituitary gland)**-11 was removed with the brain and pulled back to show the infundibulum-12. Roman numerals denote the 12 cranial nerves.

1 **Olfactory Bulb**
*bulbus olfactorius*
**Olfactory Tract**
*tractus olfactorius*
**Optic Nerve**
*nervus opticus*
**Optic Chiasma**
*chiasm opticum*

2 **Olfactory Stria**
*stria olfactoria*
**Tuber Cinereum**
*tuber cinereum*
**Maxillary Nerve**
*nervus maxillaris*
**Ophthalmic Nerve**
*nervus ophthalmicus*
**Trigeminal Nerve, Motor Root**
*portio minor*
*[radix motoria] nervi trigemini*
**Mandibular Nerve**
*n. mandibularis*

3 **Semilunar Ganglion, Trigeminal Nerve [Trigeminal Ganglion]**
*ganglion semilunare, n. trigemini [g. trigeminale]*
**Trochlear Nerve**
*n. trochlearis*

4 **Interpeduncular Fossa**
*fossa interpeduncularis*

5 **Abducens Nerve**
*nervus abducens*
**Olive**
*oliva*
**Pyramid**
*pyramis*
**Medulla Oblongata**
*medulla oblongata*
**Cerebellar Tonsil**
*tonsilla cerebelli*
**Occipital Pole**
*polus occipitalis*

6 **Spinal Cord**
*medulla spinalis*
**Cerebellar Vermis**
*vermis cerebelli*
**Pyramidal Decussation**
*decussatio pyramidum*

7 **Root Filaments of 1st Cervical Nerve**
*fila radicularia nervi cervicalis I*
**Accessory Nerve**
*nervus accessorius*
**Hypoglossal Nerve**
*nervus hypoglossus*
**Vagus Nerve**
*nervus vagus*
**Glossopharyngeal Nerve**
*nervus glossopharyngeus*
**Chorioid Plexus and Lateral Opening of the 4th Ventricle**
*plexus chorioideus + apertura lateralis ventriculi IV*

8 **Cerebellum**
*cerebellum*
**Cerebellar Flocculus**
*flocculus cerebelli*
**Vestibulocochlear Nerve**
*[n. vestibulocochlearis]*
*nerv. statoacusticus*
**Nervus Intermedius**
*nervus intermedius*

9 **Parahippocampal Gyrus**
*gyrus parahippocampalis*
**Lat. Occipitotemporal Gyrus**
*gyrus occipitotemporalis lat.*
**Facial Nerve**
*nervus facialis*
**Inferior Temporal Sulcus**
*sulcus temporalis inferior*
**Trigeminal Nerve**
*nervus trigeminus*

10 **Pons**
*pons*
**Cerebral Peduncle**
*pedunculus cerebri*
**Mammillary Body**
*corpus mamillare*
**Uncus of Parahippocampal Gyrus**
*uncus gyri parahippocampalis*
**Oculomotor Nerve**
*nervus oculomotorius*
**Anterior Perforated Substance**
*substantia perforata anterior*

11 **Temporal Pole**
*polus temporalis*
**Hypophysis (Pituitary Gland)**
*hypophysis (glandula pituitaria)*
**Orbital Gyri of Frontal Lobe**
*gyri orbitales lobi frontalis*
**Orbital Sulci of Frontal Lobe**
*sulci orbitales lobi frontalis*

12 **Infundibulum**
*infundibulum*
**Frontal Pole**
*(polus frontalis)*
**Longitudinal Cerebral Fissure**
*fissura longitudinalis cerebri*
**Olfactory Sulcus**
*sulcus olfactorius*

**Note:** 1. Portio minor-2 or **motor root** is seen as separate portion of **trigeminal nerve.**
2. The gross anatomical origin of all **cranial nerves** are clearly shown. The relationship to each other and the parts of the brain have been accurately depicted.

## 248. Sagittal Section of the Brain near the Median Plane. (1/1) (See Fig. 274)

1 **Pineal Recess**
*recessus pinealis*
**Posterior Commissure**
*commissura posterior*
**Tela Chorioidea of 3rd Ventricle**
*tela chorioidea ventriculi tertii*
**Interthalamic Adhesion**
*(massa intermedia)*
*adhesio interthalamica*
**Gyrus Cinguli**
*gyrus cinguli*
**Thalamus**
*thalamus*

2 **Trunk of Corpus Callosum**
*truncus corporis callosi*
**Body of Fornix**
*corpus fornicis*
**Lamina of Septum Pellucidum**
*lamina septi pellucidi*
**Sulcus Cinguli**
*sulcus cinguli*
**Interventricular Foramen**
*foramen interventriculare*
**Column of Fornix**
*columna fornicis*

3 **Anterior Commissure**
*commissura anterior*
**Superior Frontal Gyrus**
*gyrus frontalis superior*

4 **Frontal Pole**
*polus frontalis*
**Genu of Corpus Callosum**
*genu corporis callosi*
**Rostrum of Corpus Callosum**
*rostrum corporis callosi*
**Area Subcallosa**
*area subcallosa*
**Anterior Parolfactory Sulcus**
*(sulcus parolfactorius anterior)*
**Posterior Parolfactory Sulcus**
*(sulcus parolfactorius posterior)*
**Paraterminal Gyrus**
*gyrus paraterminalis*

5 **Hypothalamic Sulcus**
*sulcus hypothalamicus*
**Lamina Terminalis**
*lamina terminalis hypothalami*
**Optic Recess, Third Ventricle**
*recessus opticus ventriculi tertii*
**Optic Nerve**
*nervus opticus*
**Optic Chiasma**
*chiasma opticum*
**Infundibulum and Infundibular Recess**
*infundibulum + recessus infundibuli*
**Anterior Lobe**
*lobus anterior*
**Hypophysis [Pituitary Gland]**
*hypophysis [glandula pituitaria]*
**Posterior Lobe**
*lobus posterior*
**Mammillary Body**
*corpus mamillare*
**Oculomotor Nerve**
*nerv. oculomotorius*
**Posterior Perforated Substance**
*substantia perforata posterior*
**Pons**
*pons*

7 **Cerebral Aqueduct**
*aquaeductus cerebri*
**Superior Medullary Velum**
*velum medullare anterius [superior]*
**Medulla Oblongata**
*medulla oblongata*
**Fourth Ventricle**
*ventriculus quartus*
**Chorioid Membrane of 4th Ventricle**
*tela chorioidea ventriculi quarti*
**Spinal Medulla**
*medulla spinalis*

8 **Central Canal, Medulla Oblongata**
*canalis centralis medullae oblongatae*
**Obex**
*obex*
**Vermis Cerebelli**
*vermis cerebelli*
**Medullary Substance of Cerebellar Vermis**
*corpus medullare vermis cerebelli*
**Cerebellar Hemisphere**
*hemispherium cerebelli*
**Transverse Fissure**
*(fissura cerebrocerebellaris)*

9 **Medial Occipitotemporal Gyrus**
*gyrus occipitotemporalis medialis*
**Occipital Pole**
*polus occipitalis*
**Calcarine Sulcus (Fissure)**
*sulcus calcarinus*
**Vermis Cerebelli**
*vermis cerebelli*

10 **Cuneus**
*cuneus*
**Tectal Plate (Quadrigeminal Lamina)**
*lamina tecti*
**Parietooccipital Sulcus (Fissure)**
*sulcus parietooccipitalis*
**Subparietal Sulcus**
*sulcus subparietalis*

11 **Precuneus**
*precuneus*
**Splenium of Corpus Callosum**
*splenium corporis callosi*
**Sulcus of Corpus Callosum**
*sulcus corporis callosi*
**Sulcus Cinguli**
*sulcus cinguli*
**Paracentral Lobule**
*lobulus paracentralis*
**Central Sulcus**
*sulcus centralis*
**Pineal Body**
*corpus pineale*

**Note:** 1. Pronounced flexure of brain stem at the level of midbrain and the resultant angle (about 45°) between the long axis of the cerebral hemisphere and that of the midbrain pons and medulla oblongata.

2. **Lateral ventricles** are separated from each other in midline by the **fornix**-2 and **septum pellucidum**-2. The latter is so thin, it is translucent.

3. Lateral ventricles communicate with third ventricle through **interventricular foramen**-2 (Monroe).

4. **Tela chorioidea**-1 protrudes into the third ventricle through a slit between the fornix and thalamus.

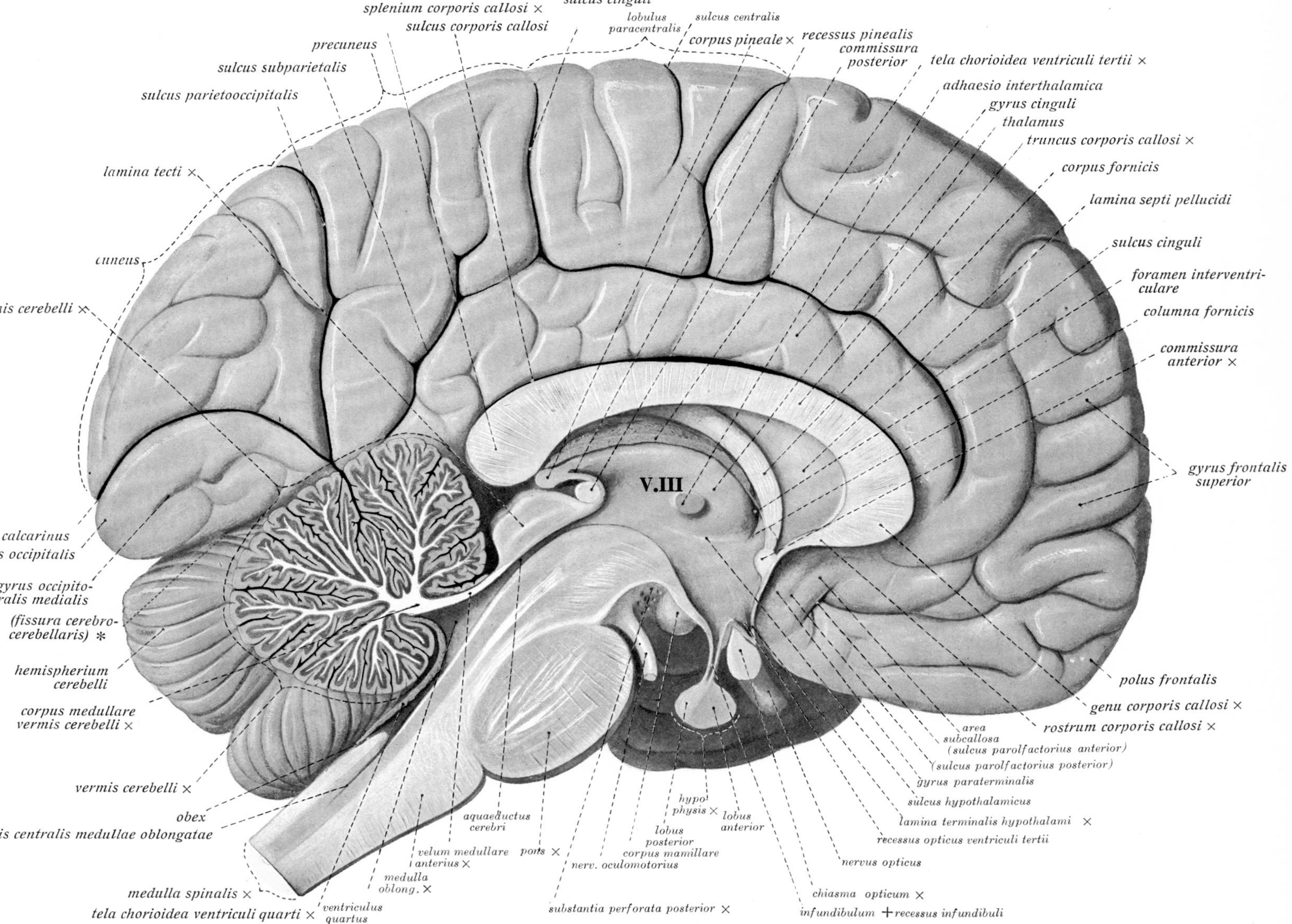
splenium corporis callosi ×
sulcus corporis callosi
sulcus cinguli
lobulus paracentralis
sulcus centralis
corpus pineale ×
recessus pinealis
commissura posterior
tela chorioidea ventriculi tertii ×
adhaesio interthalamica
gyrus cinguli
thalamus
truncus corporis callosi ×
corpus fornicis
lamina septi pellucidi
sulcus cinguli
foramen interventriculare
columna fornicis
commissura anterior ×
gyrus frontalis superior
polus frontalis
genu corporis callosi ×
rostrum corporis callosi ×
area subcallosa
(sulcus parolfactorius anterior)
(sulcus parolfactorius posterior)
gyrus paraterminalis
sulcus hypothalamicus
lamina terminalis hypothalami ×
recessus opticus ventriculi tertii
nervus opticus
chiasma opticum ×
infundibulum + recessus infundibuli
substantia perforata posterior ×
hypophysis ×
lobus anterior
lobus posterior
corpus mamillare
nerv. oculomotorius
pons ×
aquaeductus cerebri
velum medullare anterius ×
medulla oblong. ×
ventriculus quartus
V.III
precuneus
sulcus subparietalis
sulcus parietooccipitalis
lamina tecti ×
cuneus
vermis cerebelli ×
sulcus calcarinus
polus occipitalis
gyrus occipitotemporalis medialis
(fissura cerebrocerebellaris) *
hemispherium cerebelli
corpus medullare vermis cerebelli ×
vermis cerebelli ×
obex
canalis centralis medullae oblongatae
medulla spinalis ×
tela chorioidea ventriculi quarti ×

Fig. 248.

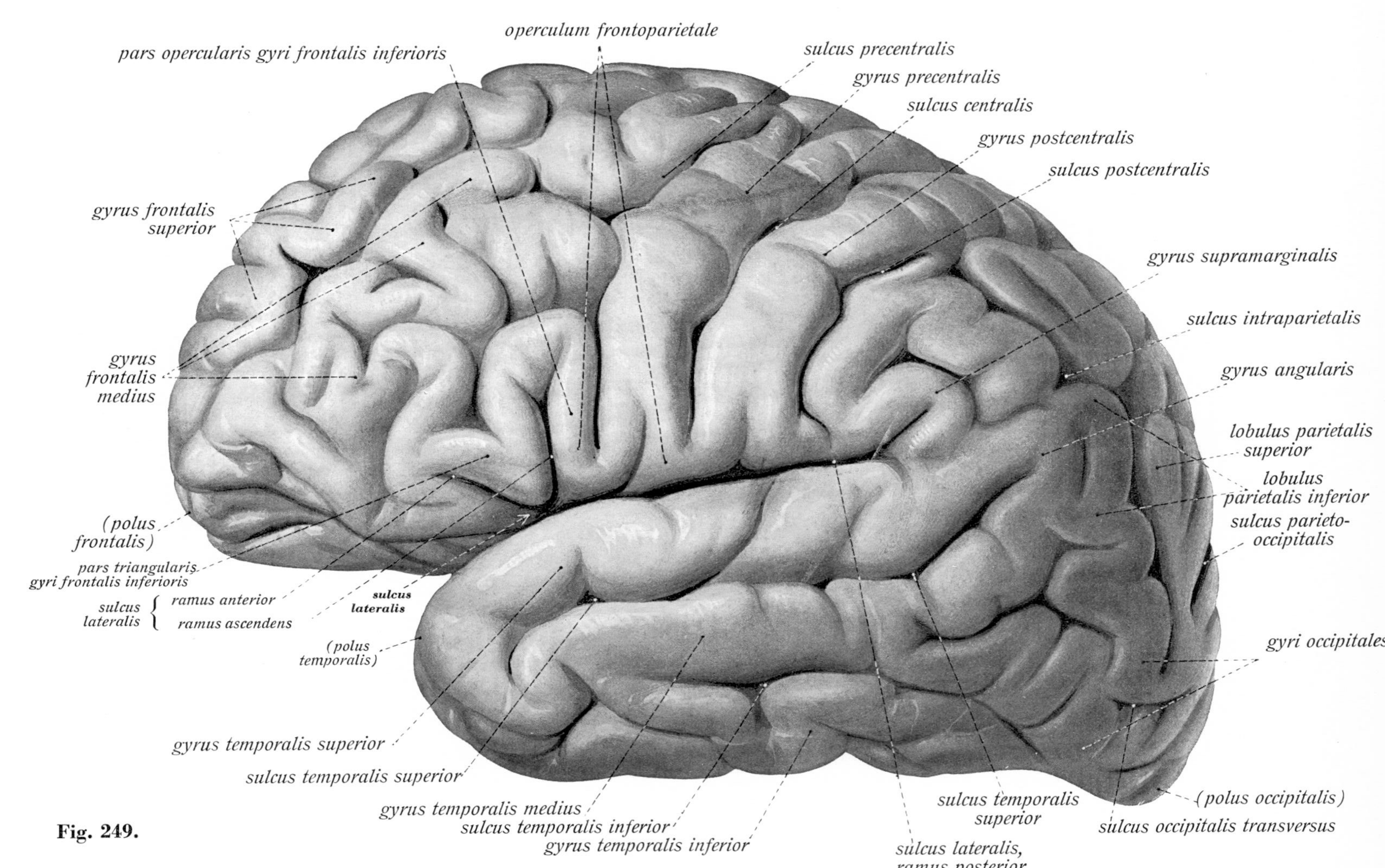

operculum frontoparietale
pars opercularis gyri frontalis inferioris
sulcus precentralis
gyrus precentralis
sulcus centralis
gyrus postcentralis
sulcus postcentralis
gyrus frontalis superior
gyrus supramarginalis
sulcus intraparietalis
gyrus frontalis medius
gyrus angularis
lobulus parietalis superior
lobulus parietalis inferior
(polus frontalis)
sulcus parieto-occipitalis
pars triangularis gyri frontalis inferioris
sulcus lateralis { ramus anterior
ramus ascendens
sulcus lateralis
(polus temporalis)
gyri occipitales
gyrus temporalis superior
sulcus temporalis superior
gyrus temporalis medius
sulcus temporalis inferior
gyrus temporalis inferior
sulcus temporalis superior
(polus occipitalis)
sulcus occipitalis transversus
sulcus lateralis, ramus posterior


**Fig. 249.**

## 249. Lateral View of a Left Cerebral Hemisphere. (See Fig. 207)

1 **Precentral Sulcus**
*sulcus precentralis*
**Precentral Gyrus**
*gyrus precentralis*
**Central Sulcus**
*sulcus centralis*
**Postcentral Gyrus**
*gyrus postcentralis*

2 **Postcentral Sulcus**
*sulcus postcentralis*
**Supramarginal Gyrus**
*gyrus supramarginalis*

3 **Intraparietal Sulcus**
*sulcus intraparietalis*
**Angular Gyrus**
*gyrus angularis*
**Superior Parietal Lobule**
*lobulus parietalis superior*
**Inferior Parietal Lobule**
*lobulus parietalis inferior*
**Parietooccipital Sulcus (Fissure)**
*sulcus parietooccipitalis*

4 **Occipital Gyri**
*gyri occipitales*
**Occipital Pole**
*(polus occipitalis)*
**Transverse Occipital Sulcus**
*sulcus occipitalis transversus*

5 **Superior Temporal Sulcus**
*sulcus temporalis superior*
**Lateral Sulcus, Posterior Br.**
*sulcus lateralis, ramus posterior*

6 **Inferior Temporal Gyrus**
*gyrus temporalis inferior*

7 **Inferior Temporal Sulcus**
*sulcus temporalis inferior*
**Middle Temporal Gyrus**
*gyrus temporalis medius*

8 **Superior Temporal Sulcus**
*sulcus temporalis superior*
**Superior Temporal Gyrus**
*gyrus temporalis superior*
**Temporal Pole**
*(polus temporalis)*
**Lateral Fissure (Sulcus)**
*sulcus lateralis (NA)*
**Lateral Fissure, Anterior and Ascending Branches**
*sulcus lateralis, ramus anterior, ramus ascendens*
**Inferior Frontal Gyrus, Triangular Part**
*pars triangularis gyri frontalis inferioris*

9 **Frontal Pole**
*(polus frontalis)*
**Middle Frontal Gyrus**
*gyrus frontalis medius*

10 **Superior Frontal Gyrus**
*gyrus frontalis superior*

11 **Opercular Part of Inferior Frontal Gyrus**
*pars opercularis gyri frontalis inferioris*

12 **Frontoparietal Operculum**
*operculum frontoparietale*

**Note:** 1. **Lateral cerebral sulcus**-5, -8 **(fissure)** between **frontoparietal** and **temporal lobes.**

2. **Central sulcus**-1, between the pre-1 and postcentral-1 gyri. It crosses the superior medial border of the cerebral hemisphere.

3. Names of sulci and gyri indicate their relative position.

**Etymology:**

*sulcus* = L. groove or furrow
gyrus = Gr. *gyros*, a convolution
fissure = L. *fissura*, a cleft or slit
*operculum* = L. a lid

## 250. Lateral View of Left Cerebral Hemisphere After Removal of the Cortex.

(Preparation, Anat. Inst., Münster) (Compare with Figures 249, 254, 258)

White medullary substance, which extends into each gyrus, remains.

1 Central sulcus
2 Lateral sulcus (fissure)
3 Lateral sulcus (fissure) ascending ramus
4 Lateral sulcus (fissure) anterior ramus

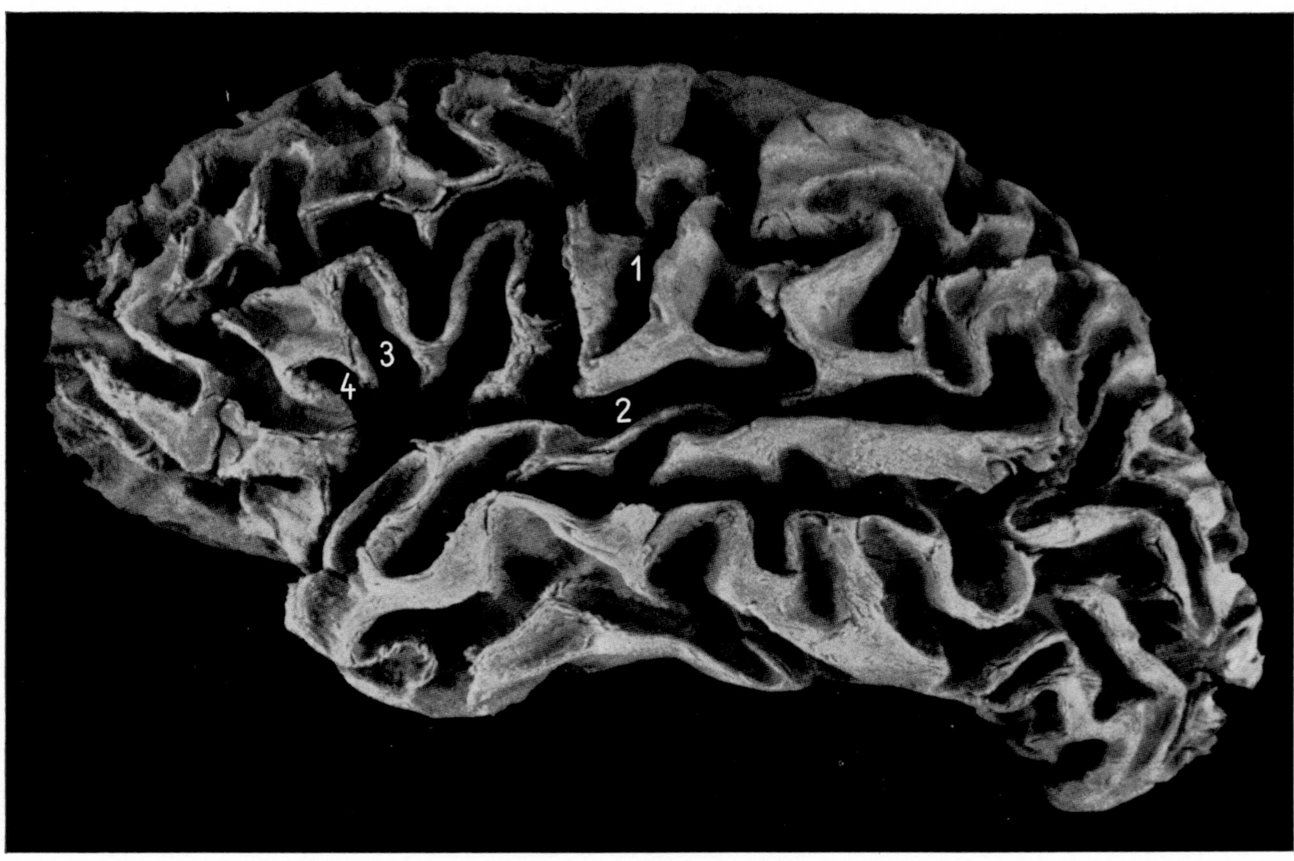
1
2
3
4

*1 sulcus centralis; 2 sulcus lateralis; 3 ramus ascendens sulci lat.; 4 ramus ant. sulci lat.*

**Fig. 250.**

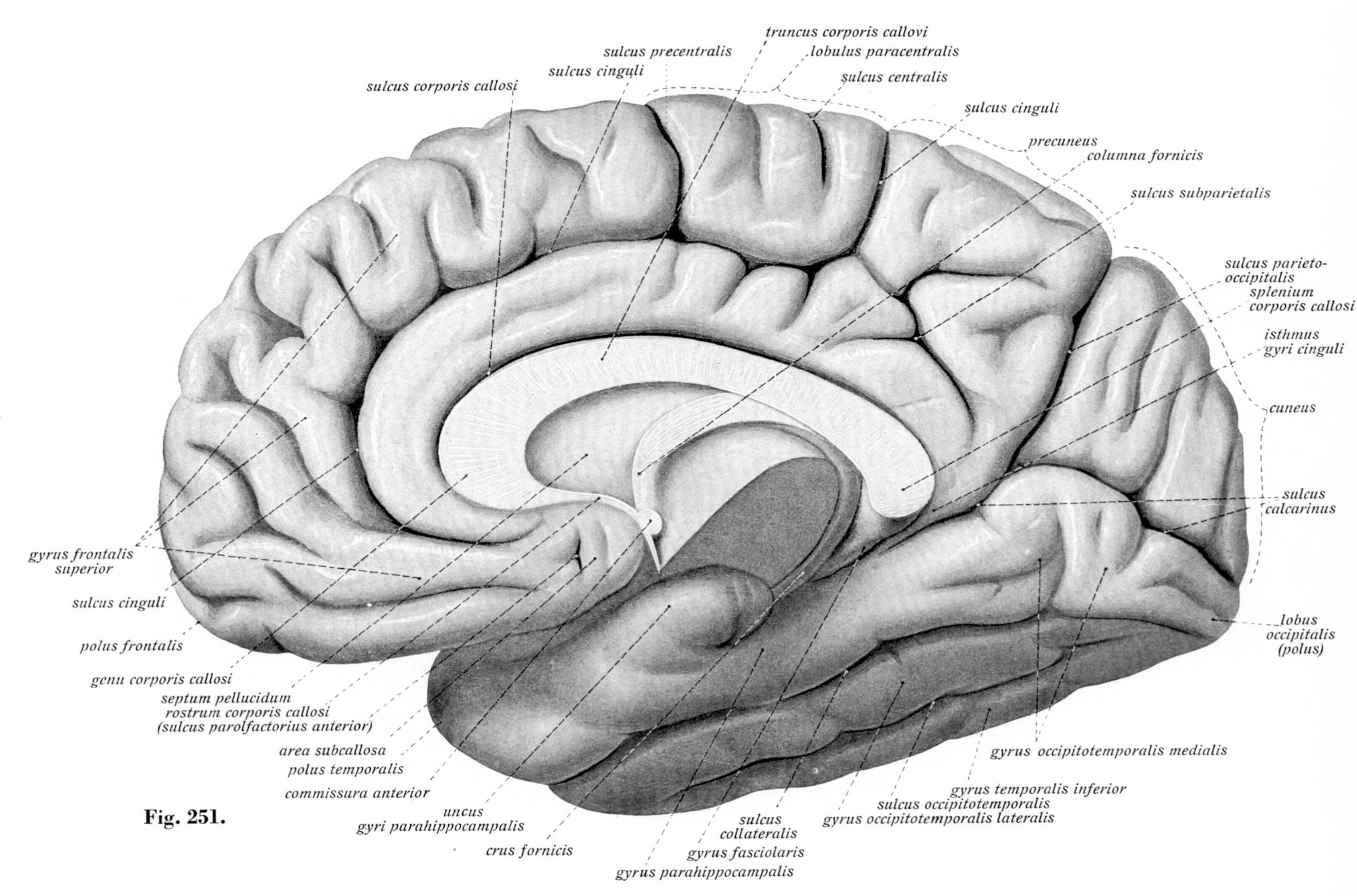
truncus corporis callovi
sulcus precentralis
lobulus paracentralis
sulcus cinguli
sulcus centralis
sulcus corporis callosi
sulcus cinguli
precuneus
columna fornicis
sulcus subparietalis
sulcus parieto-
occipitalis
splenium
corporis callosi
isthmus
gyri cinguli
cuneus
sulcus
calcarinus
lobus
occipitalis
(polus)
gyrus frontalis
superior
sulcus cinguli
polus frontalis
genu corporis callosi
septum pellucidum
rostrum corporis callosi
(sulcus parolfactorius anterior)
area subcallosa
polus temporalis
commissura anterior
uncus
gyri parahippocampalis
crus fornicis
sulcus
collateralis
gyrus fasciolaris
gyrus parahippocampalis
gyrus occipitotemporalis medialis
gyrus temporalis inferior
sulcus occipitotemporalis
gyrus occipitotemporalis lateralis

Fig. 251.

# 251. Gyri and Sulci on Medial Aspect of Cerebral Hemisphere.

(Sagittal section. Brain stem cut at thalamus) (See Fig. 210)

1 **Central Sulcus**
*sulcus centralis*

**Sulcus Cinguli**
*sulcus cinguli*

**Precuneus**
*precuneus*

2 **Column of Fornix**
*columna fornicis*

**Subparietal Sulcus**
*sulcus subparietalis*

**Parietooccipital Sulcus (Fissure)**
*sulcus parietooccipitalis*

**Splenium of Corpus Callosum**
*splenium corporis callosi*

3 **Gyrus Cinguli Isthmus**
*isthmus gyri cinguli*

**Cuneus**
*cuneus*

**Calcarine Sulcus (Fissure)**
*sulcus calcarinus*

**Occipital Lobe (Pole)**
*lobus occipitalis (polus)*

5 **Medial Occipitotemporal Gyrus**
*gyrus occipitotemporalis medialis*

**Inferior Temporal Gyrus**
*gyrus temporalis inferior*

**Occipitotemporal Sulcus**
*sulcus occipitotemporalis*

**Lateral Occipitotemporal Gyrus**
*gyrus occipitotemporalis lateralis*

6 **Collateral Sulcus (Fissure)**
*sulcus collateralis*

**Fasciola Gyrus**
*gyrus fasciolaris*

**Parahippocampal Gyrus**
*gyrus parahippocampalis*

7 **Crus of Fornix**
*crus fornicis*

**Uncus of Parahippocampal Gyrus**
*uncus gyri parahippocampalis*

8 **Anterior Commissure**
*commissura anterior*

**Temporal Pole**
*polus temporalis*

**Subcallosal Area**
*area subcallosa*

**Anterior Parolfactory Sulcus**
*(sulcus parolfactorius anterior)*

**Rostrum of the Corpus Callosum**
*rostrum corporis callosi*

**Septum Pellucidum**
*septum pellucidum*

**Genu of Corpus Callosum**
*genu corporis callosi*

**Frontal Pole**
*polus frontalis*

9 **Sulcus Cinguli**
*sulcus cinguli*

**Superior Frontal Gyrus**
*gyrus frontalis superior*

11 **Sulcus of Corpus Callosum**
*sulcus corporis callosi*

**Sulcus Cinguli**
*sulcus cinguli*

12 **Precentral Sulcus**
*sulcus precentralis*

**Trunk of the Corpus Callosum**
*truncus corporis callosi*

**Paracentral Lobule**
*lobulus paracentralis*

**Note:** 1. The central sulcus usually extends through the superior-medial border of the cerebral hemisphere.

**252. Medial Surface of Left Cerebral Hemisphere.** (After removal of the cortex to expose the white medullary substance) (Preparation, Anat. Inst., Münster) (See Figure 251)

1 Central sulcus
2 Sulcus cinguli
3 Parietooccipital sulcus
4 Calcarine sulcus (fissure)

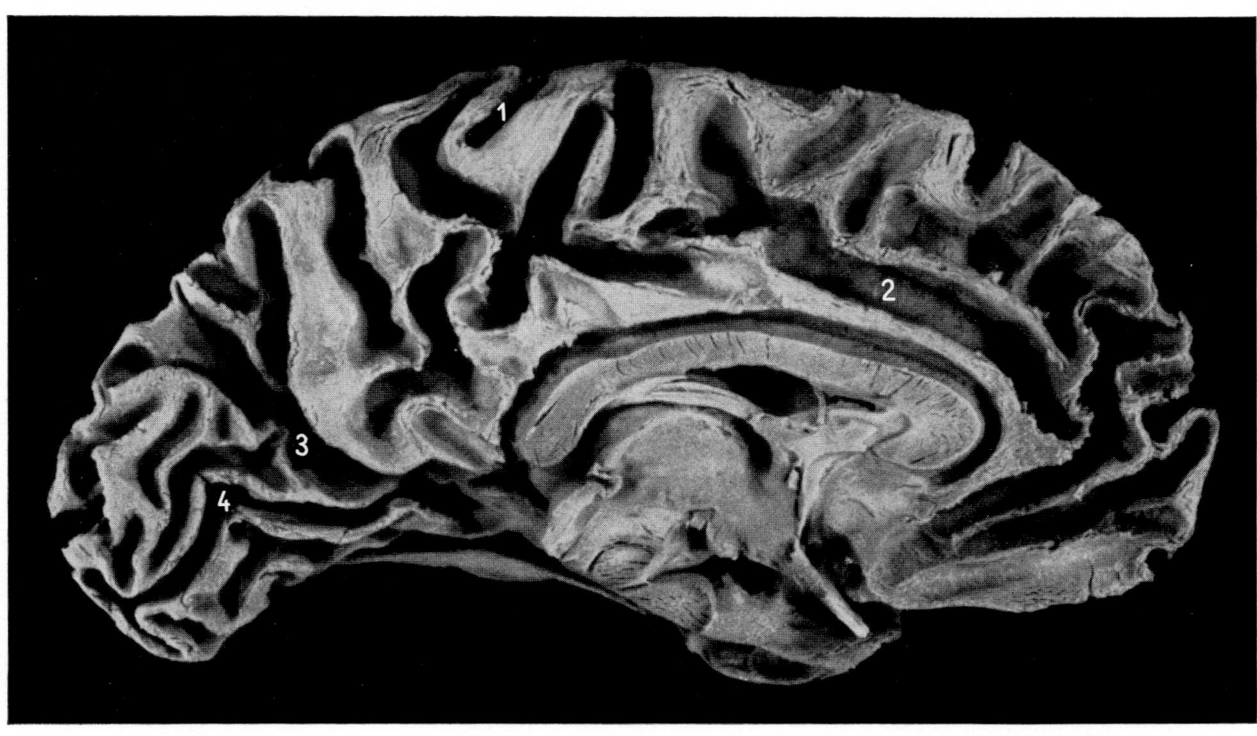
1
2
3
4

*1 sulcus centralis; 2 sulcus cinguli; 3 sulcus parieto-occipitalis; 4 sulcus calcarinus*

**Fig. 252.**

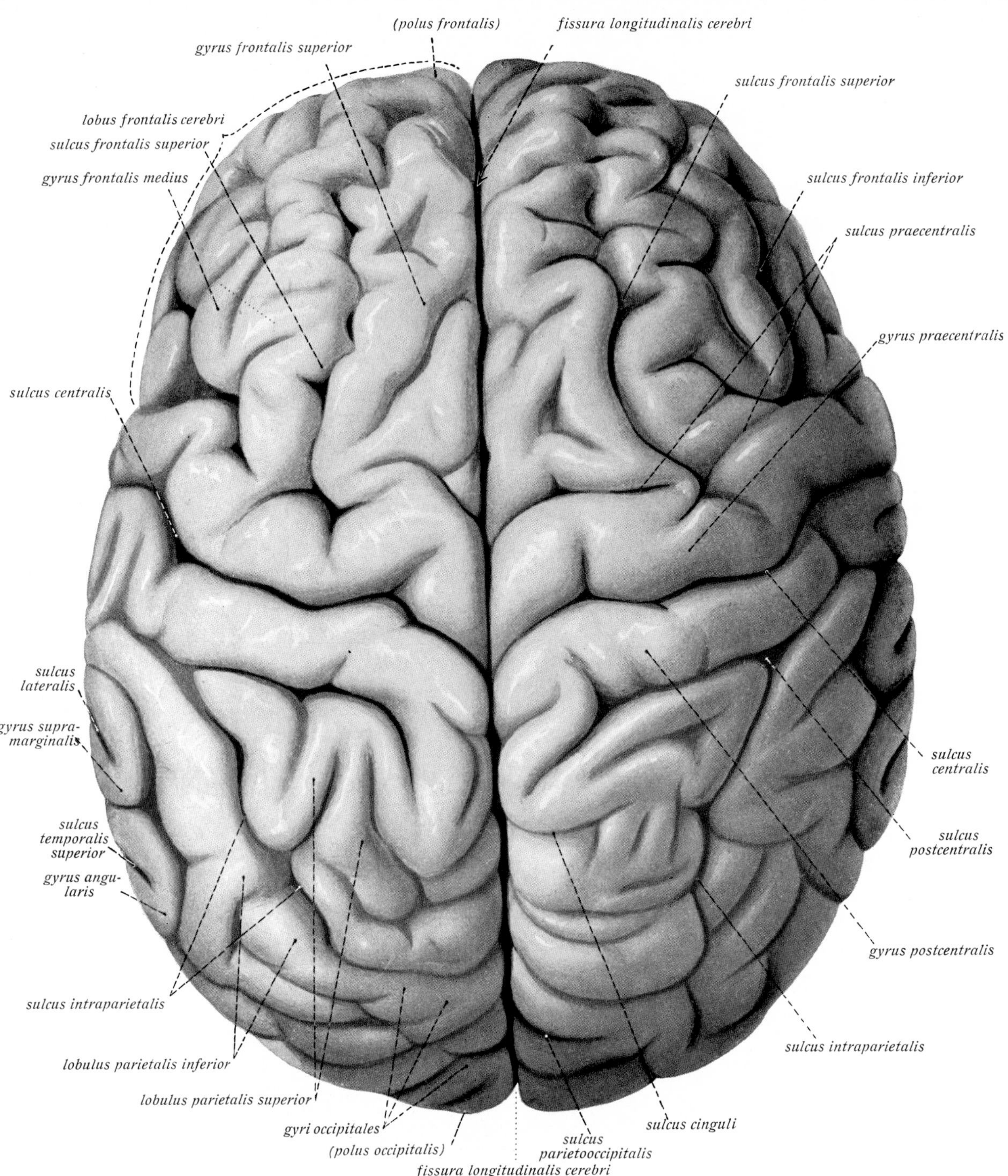
(polus frontalis)
fissura longitudinalis cerebri
gyrus frontalis superior
sulcus frontalis superior
lobus frontalis cerebri
sulcus frontalis superior
gyrus frontalis medius
sulcus frontalis inferior
sulcus praecentralis
gyrus praecentralis
sulcus centralis
sulcus lateralis
gyrus supramarginalis
sulcus centralis
sulcus temporalis superior
gyrus angularis
sulcus postcentralis
gyrus postcentralis
sulcus intraparietalis
sulcus intraparietalis
lobulus parietalis inferior
lobulus parietalis superior
gyri occipitales
(polus occipitalis)
sulcus parietooccipitalis
sulcus cinguli
fissura longitudinalis cerebri

**Fig. 253.**

# 253. Sulci and Gyri of Cerebral Cortex.

(Viewed from above) (See Figs. 208–254)

1 **Superior Frontal Sulcus**
*sulcus frontalis superior*

**Inferior Frontal Sulcus**
*sulcus frontalis inferior*

2 **Precentral Sulcus**
*sulcus precentralis*

**Precentral Gyrus**
*gyrus precentralis*

4 **Central Sulcus**
*sulcus centralis*

**Postcentral Sulcus**
*sulcus postcentralis*

**Postcentral Gyrus**
*gyrus postcentralis*

5 **Intraparietal Sulcus**
*sulcus intraparietalis*

6 **Sulcus Cinguli**
*sulcus cinguli*

**Parietooccipital Sulcus (Fissure)**
*sulcus parietooccipitalis*

**Longitudinal Cerebral Fissure**
*fissura longitudinalis cerebri*

7 **Occipital Pole**
*(polus occipitalis)*

**Occipital Gyri**
*gyri occipitales*

**Superior Parietal Lobule**
*lobulus parietalis superior*

**Inferior Parietal Lobule**
*lobulus parietalis inferior*

8 **Intraparietal Sulcus**
*sulcus intraparietalis*

**Angular Gyrus**
*gyrus angularis*

**Superior Temporal Sulcus**
*sulcus temporalis superior*

**Supramarginal Gyrus**
*gyrus supramarginalis*

9 **Lateral Sulcus (Fissure)**
*sulcus lateralis*

10 **Central Sulcus**
*sulcus centralis*

**Middle Frontal Gyrus**
*gyrus frontalis medius*

11 **Superior Frontal Sulcus**
*sulcus frontalis superior*

**Superior Frontal Gyrus**
*gyrus frontalis superior*

12 **(Frontal Pole)**
*(polus frontalis)*

**Longitudinal Cerebral Fissure**
*fissura longitudinalis cerebri*

**Note:** 1. **Central sulcus**-4, -10, between the **precentral**-2 and **postcentral**-4 **gyri**, crosses the superior cerebral border.

## 254. The Cerebral Hemispheres. (Viewed from above) (1/1)

(Preparation, Anat. Inst., Münster)

**Note:** 1. The right hemisphere has been decorticated.

2. The white medullary lamellae appear as small ridges between the wide, deep sulci.

3. The small irregular abrasions on the cortex of the left hemisphere are artifacts that resulted from the removal of pia-arachnoid and other preparative procedures.

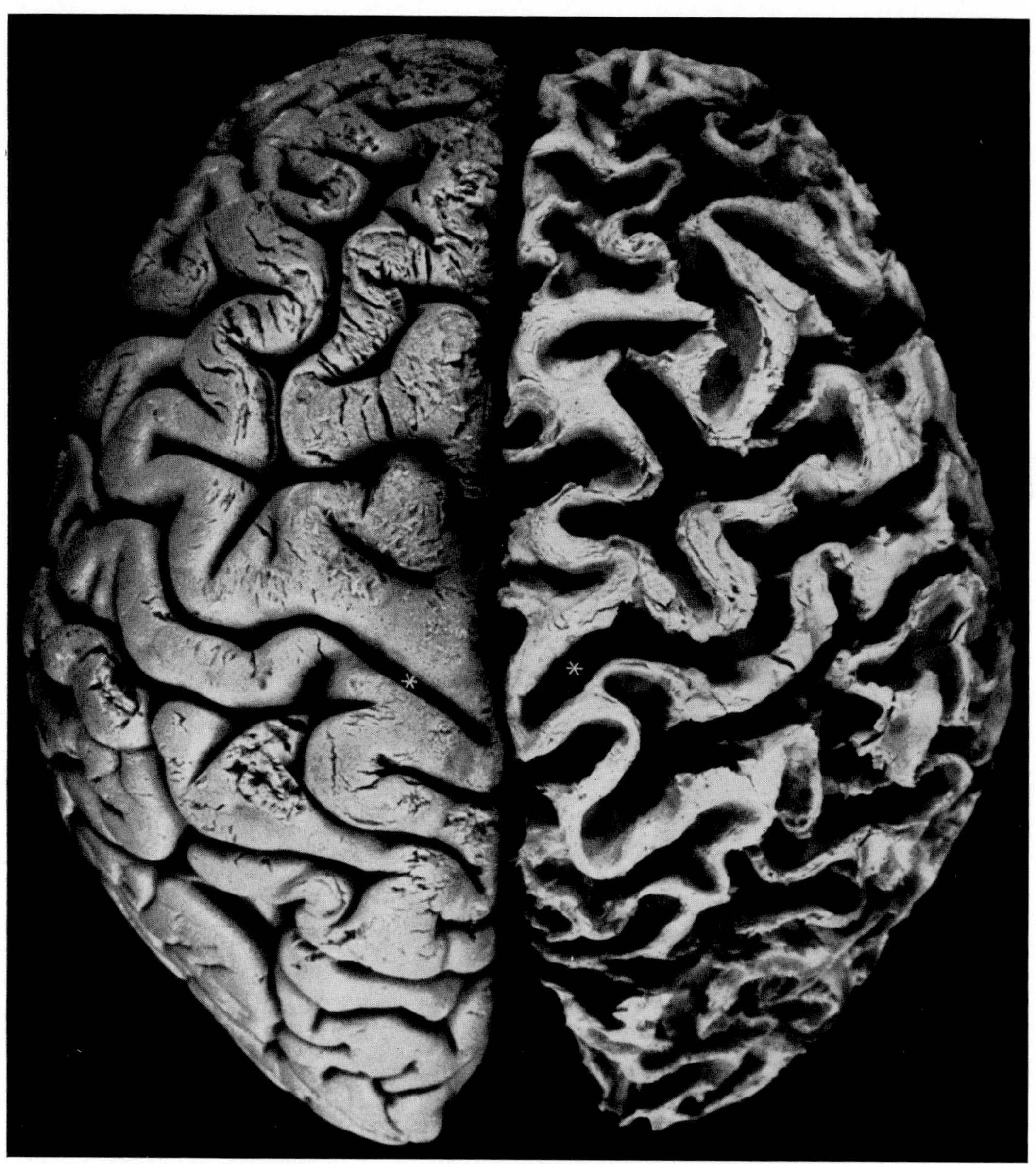
*
*

* *sulcus centralis*

**Fig. 254.**

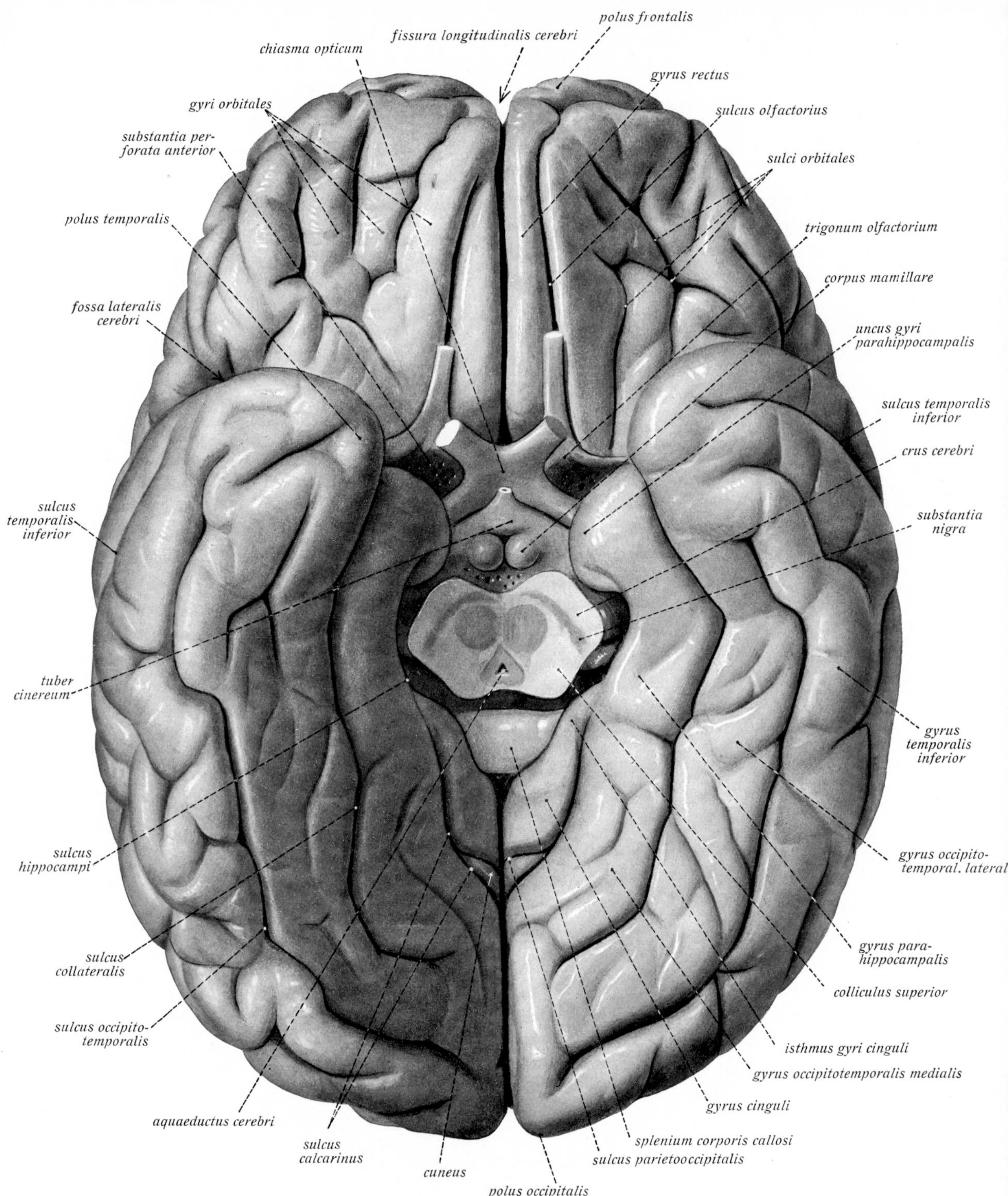

polus frontalis
fissura longitudinalis cerebri
chiasma opticum
gyrus rectus
gyri orbitales
sulcus olfactorius
substantia perforata anterior
sulci orbitales
polus temporalis
trigonum olfactorium
corpus mamillare
fossa lateralis cerebri
uncus gyri parahippocampalis
sulcus temporalis inferior
crus cerebri
sulcus temporalis inferior
substantia nigra
tuber cinereum
gyrus temporalis inferior
sulcus hippocampi
gyrus occipitotemporal. lateral
gyrus parahippocampalis
sulcus collateralis
colliculus superior
sulcus occipitotemporalis
isthmus gyri cinguli
gyrus occipitotemporalis medialis
gyrus cinguli
aquaeductus cerebri
splenium corporis callosi
sulcus calcarinus
sulcus parietooccipitalis
cuneus
polus occipitalis


Fig. 255.

# 255. Ventral View of Forebrain. (Brain stem and cerebellum removed)

(See Figure 209)

1 **Gyrus Rectus**
*gyrus rectus*

**Olfactory Sulcus**
*sulcus olfactorius*

**Orbital Sulci**
*sulci orbitales*

**Olfactory Trigone**
*trigonum olfactorium*

2 **Mammillary Body**
*corpus mamillare*

**Uncus (of Parahippocampal Gyrus)**
*uncus gyri parahippocampalis*

**Inferior Temporal Sulcus**
*sulcus temporalis inferior*

**Cerebral Crus** (peduncle)
*crus cerebri*

3 **Substantia Nigra**
*substantia nigra*

4 **Inferior Temporal Gyrus**
*gyrus temporalis inferior*

**Lateral Occipitotemporal Gyrus**
*gyrus occipitotemporal. lateral.*

**Parahippocampal Gyrus**
*gyrus parahippocampalis*

5 **Superior Colliculus**
*colliculus superior*

**Isthmus of Cingulate Gyrus**
*isthmus gyri cinguli*

**Medial Occipitotemporal Gyrus**
*gyrus occipitotemporalis medialis*

**Gyrus Cinguli**
*gyrus cinguli*

6 **Splenium of Corpus Callosum**
*splenium corporis callosi*

**Parietooccipital Sulcus (Fissure)**
*sulcus parietooccipitalis*

**Occipital Pole**
*polus occipitalis*

**Cuneus**
*cuneus*

7 **Calcarine Sulcus (Fissure)**
*sulcus calcarinus*

**Cerebral Aqueduct**
*aquaeductus cerebri*

**Occipitotemporal Sulcus**
*sulcus occipitotemporalis*

8 **Collateral Sulcus (Fissure)**
*sulcus collateralis*

**Hippocampal Sulcus**
*sulcus hippocampi*

9 **Tuber Cinereum**
*tuber cinereum*

**Inferior Temporal Sulcus**
*sulcus temporalis inferior*

10 **Lateral Cerebral Fossa**
*fossa lateralis cerebri*

**Temporal Pole**
*polus temporalis*

11 **Anterior Perforated Substance**
*substantia perforata anterior*

**Orbital Gyri**
*gyri orbitales*

12 **Optic Chiasma**
*chiasma opticum*

**Longitudinal Cerebral Fissure**
*fissura longitudinalis cerebri*

**Frontal Pole**
*polus frontalis*

**Note:** 1. **Posterior perforated substance** (near mammillary bodies-2) for arteries to midbrain and thalamus.

2. **Anterior perforated substance**-11 is arterial hilus for internal capsule and corpus striatum. (See Fig. 204).

## Etymology:

uncus = L. a hook
hippocampus = Gr. *hippos*, horse
*kampos*, seamonster
Parahippocampal gyrus has this name because it resembles a seahorse.

*tuber* = L. a knot or swelling
cinereum = L. *cinereus*, ashy, gray
chiasma = Gr. two crossing lines, as Greek *chi*

## 256. Right Cerebral Hemisphere. (Lateral view)

The **insula** surrounded by the **circular sulcus**-2 was exposed by removal of the **opercula.**

2 **Circular Sulcus of Insula**
*sulcus circularis insulae*

3 **Frontal Lobe**
*lobus frontalis*

4 **Short Gyrus of Insula**
*gyri breves insulae*

6 **Long Gyrus of the Insula**
*gyrus longus insulae*

7 **Temporal Lobe**
*lobus temporalis*

9 **Occipital Lobe**
*lobus occipitalis*

12 **Parietal Lobe**
*lobus parietalis*

**Note:** 1. Long-6 and short-4 insular gyri.

## 257. A Dissection of Fornix and Mammillothalamic Tract.
(Viewed from medial side and below)

This figure resembles Fig. 251 but, in addition, part of the parahippocampal gyrus was removed to expose the gyrus dentatus-7, and hippocampal fimbria-8.

1 **Trunk of Corpus Callosum**
*truncus corporis callosi*

**Columns of Fornix**
*columna fornicis*

**Septum Pellucidum**
*septum pellucidum*

2 **Interventricular Foramen**
*foramen interventriculare*

**Anterior Commissure**
*commissura anterior*

**Genus of Corpus Callosum**
*genus corporis callosi*

4 **Olfactory Bulb**
*bulbus olfactorius*

**Olfactory Tract**
*tractus olfactorius*

**Rostrum of Corpus Callosum**
*rostrum corporis callosi*

**Lamina Terminalis**
*lamina terminalis*

**Optic Nerve**
*nervus opticus*

5 **Columns of Fornix**
*columna fornicis*

**Mammillary Body**
*corpus mamillare*

**Uncus of Parahippocampal Gyrus**
*uncus gyri parahippocampalis*

7 **Mammillothalamic Fasciculus**
*fasciculus mamillothalamicus*

**Dentate Gyrus**
*gyrus dentatus*

8 **Fimbria of Hippocampus**
*fimbria hippocampi*

**Thalamus**
*thalamus*

**Crus of Fornix**
*crus fornicis*

**Occipital Lobe**
*lobus occipitalis*

9 **Calcarine Sulcus (Fissure)**
*sulcus calcarinus*

10 **Cuneus**
*cuneus*

**Parietooccipital Sulcus**
*sulcus parietooccipitalis*

11 **Sulcus Cinguli**
*sulcus cinguli*

**Splenium of Corpus Callosum**
*splenium corporis callosi*

12 **Body of Fornix**
*corpus fornicis*

**Note:** 1. The columns of the fornix-5 and the mammillothalamic fasciculus-7 have been exposed by removal of the gray matter of the hypothalamus which covered these bundles and formed the lateral wall of the third ventricle.

### Etymology:

*fornix* = L., arch, vault. Applied to various anatomical structures of this shape. According to Pepper: In ancient Rome, prostitutes plied their trade in the vaulted arches opening on the street under many public buildings. The term "fornication" came from this meaning and not directly from the word "fornix" in its medical sense. (**Medical Etymology**, Philadelphia, 1949.)

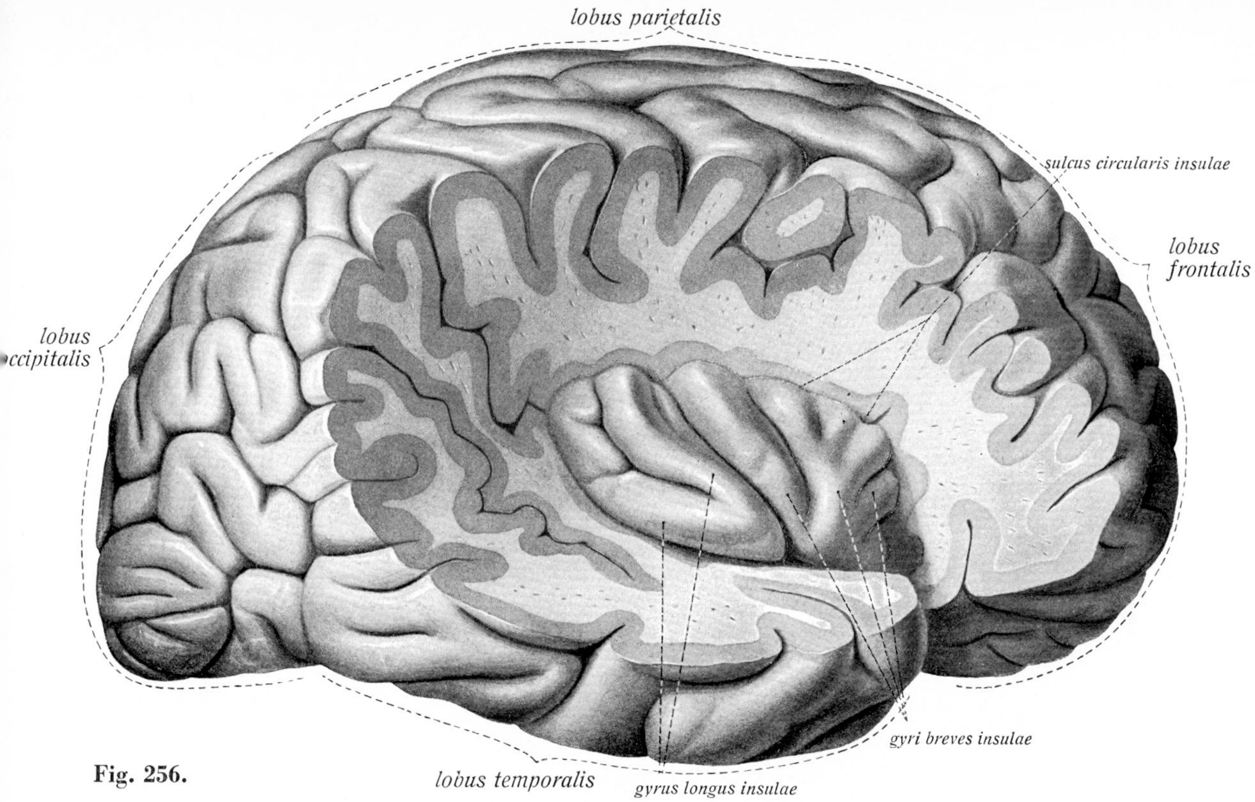

lobus parietalis
sulcus circularis insulae
lobus frontalis
lobus occipitalis
gyri breves insulae
lobus temporalis
gyrus longus insulae

**Fig. 256.**

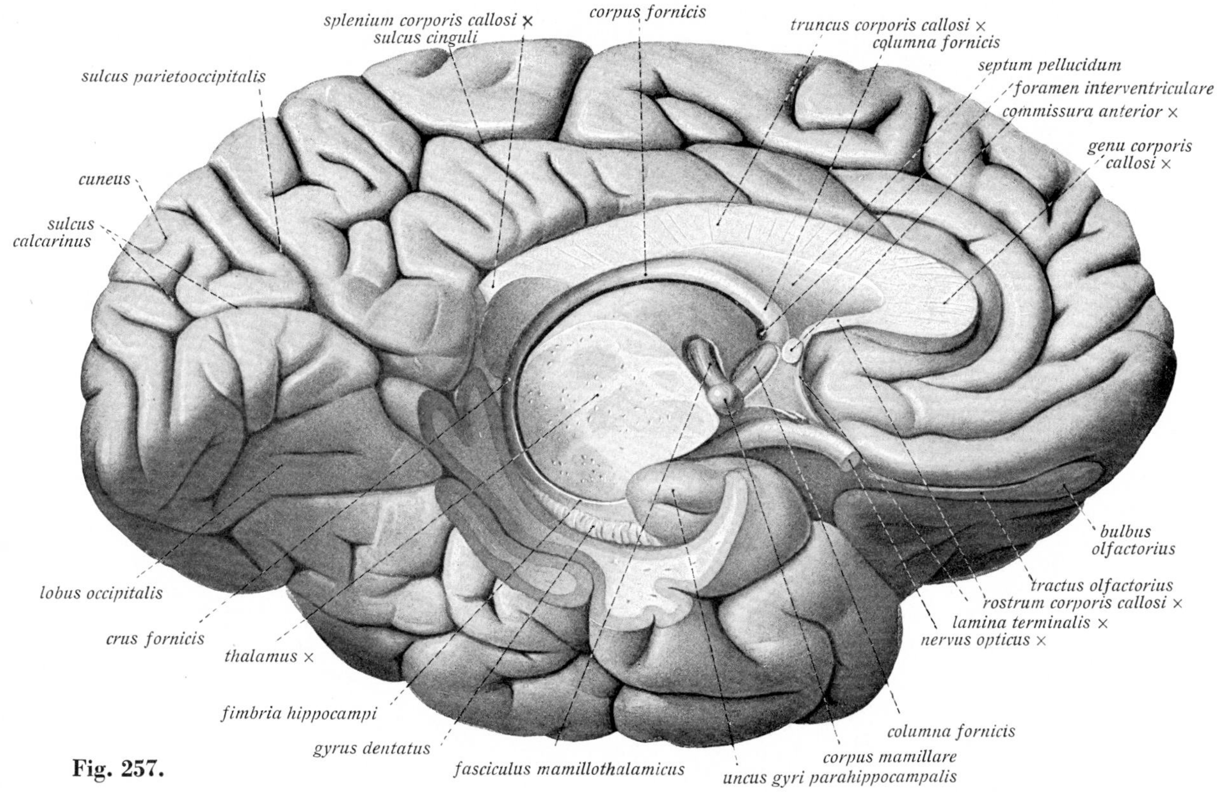

splenium corporis callosi ×
sulcus cinguli
corpus fornicis
truncus corporis callosi ×
columna fornicis
septum pellucidum
foramen interventriculare
commissura anterior ×
genu corporis callosi ×
sulcus parietooccipitalis
cuneus
sulcus calcarinus
bulbus olfactorius
tractus olfactorius
rostrum corporis callosi ×
lamina terminalis ×
nervus opticus ×
lobus occipitalis
crus fornicis
thalamus ×
fimbria hippocampi
gyrus dentatus
fasciculus mamillothalamicus
columna fornicis
corpus mamillare
uncus gyri parahippocampalis

**Fig. 257.**

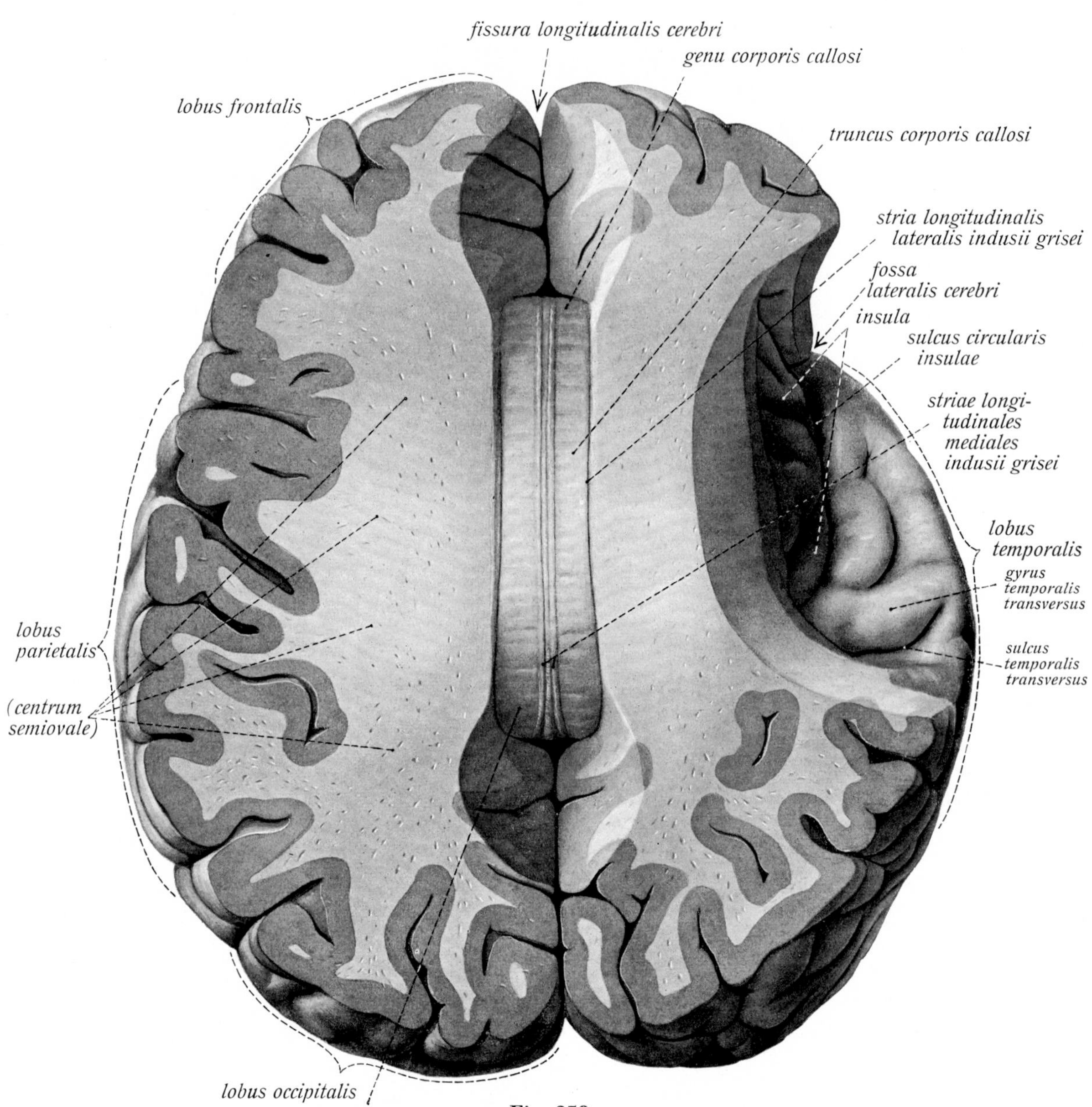

fissura longitudinalis cerebri
genu corporis callosi
lobus frontalis
truncus corporis callosi
stria longitudinalis
lateralis indusii grisei
fossa
lateralis cerebri
insula
sulcus circularis
insulae
striae longi-
tudinales
mediales
indusii grisei
lobus
temporalis
gyrus
temporalis
transversus
sulcus
temporalis
transversus
lobus
parietalis
(centrum
semiovale)
lobus occipitalis
splenium corporis callosi


**Fig. 258.**

## 258. Corpus Callosum. (From above)

The dorsal parts of the hemispheres have been sliced away and the **centrum semiovale**-9 dissected to expose the **corpus callosum**-1. On the right, the fronto-parietal operculum has been cut away to display the dorsal surface of the temporal lobe-3 and the insula-2, which are normally hidden in the lateral fissure (sulcus).

1 **Genus of Corpus Callosum**
*genus corporis callosi*

**Trunk of Corpus Callosum**
*truncus corporis callosi*

**Lateral Longitudinal Stria in Indusium Griseum** (supracallosal gyrus)
*stria longitudinalis lateralis indusii grisei*

2 **Lateral Cerebral Fossa**
*fossa lateralis cerebri*

**Insula**
*insula*

**Circular Sulcus of Insula**
*sulcus circularis insulae*

**Medial Longitudinal Stria of Indusium Griseum**
*striae longitudinales mediales indusii grisei*

3 **Temporal Lobe**
*lobus temporalis*

**Transverse Temporal Gyrus**
*gyrus temporalis transversus*

**Transverse Temporal Sulcus**
*sulcus temporalis transversus*

7 **Splenium of Corpus Callosum**
*splenium corporis callosi*

**Occipital Lobe**
*lobus occipitalis*

9 **Centrum Semiovale**
*(centrum semiovale)*

**Parietal Lobe**
*lobus parietalis*

11 **Frontal Lobe**
*lobus frontalis*

12 **Longitudinal Cerebral Fissure**
*fissura longitudinalis cerebri*

**Note:** 1. The **genu**-1 or knee and **splenium**-7 of the **corpus callosum** and the **medial longitudinal stria**-2 and the very thin layer of gray matter called **indusium griseum**-2.

2. The **corpus callosum** is by far the largest commissure or interconnection between the two cerebral hemispheres (see Fig. 286). Its radiating fibers mix with those of the internal capsule to form the corona radiata and it thus contributes heavily to the formation of the fibrous **centrum semiovale**-9. Most of the fibers of the corpus callosum connect corresponding areas in the two hemispheres, and most of the cortical areas are connected, but some more profusely than others. Few, if any, fibers connect the visual areas near the calcarine fissures (sulcus) of the two hemispheres.

## 259. Corpus Callosum and Left Lateral Ventricle. (From above and left)

The dorsal (upper) parts of the cerebral hemispheres were sliced off to expose the **corpus callosum**-2. The corpus callosum-2 has been removed where it formed the roof of the left **lateral ventricle**. The **inferior**-7 or **temporal horn** of the lateral ventricle was exposed and opened by removing a large part of the occipital and temporal lobes of the cerebral hemisphere.

1 **Genus of Corpus Callosum**
*genus corporis callosi*

**Lamina of Septum Pellucidum**
*lamina septi pellucidi*

**Medial Longitudinal Stria in Indusium Griseum of Corpus Callosum**
*striae longitudinales mediales indusii grisei corporis callosi*

**Interventricular Foramen**
*foramen interventriculare*

2 **Lateral Longitudinal Stria of Indusium Griseum of Corpus Callosum**
*stria longitudinalis lateralis indusii grisei corporis callosi*

**Corpus Callosum**
*corpus callosum*

**Crus of Fornix**
*crus fornicis*

3 **Hippocampal Commissure**
*(commissura hippocampi)*

**Splenium of Corpus Callosum**
*splenium corporis callosi*

4 **Longitudinal Fissure of Cerebrum**
*fissura longitudinalis cerebri*

5 **Occipital Gyrus**
*gyri occipitales*

6 **Bulb of Posterior Horn**
*bulbus cornus posterioris*

**Posterior Horn, Lateral Ventricle**
*cornu posterius ventriculi lateralis*

**Calcarine Sulcus (Fissure)**
*sulcus calcarinus*

**Calcar Avis**
*calcar avis*

7 **Chorioid Body**
*glomus chorioideum*

**Collateral Eminence**
*eminentia collateralis*

**Hippocampus**
*hippocampus*

**Inferior Horn of Lateral Ventricle**
*cornu inferius ventriculi lateralis*

8 **Chorioid Plexus of Lateral Ventricle**
*plexus chorioideus ventriculi lateralis*

**Anterior Chorioid Artery**
*arteria chorioidea [anterior]*

**Caudate Nucleus (Body)**
*nucleus caudatus (corpus)*

10 **Central Portion of Lateral Ventricle**
*pars centralis ventriculi lateralis*

**Lamina Affixa**
*lamina affixa*

**Caudate Nucleus (Head)**
*nucleus caudatus (caput)*

11 **Anterior Horn of Lateral Ventricle**
*cornu anterius ventriculi lateralis*

12 **Longitudinal Fissure of Cerebrum**
*fissura longitudinalis cerebri*

**Note:** 1. **Interventricular foramen**-1 (Monroe), through which the lateral ventricle communicates with the third ventricle.

2. **Chorioid plexus**-8 in the central inferior part of the lateral ventricle does not extend into the anterior horn of the ventricle-11.

3. In the anterior horn of the lateral ventricle-11, the bulging **head** of the **caudate nucleus**-10 which tapers off to its **body**-8 in the central part of the ventricle and to its very narrow **tail** in the roof of the inferior horn-7 of the lateral ventricle.

### Etymology:

callosum = L. *callum*, horny skin (callous)
chorioid = Gr. *chorion*, skin
*eidos*, resemblance

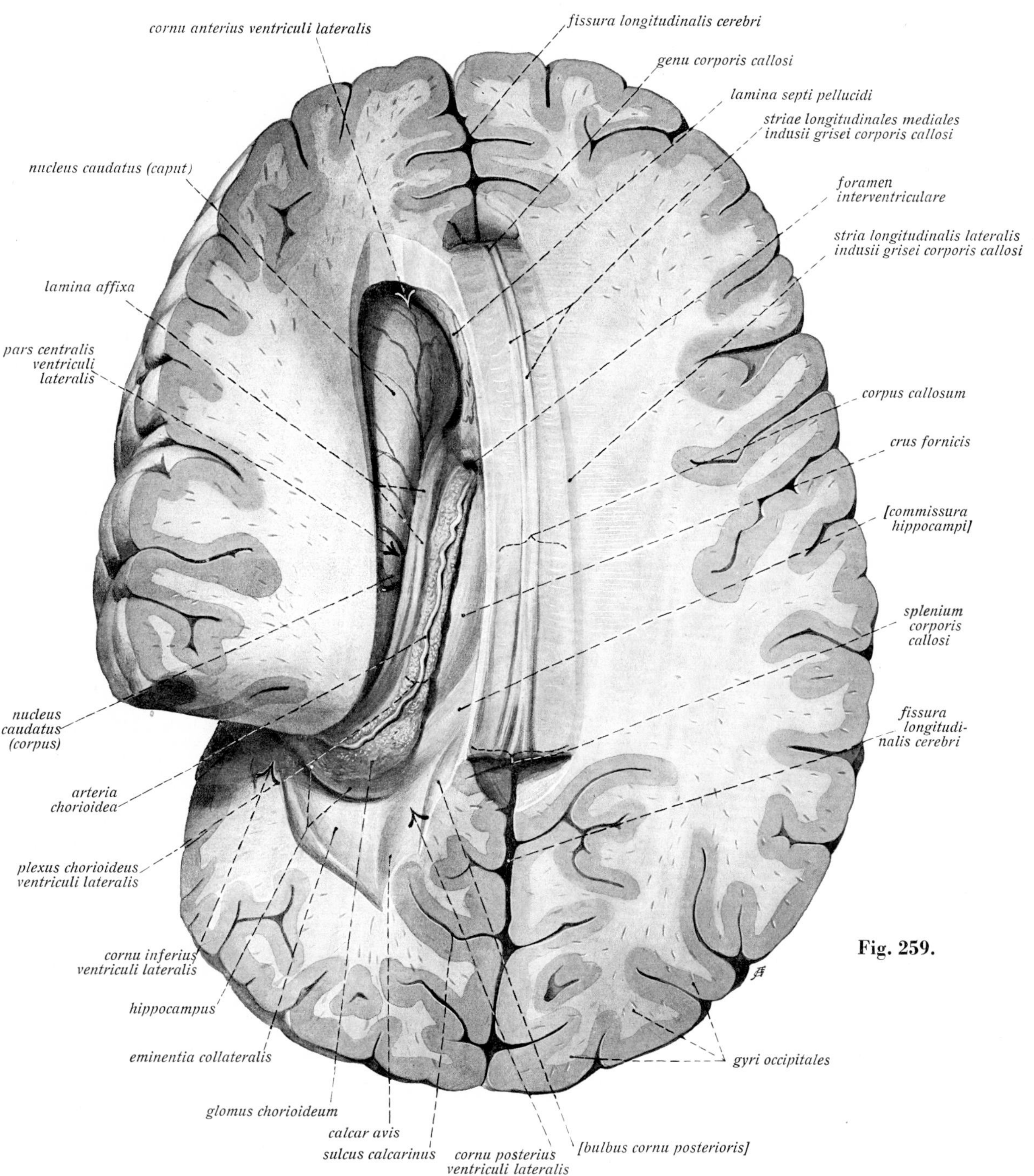
cornu anterius ventriculi lateralis
fissura longitudinalis cerebri
genu corporis callosi
lamina septi pellucidi
striae longitudinales mediales indusii grisei corporis callosi
nucleus caudatus (caput)
foramen interventriculare
stria longitudinalis lateralis indusii grisei corporis callosi
lamina affixa
pars centralis ventriculi lateralis
corpus callosum
crus fornicis
[commissura hippocampi]
splenium corporis callosi
nucleus caudatus (corpus)
fissura longitudinalis cerebri
arteria chorioidea
plexus chorioideus ventriculi lateralis
cornu inferius ventriculi lateralis
hippocampus
eminentia collateralis
gyri occipitales
glomus chorioideum
calcar avis
sulcus calcarinus
cornu posterius ventriculi lateralis
[bulbus cornu posterioris]

**Fig. 259.**

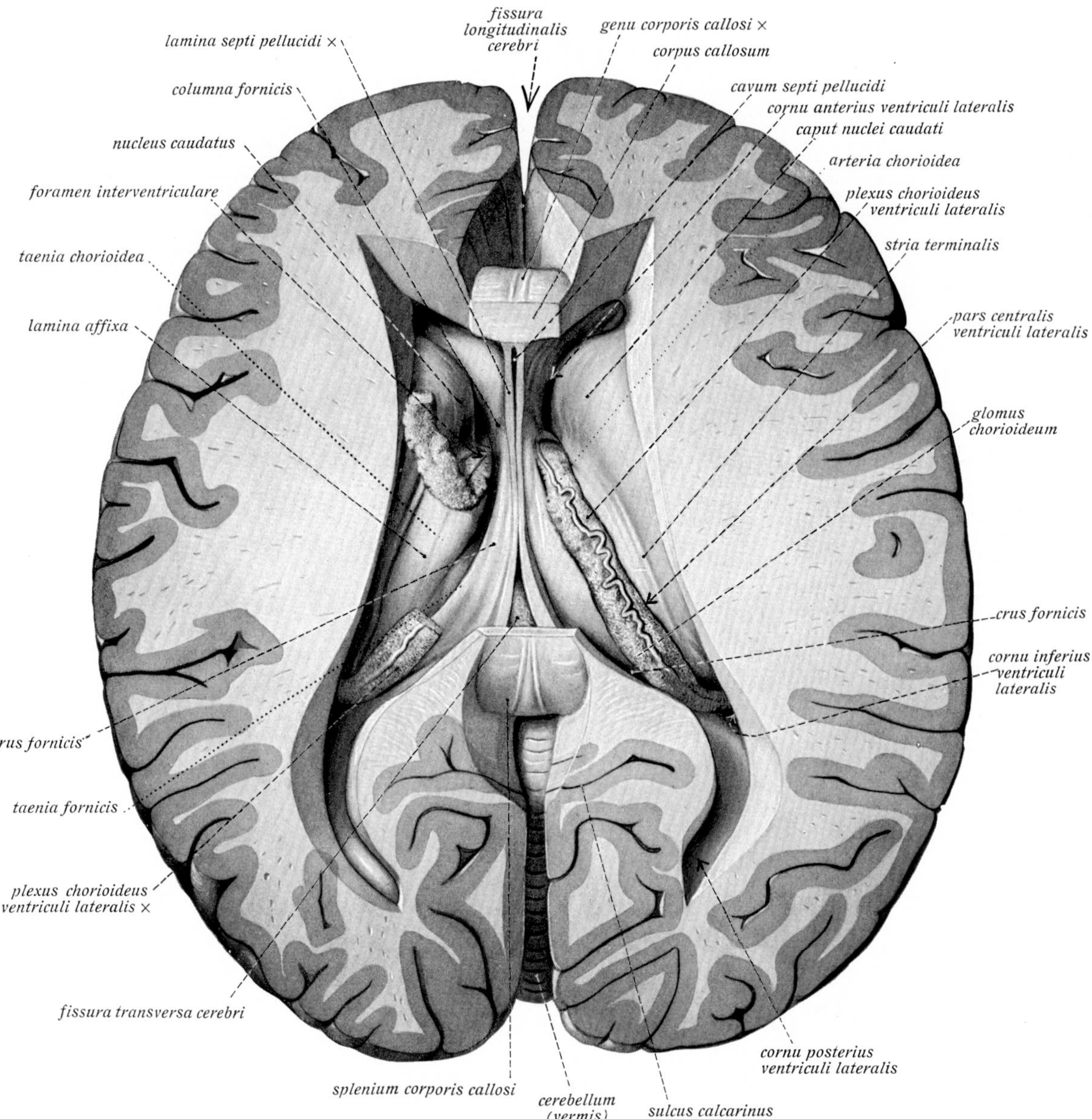
fissura
longitudinalis
cerebri
lamina septi pellucidi ×
genu corporis callosi ×
corpus callosum
columna fornicis
cavum septi pellucidi
cornu anterius ventriculi lateralis
caput nuclei caudati
nucleus caudatus
arteria chorioidea
foramen interventriculare
plexus chorioideus
ventriculi lateralis
taenia chorioidea
stria terminalis
lamina affixa
pars centralis
ventriculi lateralis
glomus
chorioideum
crus fornicis
cornu inferius
ventriculi
lateralis
crus fornicis
taenia fornicis
plexus chorioideus
ventriculi lateralis ×
fissura transversa cerebri
cornu posterius
ventriculi lateralis
splenium corporis callosi
cerebellum
(vermis)
sulcus calcarinus

**Fig. 260.**

## 260. The Two Lateral Ventricles. The Fornices and the Septum Pellucidum. (Exposed from above by the partial removal of the corpus callosum.)

1 **Corpus Callosum**
*corpus callosum*

**Cavity of Septum Pellucidum**
*cavum septi pellucidi*

**Anterior Horn of Lateral Ventricle**
*cornu anterius ventriculi lateralis*

**Caudate Nucleus, Head of**
*caput nuclei caudati*

**Anterior Chorioidal Artery**
*arteria chorioidea anterior*

**Chorioid Plexus of Lateral Ventricle**
*plexus chorioideus ventriculi lateralis*

2 **Stria Terminalis**
*stria terminalis*

**Central Portion of Lateral Ventricle**
*pars centralis ventriculi lateralis*

**Chorioid Glomus**
*glomus chorioideum*

3 **Crus of Fornix**
*crus fornicis*

**Inferior Horn of Lateral Ventricle**
*cornu inferius ventriculi lateralis*

5 **Posterior Horn of Lateral Ventricle**
*cornu posterius ventriculi lateralis*

6 **Calcarine Sulcus (Fissure)**
*sulcus calcarinus*

**Cerebellum (Vermis)**
*cerebellum (vermis)*

7 **Splenium of Corpus Callosum**
*splenium corporis callosi*

8 **Transverse Fissure of Cerebrum**
*fissura transversa cerebri*

**Chorioid Plexus of Lateral Ventricle**
*plexus chorioideus ventriculi lateralis*

**Crus of Fornix**
*crus fornicis*

**Tenia Fornicis**
*tenia fornicis*

10 **Lamina Affixa**
*lamina affixa*

**Tenia Chorioidea**
*tenia chorioidea*

**Interventricular Foramen**
*foramen interventriculare*

11 **Caudate Nucleus**
*nucleus caudatus*

**Column of Fornix**
*columna fornicis*

**Lamina of Septum Pellucidum**
*lamina septi pellucidi*

12 **Longitudinal Cerebral Fissure**
*fissura longitudinalis cerebri*

**Genu of Corpus Callosum**
*genu corporis callosi*

**Note:** 1. Curve of **occipital horn** of **lateral ventricle** correlated with deep penetration of parietooccipital and calcarine sulcus (fissures) from the medial aspect.

2. **Chorioid plexus** in left lateral ventricle has been cut and turned forward. The line for "interventricular foramen"-10, points to part of the chorioid plexus. The interventricular foramen is not readily seen.

3. The **lateral ventricles** are relatively large cavities in each cerebral hemisphere. They have an ependymal lining which is continuous with the lining of the third ventricle at the interventricular foramen. They contain cerebrospinal fluid which is introduced at the chorioid plexus and which normally flows out into the third ventricle through the interventricular foramen.

4. The lateral ventricles appear large when opened, but are almost slit-like in some areas. The irregular shape and extensive distribution of the cavities in the substance of the cerebral hemispheres makes possible the recognition of the following named parts of a **lateral ventricle**:

a. The **anterior horn**-1, extending into the frontal lobe.

b. The **central portion**-2, (or body) in contact with septum pellucidum.

c. The **posterior horn**-5, curving into the occipital lobe.

d. The **inferior horn**-3, extending into the temporal lobe (the latter indicated but not opened). (see Fig. 261-3).

## 261. Dissection of Brain: Exposure of Third Ventricle and Related Structures.

The body and splenium of the corpus callosum-1, the tela chorioidea of the third ventricle-2, and a portion of the fornices-10 were removed. This exposed most of the dorsal surface of the thalamus-10. Further dissection involved the removal of large portions of the parietal and temporal lobes of the cerebral hemispheres. This exposed the inferior horn of the lateral ventricle-2 and the fimbria hippocampi-8 which is the continuation of the crus of the fornix. Figure 266 gives an especially good view of these structures, which were exposed in the floor of the inferior horn of the lateral ventricle.

1 **Corpus Callosum**
*corpus callosum*
**Cavity of Septum Pellucidum**
*cavum septi pellucidi*
**Interventricular Foramen**
*foramen interventriculare*
**Anterior Horn of Lateral Ventricle**
*cornu anterius ventriculi lateralis*
**Head of Caudate Nucleus**
*caput nuclei caudati*

2 **Interthalamic Adhesion**
*adhesio interthalamica*
**Third Ventricle**
*ventriculus tertius*
**Habenular Commissure**
*commissura habenularum*
**Habenular Trigone**
*trigonum habenulae*
**Inferior Horn of Lateral Ventricle**
*cornu inferius ventriculi lateralis*

3 **Posterior Horn of Lateral Ventricle**
*cornu posterius ventriculi lateralis*

5 **Pineal Body**
*corpus pineale*
**Lamina of Tectum**
*lamina tecti*

6 **Vermis of Cerebellum**
*vermis cerebelli*

7 **Posterior Horn of Lateral Ventricle**
*cornu posterius ventriculi lateralis*

8 **Calcar Avis**
*calcar avis*
**Pes Hippocampi**
*pes hippocampi*
**Inferior Commissure**
*commissura inferior*
**Fimbria of Hippocampus**
*fimbria hippocampi*
**Collateral Eminence**
*eminentia collateralis*

9 **Parahippocampal Gyrus**
*gyrus parahippocampalis*

10 **Hippocampal Digitations**
*(digitationes hippocampi)*
**Uncus of Parahippocampal Gyrus**
*uncus gyri parahippocampalis*
**Anterior Tubercle of Thalamus**
*tuberculum anterius thalami*
**Columns of Fornix**
*columnae fornicis*

11 **Lamina of Septum Pellucidum**
*lamina septi pellucidi*

12 **Longitudinal Fissure of Cerebrum**
*fissura longitudinalis cerebri*

**Note:** 1. The **pineal body**-5 attached near the **habenular trigone**-2 and **commissure**-2 which form part of the dorsal wall of the third ventricle. The pineal body-5 is frequently calcified and therefore serves as a landmark in a roentgenogram. Any deviation from the midline indicates abnormal pressures in one or the other ventricle or the presence of a tumor mass which has displaced the pineal body from the midline.

2. The relationship of the **pineal body** to the **tectal lamina** (quadrigeminal plate) is also depicted.

3. Probes in the **interventricular foramina**-1. Through these openings-1, the lateral ventricles communicate with the third ventricle-2.

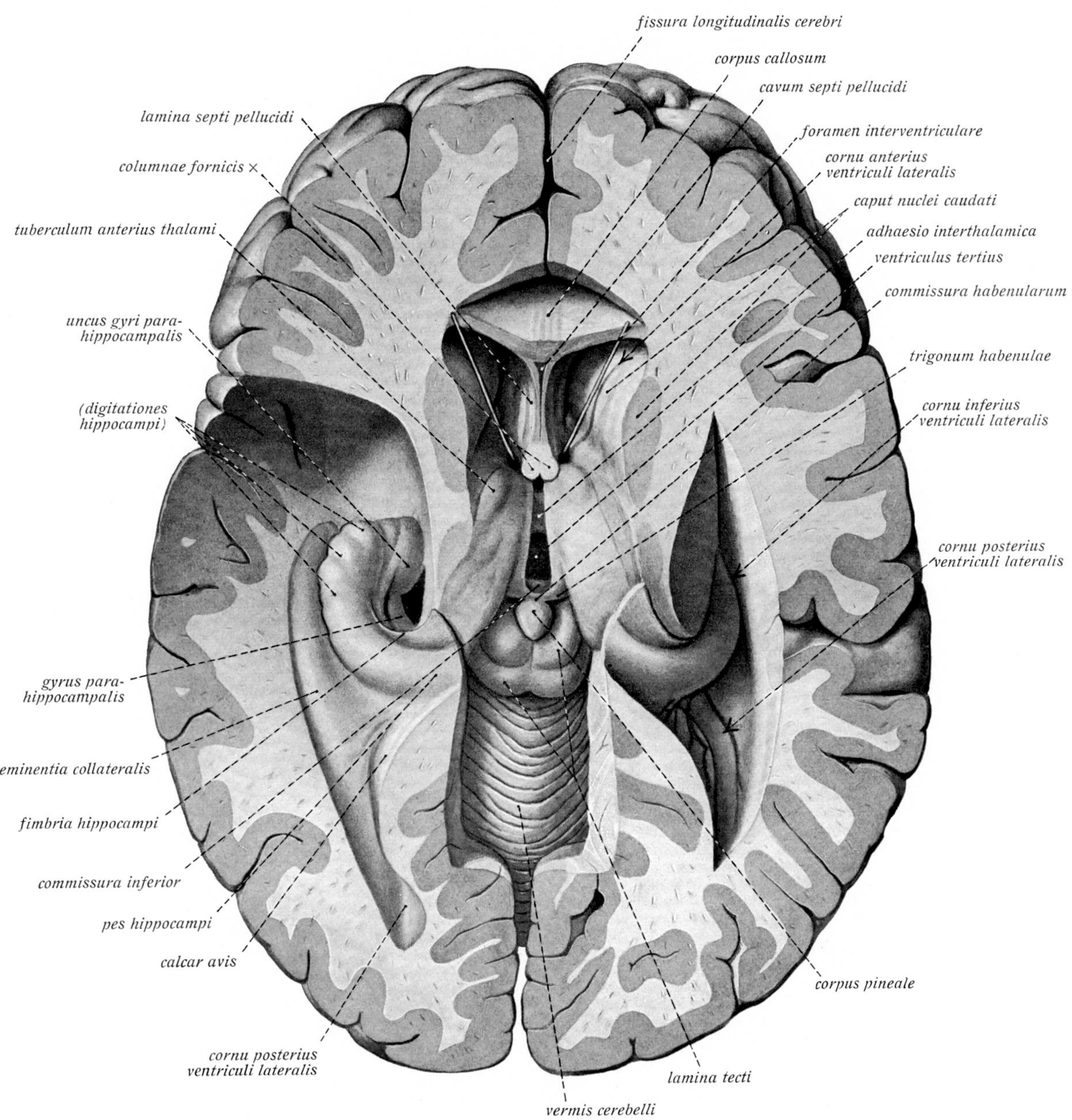
fissura longitudinalis cerebri
corpus callosum
cavum septi pellucidi
lamina septi pellucidi
foramen interventriculare
cornu anterius
ventriculi lateralis
columnae fornicis ×
caput nuclei caudati
tuberculum anterius thalami
adhaesio interthalamica
ventriculus tertius
commissura habenularum
uncus gyri para-
hippocampalis
trigonum habenulae
(digitationes
hippocampi)
cornu inferius
ventriculi lateralis
cornu posterius
ventriculi lateralis
gyrus para-
hippocampalis
eminentia collateralis
fimbria hippocampi
commissura inferior
pes hippocampi
calcar avis
corpus pineale
cornu posterius
ventriculi lateralis
lamina tecti
vermis cerebelli

**Fig. 261.**

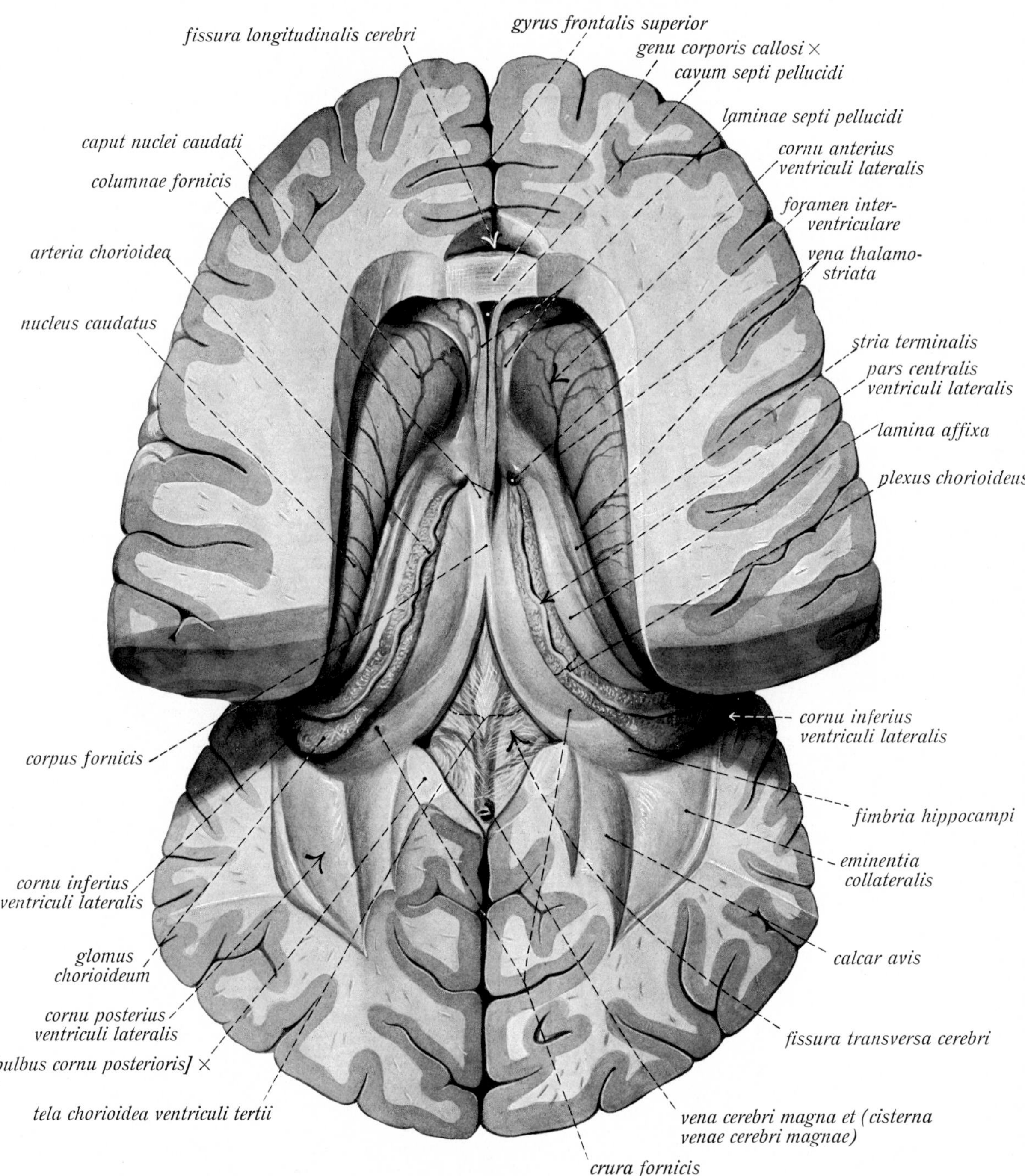

fissura longitudinalis cerebri
gyrus frontalis superior
genu corporis callosi ×
cavum septi pellucidi
laminae septi pellucidi
caput nuclei caudati
cornu anterius ventriculi lateralis
columnae fornicis
foramen interventriculare
arteria chorioidea
vena thalamostriata
nucleus caudatus
stria terminalis
pars centralis ventriculi lateralis
lamina affixa
plexus chorioideus
cornu inferius ventriculi lateralis
corpus fornicis
fimbria hippocampi
eminentia collateralis
cornu inferius ventriculi lateralis
calcar avis
glomus chorioideum
cornu posterius ventriculi lateralis
fissura transversa cerebri
[bulbus cornu posterioris] ×
tela chorioidea ventriculi tertii
vena cerebri magna et (cisterna venae cerebri magnae)
crura fornicis


**Fig. 262.**

# 262. Dissection of Lateral Ventricles in the Cerebral Hemispheres.

(See Fig. 260)

A dorsal view of the cavities of the lateral ventricles. The body and splenium of the corpus callosum and large portions of occipital and temporal lobes were removed to expose the posterior horns and part of the inferior horns of the lateral ventricles.

1 **Genu of Corpus Callosum**
*genu corporis callosi*

**Cavity of Septum Pellucidum**
*cavum septi pellucidi*

**Laminae of Septum Pellucidum**
*laminae septi pellucidi*

**Anterior Horn, Lateral Ventricle**
*cornu anterius ventriculi lateralis*

**Interventricular Foramen**
*foramen interventriculare*

**Thalamostriate Vein**
*vena thalamostriata*

2 **Stria Terminalis**
*stria terminalis*

**Lateral Ventricle (Central Part)**
*pars centralis ventriculi lateralis*

**Lamina Affixa**
*lamina affixa*

3 **Chorioid Plexus**
*plexus chorioideus*

**Lateral Ventricle, Inferior Horn**
*cornu inferius ventriculi lateralis*

4 **Fimbria of Hippocampus**
*fimbria hippocampi*

**Collateral Eminence**
*eminentia collateralis*

**Calcar Avis**
*calcar avis*

5 **Transverse Cerebral Fissure**
*fissura transversa cerebri*

**Great Cerebral Vein and Cistern**
*vena cerebri magna (cisterna venae cerebri magnae)*

6 **Crura of Fornix**
*crura fornicis*

7 **Tela Chorioid of Third Ventricle**
*tela chorioidea ventriculi tertii*

**Bulb of Posterior Horn**
*(bulbus cornus posterioris)*

**Posterior Horn, Lateral Ventricle**
*cornu posterius ventriculi lateralis*

**Chorioid Glomus**
*glomus chorioideum*

8 **Lateral Ventricle, Inferior Horn**
*cornu inferius ventriculi lateralis*

**Body of Fornix**
*corpus fornicis*

10 **Caudate Nucleus**
*nucleus caudatus*

**Anterior Chorioidal Artery**
*arteria chorioidea [anterior]*

11 **Columns of Fornix**
*columnae fornicis*

**Head of Caudate Nuclei**
*caput nuclei caudati*

**Longitudinal Cerebral Fissure**
*fissura longitudinalis cerebri*

12 **Superior Frontal Gyrus**
*gyrus frontalis superior*

**Note:** 1. Excellent view of the **tela chorioidea of the third ventricle**-7 (velum interpositum). This leptomeningeal extension into the **transverse cerebral fissure**-5 contains the **great cerebral vein**-5 (of Galen). The so-called tela chorioidea of the third ventricle-7 is not in itself "chorioidal", but the chorioidal plexus of vessels extends into the third ventricle from it by invaginating the ependymal roof of the third ventricle. (See Figs. 219, 283). The vessels at the lateral edges of the tela chorioidea invaginate the ependyma of the lateral ventricles to form the **chorioidal plexus**-3 of the **lateral ventricles.**

## 263 and 264. Ventriculograms of the Lateral and Third Ventricles.

(Lateral and anteroposterior projections, respectively)

The ventricular system of the brain is visualized by increasing the contrast with the surrounding tissues. The process is called intracranial pneumography.

### 263:

1 **Lateral Ventricle,** Left
*ventriculus lateralis sinister*

2 **Suprapineal Recess**
*recessus suprapinealis*

3 **Pineal Recess**
*rec. pinealis*

**Collateral Trigone**
*trigonum collaterale*

**Posterior Horn**
*cornu posterius*

4 **Cerebral Aqueduct**
*aqueductus cerebri (Sylvii)*

**Fourth Ventricle**
*ventriculus quartus*

8 **Sella Turcica**
*sella turcica*

**Inferior Horn (Lateral Ventricle)**
*cornu inferius*

9 **Infundibular Recess**
*rec. infundibuli.*

**Optic Recess**
*recessus fasciculi optici*

**Roof of Orbital Cavity**
*paries sup. orbitae*

10 **Anterior Horn**
*cornu ant.*

**Anterior Commissure**
*commissura ant.*

11 **Interventricular Foramen**
*foramen interventriculare* (Monroi)

**Lateral Ventricle,** Right
*ventriculus lateralis dexter*

12 **Third Ventricle**
*ventriculus tertius*

6C **Petrosal Bone**
*os petrosum*

C **Hypothalamic Sulcus**
*sulc. hypothalam.*

### 264:

1 **Lateral Ventricle** *ventriculi lateralis*: **Parietal Portion** *pars parietalis*; **Frontal Portion** *pars frontalis*

2 **Third Ventricle**
*ventriculus tertius*

3 **Supraorbital Margin**
*margo supraorbitalis*

**Great Wing of Sphenoid** (Edge View)
*ala major ossis sphenoidalis***

4 **Sella Turcica**
*sella turcica*

**Nasal Septum**
*septum nasi*

**Inferior Nasal Concha**
*concha nasalis inferior*

6 **Dens of Axis**
*axis*

8 **Foramen Rotundum**
*foramen rotundum*

**Ethmoidal Air Cells**
*cellulae ethmoidales*

**Temporal Bone, Petrosal Portion**
*pars petrosa ossis temp.*

9 **Lesser Wing of Sphenoid**
*ala minor ossis sphenoidalis*

**Frontal Sinus**
*sinus frontalis*

10 **Caudate Nucleus, Head**
*caput nuclei caudati*

11 **Septum Pellucidum**
*septum pellucidum*

12 **Subarachnoid Space** (filled with air)
*cavum leptomeningicum*

**Note:** 1. In these figures, the ventricular cavities were filled with air through holes drilled through the skull. The fluid is removed and air is introduced by a needle which penetrates the brain to the lateral ventricle. This procedure is called ventriculography; the roentgenogram, following replacement of cerebrospinal fluid by air or oxygen, is called a ventriculogram. This is an important diagnostic procedure, particularly with respect to localization of tumors and diagnosis of obstruction of the ventricular system. This procedure is usually considered safer than encephalography.

2. An encephalogram is a roentgenogram of the skull following the replacement of cerebrospinal fluid by air or oxygen, but the procedure is carried out by means of lumbar puncture. The cerebrospinal fluid is removed from the lumbar region with the patient in a sitting or reclining position. As the fluid is removed, it is replaced by air or oxygen. In preparation for an encephalogram, the cerebrospinal fluid pressure is measured. This procedure must never be used when lumbar puncture is not safe nor when there is evidence of an increase in intracranial pressure.

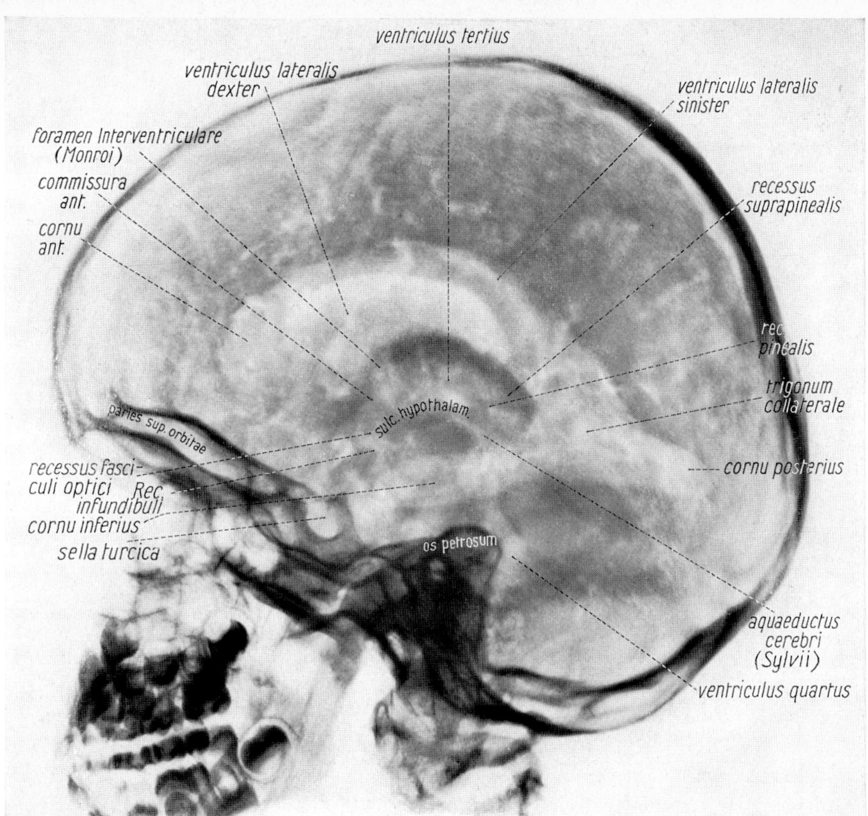
ventriculus tertius
ventriculus lateralis dexter
ventriculus lateralis sinister
foramen Interventriculare (Monroi)
commissura ant.
cornu ant.
recessus suprapinealis
rec. pinealis
trigonum collaterale
sulc. hypothalam.
paries sup. orbitae
cornu posterius
recessus fasciculi optici
Rec. infundibuli
cornu inferius
sella turcica
os petrosum
aquaeductus cerebri (Sylvii)
ventriculus quartus

Fig. 263.

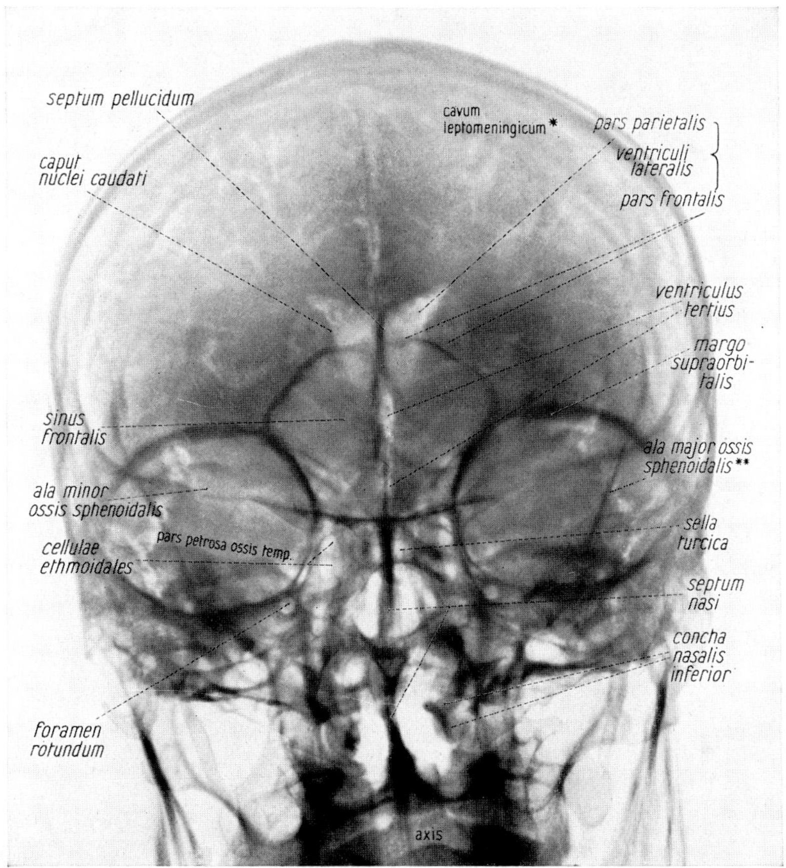
septum pellucidum
cavum leptomeningicum *
pars parietalis
ventriculi lateralis
pars frontalis
caput nuclei caudati
ventriculus tertius
margo supraorbitalis
sinus frontalis
ala major ossis sphenoidalis **
ala minor ossis sphenoidalis
sella turcica
pars petrosa ossis temp.
cellulae ethmoidales
septum nasi
concha nasalis inferior
foramen rotundum
axis

Fig. 264.

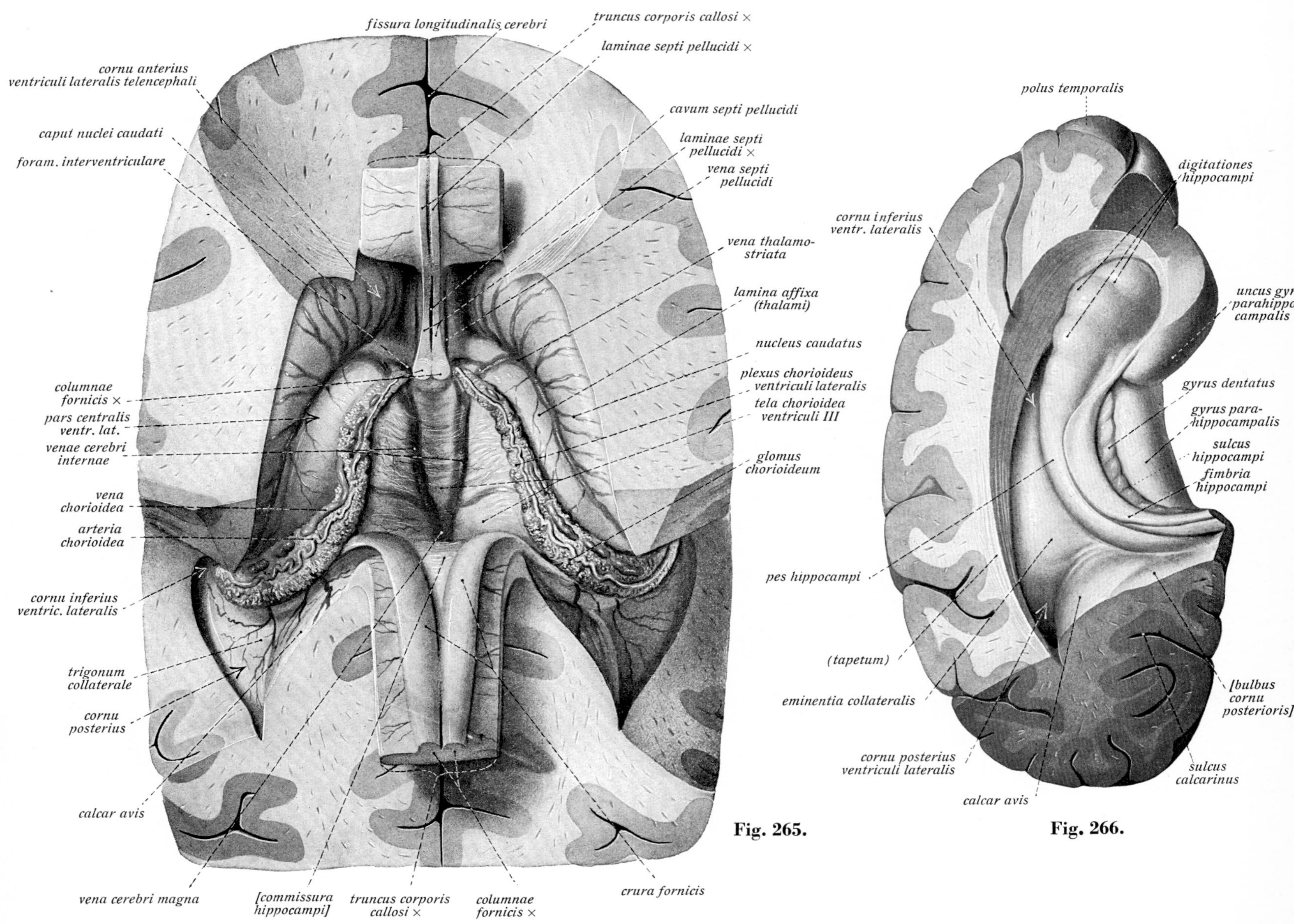
fissura longitudinalis cerebri
truncus corporis callosi ×
laminae septi pellucidi ×
cornu anterius ventriculi lateralis telencephali
cavum septi pellucidi
caput nuclei caudati
laminae septi pellucidi ×
foram. interventriculare
vena septi pellucidi
vena thalamostriata
lamina affixa (thalami)
nucleus caudatus
columnae fornicis ×
plexus chorioideus ventriculi lateralis
pars centralis ventr. lat.
tela chorioidea ventriculi III
venae cerebri internae
glomus chorioideum
vena chorioidea
arteria chorioidea
cornu inferius ventric. lateralis
trigonum collaterale
cornu posterius
calcar avis
vena cerebri magna
[commissura hippocampi]
truncus corporis callosi ×
columnae fornicis ×
crura fornicis
polus temporalis
digitationes hippocampi
cornu inferius ventr. lateralis
uncus gyri parahippocampalis
gyrus dentatus
gyrus parahippocampalis
sulcus hippocampi
fimbria hippocampi
pes hippocampi
(tapetum)
eminentia collateralis
[bulbus cornu posterioris]
cornu posterius ventriculi lateralis
sulcus calcarinus
calcar avis

**Fig. 265.**

**Fig. 266.**

## 265. Lateral Ventricles, Corpus Callosum. Fornix and Tela Chorioidea of Third Ventricle. (5/4)

1 **Trunk of Corpus Callosum**
*truncus corporis callosi*
**Laminae of Septum Pellucidum**
*laminae septi pellucidi*
**Cavity of Septum Pellucidum**
*cavum septi pellucidi*
**Laminae of Septum Pellucidum**
*laminae septi pellucidi*
**Vein of Septum Pellucidum**
*vena septi pellucidi*

2 **Thalamostriate Vein**
*vena thalamostriata*
**Lamina Affixa (Thalamus)**
*lamina affixa (thalami)*
**Caudate Nucleus**
*nucleus caudatus*

3 **Chorioid Plexus of Lateral Ventricle**
*plexus chorioideus ventriculi lateralis*
**Tela Chorioidea of Third Ventricle**
*tela chorioidea ventriculi III*
**Chorioid Glomus**
*glomus chorioideum*

5 **Crura of Fornix**
*crura fornicis*

6 **Columns of the Fornix**
*columnae fornicis*
**Trunk of Corpus Callosum**
*truncus corporis callosi*

7 **Hippocampal Commissure**
*[commissura hippocampi]*
**Great Cerebral Vein**
*vena cerebri magna*
**Calcar Avis**
*calcar avis*

8 **Posterior Horn**
*cornu posterius*
**Collateral Trigone**
*trigonum collaterale*
**Inferior Horn of Lateral Ventricle**
*cornu inferius ventric. lateralis*

9 **Chorioid Artery [Anterior]**
*arteria chorioidea [anterior]*
**Chorioid Vein**
*vena chorioidea*
**Internal Cerebral Veins**
*venae cerebri internae*
**Central Part of Lateral Ventricle**
*pars centralis ventr. lat.*
**Columns of Fornix**
*columnae fornicis*

10 **Interventricular Foramen**
*foram. interventriculare*

11 **Head of Caudate Nucleus**
*caput nuclei caudati*

**Anterior Horn of Lateral Ventricle of Telencephali**
*cornu anterius ventriculi lateralis telencephali*

12 **Longitudinal Cerebral Fissure**
*fissura longitudinalis cerebri*

The **corpus callosum**-1, -6, together with the fornices-6, -9, were divided and the two parts reflected forward and backward to display the tela chorioidea of the 3rd ventricle-3 in the transverse cerebral fissure.

**Note:** 1. **Deep internal cerebral veins**-9 uniting to form **great cerebral vein**-7 within the **tela chorioidea**-3 of the **third ventricle**.

2. **Tela chorioidea of 3rd ventricle** extends forward caudal to **corpus callosum** and **hippocampal commissure**-7, separating those structures from the **thalamus** which it covers. It extends to **chorioidal plexus of lateral ventricles**-9. Ventrally, it is attached to **columns of fornices**-9 near **interventricular foramina**-10. (See Fig. 219)

## 266. Temporal Lobe: Shows Floor of Inferior and Posterior Horns of Lateral Ventricle. (5/4)

1 **Hippocampal Digitations**
*digitationes hippocampi*
**Uncus of Parahippocampal Gyrus**
*uncus gyri parahippocampalis*

2 **Dentate Gyrus**
*gyrus dentatus*
**Parahippocampal Gyrus**
*gyrus parahippocampalis*

3 **Hippocampal Sulcus**
*sulcus hippocampi*
**Fimbria of Hippocampus**
*fimbria hippocampi*

5 **Posterior Horn Bulb**
*[bulbus cornu posterioris]*
**Calcarine Sulcus (Fissure)**
*sulcus calcarinus*

6 **Calcar Avis**
*calcar avis*

7 **Post. Horn of Lat. Ventricle**
*cornu posterius ventriculi lat.*
**Collateral Eminence**
*eminentia collateralis*
**Tapetum**
*(tapetum)*

8 **Pes Hippocampi**
*pes hippocampi*

11 **Lat. Ventricle, Inferior Horn**
*cornu inferius ventr. lateralis*

12 **Temporal Pole**
*polus temporalis*

The chorioid plexus was removed to display structures on floor of inferior horn of lateral ventricle.

**Note:** 1. Hippocampal structures form part of floor. From medial to lateral, they are: **fimbria**-3, **hippocampus**-8, and **hippocampal digitations**-1.

2. **Collateral eminence** is located at junction of posterior-7 and inferior horns-11.

## 267. Floor of Inferior Horn of Lateral Ventricle. (2/1)

Shows relationships of **pes hippocampi**-8, **parahippocampal gyrus**-3, and **hippocampal fimbria**-4.

2 **Velum Terminale**
*[velum terminale]*

3 **Parahippocampal Gyrus**
*gyrus parahippocampalis*

4 **Fimbria of Hippocampus**
*fimbria hippocampi*

7 **Calcar Avis**
*calcar avis*

**Posterior Horn of Lateral Ventricle**
*cornu posterius ventr. lat.*

8 **Collateral Trigone**
*trigonum collaterale*

**Pes Hippocampi**
*pes hippocampi*

10 **Hippocampal Digitations**
*digitationes hippocampi*

12 **Inferior Horn of Lateral Ventricle**
*cornu inferius ventriculi lat.*

## 268. Ventral End of Temporal Lobe with Inferior Horn of Lateral Ventricle Opened. (2/1)

1 **Hippocampal Digitations**
*digitationes hippocampi*

2 **Uncus of Parahippocampal Gyrus**
*uncus gyri parahippocampalis*

3 **Fimbria of Hippocampus**
*fimbria hippocampi*

4 **Hippocampal Sulcus**
*sulcus hippocampi*

**Dentate Gyrus**
*gyrus dentatus*

**Parahippocampal Gyrus**
*gyrus parahippocampalis*

5 **White Reticular Substance**
*(substantia reticularis alba)*

6 **Collateral Sulcus**
*sulcus collateralis*

7 **Fimbria of Hippocampus**
*fimbria hippocampi*

10 **Trigone Collateral**
*trigonum collaterale*

12 **Pes Hippocampi**
*pes hippocampi*

## 269. Frontal End of Inferior Horn of Lateral Ventricle. (2/1)

Dissection similar to Figure 267, but shows more detail. Uncus of parahippocampal gyrus resected to display an uncus band of Giacomini *-3.

1 **Transverse Temporal Gyri**
*gyri temporales transversi*

**Pes Hippocampi**
*pes hippocampi*

3 **Uncus Band of Giacomini**
*

**Dentate Gyrus**
*gyrus dentatus*

**Parahippocampal Gyrus**
*gyrus parahippocampalis*

**Fimbria of Hippocampus**
*fimbria hippocampi*

4 **Hippocampal Sulcus**
*sulcus hippocampi*

5 **Pes Hippocampi**
*pes hippocampi*

6 **Pes Hippocampi**
*pes hippocampi*

**Inferior Horn of Lateral Ventricle**
*cornu inferius ventriculi lateralis*

7 **Temporal Gyri**
*gyri temporales*

## 270. Frontal End of Temporal Lobe. (Viewed from behind and below) (2/1)

Demonstrates continuity of dentate gyrus-1 and fasciolar gyrus-12.

1 **Dentate Gyrus**
*gyrus dentatus*

**Parahippocampal Gyrus**
*gyrus parahippocampalis*

5 **White Line of Cortex**
*(stratum album [principale] corticis)*

6 **White Matter**
*substantia alba*

8 **Fimbria of Hippocampus**
*fimbria hippocampi*

9 **Dentate Gyrus**
*gyrus dentatus*

10 **Fimbria of Hippocampus**
*fimbria hippocampi*

11 **Corpus Callosum**
*corpus callosum*

**Splenium of Corpus Callosum**
*splenium corporis callosi*

12 **Fasciolar Gyrus**
*gyrus fasciolaris*

**Parahippocampal Gyrus**
*gyrus parahippocampalis*

### Etymology:

splenium = Gr. *splenion*, bandage (a roll-shaped swelling)

*fimbria* = L. fringe
*pes* = L. foot (pl. *pedes*)

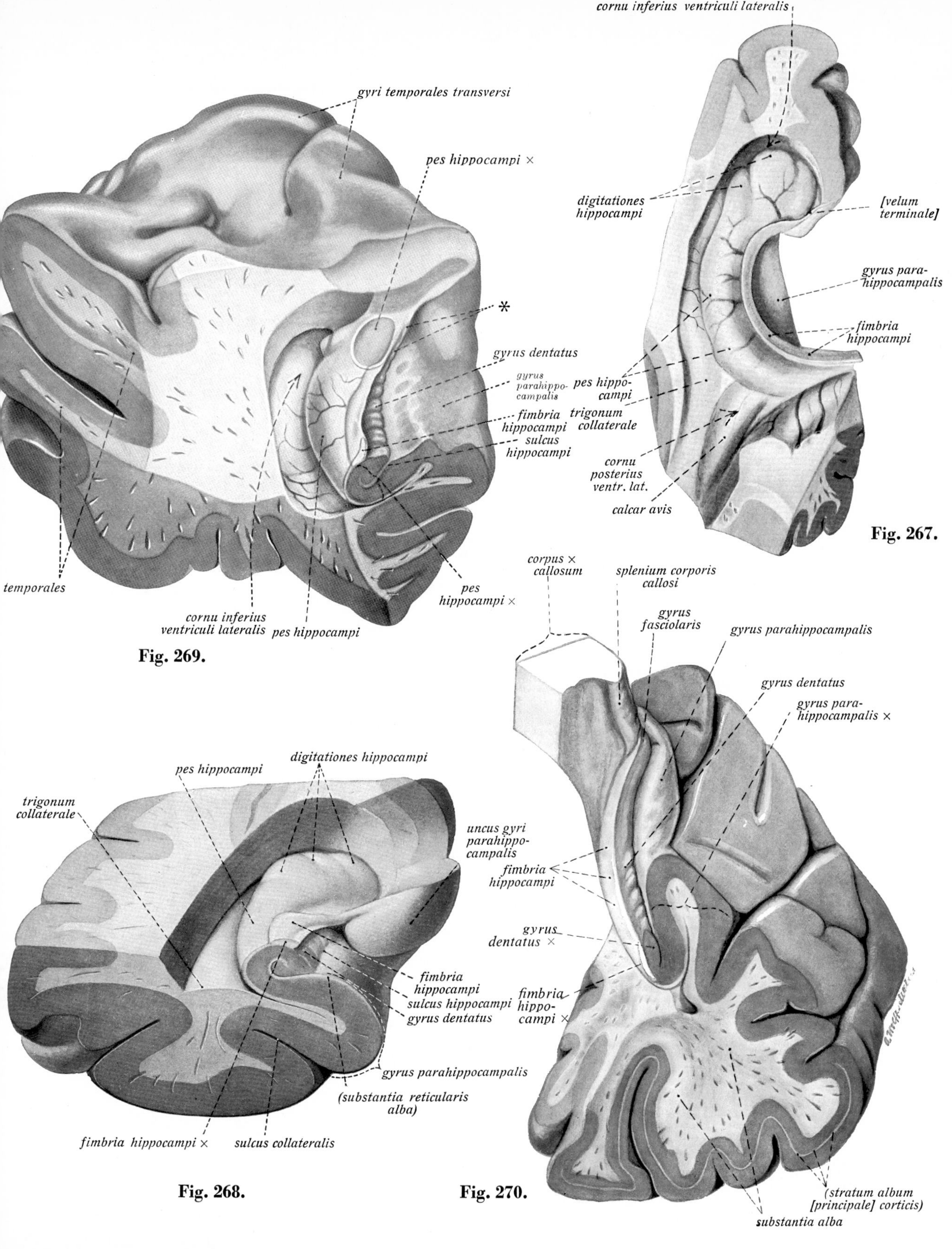

cornu inferius ventriculi lateralis
digitationes hippocampi
[velum terminale]
gyrus parahippocampalis
fimbria hippocampi
pes hippocampi
trigonum collaterale
cornu posterius ventr. lat.
calcar avis
gyri temporales transversi
pes hippocampi ×
*
gyrus dentatus
gyrus parahippocampalis
fimbria hippocampi
sulcus hippocampi
temporales
cornu inferius ventriculi lateralis
pes hippocampi
pes hippocampi ×
corpus × callosum
splenium corporis callosi
gyrus fasciolaris
gyrus parahippocampalis
gyrus dentatus
gyrus parahippocampalis ×
fimbria hippocampi
gyrus dentatus ×
fimbria hippocampi ×
(stratum album [principale] corticis)
substantia alba
pes hippocampi
digitationes hippocampi
trigonum collaterale
uncus gyri parahippocampalis
fimbria hippocampi
sulcus hippocampi
gyrus dentatus
gyrus parahippocampalis
(substantia reticularis alba)
fimbria hippocampi ×
sulcus collateralis


Fig. 267.

Fig. 269.

Fig. 268.

Fig. 270.

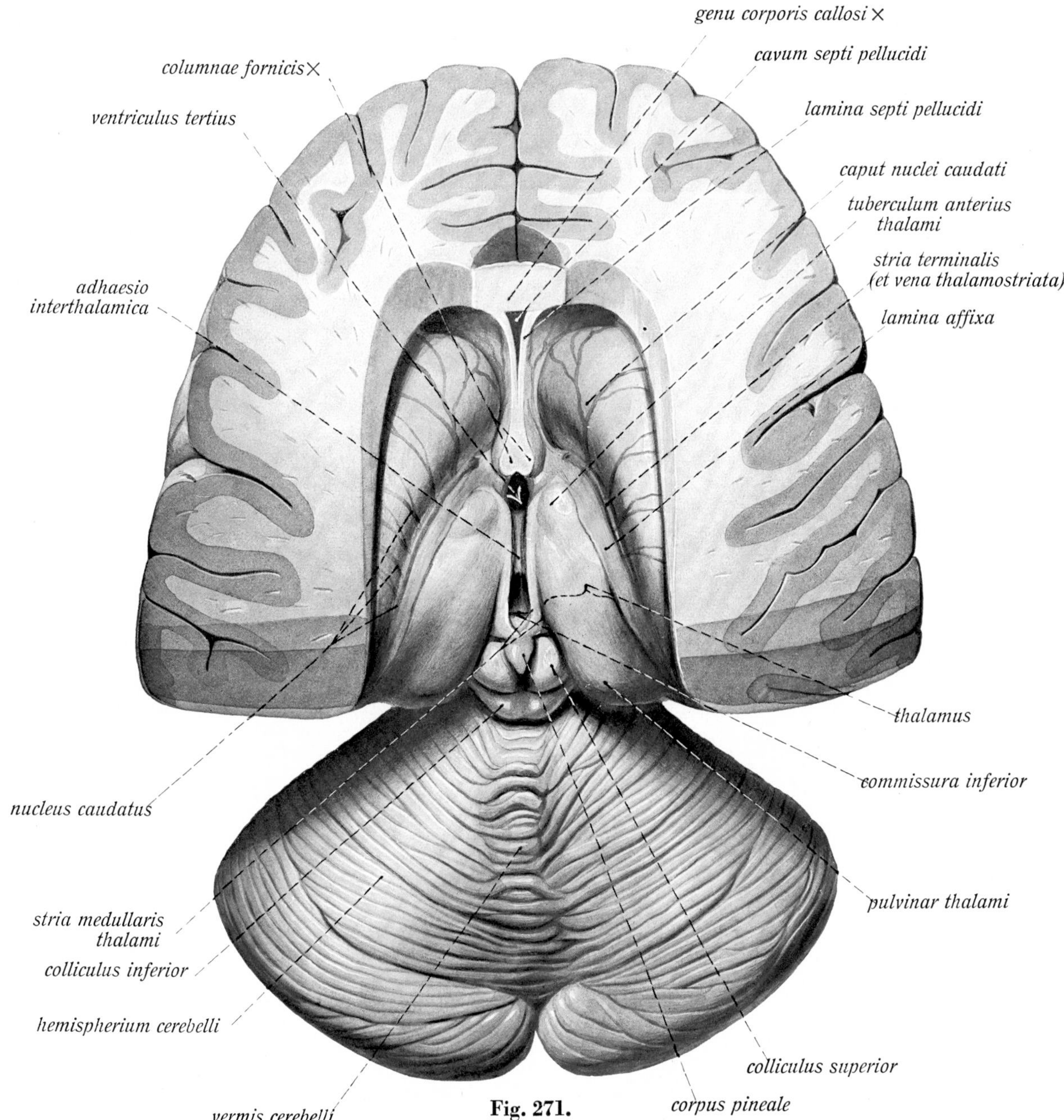
genu corporis callosi ×
columnae fornicis ×
cavum septi pellucidi
ventriculus tertius
lamina septi pellucidi
caput nuclei caudati
tuberculum anterius thalami
stria terminalis (et vena thalamostriata)
adhaesio interthalamica
lamina affixa
thalamus
commissura inferior
nucleus caudatus
pulvinar thalami
stria medullaris thalami
colliculus inferior
hemispherium cerebelli
colliculus superior
vermis cerebelli
corpus pineale

**Fig. 271.**

# 271. Dissection to Show the Lateral Ventricles, Third Ventricle, Quadrigeminal Plate, and Cerebellum. (Viewed from above) (4/5)

Dissection similar to that in Figures 262, 265 but, in addition, the fornices, and the tela chorioidea of third ventricle, temporal and occipital lobes of cerebral hemispheres were removed.

1 **Genu of Corpus Callosum**
*genu corporis callosi*

**Cavity of Septum Pellucidum**
*cavum septi pellucidi*

**Lamina of Septum Pellucidum**
*lamina septi pellucidi*

**Head of Caudate Nucleus**
*caput nuclei caudati*

**Anterior Tubercle of Thalamus**
*tuberculum anterius thalami*

2 **Stria Terminalis + Thalamo-striate Vein**
*stria terminalis (+ vena thalamostriata)*

**Lamina Affixa**
*lamina affixa*

4 **Thalamus**
*thalamus*

**Inferior Commissure**
*comissura inferior*

**Pulvinar of Thalamus**
*pulvinar thalami*

5 **Superior Colliculus**
*colliculus superior*

**Pineal Body**
*corpus pineale*

7 **Vermis of Cerebellum**
*vermis cerebelli*

**Cerebellar Hemisphere**
*hemispherium cerebelli*

8 **Inferior Colliculus**
*colliculus inferior*

**Stria Medullaris Thalami**
*stria medullaris thalami*

**Caudate Nucleus**
*nucleus caudatus*

10 **Interthalamic Adhesion**
*adhesio interthalamica*

11 **Third Ventricle**
*ventriculus tertius*

**Columns of Fornix**
*columnae fornicis*

## Etymology:

*thalamus* = Gr. *thalamos* an inner chamber. Word does not mean a cavity, but two massive bodies forming walls of the third ventricle

pellucidus = L. translucent (*pellucere,* to shine through)

*vermis* = L. a worm

## 272. Structures at Base of Brain. (Cranial nerves removed, right side) (Somewhat enlarged)

1 **Olfactory Stria**
*striae olfactoriae*

**Limen Insula**
*limen insulae*

**Lateral Cerebral Fossa**
*fossa lateralis cerebri*

2 **Interpeduncular Fossa**
*fossa interpeduncularis*

**Anterior Perforated Substance**
*substantia perforata anterior*

**Lateral Ventricle, Chorioid Plexus**
*plexus chorioideus ventriculi lateralis*

**Inferior Horn of Lateral Ventricle**
*cornu inferius ventriculi lateralis*

**Pes Hippocampi**
*pes hippocampi*

4 **Trochlear Nerve**
*n. trochlearis*

**Trigeminal Nerve**
*n. trigeminus*

**Nervus Intermedius**
*n. intermedius*

**Vestibulocochlear Nerve**
*n. statoacusticus [vestibulocochlearis]*

**Facial Nerve**
*n. facialis*

**Cerebellar Flocculus**
*flocculus cerebelli*

**Chorioid Plexus and Lateral Rhombencephalic Aperture**
*plexus chorioideus + apertura lateralis rhombencephali*

5 **Glossopharyngeal Nerve**
*nervus glossopharyngeus*

**Vagus Nerve**
*nervus vagus*

**Hypoglossal Nerve**
*nervus hypoglossus*

**Spinal Accessory Nerve**
*nervus accessorius*

**Medulla Oblongata**
*medulla oblongata*

6 **Pyramidal Decussation**
*decussatio pyramidum*

**Spinal Cord**
*medulla spinalis*

**Pyramid**
*pyramis medullae oblongatae*

7 **Olive**
*oliva*

**Lateral Funiculus of Medulla Oblongata**
*funiculus lateralis medullae oblongatae*

**Foramen Cecum**
*foramen cecum*

8 **Basilar Sulcus of Pons**
*sulcus basilaris pontis*

**Pons**
*pons*

**Transverse Pontine Fibers**
*fibrae pontis transversae*

**Posterior Perforated Substance**
*substantia perforata posterior*

**Cerebral Peduncle**
*pedunculus cerebri*

10 **Oculomotor Nerve Sulcus**
*sulcus nervi oculomotorii*

**Optic Tract**
*tractus opticus*

11 **Mammillary Peduncle**
*pedunculus corporis mamillaris*

**Mammillary Body**
*corpus mamillare*

**Olfactory Trigone**
*trigonum olfactorium*

**Infundibulum**
*infundibulum*

**Optic Chiasma**
*chiasma opticum*

12 **Olfactory Sulcus**
*sulcus olfactorius*

**Longitudinal Cerebral Fissure**
*fissura longitudinalis cerebri*

**Lamina Terminalis Hypothalami**
*lamina terminalis hypothalami*

**Tuber Cinereum**
*tuber cinereum*

**Olfactory Bulb**
*bulbus olfactorius*

**Olfactory Tract**
*tractus olfactorius*

**Note:** 1. **Hypoglossal nerve**-5 is a cranial extension of spinal nerve series.

2. **Accessory nerve**-5 is a cervical extension of vagus nerve-5 complex.

3. Last 7 cranial nerves exit near cerebello-pontine angle.

4. Anterior perforated substance where lateral striate arteries entered brain substance.

### Etymology:

flocculus = L. diminutive of *floccus*, flock or tuft

funiculus = L. diminutive of *funis*, a cord

*medulla* = L. marrow

oblongata = L. *oblongus*, rather long or oblong

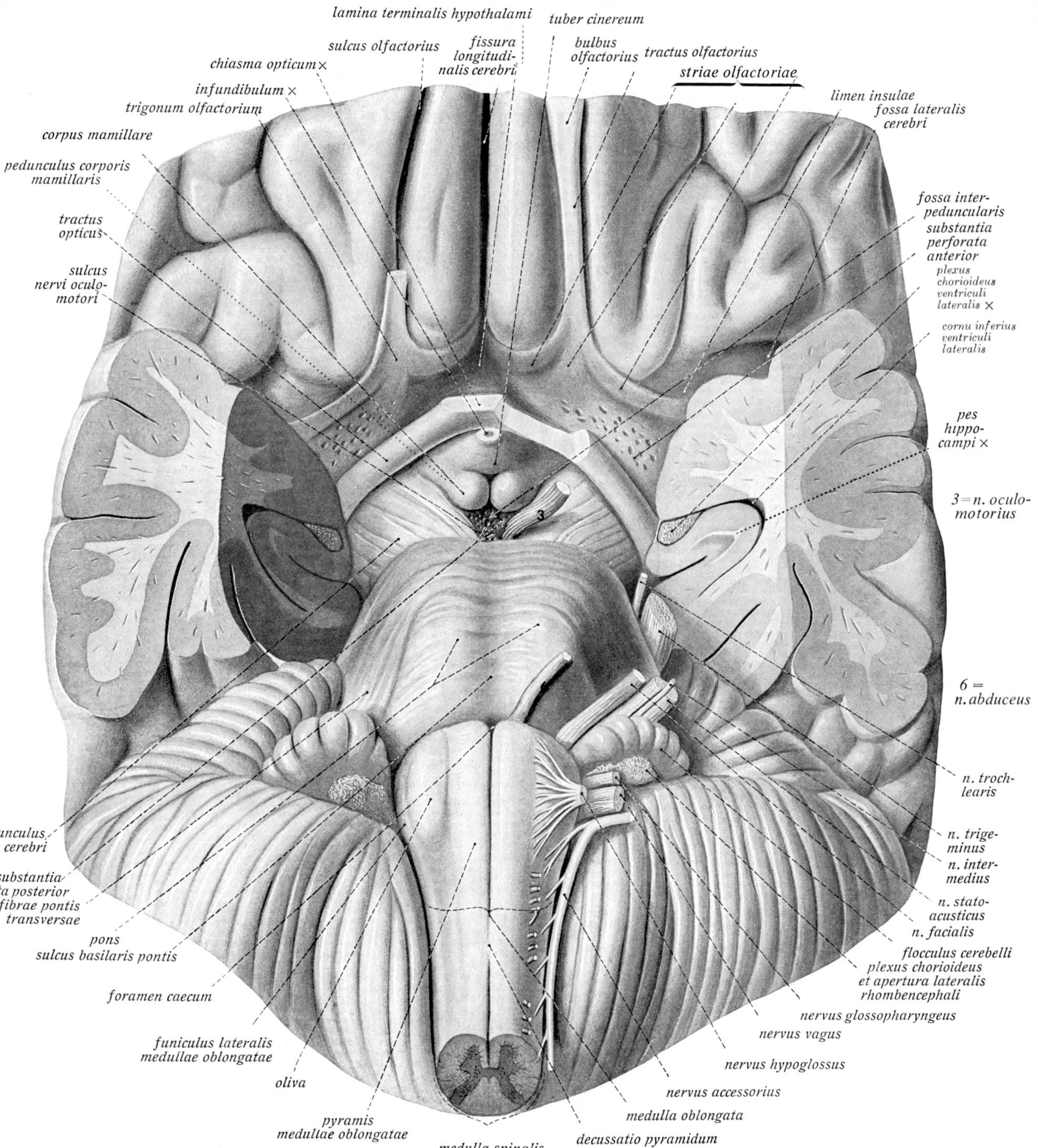

lamina terminalis hypothalami
tuber cinereum
sulcus olfactorius
fissura longitudinalis cerebri
bulbus olfactorius
tractus olfactorius
chiasma opticum ×
striae olfactoriae
infundibulum ×
trigonum olfactorium
limen insulae
fossa lateralis cerebri
corpus mamillare
pedunculus corporis mamillaris
tractus opticus
fossa interpeduncularis
substantia perforata anterior
plexus chorioideus ventriculi lateralis ×
sulcus nervi oculomotori
cornu inferius ventriculi lateralis
pes hippocampi ×
3
3 = n. oculomotorius
6 = n. abduceus
n. trochlearis
edunculus cerebri
n. trigeminus
n. intermedius
substantia
ata posterior
fibrae pontis transversae
n. statoacusticus
n. facialis
pons
sulcus basilaris pontis
flocculus cerebelli
plexus chorioideus et apertura lateralis rhombencephali
foramen caecum
nervus glossopharyngeus
nervus vagus
funiculus lateralis medullae oblongatae
nervus hypoglossus
oliva
nervus accessorius
medulla oblongata
pyramis medullae oblongatae
decussatio pyramidum
medulla spinalis


**Fig. 272.**

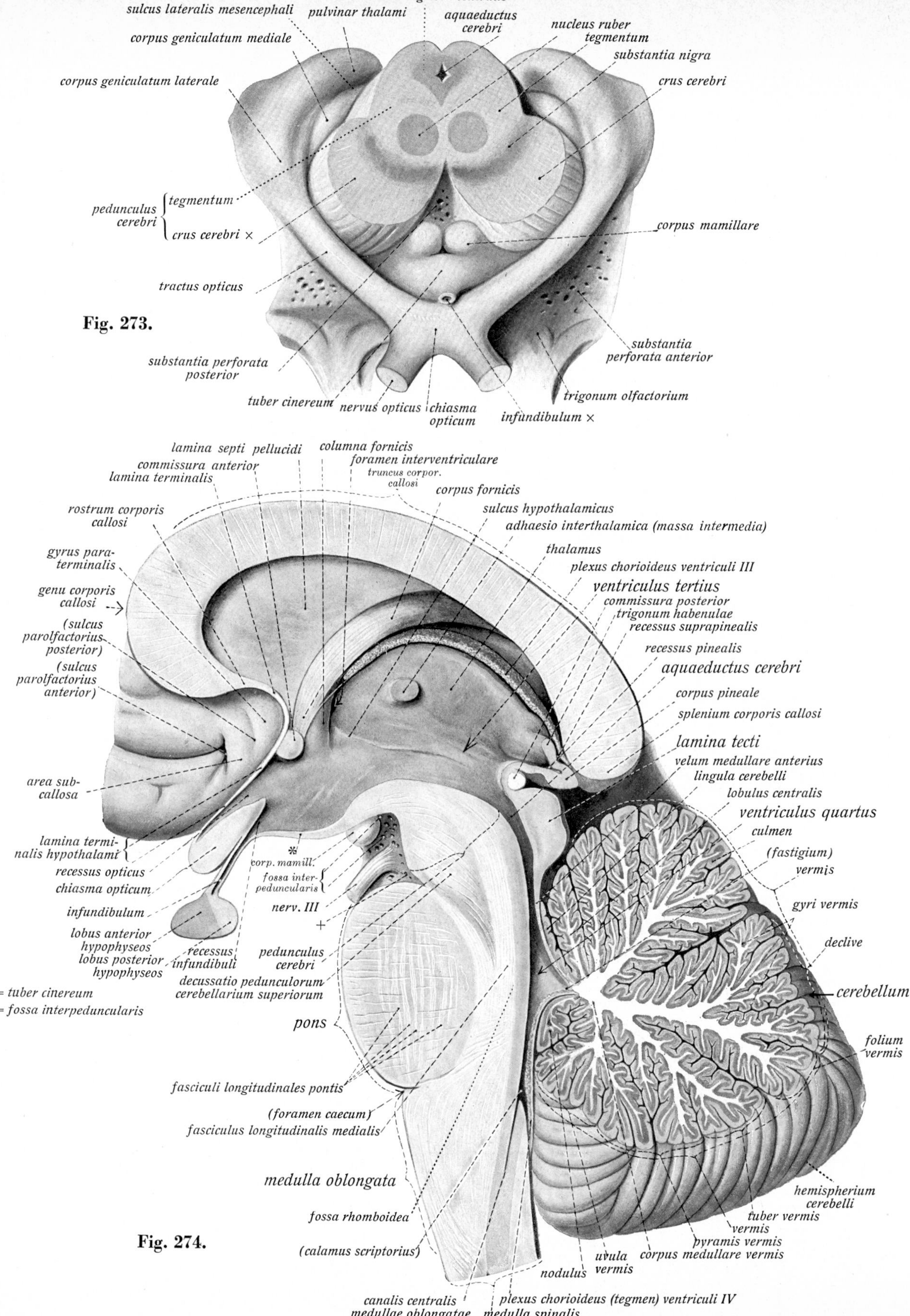
substantia grisea centralis
sulcus lateralis mesencephali
pulvinar thalami
aquaeductus cerebri
corpus geniculatum mediale
nucleus ruber
tegmentum
substantia nigra
corpus geniculatum laterale
crus cerebri
pedunculus cerebri
tegmentum
crus cerebri ×
corpus mamillare
tractus opticus
substantia perforata anterior
substantia perforata posterior
trigonum olfactorium
tuber cinereum
nervus opticus
chiasma opticum
infundibulum ×
lamina septi pellucidi
columna fornicis
foramen interventriculare
commissura anterior
lamina terminalis
truncus corpor. callosi
corpus fornicis
rostrum corporis callosi
sulcus hypothalamicus
adhaesio interthalamica (massa intermedia)
thalamus
gyrus para-terminalis
plexus chorioideus ventriculi III
ventriculus tertius
genu corporis callosi
commissura posterior
trigonum habenulae
recessus suprapinealis
(sulcus parolfactorius posterior)
recessus pinealis
(sulcus parolfactorius anterior)
aquaeductus cerebri
corpus pineale
splenium corporis callosi
lamina tecti
area sub-callosa
velum medullare anterius
lingula cerebelli
lobulus centralis
ventriculus quartus
culmen
lamina termi-nalis hypothalami
(fastigium)
recessus opticus
corp. mamill.
vermis
chiasma opticum
fossa inter-peduncularis
infundibulum
nerv. III
gyri vermis
lobus anterior hypophyseos
lobus posterior hypophyseos
recessus infundibuli
pedunculus cerebri
declive
decussatio pedunculorum cerebellarium superiorum
cerebellum
* = tuber cinereum
+ = fossa interpeduncularis
pons
folium vermis
fasciculi longitudinales pontis
(foramen caecum)
fasciculus longitudinalis medialis
medulla oblongata
hemispherium cerebelli
fossa rhomboidea
tuber vermis
vermis
pyramis vermis
(calamus scriptorius)
uvula vermis
corpus medullare vermis
nodulus
canalis centralis medullae oblongatae
plexus chorioideus (tegmen) ventriculi IV
medulla spinalis

**Fig. 273.**

**Fig. 274.**

## 273. Transverse Section of Mesencephalon. (2/1)

1 **Red Nucleus**
*nucleus ruber*
**Tegmentum**
*tegmentum*

2 **Substantia Nigra**
*substantia nigra*
**Crus Cerebri**
*crus cerebri*

3 **Mammillary Body**
*corpus mamillare*

4 **Anterior Perforated Substance**
*substantia perforata anterior*

5 **Olfactory Trigone**
*trigonum olfactorium*
**Infundibulum**
*infundibulum*

6 **Optic Chiasma**
*chiasma opticum*

7 **Optic Nerve**
*nervus opticus*
**Tuber Cinereum**
*tuber cinereum*

8 **Posterior Perforated Substance**
*substantia perforata posterior*
**Optic Tract**
*tractus opticus*

9 **Cerebral Peduncles** { **crus cerebri** | **tegmentum** }
*pedunculus cerebri* { *crus cerebri* | *tegmentum* }

10 **Lateral Geniculate Body**
*corpus geniculatum laterale*

11 **Medial Geniculate Body**
*corpus geniculatum mediale*

**Lat. Sulcus of Mesencephalon**
*sulcus lateralis mesencenphali*

**Pulvinar of Thalamus**
*pulvinar thalami*

12 **Central Gray Matter**
*substantia grisea centralis*

**Cerebral Aqueduct**
*aqueductus cerebri*

## 274. Part of Sagittal Section of Brain. (Slightly enlarged)

1 **Thalamus**
*thalamus*
**Chorioid Plexus of Ventricle III**
*plexus choriodeus ventriculi III*
**Third Ventricle**
*ventriculus tertius*
**Posterior Commissure**
*commissura posterior*
**Habenular Trigone**
*trigonum habenulae*
**Suprapineal Recess**
*recessus suprapinealis*

2 **Pineal Recess**
*recessus pinealis*
**Cerebral Aqueduct**
*aqueductus cerebri*
**Pineal Body**
*corpus pineale*
**Splenium of Corpus Callosum**
*splenium corporis callosi*
**Tectal Lamina**
*lamina tecti*
**[Sup.] Ant. Medullary Velum**
*velum medullare anterius [sup.]*
**Cerebellar Lingula**
*lingula cerebelli*
**Central Lobule**
*lobulus centralis*
**Fourth Ventricle**
*ventriculus quartus*

3 **Culmen**
*culmen*
**(Fastigium)**
*(fastigium)*
**Vermis**
*vermis*
**Gyri Vermis**
*gyri vermis*
**Declive**
*declive*
**Cerebellum**
*cerebellum*

4 **Folium Vermis**
*folium vermis*
**Cerebellar Hemisphere**
*hemispherium cerebelli*
**Tuber Vermis**
*tuber vermis*

5 **Vermis**
*vermis*
**Pyramid Vermis**
*pyramis vermis*
**Medullary Body of Vermis**
*corpus medullare vermis*
**Uvula (Vermis)**
*uvula vermis*

6 **Nodulus**
*nodulus*
**Chorioid Plexus of 4th Ventricle**
*plexus chorioideus (tegmen) ventriculi IV*
**Spinal Medulla**
*medulla spinalis*
**Centr. Can. Medulla Oblongata**
*canalis centralis medullae oblongatae*
**(Calamus Scriptorius)**
*(calamus scriptorius)*

7 **Rhomboid Fossa**
*fossa rhomboidea*
**Medulla Oblongata**
*medulla oblongata*
**Medial Longitudinal Fasciculus**
*fascic. longitudinalis medialis*
**Foramen Cecum**
*(foramen cecum)*
**Longitudinal Fasciculi of Pons**
*fasciculi longitudinales pontis*
**Pons**
*pons*

8 **Dec. of Sup. Cerebellar Ped.**
*decussatio pedunculorum cerebellarium superiorum*
**Cerebral Peduncle**
*pedunculus cerebri*
**Interpeduncular Fossa**
*+fossa interpeduncularis*
**Oculomotor Nerve III**
*nerv. III*
**Interpeduncular Fossa**
*fossa interpeduncularis*

9 **Mammillary Body**
*corpus mamillare*
**Tuber Cinereum**
*

8 **Infundibular Recess**
*recessus infundibuli*
**Hypophysis (Pit. Gl.) Post. Lobe**
*lobus posterior hypophyseos*
**Hypophysis, (Pit. Gl.) Ant. Lobe**
*lobus anterior hypophyseos*

9 **Infundibulum**
*infundibulum*
**Optic Chiasma**
*chiasma opticum*
**Optic Recess**
*recessus opticus*
**Hypothalamic Lamina Terminalis**
*lamina terminalis hypothalami*
**Subcallosa Area**
*area subcallosa*

10 **Anterior Parolfactory Sulcus**
*(sulcus parolfactorius anterior)*
**Posterior Parolfactory Sulcus**
*(sulcus parolfactorius posterior)*
**Genus of Corpus Callosum**
*genus corporis callosi*
**Paraterminal Gyrus**
*gyrus paraterminalis*

11 **Rostrum of Corpus Callosum**
*rostrum corporis callosi*
**Lamina Terminalis**
*lamina terminalis*
**Anterior commissure**
*commissura anterior*
**Lamina of Septum Pellucidum**
*lamina septi pellucidi*

12 **Columns of Fornix**
*columna fornicis*
**Interventricular Foramen**
*foramen interventriculare*
**Body of Corpus Callosum**
*truncus corpor. callosi*
**Body of Fornix**
*corpus fornicis*
**Hypothalamic Sulcus**
*sulcus hypothalamicus*
**Interthalamic Adhesion**
*adhesio interthalamica (massa intermedia)*

## 275. Sagittal Section Through Hypophysis in Sella Turcica. (2/1)

1 **Optic Nerve**
*nervus opticus*
3 **Sphenoidal Sinus**
*sinus sphenoidalis*
7 **Body of Sphenoid Bone**
*corpus ossis sphenoidalis*
9 **Anterior Lobe of Hypophysis**
*lobus anterior hypophyseos*
**Intermediate Part of Hypophysis**
*pars intermedia hypophyseos*
10 **Posterior Lobe of Hypophysis**
*lobus posterior hypophyseos*
12 **Infundibulum**
*infundibulum*
**Dura Mater, Diaphragm of Sella**
*dura mater, diaphragma sellae*

**Note:** 1. Close relationship of hypophysis-9 to optic nerve-1 and optic chiasma.

## 276. Dorsal View of Brain Stem Showing Caudate Nuclei, Thalami, Tectal Lamina, and Medulla Oblongata. (1/1)

**Caudate nucleus**-11, **thalami** (anterior tubercle-1), **third ventricle**-11, and other structures of brain stem displayed by removing outer parts of cerebral hemispheres, corpus callosum, fornix, and roof of third ventricle. Cerebellum removed except for flocculus-5 on right and a part of the cortex and medullary body of cerebellar hemisphere on left. **Roof of fourth ventricle**-7 cut in midsagittal line and pulled caudally on right side to display **rhomboid fossa**-5 or floor of fourth ventricle and its **lateral aperture**-5. The incision was stopped short of caudal extremity of fourth ventricle in order to display the intact **median aperture of fourth ventricle**-6.

1 **Columns of the Fornix**
*columnae fornicis*
**Anterior Commissure**
*commissura anterior*
**Optic Recess of Ventricle III**
*recessus opticus ventriculi III*
**Anterior Tubercle of Thalamus**
*tuberculum anterius thalami*
**Stria Terminalis**
*stria terminalis*
**Tenia Chorioidea**
*tenia chorioidea*
2 **Habenular Commissure**
*commissura habenularum*
**Lamina Affixa**
*lamina affixa*
**Brachium of Superior Colliculus**
*brachium colliculi superioris*
**Pulvinar of Thalamus**
*pulvinar thalami*
3 **Lateral Geniculate Body**
*corpus geniculatum laterale*
**Medial Geniculate Body**
*corpus geniculatum mediale*
**Inferior Colliculus**
*colliculus inferior*
**Trochlear Nerve**
*nervus trochlearis*
4 **Superior Cerebellar Peduncle (Brachium Conjunctivum)**
*pedunculus cerebellaris superior (brachium conjunctivum)*
**Lateral Recess of Ventricle IV**
*recessus lateralis ventriculi quarti*
**Middle Cerebellar Peduncle (Brachium Pontis)**
*pedunculus cerebellaris medius (brachium pontis)*
**Peduncle of Flocculus**
*pedunculus flocculi*
5 **Cerebellar Flocculus**
*flocculus cerebelli*
**Lat. Aperture of 4th Ventricle**
*apertura lateralis ventriculi quarti*
**Chorioid Plexus of 4th Ventricle**
*plexus chorioideus ventriculi IV*
**Rhomboid Fossa**
*fossa rhomboidea*
6 **Median Aperture, Ventricle IV**
*apertura mediana ventriculi quarti*
**Fasciculus Gracilis of Posterior Funiculus**
*fasciculus gracilis funiculi posterioris*
**Medulla Oblongata**
*medulla oblongata*
7 **Roof of 4th Ventricle**
*tegmen ventriculi quarti*
8 **Lingula of Cerebellum**
*lingula cerebelli*
**[Sup.] Ant. Medullary Velum**
*velum medullare anterius [sup.]*
**Lateral Pontine Fila**
*(fila lateralia pontis)*
**Tectum (Quadrigeminal Body)**
*lamina tecti*
9 **Cerebral Peduncle**
*pedunculus cerebri*
**Brachium of Inferior Colliculus**
*brachium colliculi inferioris*
**Brachium of Superior Colliculus**
*brachium colliculi superioris*
**Tail of Caudate Nucleus**
*cauda nuclei caudati*
10 **Superior Colliculus**
*colliculus superior*
**Pineal Body**
*corpus pineale*
11 **Habenular Trigone**
*trigonum habenulae*
**Ventricle III**
*ventriculus III*
**Medullary Stria (Thalamus)**
*stria medullaris thalami*
**Head of Caudate Nucleus**
*caput nuclei caudati*
**Columns of Fornix**
*columnae fornicis*
12 **Corpus Callosum**
*corpus callosum*
**Laminae of Septum Pellucidum**
*laminae septi pellucidi*

**Note:** 1. Median and lateral apertures of fourth ventricle are openings in the pia and ependymal lining of fourth ventricle through which cerebrospinal fluid flows out of the brain ventricles to subarachnoid spaces. This not only permits a continuous flow of cerebrospinal fluid, but provides for pulsation of the brain (volume changes) coincident with pulsatile changes in size of tremendous numbers of blood channels that supply the brain.

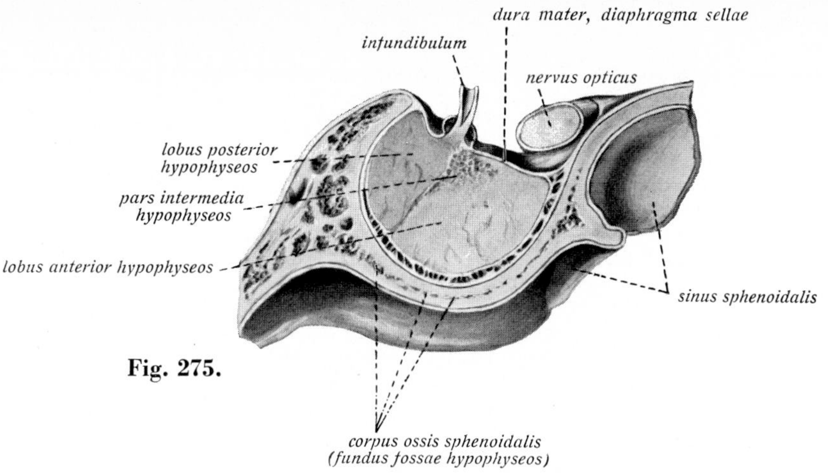
dura mater, diaphragma sellae
infundibulum
nervus opticus
lobus posterior hypophyseos
pars intermedia hypophyseos
lobus anterior hypophyseos
sinus sphenoidalis
corpus ossis sphenoidalis (fundus fossae hypophyseos)

**Fig. 275.**

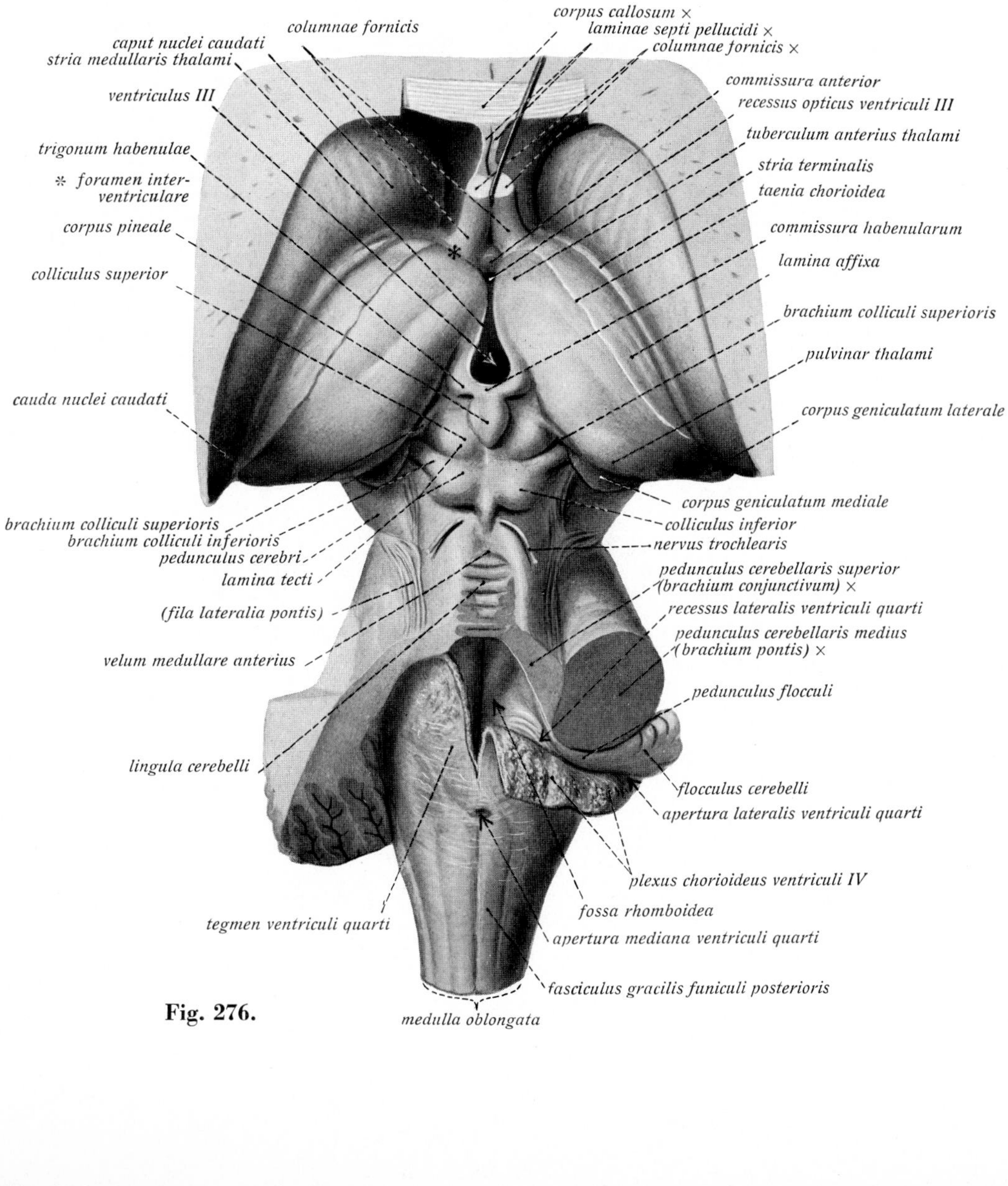

corpus callosum ×
columnae fornicis
laminae septi pellucidi ×
caput nuclei caudati
columnae fornicis ×
stria medullaris thalami
commissura anterior
ventriculus III
recessus opticus ventriculi III
tuberculum anterius thalami
trigonum habenulae
stria terminalis
* foramen interventriculare
taenia chorioidea
corpus pineale
commissura habenularum
lamina affixa
colliculus superior
brachium colliculi superioris
pulvinar thalami
cauda nuclei caudati
corpus geniculatum laterale
corpus geniculatum mediale
brachium colliculi superioris
colliculus inferior
brachium colliculi inferioris
nervus trochlearis
pedunculus cerebri
pedunculus cerebellaris superior (brachium conjunctivum) ×
lamina tecti
(fila lateralia pontis)
recessus lateralis ventriculi quarti
pedunculus cerebellaris medius (brachium pontis) ×
velum medullare anterius
pedunculus flocculi
lingula cerebelli
flocculus cerebelli
apertura lateralis ventriculi quarti
plexus chorioideus ventriculi IV
fossa rhomboidea
tegmen ventriculi quarti
apertura mediana ventriculi quarti
fasciculus gracilis funiculi posterioris
medulla oblongata

**Fig. 276.**

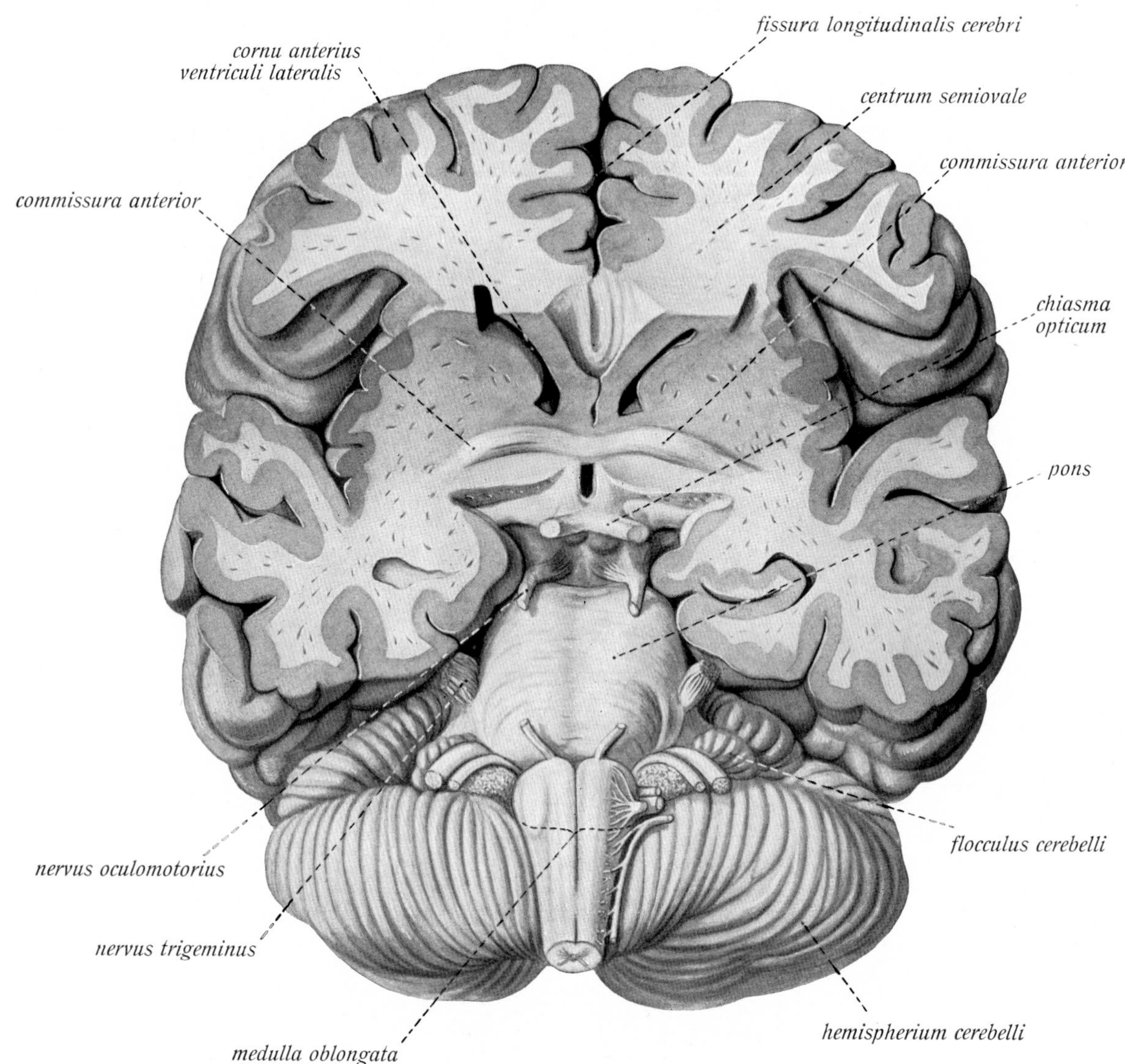
fissura longitudinalis cerebri
cornu anterius
ventriculi lateralis
centrum semiovale
commissura anterior
commissura anterior
chiasma
opticum
pons
flocculus cerebelli
nervus oculomotorius
nervus trigeminus
hemispherium cerebelli
medulla oblongata

**Fig. 277.**

## 277. The Dissection of the Anterior Commissure and Display of Other Structures. (1/1)

The frontal lobes and ventral ends of the temporal lobes were sliced off to expose the **anterior commissure**-2. This procedure opened the **third ventricle** and the anterior horns of the **lateral ventricles**-11. Only the middle portion of the anterior commissure has been exposed. The lateral radiations of the anterior commissure are not seen in the plane of this dissection.

1 **Longitudinal Cerebral Fissure**
*fissura longitudinalis cerebri*
**Centrum Semiovale**
*centrum semiovale*
2 **Anterior Commissure**
*commissura anterior*
**Optic Chiasma**
*chiasma opticum*

3 **Pons**
*pons*
4 **Cerebellar Flocculus**
*flocculus cerebelli*
5 **Cerebellar Hemisphere**
*hemispherium cerebelli*
7 **Medulla Oblongata**
*medulla oblongata*

8 **Trigeminal Nerve**
*nervus trigeminus*
**Oculomotor Nerve**
*nervus oculomotorius*
10 **Anterior Commissure**
*commissura anterior*
11 **Lateral Ventricle, Anterior Horn**
*cornu anterius ventriculi lateralis*

**Note:** 1. The **anterior commissure**-2, -10 is a conspicuous rounded fascicle (and, therefore, a landmark) which crosses the midline in the dorsal part of the lamina terminalis, just rostral to the columns of the fornix (see Fig. 276-1, -11).

2. The **anterior commissure** is a part of the rhinencephalon. The ventral portion connects the two olfactory bulbs. The dorsal portion has been traced laterally through the lentiform nucleus to the pyriform area of the cortex to the middle temporal gyrus and, in some animals, to the amygdaloid bodies (see Fig. 286-5, -7, -8).

**Etymology:** (see Fig. 278)

*claustrum* = L. *claudere*, to close (a barrier)
*lentiformis* = L. *lens, lentis*, lentil, therefore lentil or bean-shaped.
*putamen* = L. *puto*, to prune, therefore a shell, covering.
*pallidus* = L. pale

## 278. Horizontal Cross-Section of Brain just above Interventricular Foramen. Pia and arachnoid left in place. (1/1)

1 **Lateral Ventricle, Anterior Horn**
*cornu anterius ventriculi lateralis*
**Head of Caudate Nucleus**
*caput nuclei caudati*
**Third Ventricle**
*ventriculus tertius*
**Internal Capsule, Anterior Limb**
*crus anterius capsulae internae*

2 **Genu of Internal Capsule**
*genus capsulae internae*
**Internal Capsule, Posterior Limb**
*crus posterius capsulae internae*
**Putamen of Lentiform Nucleus**
*putamen nuclei lentiformis*
**Claustrum**
*claustrum*

3 **Globus Pallidus**
*globus pallidus*
**Lateral Medullary Lamina**
*lamina medullaris lateralis*
**Medial Medullary Lamina**
*lamina medullaris medialis*
**Tail of Caudate Nucleus**
*cauda nuclei caudati*

4 **Chorioid Plexus**
*plexus chorioideus*
**Lateral Ventricle Post. Horn**
*cornu posterius ventriculi lateralis*
**Pes Hippocampi**
*pes hippocampi*

5 **Superior Cerebellar Artery**
*arteria cerebelli superior*

6 **Cerebellum**
*cerebellum*

7 **Cerebellar Gyri**
*gyri cerebelli*
**Superior Colliculi**
*colliculi superiores*
**Third Ventricle**
*ventriculus tertius*

8 **Thalamic Nuclei**
*nuclei thalami*
**Nucleus of Lateral Geniculate Body**
*nucleus corporis geniculati lateralis*
**Interventricular Foramen**
*foramen interventriculare*
**Columns of Fornix**
*columnae fornicis*

9 **Lentiform Nucleus**
*nucleus lentiformis*
**Insular Gyri**
*gyri insulae*

10 **External Capsule**
*capsula externa*
**Claustrum**
*claustrum*

11 **Lamina of Septum Pellucidum**
*lamina septi pellucidi*
**Corpus Callosum**
*corpus callosum*
**Cavity of Septum Pellucidum**
*cavum septi pellucidi*
**Longitudinal Cerebral Fissure**
*fissura longitudinalis cerebri*

12 **Cerebral Vessels**
*vasa cerebri*

**Note:** 1. Body and **anterior horn**-1 of **lateral ventricle, interventricular foramen**-8 and upper part of **third ventricle**-1, -7.

2. **Septum pellucidum**-11 separates lateral ventricles. It is double layered, but relatively thin and translucent, when viewed in transmitted light.

3. **Lateral ventricle**-4 near junction of its posterior and inferior horns.

4. **Basal ganglia of the telencephalon.** This section displays three **(caudate nucleus**-1, -3; **lentiform nucleus**-9; **claustrum**-10**)** of the four nuclear masses located deep in each cerebral hemisphere and commonly called the basal ganglia of the telencephalon. The fourth **(amygdaloid body),** does not appear in this section because it is located at end of the tail of the caudate nucleus-3 in ventral end of the temporal lobe.

a) Head of **caudate nucleus**-1 bulges into the lateral ventricle. It is a long, tapering, horseshoe-shaped mass that follows lateral ventricle as its inferior horn penetrates the temporal lobe.

b) **Lentiform nucleus**-9 is a large nucleus wedged into the lateral concavity of the internal capsule-2 and subdivided by white fiber lines into a smaller medial pale portion, the globus pallidus-3, and a large, lateral dark grey nucleus, the putamen-2. It is separated from the caudate nucleus and thalamus by the internal capsule.

c) **Claustrum,** just deep to insula, is completely "walled in" by white matter.

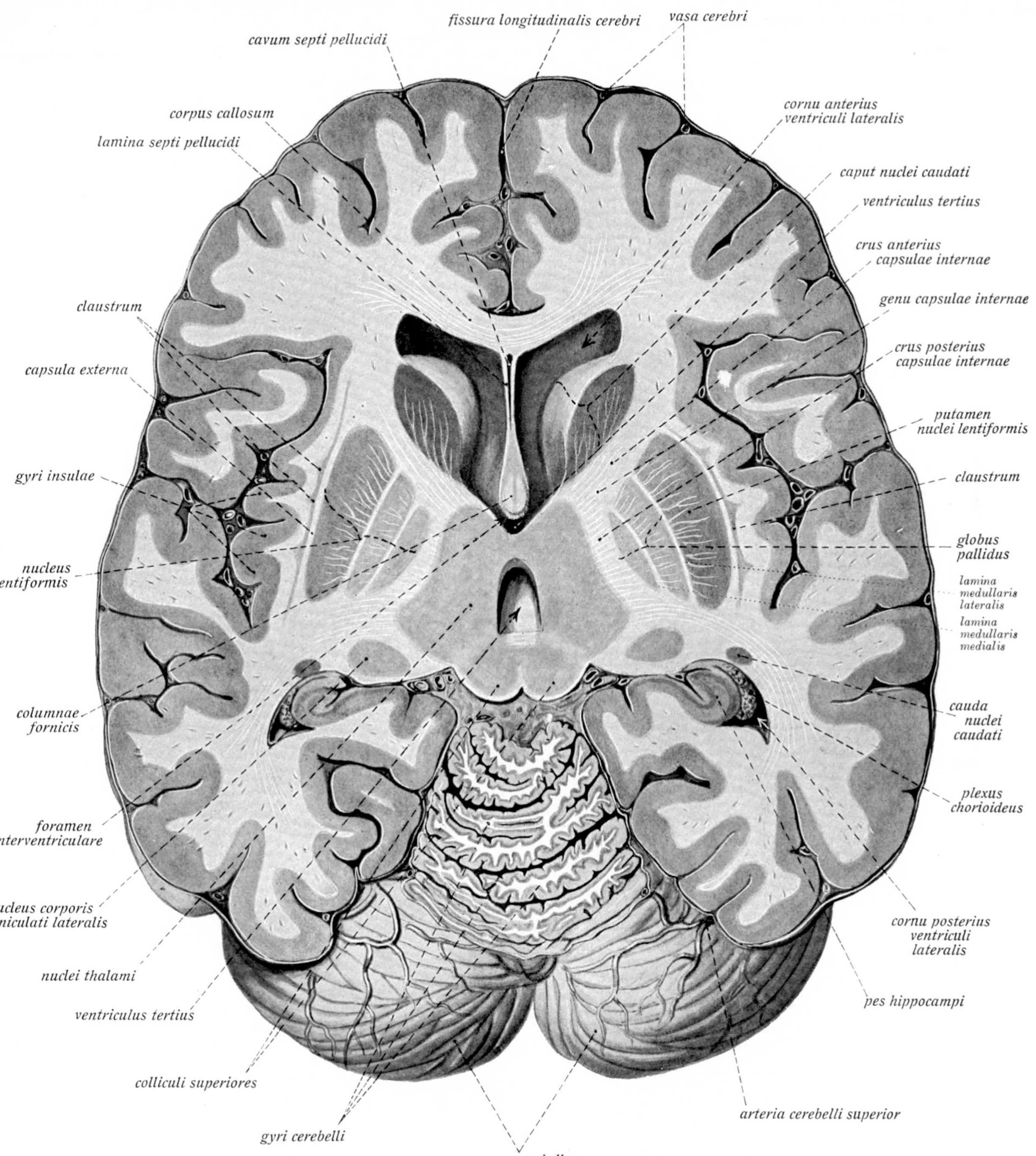

fissura longitudinalis cerebri
vasa cerebri
cavum septi pellucidi
corpus callosum
lamina septi pellucidi
cornu anterius ventriculi lateralis
caput nuclei caudati
ventriculus tertius
crus anterius capsulae internae
genu capsulae internae
crus posterius capsulae internae
putamen nuclei lentiformis
claustrum
globus pallidus
lamina medullaris lateralis
lamina medullaris medialis
cauda nuclei caudati
plexus chorioideus
cornu posterius ventriculi lateralis
pes hippocampi
arteria cerebelli superior
cerebellum
gyri cerebelli
colliculi superiores
ventriculus tertius
nuclei thalami
nucleus corporis geniculati lateralis
foramen interventriculare
columnae fornicis
nucleus lentiformis
gyri insulae
capsula externa
claustrum


**Fig. 278.**

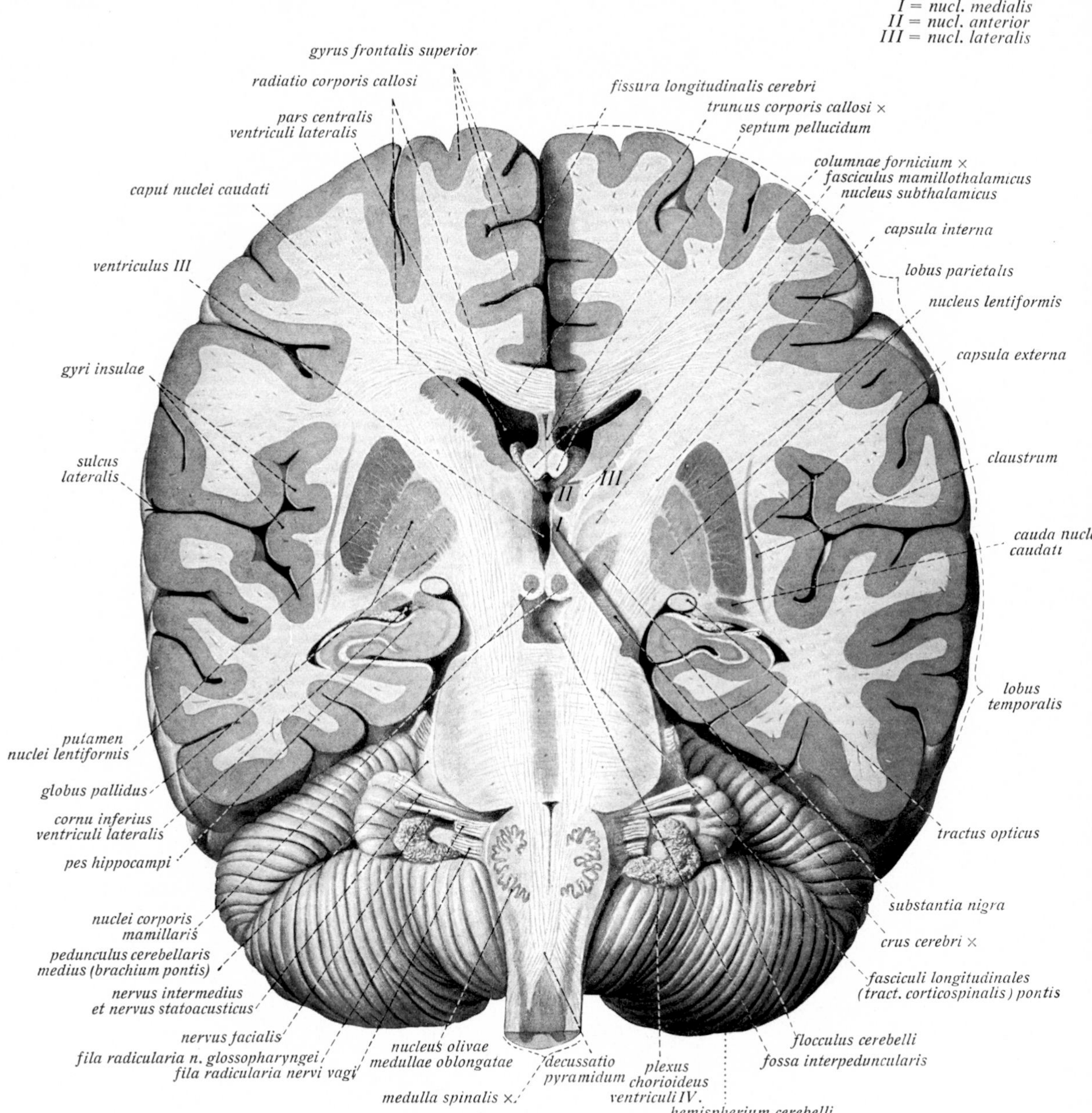
I-III = nuclei thalami
I = nucl. medialis
II = nucl. anterior
III = nucl. lateralis
gyrus frontalis superior
radiatio corporis callosi
pars centralis
ventriculi lateralis
caput nuclei caudati
ventriculus III
gyri insulae
sulcus
lateralis
putamen
nuclei lentiformis
globus pallidus
cornu inferius
ventriculi lateralis
pes hippocampi
nuclei corporis
mamillaris
pedunculus cerebellaris
medius (brachium pontis)
nervus intermedius
et nervus statoacusticus
nervus facialis
fila radicularia n. glossopharyngei
fila radicularia nervi vagi
nucleus olivae
medullae oblongatae
medulla spinalis ×
decussatio
pyramidum
plexus
chorioideus
ventriculi IV.
hemispherium cerebelli
fissura longitudinalis cerebri
truncus corporis callosi ×
septum pellucidum
columnae fornicium ×
fasciculus mamillothalamicus
nucleus subthalamicus
capsula interna
lobus parietalis
nucleus lentiformis
capsula externa
claustrum
cauda nuclei
caudati
lobus
temporalis
tractus opticus
substantia nigra
crus cerebri ×
fasciculi longitudinales
(tract. corticospinalis) pontis
flocculus cerebelli
fossa interpeduncularis
I
II
III

**Fig. 279.**

# 279. Section of the Brain Along the Axis of the Cerebral Peduncles. (Viewed from in front) (1/2)

On the left side, an additional slice of the cerebral hemisphere was cut off. I, II, and III indicate respectively the medial, anterior, and lateral thalamic nuclei.

1 **Trunk of the Corpus Callosum**
*truncus corporis callosi*

**Septum Pellucidum**
*septum pellucidum*

**Columns of Fornix**
*columnae fornicium*

**Mamillothalamic Fasciculus**
*fasciculus mamillothalamicus*

**Subthalamic Nucleus**
*nucleus subthalamicus*

2 **Internal Capsule**
*capsula interna*

**Parietal Lobe**
*lobus parietalis*

**Lentiform Nucleus**
*nucleus lentiformis*

**External Capsule**
*capsula externa*

3 **Claustrum**
*claustrum*

**Tail of Caudate Nucleus**
*cauda nuclei caudati*

**Temporal Lobe**
*lobus temporalis*

4 **Optic Tract**
*tractus opticus*

**Substantia Nigra**
*substantia nigra*

5 **Crus Cerebri**
*crus cerebri*

**Longitudinal Fasciculus (Corticospinal Tract) of Pons**
*fasciculi longitudinales (tract. corticospinalis) pontis*

**Flocculus Cerebelli**
*flocculus cerebelli*

**Interpeduncular Fossa**
*fossa interpeduncularis*

**Cerebellar Hemisphere**
*hemispherium cerebelli*

**Chorioid Plexus of Ventricle IV**
*plexus chorioideus IV ventriculi*

**Pyramidal Decussation**
*decussatio pyramidum*

7 **Spinal Medulla**
*medulla spinalis*

**Olivary Nucleus (of Medulla Oblongata)**
*nucleus olivae medullae oblongatae [olivaris]*

**Vagus Nerve, Rootlets**
*fila radicularia nervi vagi*

**Glossopharyngeal Nerve, Rootlets**
*fila radicularia n. glosso-pharyngei*

**Facial Nerve**
*nervus facialis*

**Intermedius Nerve and Vestibulocochlear Nerve**
*nervus intermedius + nervus vestibulocochlearis*

8 **Middle Cerebellar Peduncle (Brachium Pontis)**
*pedunculus cerebellaris medius (brachium pontis)*

8 **Mammillary Body, Nuclei**
*nuclei corporis mamillaris*

**Pes Hippocampi**
*pes hippocampi*

**Lateral Ventricle, Inferior Horn**
*cornu inferius ventriculi lateralis*

**Globus Pallidus**
*globus pallidus*

**Putamen Lentiform Nucleus**
*putamen nuclei lentiformis*

9 **Lateral Sulcus (Fissure)**
*sulcus lateralis*

10 **Insular Gyrus**
*gyri insulae*

**Third Ventricle**
*ventriculus III*

**Head of Caudate Nucleus**
*caput nuclei caudati*

11 **Lateral Ventricle, Central Part**
*pars centralis ventriculi lateralis*

**Radiation of Corpus Callosum**
*radiatio corporis callosi*

12 **Superior Frontal Gyrus**
*gyrus frontalis superior*

**Longitudinal Cerebral Fissure**
*fissura longitudinalis cerebri*

**Note:** The **corticospinal fibers (pyramidal)**-6 pass from the cortex through the **internal capsule**-2; **cerebral peduncles** (crus cerebri-5); the **longitudinal fascicles of the pons**-5 and on into the medulla oblongata where most of the fibers decussate or cross to the opposite side as the **decussation of the pyramids**-6. Most of the fibers then pass into the lateral funiculus of the spinal cord and descend as the lateral **cortico-spinal (pyramidal) tract.** (see Fig. 315) Those fibers that do not cross in the decussation continue on as the anterior corticospinal tract.

# 280. Horizontal Cross-Section of Head with Brain and Meninges *in situ* (1/1)

This section was cut through the interventricular foramina-3 and the lentiform nuclei-10. In the region of the frontal sinus, it may be observed that parts of the orbital plates-1 were cut asymmetrically. Some asymmetry of the frontal lobes is also seen. The irregularities indicate that the section may not be at exactly the same level on both sides.

1 **Falx Cerebri**
*falx cerebri*

**Frontal Bone, Orbital Portion**
*pars orbitalis ossis frontalis*

**Longitudinal Cerebral Fissure**
*fissura longitudinalis cerebri*

**Frontal Lobe**
*lobus frontalis*

**Head of Caudate Nucleus**
*caput nuclei caudati*

2 **Temporal Muscle**
*musc. temporalis*

**Septum Pellucidum**
*septum pellucidum*

**Claustrum**
*claustrum*

**Insular Gyri**
*gyri insulae*

**Dura Mater**
*dura mater*

3 **Interventricular Foramen**
*foram. interventriculare*

**Tail of Caudate Nucleus**
*cauda nuclei caudati*

**Lateral Ventricle, Posterior Horn**
*cornu posterius ventriculi lateralis*

4 **Pia Mater and Arachnoid**
*pia mater + arachnoidea*

**Dura Mater**
*dura mater*

5 **Crus of Fornix**
*crus fornicis*

**Occipital Gyri**
*gyri occipitales*

6 **Falx Cerebri**
*falx cerebri*

7 **Superior Sagittal Sinus**
*sinus sagittalis superior*

**Calvarium (Occipital Bone)**
*calvaria (os occipitale)*

**Inferior Sagittal Sinus**
*sinus sagittalis inferior*

8 **Splenium of Corpus Callosum**
*splenium corporis callosi*

**Anterior Chorioid Artery**
*arteria chorioidea [anterior]*

**Chorioid Plexus**
*plexus chorioideus*

**Third Ventricle**
*ventriculus tertius*

**Thalamus**
*thalamus*

**Internal Capsule, Posterior Limb**
*crus posterius capsul. internae*

9 **Column of Fornix**
*columna fornicis*

9 **Lentiform Nucleus, Globus Pallidus**
*globus pallidus nucl. lentiform.*

**Lentiform Nucleus, Putamen**
*putamen nucl. lentiformis*

10 **Calvarium**
*calvaria*

**Substantia Medullaris**
*substantia medullaris*

**Lentiform Nucleus**
*nucleus lentiformis*

11 **External Capsule**
*capsula externa*

**Genu of Internal Capsule**
*genu capsulae internae*

**Internal Capsule, Anterior Limb**
*crus anterius capsulae internae*

**Head of Caudate Nucleus**
*caput nuclei caudati*

**Lateral Ventricle, Anterior Horn**
*cornu anterius ventriculi lateralis*

12 **Frontal Sinus**
*sinus frontalis*

**Frontal Muscle**
*musc. frontalis*

**Note:** 1. Head of **caudate nucleus**-1, -11 bulging into the **lateral ventricles**-11 which are separated from each other by the septum pellucidum-2 and the **columns of the fornix**-9.

2. The **internal capsule**-11 separates the **lentiform nucleus**-10 from the **thalamus**-8 and the **caudate nucleus**-11.

3. **Corpus striatum.** The two largest nuclear masses of the basal ganglia, the **caudate**-11 **and lentiform nuclei**-11 together with the **white fascicles from the internal capsule**-8, -11 which separate and permeate them, are called the corpus striatum or striate body.

4. The **internal capsule** appears to have an angle in a horizontal section of the brain. The bend is called the genu-11 or knee. The extensions are called the anterior-11 and posterior-8 crura or legs.

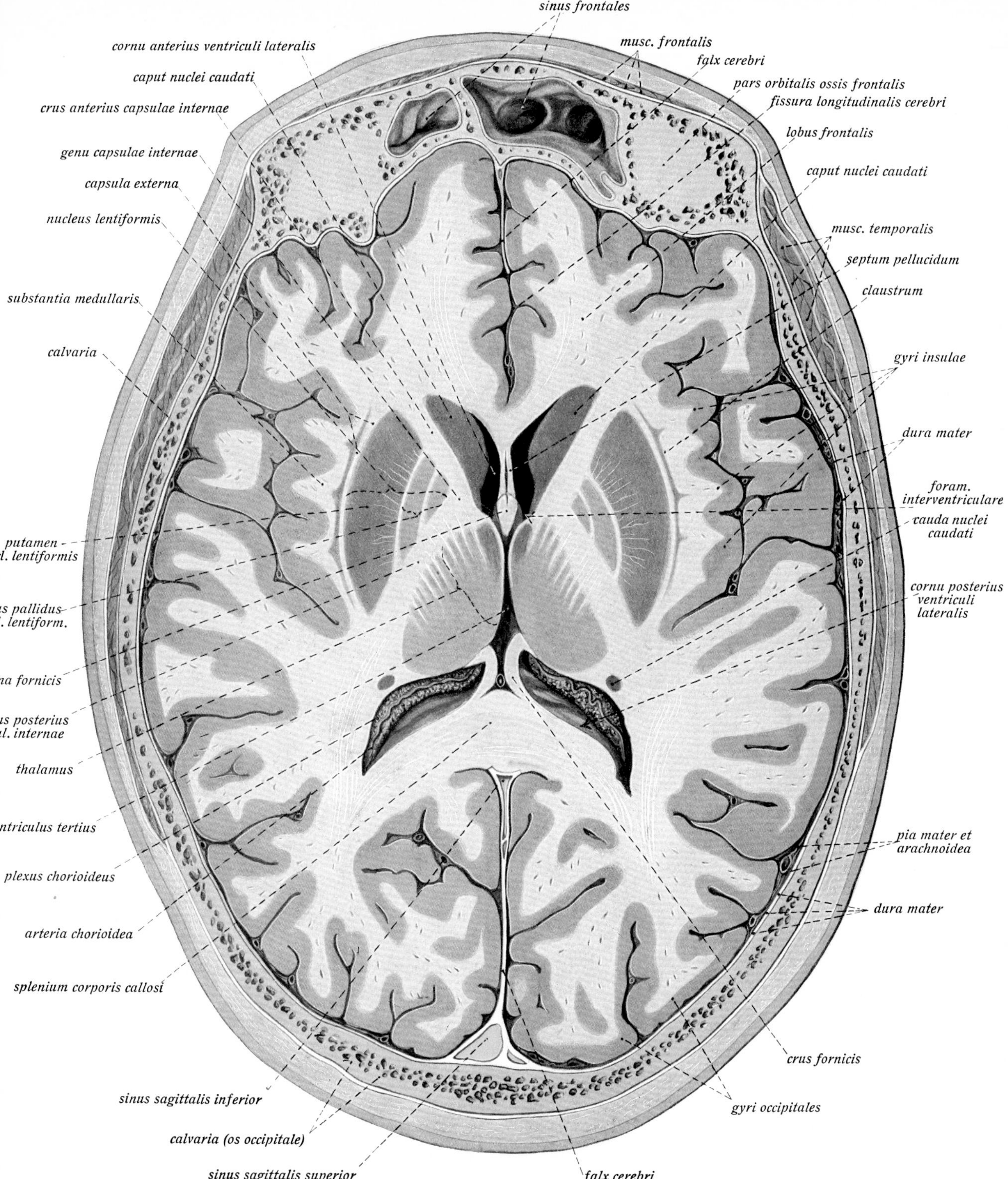

sinus frontales
cornu anterius ventriculi lateralis
musc. frontalis
falx cerebri
caput nuclei caudati
pars orbitalis ossis frontalis
crus anterius capsulae internae
fissura longitudinalis cerebri
lobus frontalis
genu capsulae internae
caput nuclei caudati
capsula externa
nucleus lentiformis
musc. temporalis
septum pellucidum
substantia medullaris
claustrum
calvaria
gyri insulae
dura mater
foram. interventriculare
putamen - cl. lentiformis
cauda nuclei caudati
cornu posterius ventriculi lateralis
us pallidus- l. lentiform.
na fornicis
us posterius ul. internae
thalamus
entriculus tertius
pia mater et arachnoidea
plexus chorioideus
dura mater
arteria chorioidea
splenium corporis callosi
crus fornicis
sinus sagittalis inferior
gyri occipitales
calvaria (os occipitale)
sinus sagittalis superior
falx cerebri


**Fig. 280.**

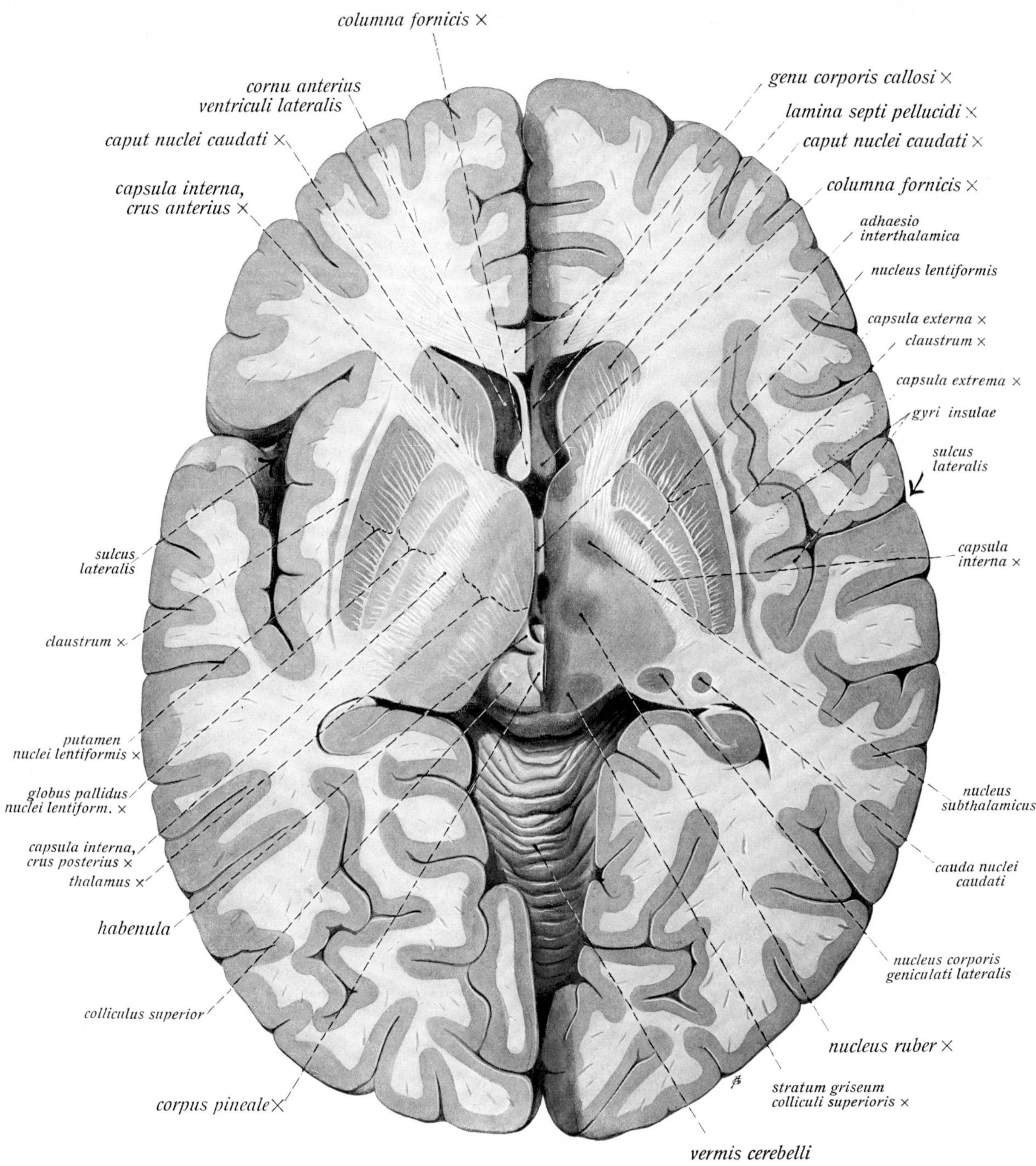
columna fornicis ×
cornu anterius
ventriculi lateralis
caput nuclei caudati ×
capsula interna,
crus anterius ×
genu corporis callosi ×
lamina septi pellucidi ×
caput nuclei caudati ×
columna fornicis ×
adhaesio
interthalamica
nucleus lentiformis
capsula externa ×
claustrum ×
capsula extrema ×
gyri insulae
sulcus
lateralis
sulcus
lateralis
capsula
interna ×
claustrum ×
putamen
nuclei lentiformis ×
globus pallidus
nuclei lentiform. ×
nucleus
subthalamicus
capsula interna,
crus posterius ×
thalamus ×
cauda nuclei
caudati
habenula
nucleus corporis
geniculati lateralis
colliculus superior
nucleus ruber ×
stratum griseum
colliculi superioris ×
corpus pineale ×
vermis cerebelli

Fig. 281.

## 281. Horizontal Cross Section of the Brain. (1/1)

On the left side, the section is cut through the thalamus. On the right side, the section is cut through the thalamus 1 cm more caudally. This exposed the subthalamic nucleus-4 and the superior colliculus (stratum griseum-5).

1 **Corpus Callosum, Genu**
*genu corporis callosi*

**Septum Pellucidum Lamina**
*lamina septi pellucidi*

**Head of Caudate Nucleus**
*caput nuclei caudati*

**Column of Fornix**
*columna fornicis*

**Adhesio Interthalamica**
*adhesio interthalamica*

**Lentiform Nucleus**
*nucleus lentiformis*

2 **External Capsule**
*capsula externa*

**Claustrum**
*claustrum*

**Insular Gyri**
*gyri insulae*

**Lateral Sulcus (Fissure)**
*sulcus lateralis*

3 **Internal Capsule**
*capsula interna*

4 **Subthalamic Nucleus**
*nucleus subthalamicus*

**Caudate Nucleus, Tail**
*cauda nuclei caudati*

5 **Nucleus of Lateral Geniculate Bodies**
*nucleus corporis geniculati lateralis*

**Red Nucleus**
*nucleus ruber*

**Stratum Griseum of Superior Colliculi**
*stratum griseum colliculi superioris*

6 **Cerebellar Vermis**
*vermis cerebelli*

7 **Pineal Body**
*corpus pineale*

8 **Superior Colliculus**
*colliculus superior*

**Habenula**
*habenula*

**Thalamus**
*thalamus*

**Internal Capsule, Posterior Limb**
*capsule interna, crus posterius*

**Lentiform Nuclei, Globus Pallidus**
*globus pallidus nuclei lentiformis*

**Lentiform Nucleus, Putamen**
*putamen nuclei lentiformis*

9 **Claustrum**
*claustrum*

**Lateral Sulcus (Fissure)**
*sulcus lateralis*

10 **Internal Capsule, Anterior Limb**
*capsula interna crus anterius*

11 **Caudate Nucleus, Head**
*caput nuclei caudati*

**Lateral Ventricle, Anterior Horn**
*cornu anterius ventriculi lateralis*

**Column of Fornix**
*columna fornicis*

**Note:** 1. Relationships of:

a) **Superior colliculus**-5 (stratum griseum).

b) **Lateral geniculate body**-5.

c) **Red nucleus**-5.

d) **Subthalamic nucleus**-4.

e) **Tail of caudate nucleus**-4.

**Fig. 282**

## 282. Horizontal Section of the Brain at the Level of the Basal Ganglia. (Viewed from below) (Prep. Anat. Inst., Münster)

**Note:** 1. On the **right** side: The nuclei, except for the claustrum, have been shelled out.

2. The white fiber connections, between the caudate nucleus and putamen, give rise to the name "corpus striatum".

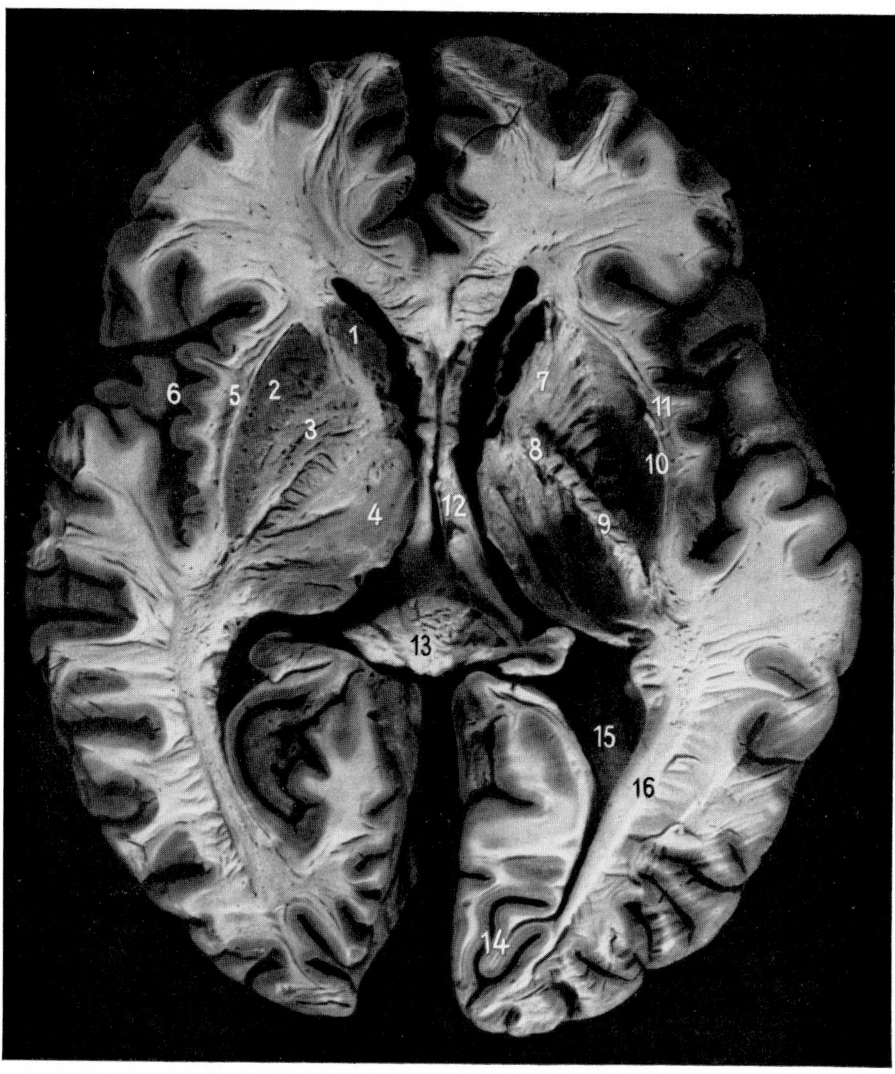
1
2
3
4
5
6
7
8
9
10
11
12
13
14
15
16

1 *caput nuclei caudati*
2 *putamen*
3 *nuclei pallidi*
4 *thalamus*
5 *claustrum*
6 *cortex insulae*
7 *crus anterius capsulae internae*
8 *genu capsulae internae*
9 *crus posterius capsulae internae*
10 *capsula externa*
11 *capsula extrema*
12 *crura fornicis*
13 *splenium corporis callosi*
14 *sulcus calcarinus*
15 *trigonum collaterale ventriculi lateralis*
16 *radiatio optica (Gratiolet)*

**Fig. 282.**

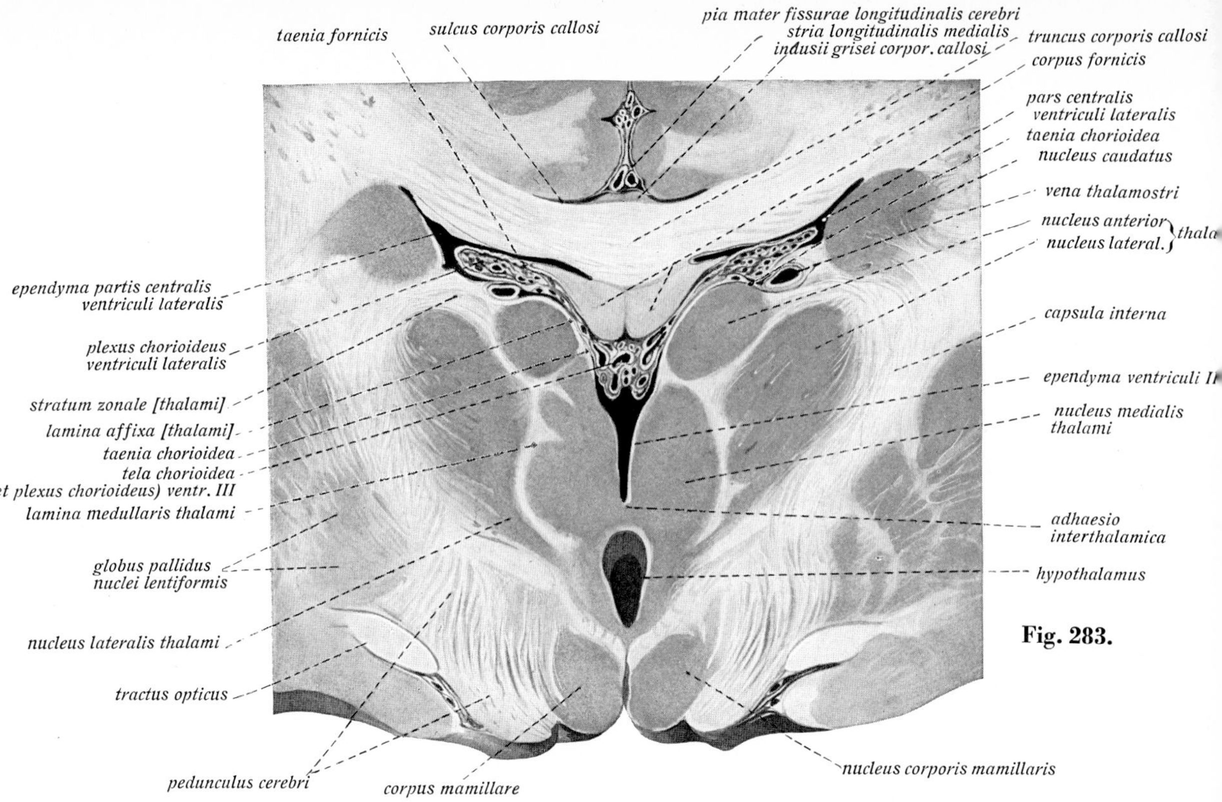

taenia fornicis
sulcus corporis callosi
pia mater fissurae longitudinalis cerebri
stria longitudinalis medialis
indusii grisei corpor. callosi
truncus corporis callosi
corpus fornicis
pars centralis
ventriculi lateralis
taenia chorioidea
nucleus caudatus
vena thalamostri
nucleus anterior
nucleus lateral. } thala
capsula interna
ependyma ventriculi II
nucleus medialis
thalami
adhaesio
interthalamica
hypothalamus
ependyma partis centralis
ventriculi lateralis
plexus chorioideus
ventriculi lateralis
stratum zonale [thalami]
lamina affixa [thalami]
taenia chorioidea
tela chorioidea
(et plexus chorioideus) ventr. III
lamina medullaris thalami
globus pallidus
nuclei lentiformis
nucleus lateralis thalami
tractus opticus
pedunculus cerebri
corpus mamillare
nucleus corporis mamillaris

**Fig. 283.**

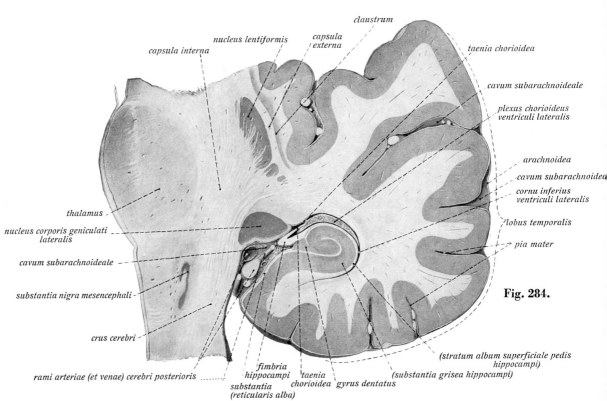

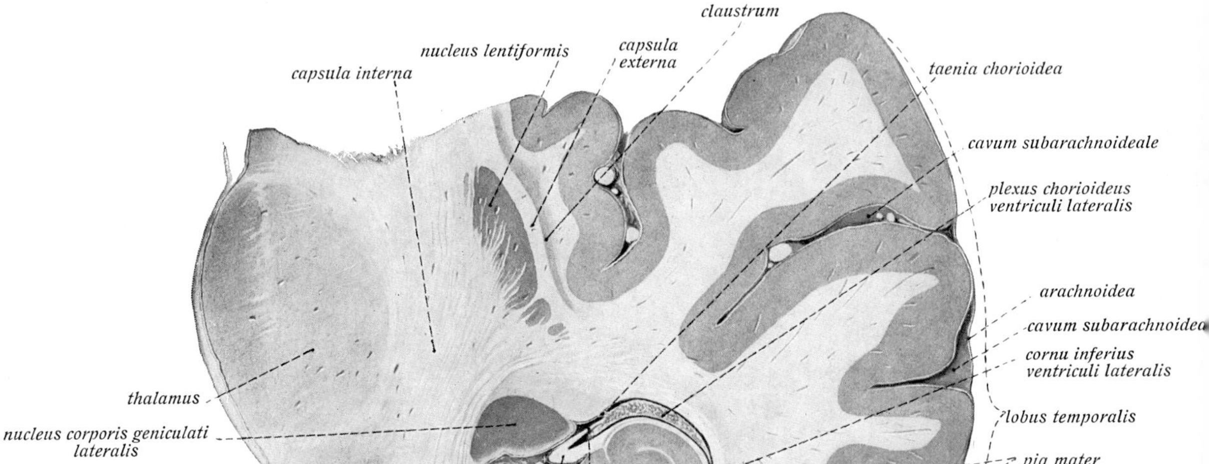

claustrum
nucleus lentiformis
capsula
externa
capsula interna
taenia chorioidea
cavum subarachnoideale
plexus chorioideus
ventriculi lateralis
arachnoidea
cavum subarachnoidea
cornu inferius
ventriculi lateralis
lobus temporalis
pia mater
thalamus
nucleus corporis geniculati
lateralis
cavum subarachnoideale
substantia nigra mesencephali
crus cerebri
rami arteriae (et venae) cerebri posterioris
fimbria
hippocampi
substantia
(reticularis alba)
taenia
chorioidea
gyrus dentatus
(substantia grisea hippocampi)
(stratum album superficiale pedis
hippocampi)

**Fig. 284.**

## 283. Frontal Section of Brain Through Mammillary Bodies showing Relationships of Thalamic Nuclei, Third Ventricle, Hypothalamic Region, Fornix, and Corpus Callosum. (2/1)

(Compare with Fig. 279)

Only the central portion of the section has been depicted. For details of the tela chorioidea and the relationships of the **chorioid plexuses of the lateral and third ventricles,** see diagram, Figure 219.

1 **Medial Longitudinal Stria in Indusium Griseum**
*stria longitudinalis medialis indusii grisei corpor. callosi*

2 **Body of Corpus Callosum**
*truncus corporis callosi*
**Body of Fornix**
*corpus fornicis*
**Lat. Ventricle, Central Portion**
*pars centralis ventriculi lateralis*
**Tenia Chorioidea**
*tenia chorioidea*
**Caudate Nucleus**
*nucleus caudatus*
**Thalamostriate Vein**
*vena thalamostriata*
**Ant. and Lat. Thalamic Nuclei**
*nucleus anterior* } *thalami*
*nucleus lateral.*

3 **Internal Capsule**
*capsula interna*
**Ependyma of Third Ventricle**
*ependyma ventriculi III*
**Medial Thalamic Nucleus**
*nucleus medialis thalami*
**Interthalamic Adhesion**
*adhesio interthalamica*

4 **Hypothalamus**
*hypothalamus*

5 **Nucleus of Mammillary Body**
*nucleus corporis mamillaris*

7 **Mammillary Body**
*corpus mamillare*

8 **Cerebral Peduncle**
*pedunculus cerebri*
**Optic Tract**
*tractus opticus*
**Lateral Thalamic Nucleus**
*nucleus lateralis thalami*
**Lentiform Nucleus, Globus Pallidus**
*globus pallidus nuclei lentiformis*

9 **Internal Medullary Lamina**
*lamina medullaris thalami*
**Tela Chorioidea + Chorioid Plexus of Third Ventricle**
*tela chorioidea (et plexus chorioideus) ventr. III*
**Tenia Chorioidea**
*tenia chorioidea*
**Lamina Affixa [Thalamic]**
*lamina affixa [thalami]*
**Stratum Zonale, Thalamic**
*stratum zonale [thalami]*
**Lat. Ventricle, Chorioid Plexus**
*plexus chorioideus ventriculi lat.*
**Ependyma of Central Part of Lateral Ventricle**
*ependyma partis centralis ventriculi lateralis*

11 **Tenia Fornicis**
*tenia fornicis*
**Sulcus of Corpus Callosum**
*sulcus corporis callosi*

12 **Pia Mater of Longitudinal Cerebral Fissure**
*pia mater fissurae longitudinalis cerebri*

## 284. Frontal Section Through Temporal Lobe and Adjacent Parts of Diencephalon and the Midbrain. (slightly enlarged)

The pia mater and blood vessels were left in place. Compare with Figure 220, which is an enlarged mirror-image diagram of a similar frontal section of the hippocampal region, to show the details of the invagination of the **inferior horn of the lateral ventricles** by the **chorioid plexus**-2.

1 **Tenia Chorioidea**
*tenia chorioidea*

2 **Subarachnoid Space**
*cavum subarachnoideale*
**Lateral Ventricle, Chorioid Plexus**
*plexus chorioideus ventriculi lateralis*

3 **Arachnoid**
*arachnoidea*
**Subarachnoid Space**
*cavum subarachnoideale*
**Lateral Ventricle, Inferior Horn**
*cornu inferius ventriculi lateralis*
**Temporal Lobe**
*lobus temporalis*
**Pia Mater**
*pia mater*

4 **Superficial White Layer of Hippocampus**
*(stratum album superficiale pedis hippocampi)*

5 **Gray Matter of Hippocampus**
*(substantia grisea hippocampi)*

6 **Dentate Gyrus**
*gyrus dentatus*
**Tenia Chorioidea**
*tenia chorioidea*
**Fimbria of Hippocampus**
*fimbria hippocampi*
**White Reticular Substance**
*substantia (reticularis alba)*

8 **Posterior Cerebral Arteries (and Veins), Branches**
*r. art. (et venae) cerebri post.*
**Crus Cerebri**
*crus cerebri*
**Substantia Nigra of Mesencephalon**
*substantia nigra mesencephali*

9 **Subarachnoid Space**
*cavum subarachnoidale*
**Nucleus of Lateral Geniculate Body**
*nucleus corporis geniculati lateralis*
**Thalamus**
*thalamus*

10 **Internal Capsule**
*capsula interna*

11 **Lentiform Nucleus**
*nucleus lentiformis*

12 **External Capsule**
*capsula externa*
**Claustrum**
*claustrum*

## 285. Frontal Section of Brain through Part of Septum Pellucidum.

Figures 285 to 288 are consecutive frontal sections of the brain. They are arranged so that the higher figure numbers are given to the more dorsal sections. The dorsal surface of the sections have been depicted and labeled.

1 **Cavity of Septum Pellucidum**
*cavum septi pellucidi*

**Radiation of Corpus Callosum**
*radiatio corporis callosi*

**Middle Frontal Gyrus**
*gyrus frontalis medius*

2 **Head of Caudate Nucleus**
*caput nuclei caudati*

**Corpus Striatum**
*corpus striatum*

**Lentiform Nucleus**
*nucleus lentiformis*

**Inferior Frontal Gyrus**
*gyrus frontalis inferior*

3 **Lateral Sulcus (Fissure)**
*sulcus lateralis*

**Temporal Lobe**
*lobus temporalis*

5 **Orbital Gyri**
*gyri orbitales*

6 **Subcallosal Area**
*area subcallosa*

**Olfactory Sulcus**
*sulcus olfactorius*

7 **Olfactory Tract**
*tractus olfactorius*

8 **Rostrum of Corpus Callosum**
*rostrum corporis callosi*

9 **Claustrum**
*claustrum*

10 **External Capsule**
*capsula externa*

**Lateral Ventricle, Anterior Horn**
*cornu anterius ventriculi lateralis*

**Frontal Lobe**
*lobus frontalis*

11 **Lamina of Septum Pellucidum**
*laminae septi pellucidi*

12 **Superior Frontal Gyrus**
*gyrus frontalis superior*

**Note:** 1. Cavity-1 and laminae-11 of **septum pellucidum** separate the **lateral ventricles.**

2. The **corpus striatum** is represented here by the head of the **caudate nucleus**-2, and the beginning **lentiform nucleus**-2 (putamen), and the white fascicles of the anterior limb of the **internal capsule**-2 (labeled corpus striatum-2).

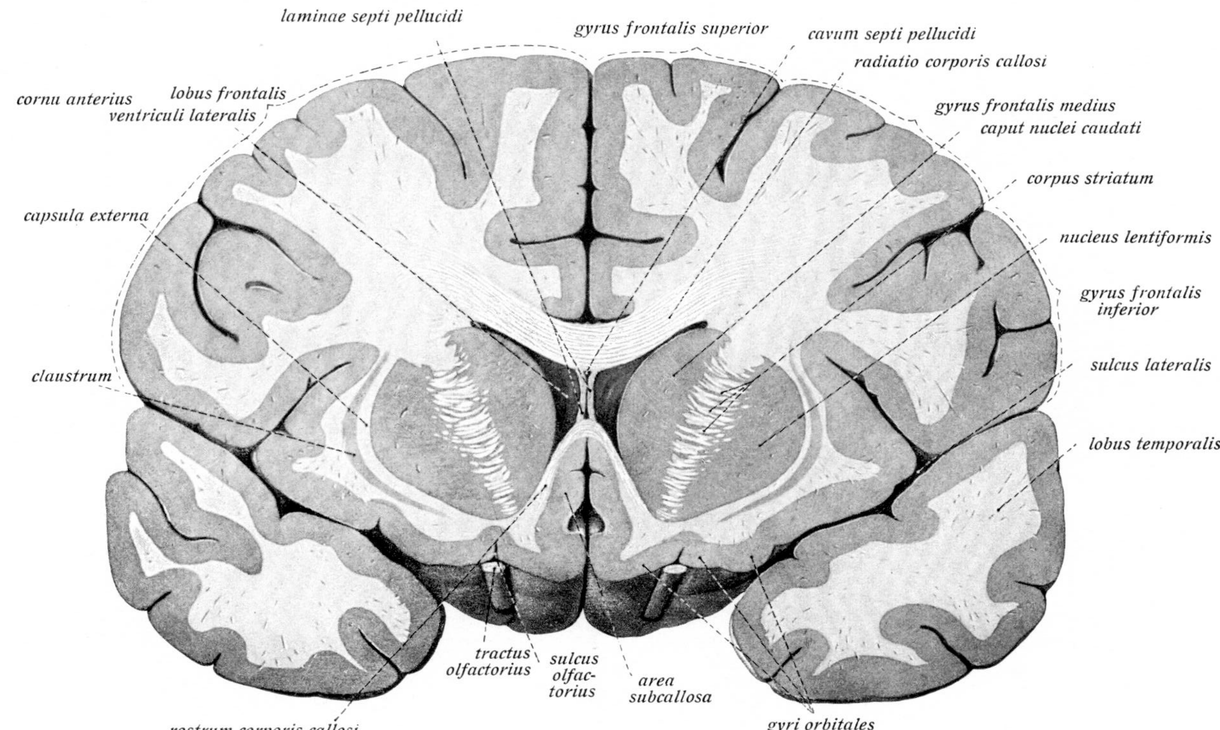
laminae septi pellucidi
gyrus frontalis superior
cavum septi pellucidi
radiatio corporis callosi
cornu anterius
lobus frontalis
ventriculi lateralis
gyrus frontalis medius
caput nuclei caudati
corpus striatum
capsula externa
nucleus lentiformis
gyrus frontalis inferior
claustrum
sulcus lateralis
lobus temporalis
tractus olfactorius
sulcus olfactorius
area subcallosa
rostrum corporis callosi
gyri orbitales

**Fig. 285.**

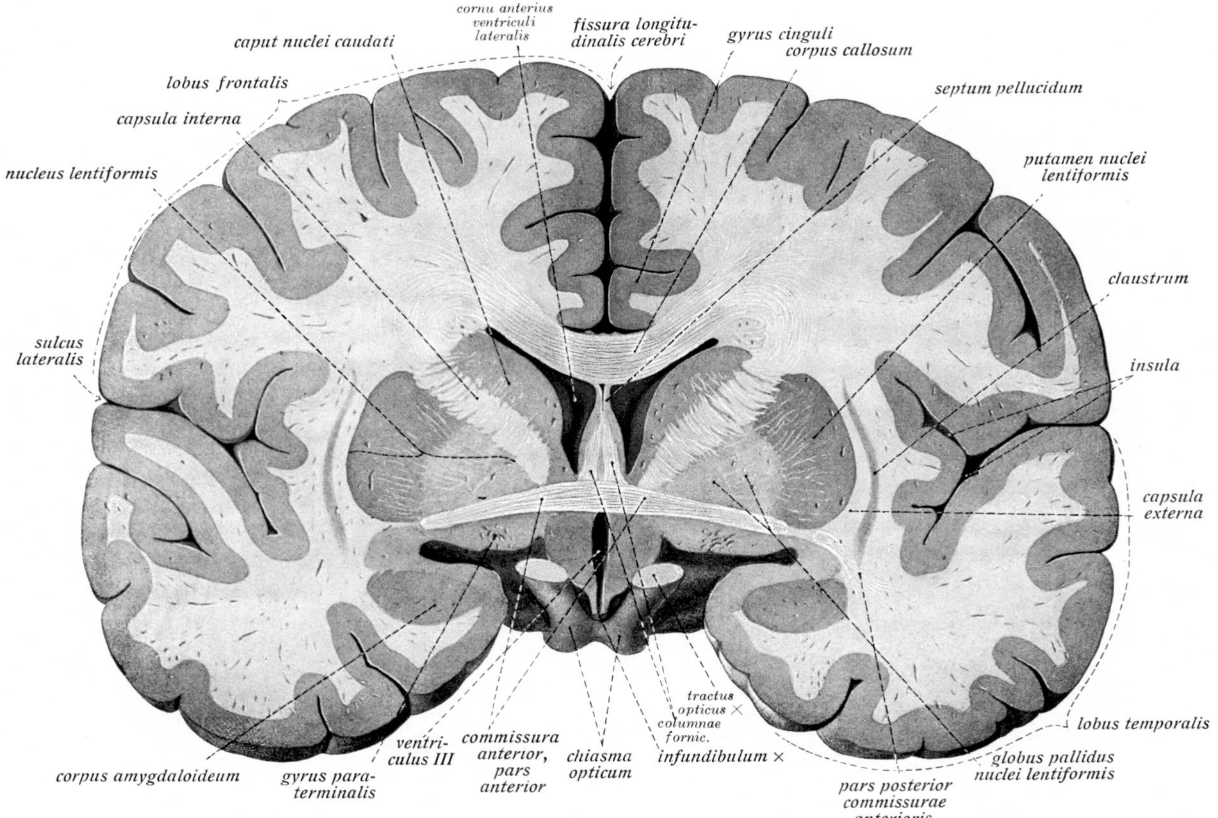
cornu anterius ventriculi lateralis
fissura longitudinalis cerebri
caput nuclei caudati
gyrus cinguli
corpus callosum
lobus frontalis
septum pellucidum
capsula interna
putamen nuclei lentiformis
nucleus lentiformis
claustrum
sulcus lateralis
insula
capsula externa
tractus opticus ×
columnae fornic.
lobus temporalis
ventriculus III
commissura anterior, pars anterior
chiasma opticum
infundibulum ×
globus pallidus nuclei lentiformis
corpus amygdaloideum
gyrus paraterminalis
pars posterior commissurae anterioris

**Fig. 286.**

## 286. Frontal Section of Brain through Anterior Commissure. (dorsal aspect)

1 **Gyrus Cinguli**
*gyrus cinguli*

**Corpus Callosum**
*corpus callosum*

2 **Septum Pellucidum**
*septum pellucidum*

**Putamen of Lentiform Nucleus**
*putamen nuclei lentiformis*

3 **Claustrum**
*claustrum*

**Insula**
*insula*

4 **External Capsule**
*capsula externa*

**Temporal Lobe**
*lobus temporalis*

5 **Lentiform Nucleus, Globus Pallidus**
*globus pallidus nuclei lentiformis*

**Anterior Commissure, Posterior Portion**
*pars posterior commissurae anterioris*

6 **Optic Tract**
*tractus opticus*

**Columns of Fornix**
*columnae fornicis*

**Infundibulum**
*infundibulum*

**Optic Chiasma**
*chiasma opticum*

7 **Anterior Commissure, Anterior Portion**
*commissura anterior, pars anterior*

**Third Ventricle**
*ventriculus III*

**Paraterminal Gyrus**
*gyrus paraterminalis*

8 **Amygdaloid Body**
*corpus amygdaloideum*

9 **Lateral Sulcus (Fissure)**
*sulcus lateralis*

10 **Lentiform Nucleus**
*nucleus lentiformis*

**Internal Capsule**
*capsula interna*

**Frontal Lobe**
*lobus frontalis*

**Caudate Nucleus, Head of**
*caput nuclei caudati*

11 **Lateral Ventricle, Anterior Horn**
*cornu anterius ventriculi lateralis*

12 **Longitudinal Cerebral Fissure**
*fissura longitudinalis cerebri*

**Note:** 1. **Infundibulum**-6 between the two converging optic tracts-6.

2. **Amygdaloid body**-8 (sometimes called "archistriatum") at anterior end of temporal lobe-4, is a nuclear mass at the anterior end of the tail of the caudate nucleus. It is included with the basal ganglia of the telencephalon and is a football-shaped mass (almond shape) indenting the roof of the inferior horn of the lateral ventricle (near end). It is very close to area where the hippocampus bulges up from floor of the inferior horn.

3. Investigations indicate that the **amygdaloid body** is related to a number of functions. In conjunction with other parts of the limbic lobe, it appears to be involved in emotional responses and alerting reactions. It is of even greater importance in lower forms, in which the cortex and thalamus have not reached a stage of development that permits a greater latitude of modification of response with change in environment.

**Etymology:**

amygdaloid = Gr. *amygdale*, almond
*eidos*, resemblance

## 287. Frontal Section of the Brain Through the Third Ventricle. (1/1)

This section was cut just dorsal to the anterior commissure-4 or through the anterior part of the third ventricle-6.

1 **Longitudinal Cerebral Fissure**
*fissura longitudinalis cerebri*

2 **Corpus Callosum**
*corpus callosum*

**Radiation of Corpus Callosum**
*radiatio corporis callosi*

**Caudate Nucleus, Head of**
*caput nuclei caudati*

**Interventricular Foramen**
*foramen interventriculare*

3 **External Capsule**
*capsula externa*

**Lentiform Nucleus Putamen**
*putamen nuclei lentiformis*

4 **Lentiform Nucleus, Globus Pallidus**
*globus pallidus nuclei lentiformis*

**Anterior Commissure**
*commissura anterior*

6 **Optic Tract**
*tractus opticus*

**Infundibulum**
*infundibulum*

**Third Ventricle**
*ventriculus III*

7 **Columns of Fornix**
*columnae fornicis*

**Columns of Fornix**
*columnae fornicis*

8 **Lateral Ventricle, Inferior Horn**
*cornu inferius ventriculi lateralis*

**Anterior Commissure, Posterior Portion**
*pars posterior commissurae anterioris*

**Lentiform Nucleus**
*nucleus lentiformis*

**Claustrum**
*claustrum*

9 **Lateral Sulcus (Fissure)**
*sulcus lateralis*

**Insular Gyri**
*gyri insulae*

10 **Internal Capsule**
*capsula interna*

**Lateral Ventricle, Anterior Horn**
*cornu anterius ventriculi lateralis*

**Laminae of Septum Pellucidum**
*laminae septi pellucidi*

**Note:** 1. **Columns of fornix**-7 pass just dorsal to the anterior commissure-4.

2. Fibers of the posterior part of anterior commissure-8, lateral to edge of amygdaloid body (not labeled, evident on left side, but small or absent on right side). It is located between the left optic tract-6 and the inferior horn of the lateral ventricle-8. (See Fig. 286-8.)

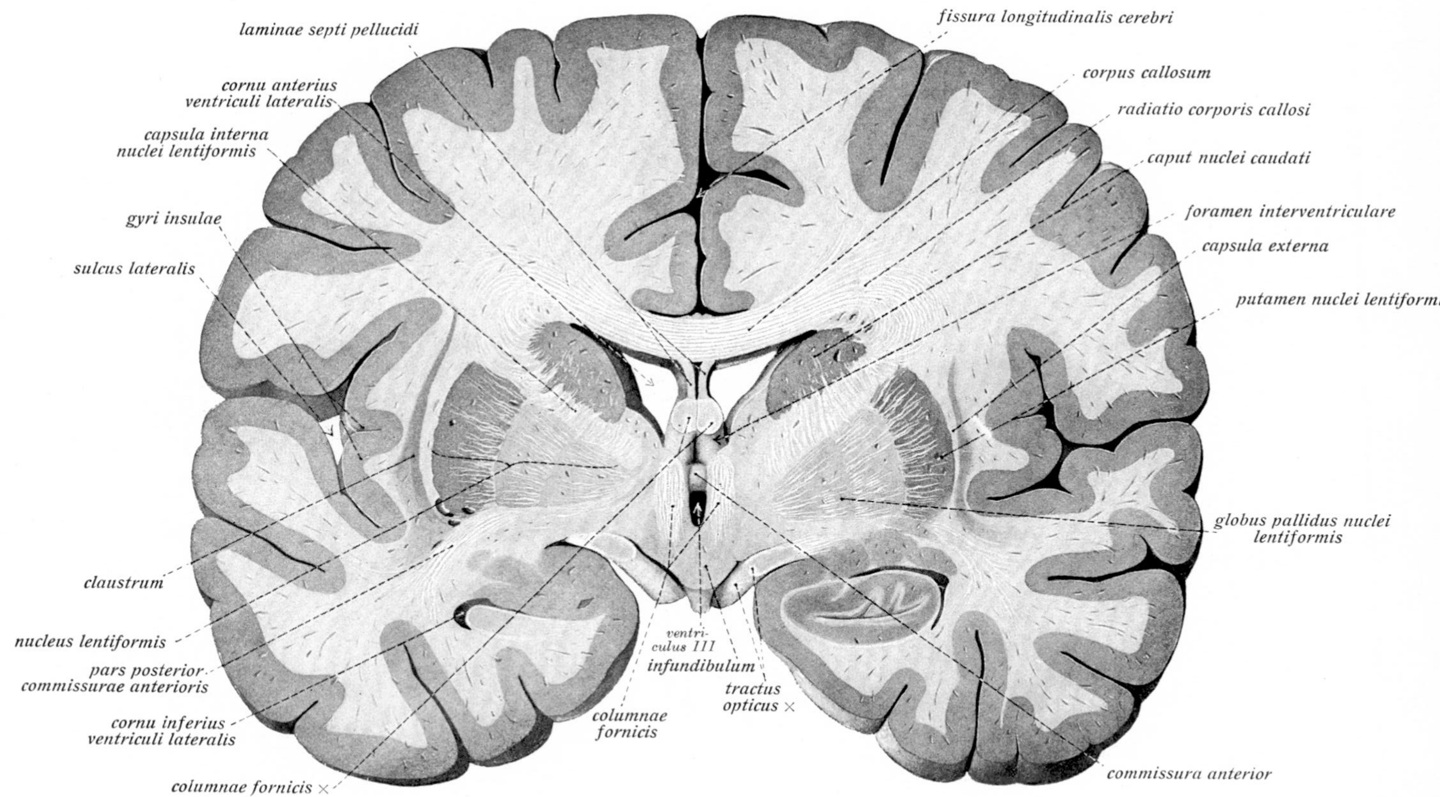
laminae septi pellucidi
cornu anterius ventriculi lateralis
capsula interna nuclei lentiformis
gyri insulae
sulcus lateralis
claustrum
nucleus lentiformis
pars posterior commissurae anterioris
cornu inferius ventriculi lateralis
columnae fornicis ×
fissura longitudinalis cerebri
corpus callosum
radiatio corporis callosi
caput nuclei caudati
foramen interventriculare
capsula externa
putamen nuclei lentiformis
globus pallidus nuclei lentiformis
commissura anterior
ventriculus III
infundibulum
tractus opticus ×
columnae fornicis

**Fig. 287.**

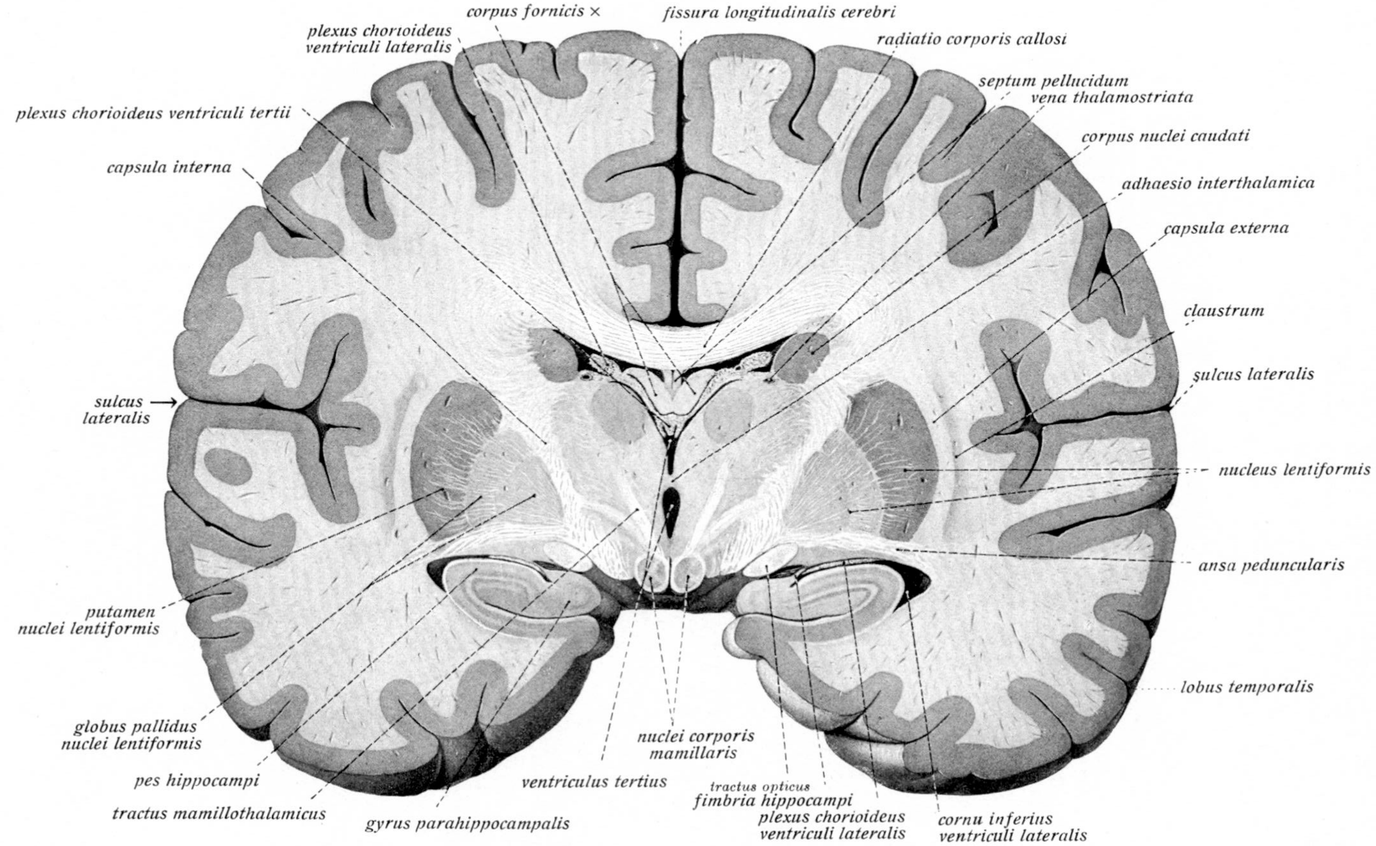
corpus fornicis ×
fissura longitudinalis cerebri
plexus chorioideus
ventriculi lateralis
radiatio corporis callosi
septum pellucidum
vena thalamostriata
plexus chorioideus ventriculi tertii
corpus nuclei caudati
capsula interna
adhaesio interthalamica
capsula externa
claustrum
sulcus lateralis
sulcus
lateralis
nucleus lentiformis
ansa peduncularis
putamen
nuclei lentiformis
lobus temporalis
globus pallidus
nuclei lentiformis
nuclei corporis
mamillaris
pes hippocampi
ventriculus tertius
tractus opticus
fimbria hippocampi
tractus mamillothalamicus
plexus chorioideus
ventriculi lateralis
cornu inferius
ventriculi lateralis
gyrus parahippocampalis

Fig. 288.

## 288. Frontal Section of Brain Through the Third Ventricle. (dorsal aspect) (1/1)

1 **Radiation of Corpus Callosum** *radiatio corporis callosi*
**Septum Pellucidum** *septum pellucidum*

2 **Thalamostriate Vein** *vena thalamostriata*
**Body of Caudate Nucleus** *corpus nuclei caudati*
**Interthalamic Adhesion (massa intermedia)** *adhesio interthalamica*
**External Capsule** *capsula externa*

3 **Claustrum** *claustrum*
**Lateral Sulcus (Fissure)** *sulcus lateralis*
**Lentiform Nucleus** *nucleus lentiformis*
**Ansa Peduncularis** *ansa peduncularis*

4 **Temporal Lobe** *lobus temporalis*

5 **Inferior Horn of Lateral Ventricle** *cornu inferius ventriculi lateralis*

6 **Chorioid Plexus, Lateral Ventricle** *plexus chorioideus ventriculi lateralis*
**Hippocampal Fimbria** *fimbria hippocampi*
**Optic Tract** *tractus opticus*
**Nuclei of Mammillary Bodies** *nuclei corporis mamillaris*

7 **Third Ventricle** *ventriculus tertius*
**Parahippocampal Gyrus** *gyrus parahippocampalis*

8 **Mammillothalamic Tract** *tractus mamillothalamicus*
**Pes Hippocampi** *pes hippocampi*
**Globus Pallidus of Lentiform Nucleus** *globus pallidus nuclei lentiformis*
**Putamen of Lentiform Nucleus** *putamen nuclei lentiformis*

9 **Lateral Sulcus (Fissure)** *sulcus lateralis*

10 **Internal Capsule** *capsula interna*
**Chorioid Plexus of Third Ventricle** *plexus chorioideus ventriculi tertii*

11 **Lateral Ventricle, Chorioid Plexus** *plexus chorioideus ventriculi lateralis*
**Body of Fornix** *corpus fornicis*

12 **Longitudinal Cerebral Fissure** *fissura longitudinalis cerebri*

**Note:** 1. The **mammillary bodies**-6 are a part of the hypothalamus. The fornices-11 and **mammillothalamic tract**-8 fibers carry impulses to and from the mammillary bodies.

2. The **globus pallidus**-8, as indicated by its name, is the more pale portion of the **lentiform nucleus.**

3. The **lateral sulcus** (fissure)-3 separates the parietal lobe from the temporal lobe, and leads to the insular cortex.

## 289. Dorsal and 290. Dorso-Lateral Views of Brain Stem. (see next page)

**Note:** 1. **Trochlear nerve**-1 emerges from dorsal aspect of brain stem.

2. Superior-10, middle-9, and inferior-8 **cerebellar peduncles.**

3. **Tubercles**-5 of **nuclei gracilis** and **cuneatus** at rostral ends of these fasciculi-6.

**Note:** 1. **Ventral rootlets of cervical nerves**-7 in direct line with **rootlets of hypoglossal nerve** (somatic motor column).

2. Rootlets of **accessory**-7, **vagus and glossopharyngeal**-8 emerge between rootlets for dorsal and ventral spinal roots (lateral branchiomeric column).

# 289. Dorsal and 290. Dorso-Lateral Views of Brain Stem. (slightly enlarged) (See Figs. 229–231)

1 **Sup. Colliculi, Tectal Lamina**
*colliculi superiores laminae tecti*
**Frenulum, Sup. Medullary Velum**
*frenulum veli medullaris anterioris [superioris]*
**Trochlear Nerves**
*nervi trochleares*
**Brachium, Inf. Colliculus**
*brachium colliculi inferioris*

2 **Median Sulcus**
*sulcus medianus*
**Locus Coruleus**
*locus coruleus*
**Medial Eminence**
*eminentia medialis*
**Superior Fovea**
*fovea superior*

3 **Sulcus Limitans**
*sulcus limitans*

4 **Rhomboid Fossa**
*fossa rhomboidea*
**Lateral Recess, IV Ventricle**
*recessus lateralis ventriculi IV*
**Inferior Fovea**
*fovea inferior*

5 **Vestibular Area**
*area vestibularis*
**Tenia of IV Ventricle**
*tenia ventriculi IV*
**Median Sulcus**
*sulcus medianus*
**Calamus Scriptorius**
*(calamus scriptorius)*
**Tubercle Nucleus Cuneatus**
*tuberculum nuclei cuneati*
**Tubercle Nucleus Gracilis**
*tuberculum nuclei gracilis*

6 **Posterior Funiculus**
**Fasciculus Cuneatus**
**Fasciculus Gracilis**
*funiculi posterioris*
*fasciculus cuneatus*
*fasciculus gracilis*

7 **Posterior Median Sulcus**
*sulcus medianus posterior*
**Posterior Intermediate Sulcus**
*sulcus intermedius posterior*
**Posteriolateral Sulcus**
*sulcus lateralis posterior*
**Obex**
*obex*
**Trigone, Vagus N.**
*trigonum n. vagi*

8 **Trigone, Hypoglossal Nerve**
*trigonum nervi hypoglossi*
**(Tuberculum Cinereum)**
*(tuberculum cinereum)*
**Tenia of IV Ventricle**
*tenia ventriculi quarti*
**Striae Medullares, IV Ventr.**
*striae medullares ventr. quarti*
**Vestibular Area**
*area vestibularis*
**Facial Colliculus**
*colliculus facialis*
**Inferior Cerebellar Peduncle**
*pedunculus cerebellaris inferior*

9 **Superior Cerebellar Peduncle**
*pedunculus cerebellar. superior*
**Middle Cerebellar Peduncle**
*pedunculus cerebellaris medius*
**Middle Cerebellar Peduncle**
*pedunculus cerebellaris medius*
**Locus Coruleus**
*locus coruleus*

10 **Superior Cerebellar Peduncle**
*pedunculus cerebellaris superior (brachium conjunctivum)*
**Superior Medullary Velum**
*velum medullare ant. [sup.]*

11 **Inferior Colliculi, Tectal Lamina**
*colliculi inferiores laminae tecti*
**Third Ventricle**
*ventriculus III*

12 **Pineal Recess**
*recessus pinealis*

1 **Thalamus, Pulvinar**
*thalamus (pulvinar)*
**Brachium of Sup. Colliculus**
*brachium colliculi superioris*
**Pineal Recess**
*recessus pinealis*
**Superior Colliculi**
*colliculi superiores*
**Trigone Lemnisci**
*(trigonum lemnisci)*
**Inferior Colliculi**
*colliculi inferiores*
**Trochlear Nerve**
*nervi trochleares*

2 **Superior Cerebellar Peduncle**
*pedunculus cerebellaris superior (brachium conjunctivum)*
**Middle Cerebellar Peduncle**
*pedunculus cerebellaris medius (brachium pontis)*

4 **Rhomboid Fossa**
*fossa rhomboidea*
**Striae Medullares, IV Vent.**
*striae medullares ventriculi quarti*

5 **Tubercle, Nucleus Gracilis**
*tuberculum nuclei gracilis*
**Tubercle of Nucleus Cuneatus**
*tuberculum nuclei cuneati (fasciculus cuneatus) funiculi posterioris*
**Posterior Intermediate Sulcus**
*sulcus intermedius posterior*

6 **Dorsal Rootlets, 2nd Cerv. N.**
*fila radicularia dorsalia nervi cervicalis II*
**Spinal Medulla**
*medulla spinalis*

7 **Posteriolateral Sulcus**
*sulcus lateralis posterior*
**Anterior Lateral Sulcus**
*sulcus lateralis anterior*
**Vent. Rootlets, 2nd Cerv. N.**
*fila radicularia ventralia nervi cervicalis II*
**Accessory Nerve Rootlets**
*fila radicularia n. accessorii*
**Tuberculum Cinereum**
*(tuberculum cinereum)*
**Pyramid**
*pyramis*

8 **Medulla Oblongata**
*medulla oblongata*
**Inf. Cerebellar Peduncle**
*pedunculus cerebellaris inferior (corpus restiforme)*
**Rootlets, Vagus and Glossopharyngeal Nerve**
*fila radicularia n. vagi et n. glossopharyngei*
**Olive**
*oliva*
**Facial Nerve**
*n. facialis*
**[Vestibulocochlear Nerve]**
*n. statoacusticus*
*[n. vestibulocochlearis]*

9 **Pons**
*pons*
**Trigeminal N. [Sensory Root]**
*n. trigeminus (portio major) [radix sensoria]*
**Trigeminal Nerve, Motor Root**
*n. trigemini portio minor [radix motoria]*
**Fila Lateralis Pontis**
*(fila lateralia pontis)*

10 **Brachium, Inferior Colliculus**
*brachium colliculi inferioris*
**Cerebral Peduncle**
*pedunculus cerebri*
**Geniculate Body, Med. and Lat.**
*corpus geniculatum, lat. et med.*
**Optic Tract**
*tractus opticus*

**Notes:** See preceding page.

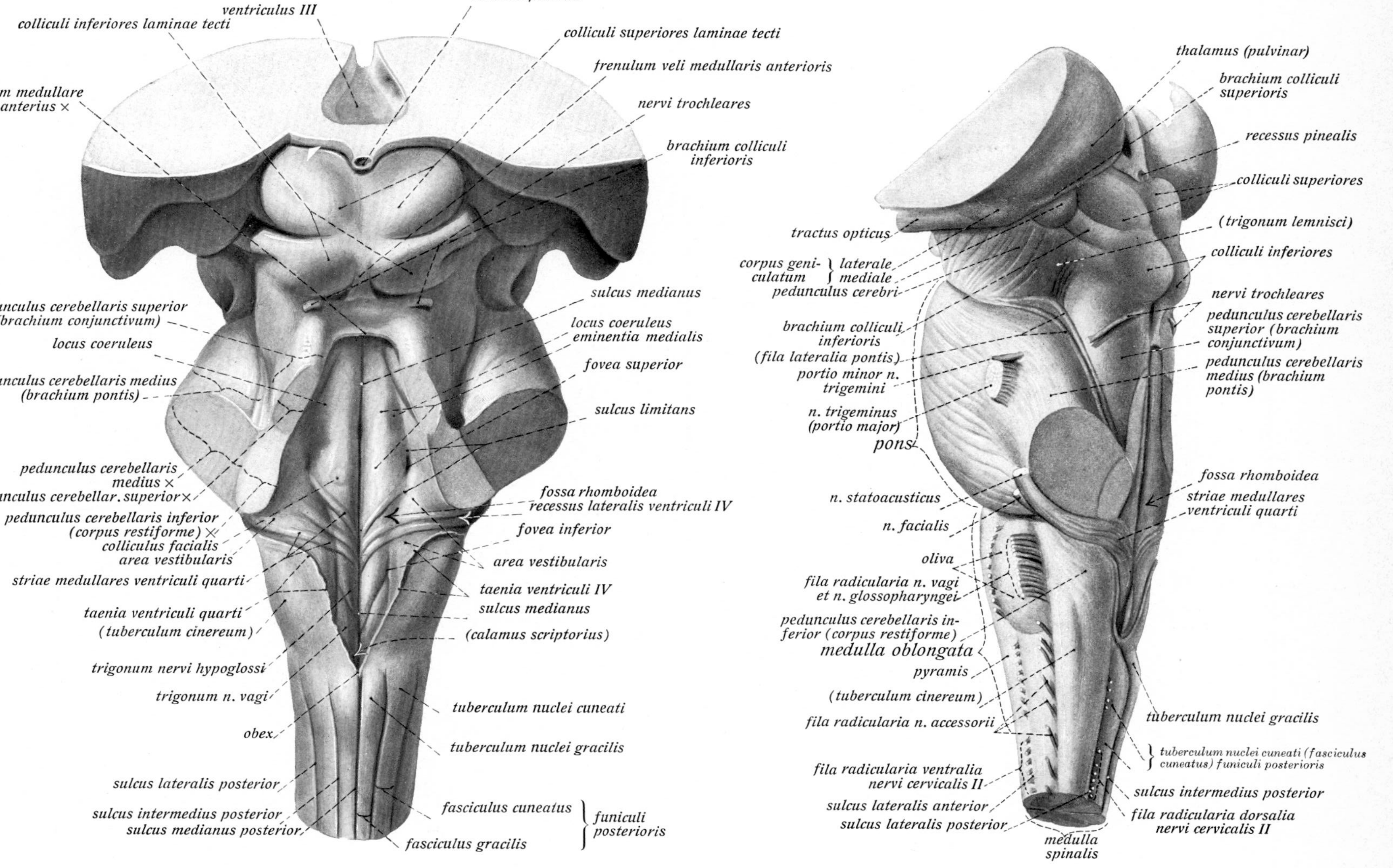

recessus pinealis
ventriculus III
colliculi inferiores laminae tecti
colliculi superiores laminae tecti
frenulum veli medullaris anterioris
velum medullare anterius ×
nervi trochleares
brachium colliculi inferioris
sulcus medianus
pedunculus cerebellaris superior (brachium conjunctivum)
locus coeruleus
locus coeruleus
eminentia medialis
fovea superior
pedunculus cerebellaris medius (brachium pontis)
sulcus limitans
pedunculus cerebellaris medius ×
pedunculus cerebellar. superior ×
fossa rhomboidea
recessus lateralis ventriculi IV
pedunculus cerebellaris inferior (corpus restiforme) ×
colliculus facialis
area vestibularis
fovea inferior
area vestibularis
striae medullares ventriculi quarti
taenia ventriculi IV
sulcus medianus
taenia ventriculi quarti
(tuberculum cinereum)
(calamus scriptorius)
trigonum nervi hypoglossi
trigonum n. vagi
tuberculum nuclei cuneati
obex
tuberculum nuclei gracilis
sulcus lateralis posterior
sulcus intermedius posterior
sulcus medianus posterior
fasciculus cuneatus
fasciculus gracilis
funiculi posterioris
thalamus (pulvinar)
brachium colliculi superioris
recessus pinealis
colliculi superiores
(trigonum lemnisci)
tractus opticus
colliculi inferiores
corpus geniculatum laterale
mediale
pedunculus cerebri
nervi trochleares
pedunculus cerebellaris superior (brachium conjunctivum)
brachium colliculi inferioris
(fila lateralia pontis)
pedunculus cerebellaris medius (brachium pontis)
portio minor n. trigemini
n. trigeminus (portio major)
pons
fossa rhomboidea
n. statoacusticus
striae medullares ventriculi quarti
n. facialis
oliva
fila radicularia n. vagi et n. glossopharyngei
pedunculus cerebellaris inferior (corpus restiforme)
medulla oblongata
pyramis
(tuberculum cinereum)
fila radicularia n. accessorii
tuberculum nuclei gracilis
tuberculum nuclei cuneati (fasciculus cuneatus) funiculi posterioris
fila radicularia ventralia nervi cervicalis II
sulcus intermedius posterior
sulcus lateralis anterior
fila radicularia dorsalia nervi cervicalis II
sulcus lateralis posterior
medulla spinalis


**Fig. 289.**

**Fig. 290.**

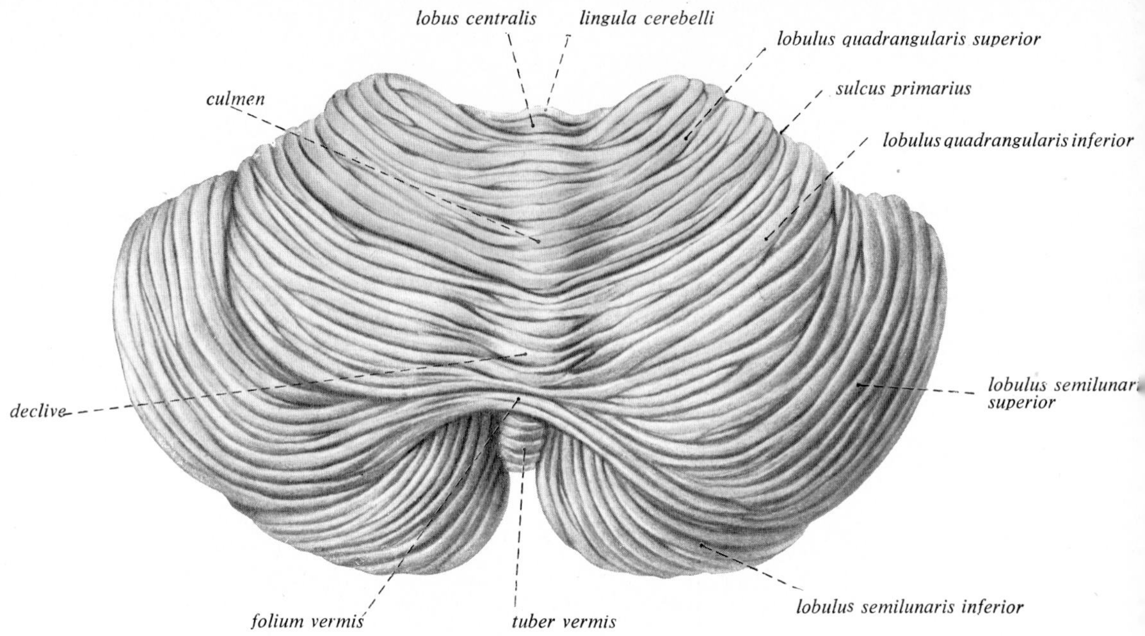
lobus centralis
lingula cerebelli
lobulus quadrangularis superior
culmen
sulcus primarius
lobulus quadrangularis inferior
lobulus semilunaris superior
declive
folium vermis
tuber vermis
lobulus semilunaris inferior

**Fig. 291.**

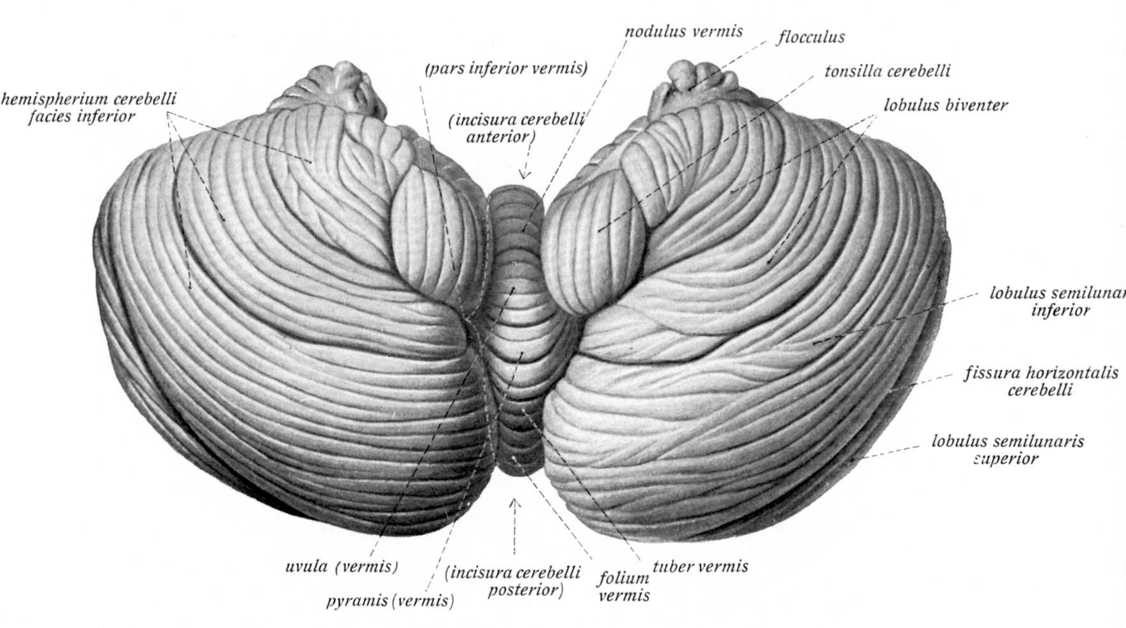
nodulus vermis
flocculus
(pars inferior vermis)
tonsilla cerebelli
hemispherium cerebelli facies inferior
lobulus biventer
(incisura cerebelli anterior)
lobulus semilunaris inferior
fissura horizontalis cerebelli
lobulus semilunaris superior
uvula (vermis)
(incisura cerebelli posterior)
folium vermis
tuber vermis
pyramis (vermis)

**Fig. 292.**

## 291. The Cerebellum. (from above and dorsally) (1/1)

**Yellow:** Primitive part of cerebellum.

1 **Quadrangular Lobules, Superior**
*lobulus quadrangularis superior*

2 **Primary Fissure**
*sulcus primarius*

3 **Quadrangular Lobule, Inferior**
*lobulus quadrangularis inferior*

**Semilunar Lobule, Superior**
*lobulus semilunaris superior*

4 **Semilunar Lobule, Inferior**
*lobulus semilunaris inferior*

6 **Tuber of Vermis**
*tuber vermis*

7 **Folium of Vermis**
*folium vermis*

9 **Declive**
*declive*

10 **Culmen**
*culmen*

11 **Central Lobule**
*lobus [lobulus] centralis*

12 **Lingula**
*lingula cerebelli*

**Note:** 1. **Cerebellar cortex** is divided by **cerebellar fissures** into narrow **cerebellar folia.** Folia correspond to gyri of cerebral hemispheres; fissures to the sulci.

2. The **cerebellum** grossly consists of three main parts: unpaired median narrow portion or **vermis of cerebellum**-6 (so-called because of its resemblance to a worm) and **paired cerebellar hemispheres** on either side. Rostrally, the boundary between hemispheres and vermis are not conspicuous. Dorsally and caudally, however, surface of the vermis is a prominent ridge and forms the floor of a relatively deep notch, the **posterior cerebellar notch** (see Fig. 292). Little valleys which separate the vermis from cerebellar hemispheres are called the vallecula or the cerebellar vallecula. (Fig. 293-5, -7). The vallecula may be partly overlapped by the convexity of the hemispheres.

## 292. The Cerebellum, Basal Surface (from below) (1/1)

1 **Nodulus Vermis**
*nodulus vermis*

**Flocculus**
*flocculus*

2 **Cerebellar Tonsil**
*tonsilla cerebelli*

**Biventral Lobule**
*lobulus biventer*

3 **Inferior Semilunar Lobule**
*lobulus semilunaris inferior*

**Horizontal Cerebellar Fissure**
*fissura horizontalis cerebelli*

**Superior Semilunar Lobule**
*lobulus semilunaris superior*

5 **Tuber Vermis**
*tuber vermis*

**Folium Vermis**
*folium vermis*

6 **Posterior Cerebellar Notch**
*(incisura cerebelli posterior)*

7 **Pyramid (Vermis)**
*pyramis (vermis)*

**Uvula (Vermis)**
*uvula (vermis)*

10 **Cerebellar Hemisphere, Inferior Surface**
*hemispherium cerebelli, facies inferior*

11 **Inferior Vermis**
*(pars inferior vermis)*

12 **Anterior Cerebellar Notch**
*(incisura cerebelli anterior)*

**Note:** 1. Conspicuous **vermis**-5, -7 separating two **cerebellar hemispheres**-10 forming floor of **posterior cerebellar notch**-6.

2. Cerebellar hemispheres exhibit a superior surface and an inferior surface-10. These surfaces are separated from each other by the **horizontal cerebellar fissure**-3.

3. Fissures on inferior surface, divide the cerebellum into inferior semilunar-3, biventral lobule-2, and **cerebellar tonsil**-2. Another very deep fissure separates the smallest cerebellar lobule, the **flocculus**-1, from the rest of the cerebellum. The flocculus extends to the lateral inferior area of the cerebellum by means of a flat stalk, the floccular peduncle. (See Fig. 293-2.)

## 293. The Cerebellum. (ventral aspect) (1/1)

Cerebellum has been removed from brain by dividing its peduncles and the anterior and posterior [superior and inferior] medullary velli.

1 **Culmen**
*culmen*

**Central Lobule**
*lobulus centralis*

**Cerebellar Lingula**
*lingula cerebelli*

**Ala of Central Lobule**
*ala lobuli centralis*

2 **Superior Cerebellar Peduncle (Brachium Conjunctivum)**
*pedunculus cerebellaris superior (brachium conjunctivum)*

**Middle Cerebellar Peduncle (Brachium Pontis)**
*pedunculus cerebellaris medius (brachium pontis)*

**Floccular Peduncle**
*pedunculus flocculi*

3 **Flocculus**
*flocculus*
**Horizontal Cerebellar Fissure**
*fissura horizontalis cerebelli*

5 **Vallecula Cerebelli**
*vallecula cerebelli*

**Nodulus**
*nodulus vermis*

6 **Posterior Cerebellar Notch**
*(incisura cerebelli posterior)*

**Uvula**
*uvula vermis*

7 **Vallecula Cerebelli**
*vallecula cerebelli*

8 **Cerebellar Hemisphere, Inferior Surface**
*facies inferior hemispherii cerebelli*

**Fourth Ventricle, Lateral Recess**
*recessus lateralis ventriculi IV*

10 **Superior Surface of Hemisphere**
*facies superior hemispherii*
**Posterior [Inferior] Medullary Velum**
*velum medullare posterius [inferius]*
**Vinculum Lingulae**
*(vinculum lingulae)*

11 **Fourth Ventricle Tegmen**
*tegmen ventriculi IV*

**Anterior [Superior] Medullary Velum**
*velum medullare anterius [superius]*

12 **Declive**
*declive*

**Note:** 1. **Horizontal fissure**-3 is more conspicuous from this view.

2. Many **subdivisions** of central or **vermian portion of cerebellum** are shown: cerebellar lingula-1, central lobule-1, culmen-1 and the declive-12. The nodulus-5 and uvula-6 are seen near the posterior. (The pyramid-7 and tuber-5 are shown on Figure 292.) (See Fig. 227.)

## 294. The Cerebellum, Basal Aspect with Pons. (1/1)

Right tonsil has been resected. The pons-1 has been left in position but cut transversely to expose the **roof of the fourth ventricle.** The roof is formed medially by **anterior** [**superior**] **medullary velum**-11, and on either side by **superior cerebellar peduncles**-2 (brachium conjunctivum).

1 **Pons**
*pons*

2 **Superior Cerebellar Peduncle (Brachium Conjunctivum)**
*pedunculus cerebellaris superior (brachium conjunctivum)*
**Flocculus**
*flocculus*

3 **Nodulus**
*nodulus*
**Horizontal Cerebellar Fissure**
*fissura horizontalis cerebelli*

**Biventral Lobule**
*lobulus biventer*

5 **Cerebellar Tonsil**
*tonsilla cerebelli*

6 **Posterior Cerebellar Notch**
*(incisura cerebelli posterior)*
**Pyramid (Vermis)**
*pyramis (vermis)*

7 **Uvula (Vermis)**
*uvula (vermis)*
**Nidus avis**
*[nidus avis]*

10 **Flocculus**
*flocculus*

**Floccular Peduncle**
*pedunculus flocculi*

**Posterior [Inferior] Medullary Velum**
*velum medullare posterius [inferius]*

11 **Anterior [Superior] Medullary Velum**
*velum medullare anterius [superius]*

**Note:** 1. **Flocculo**-10–**nodular**-3 **portion of cerebellum** is well depicted. This, with the **uvula**-7 is known as the **vestibular cerebellum.**

2. **Main portion of the cerebellum,** or middle portion has come to be recognized as the **cerebral cerebellum** (neocerebellum). The pontine-1 nuclei receive many fibers from the cerebral cortex and relay them to the middle portion of the cerebellum through the middle cerebellar peduncles (brachium pontis) (Fig. 293-2).

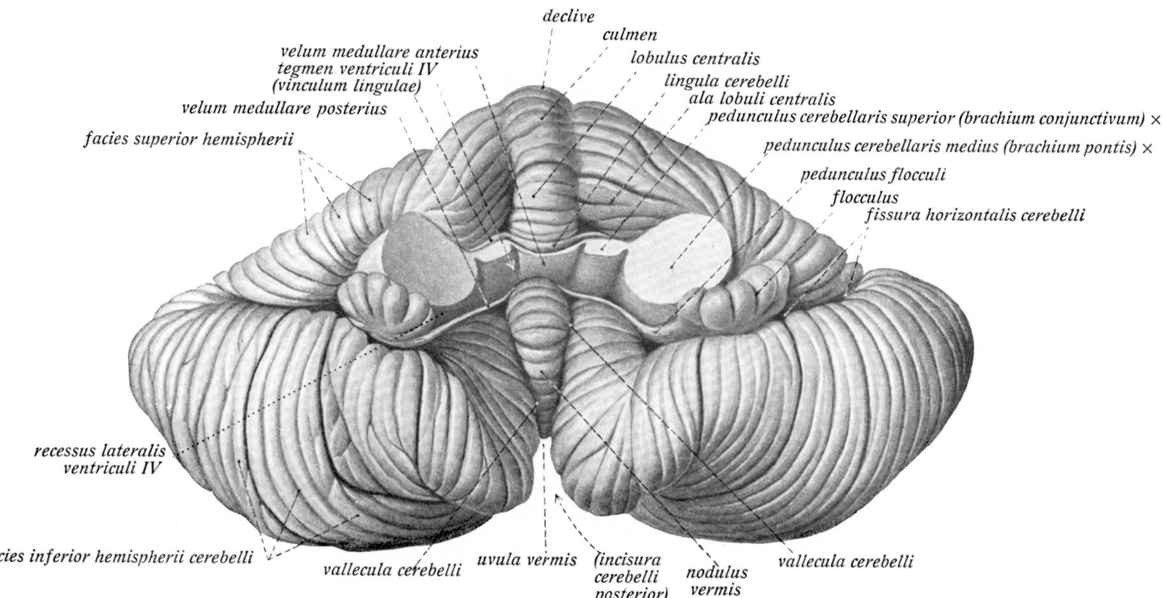
declive
culmen
velum medullare anterius
tegmen ventriculi IV
(vinculum lingulae)
lobulus centralis
lingula cerebelli
ala lobuli centralis
velum medullare posterius
pedunculus cerebellaris superior (brachium conjunctivum) ×
facies superior hemispherii
pedunculus cerebellaris medius (brachium pontis) ×
pedunculus flocculi
flocculus
fissura horizontalis cerebelli
recessus lateralis
ventriculi IV
facies inferior hemispherii cerebelli
vallecula cerebelli
uvula vermis
(incisura
cerebelli
posterior)
nodulus
vermis
vallecula cerebelli

**Fig. 293.**

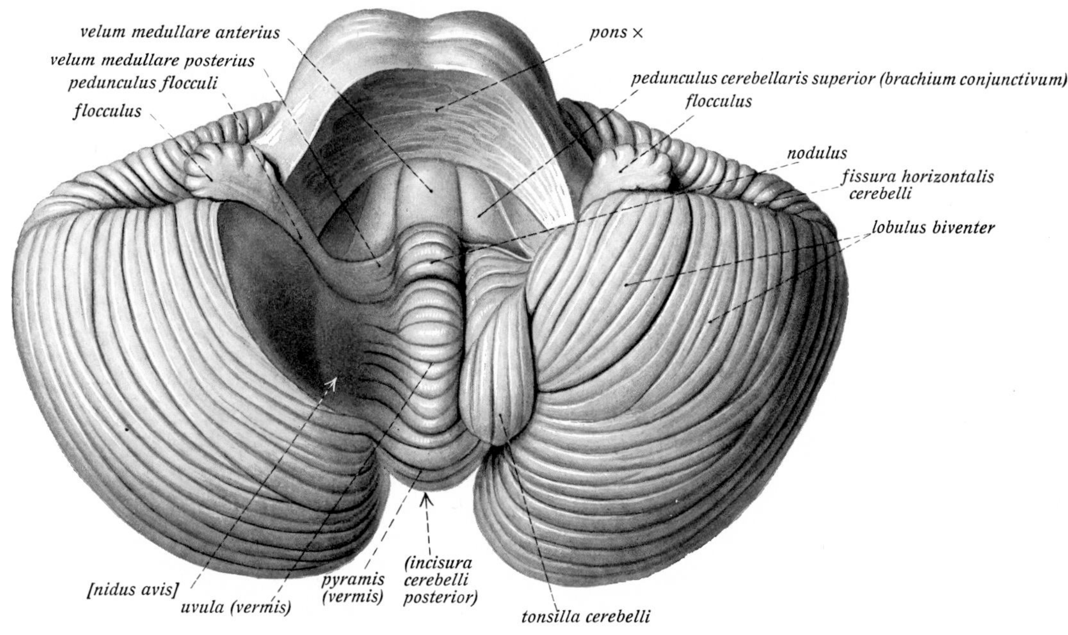
velum medullare anterius
velum medullare posterius
pedunculus flocculi
flocculus
pons ×
pedunculus cerebellaris superior (brachium conjunctivum)
flocculus
nodulus
fissura horizontalis
cerebelli
lobulus biventer
[nidus avis]
uvula (vermis)
pyramis
(vermis)
(incisura
cerebelli
posterior)
tonsilla cerebelli

**Fig. 294.**

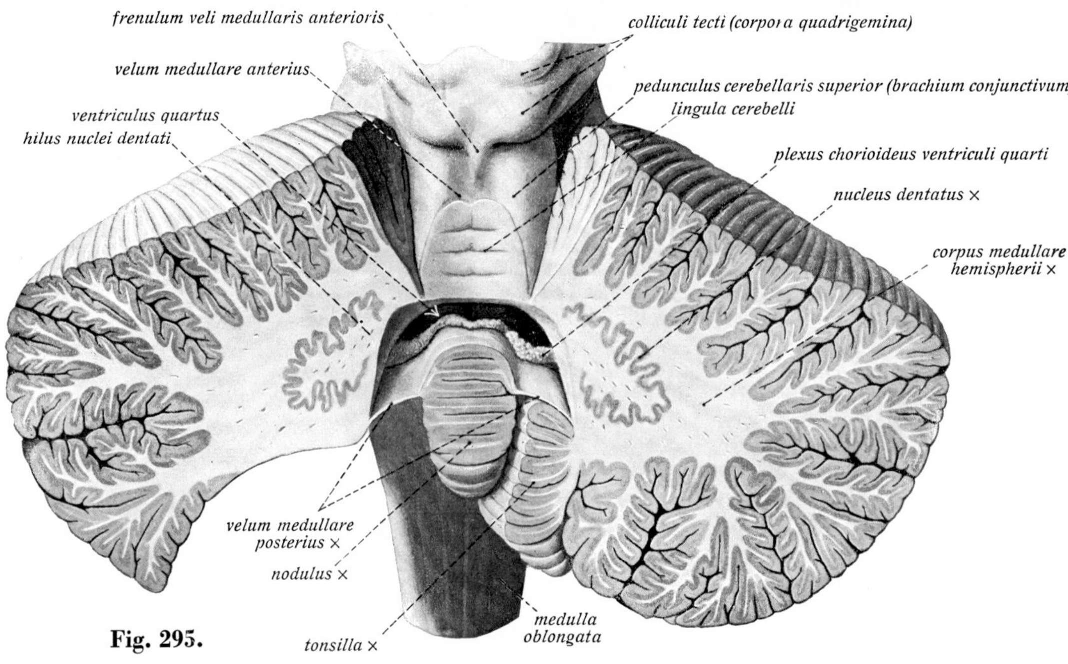
frenulum veli medullaris anterioris
velum medullare anterius
ventriculus quartus
hilus nuclei dentati
colliculi tecti (corpora quadrigemina)
pedunculus cerebellaris superior (brachium conjunctivum)
lingula cerebelli
plexus chorioideus ventriculi quarti
nucleus dentatus ×
corpus medullare hemispherii ×
velum medullare posterius ×
nodulus ×
tonsilla ×
medulla oblongata

**Fig. 295.**

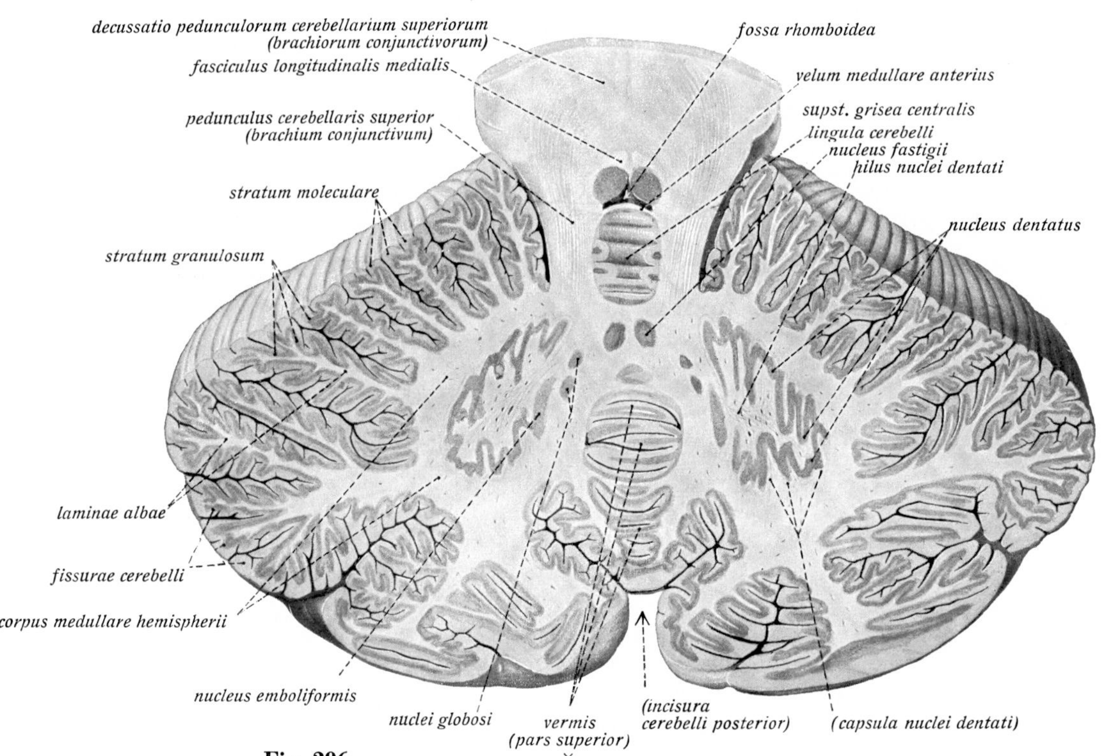
decussatio pedunculorum cerebellarium superiorum (brachiorum conjunctivorum)
fasciculus longitudinalis medialis
pedunculus cerebellaris superior (brachium conjunctivum)
stratum moleculare
stratum granulosum
fossa rhomboidea
velum medullare anterius
supst. grisea centralis
lingula cerebelli
nucleus fastigii
hilus nuclei dentati
nucleus dentatus
laminae albae
fissurae cerebelli
corpus medullare hemispherii
nucleus emboliformis
nuclei globosi
vermis (pars superior) ×
(incisura cerebelli posterior)
(capsula nuclei dentati)

**Fig. 296.**

## 295. Internal Structure of Cerebellum and Boundaries of Fourth Ventricle. (1/1)

Most of the vermis (all except the lingula-2 and the nodulus-7) were removed as well as most of the dorsal halves of the two cerebellar hemispheres-3. In addition, the tonsil-7 and the biventral lobule were removed from the left in order to display the posterior [inferior] medullary velum-8.

1 **Tectal Colliculi (Quadrigeminal Bodies)**
*colliculi tecti*
*(corpora quadrigemina)*
**Superior Cerebellar Peduncle, Brachium Conjunctivum**
*pedunculus cerebellaris superior*
*(brachium conjunctivum)*

2 **Lingula of Cerebellum**
*lingula cerebelli*
**Chorioid Plexus of Fourth Ventricle**
*plexus chorioideus ventriculi quarti*
**Dentate Nucleus**
*nucleus dentatus*

3 **Medullary Substance of Cerebellum**
*corpus medullare hemispherii*

5 **Medulla Oblongata**
*medulla oblongata*

7 **Tonsil [of Cerebellum]**
*tonsilla*
**Nodulus**
*nodulus*

8 **Inferior Medullary Velum**
*velum medullare posterius [inferius]*

10 **Hilus of Dentate Nucleus**
*hilus nuclei dentati*
**Fourth Ventricle**
*ventriculus quartus*
**Superior Medullary Velum**
*velum medullare anterius [superius]*

11 **Frenulum of Superior Medullary Velum**
*frenulum veli medullaris anterioris [superius]*

**Note:** 1. The **posterior [inferior] medullary velum** is one boundary of fourth ventricle. The ventricle contains cerebrospinal fluid and the chorioid plexus.

2. **Anterior [superior] medullary velum**-11.

3. **Superior cerebellar peduncles**-1, which convey fibers from the dentate and other nuclei of cerebellum, to red nucleus and thalamus. Here impulses are relayed to the cerebral hemispheres.

## 296. Section of Cerebellum in Plane of Superior Cerebellar Peduncles. (1/1)

1 **Rhomboid Fossa**
*fossa rhomboidea*
**Superior Medullary Velum**
*velum medullare anterius [superius]*
**Lingula of Cerebellum**
*lingula cerebelli*
**Fastigial Nucleus**
*nucleus fastigii*

2 **Hilus of Dentate Nucleus**
*hilus nuclei dentati*
**Dentate Nucleus**
*nucleus dentatus*

5 **Capsule of Dentate Nucleus**
*(capsula nuclei dentati)*

6 **Posterior Cerebellar Notch**
*(incisura cerebelli posterior)*
**Vermis, Superior Part**
*vermis (pars superior)*

7 **Globose Nuclei**
*nuclei globosi*

8 **Emboliform Nucleus**
*nucleus emboliformis*
**Medullary Substance of Cerebellum** (White Matter)
*corpus medullare hemispherii*

9 **Cerebellar Fissures**
*fissurae cerebelli*
**White Medullary Lamina**
*laminae albae*

10 **Granular Layer**
*stratum granulosum*
**Molecular Layer**
*stratum moleculare*
**Superior Cerebellar Peduncle, Brachium Conjunctivum**
*pedunculus cerebellaris superior*
*(brachium conjunctivum)*
**Medial Longitudinal Fasciculus**
*fasciculus longitudinalis medialis*

11 **Decussation of Superior Cerebellar Peduncles**
*decussatio pedunculorum cerebellarium superiorum (brachiorum conjunctivorum)*

**Note:** 1. Location of internal nuclei of cerebellum in medullary substance of cerebellar hemispheres and vermis. Names refer to shape or relative position. Large **dentate nucleus**-2 so-called because of the tooth-like appearance; **globose nuclei**-7 because of their globular shape; **fastigial nuclei**-1 because they are located in roof of fourth ventricle; **emboliform nuclei**-8 because they have a fancied resemblance to an embolus blocking mouth of dentate nucleus.

## 297. Phantom Diagram of Association Tracts of Cerebral Hemisphere.

Superior Longitudinal (Frontooccipital) and Uncinate (Frontotemporal) Fasciculi.

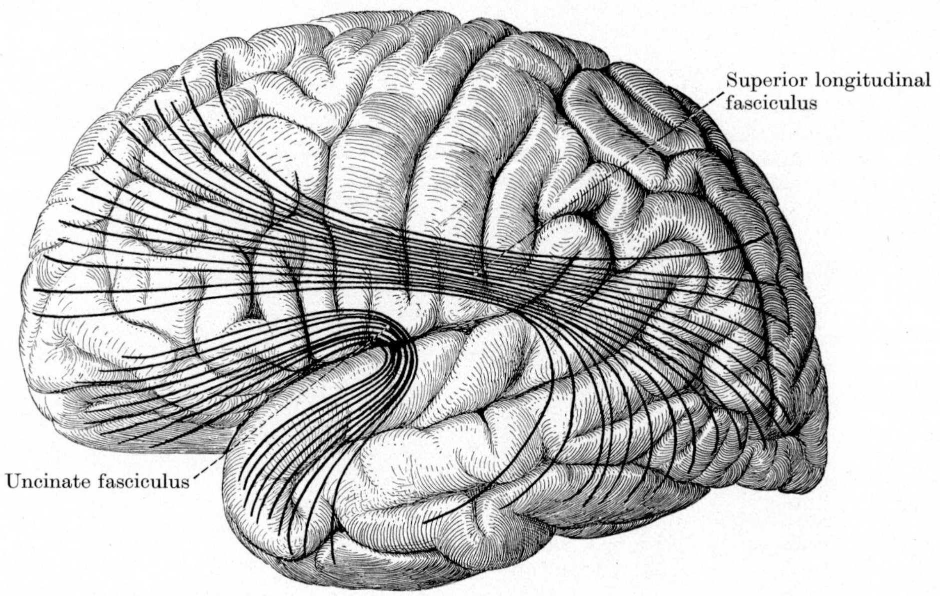
Superior longitudinal fasciculus
Uncinate fasciculus

## 298. Phantom Diagram of Association Tracts of Cerebral Hemisphere.

Cingulum, Arcuate Fibers, and Inferior Longitudinal Fasciculus.

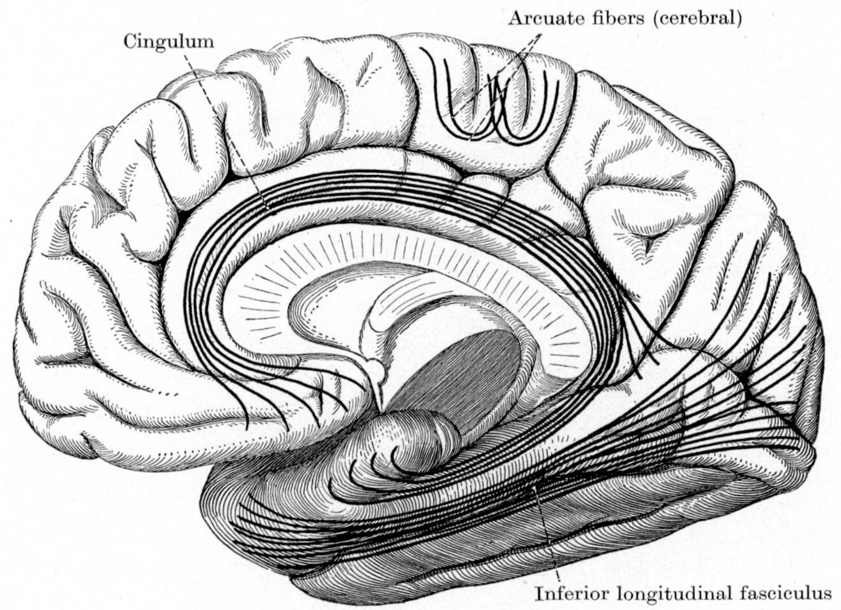
Arcuate fibers (cerebral)
Cingulum
Inferior longitudinal fasciculus

## 299. Course of the Long Cortical Projection Tracts Through the Internal Capsule and Brain Stem. (Schematic)

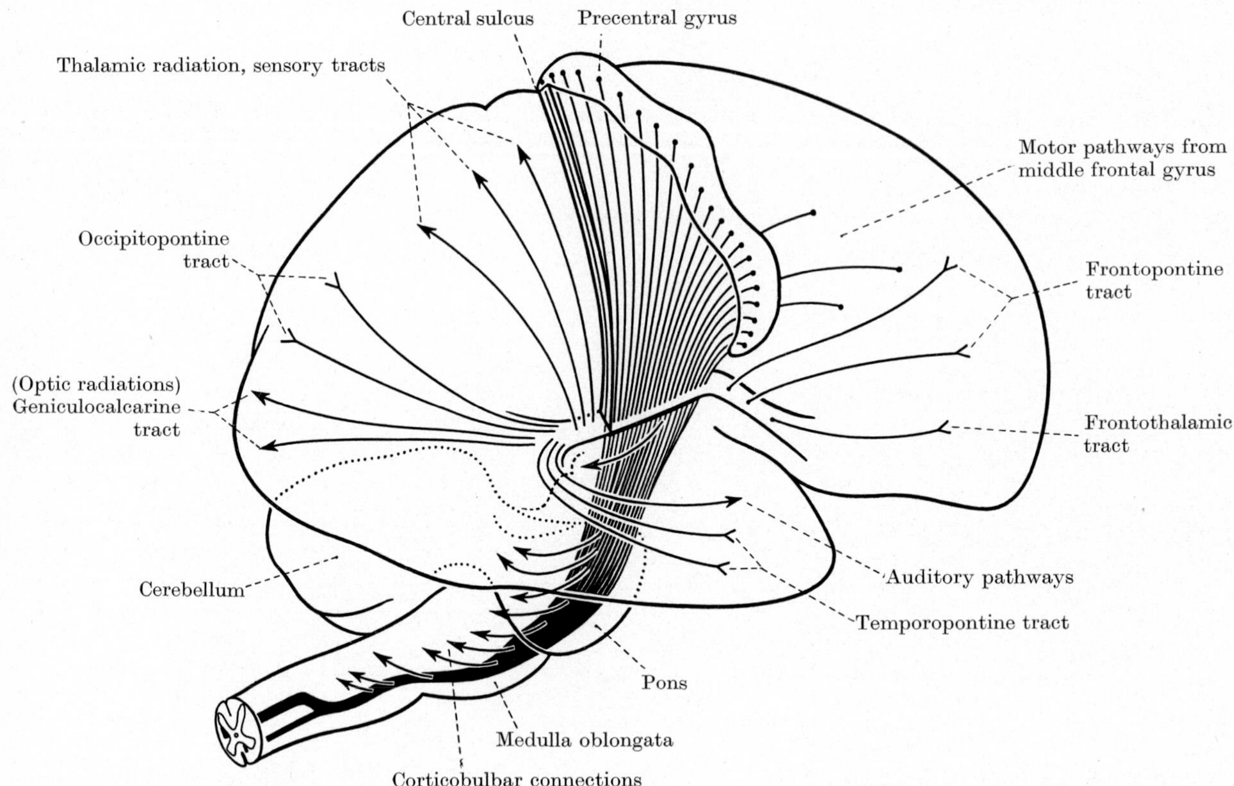
Central sulcus
Precentral gyrus
Thalamic radiation, sensory tracts
Motor pathways from middle frontal gyrus
Occipitopontine tract
Frontopontine tract
(Optic radiations) Geniculocalcarine tract
Frontothalamic tract
Auditory pathways
Cerebellum
Temporopontine tract
Pons
Medulla oblongata
Corticobulbar connections

**Note:** 1. **Arrows** – Fibers leaving the pyramidal tracts to go to the quadrigeminal plate, **corticotectal tract**; to the nuclei of the pons, **corticopontine tract**; and the cerebellum, **corticocerebellar tract;** and the nuclei of the medulla oblongata, **corticobulbar tract.** More caudally, the **pyramidal tract** continues as the crossed and uncrossed pyramidal tracts, the **lateral corticospinal** and **anterior corticospinal**, respectively.

2. Neurons in precentral gyrus are first neurons of the pyramidal tract. Their fibers converge and pass through the anterior two-thirds of the posterior limb of the internal capsule.

3. In a diagram such as this, the actual positions of the tracts cannot be accurately depicted.

# 300. Diagram of Internal Capsule to Show Arrangement of Fiber Tract Systems with Special Reference to the Sequence of Motor Fibers from the Precentral Cortex.

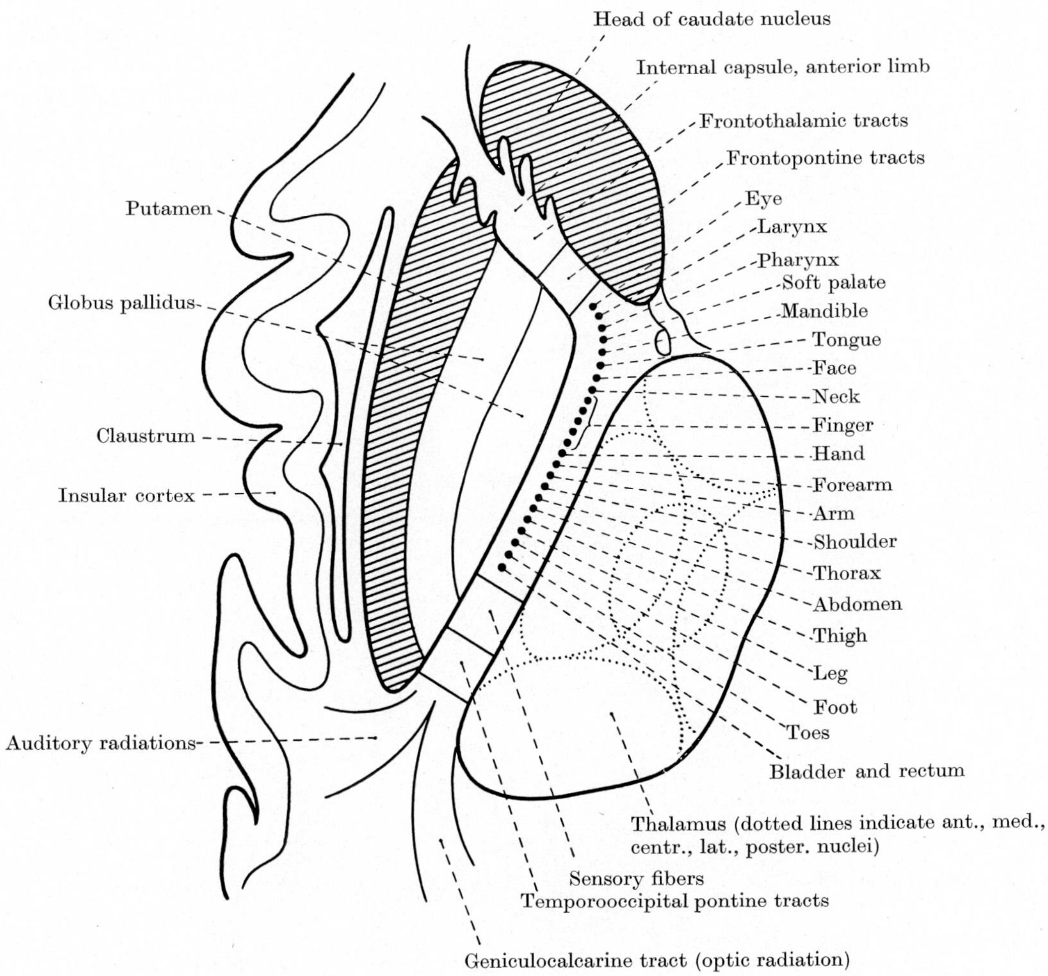
Head of caudate nucleus
Internal capsule, anterior limb
Frontothalamic tracts
Frontopontine tracts
Putamen
Eye
Larynx
Pharynx
Soft palate
Globus pallidus
Mandible
Tongue
Face
Neck
Claustrum
Finger
Hand
Insular cortex
Forearm
Arm
Shoulder
Thorax
Abdomen
Thigh
Leg
Foot
Toes
Auditory radiations
Bladder and rectum
Thalamus (dotted lines indicate ant., med., centr., lat., poster. nuclei)
Sensory fibers
Temporooccipital pontine tracts
Geniculocalcarine tract (optic radiation)

**Note:** 1. Corticobulbar and corticospinal projection tracts occupy the knee and two-thirds of posterior limb of internal capsule. The fibers to various parts of the body are arranged in definite sequence from head to foot in ventral-dorsal orientation, respectively, in the internal capsule.

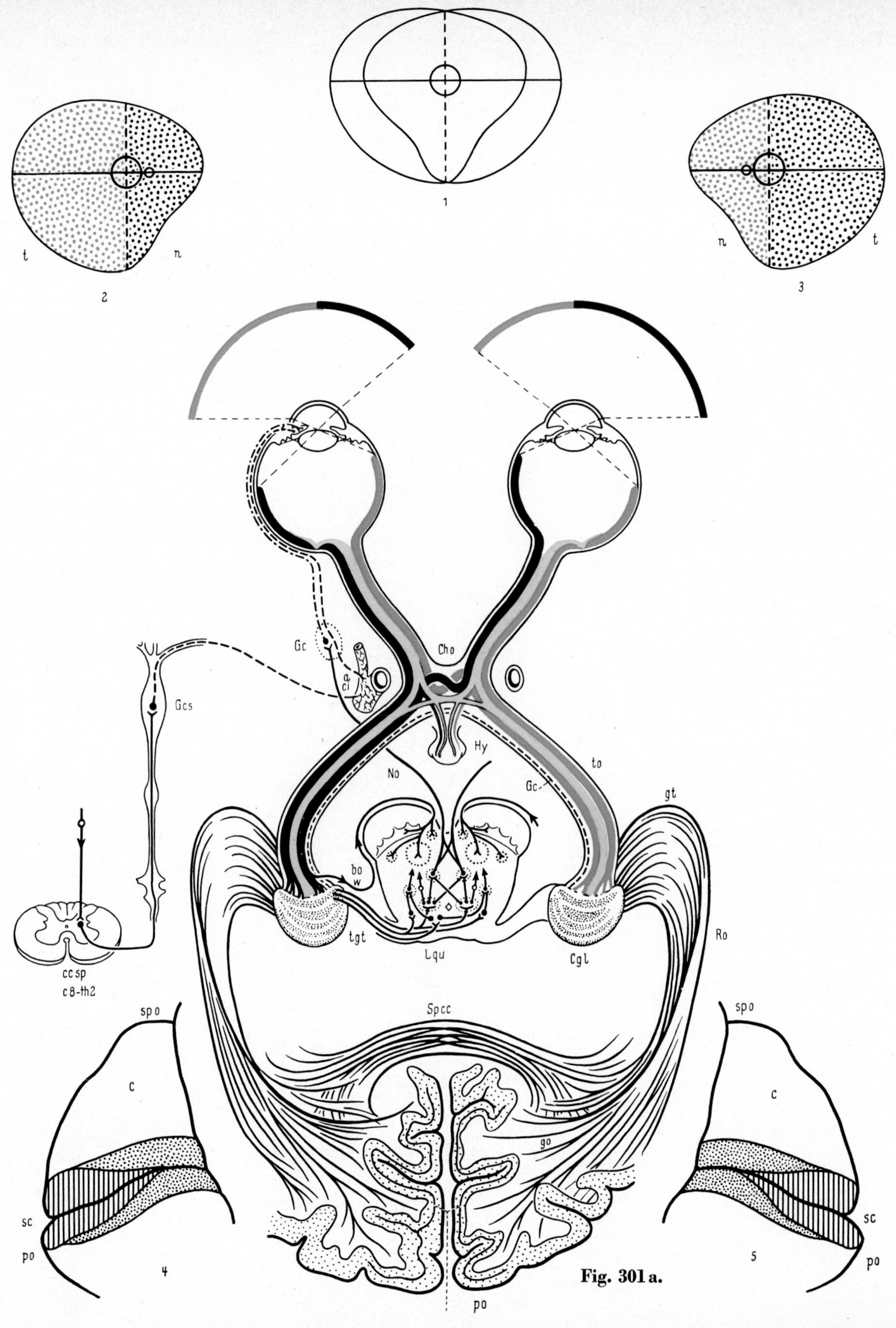
1
t
n
2
n
t
3
Gc
Cho
a
ci
Gcs
Hy
No
to
Gc
gt
bo
w
tgt
Lqu
Cgl
Ro
ccsp
c8-th2
spo
Spcc
spo
c
c
go
sc
po
4
po
5
sc
po
Fig. 301 a.

## 301 a. Optic Pathways, Visual Fields, and their Central Projections.

| | |
|---|---|
| 1 | Binocular visual field |
| 2 | Visual field of left eye |
| 3 | Visual field of right eye |
| n | Nasal |
| t | Temporal |
| 4, 5 | Medial surface of occipital lobe of cerebrum |
| Ch o | Optic chiasma |
| a c i | Internal carotid artery with plexus |
| g c | Ciliary ganglion |
| Hy | Hypophysis retinohypothalamic tract and retinohypophyseal tract |
| t o | Optic tract |
| Gc | Gudden's commissure (connecting lateral geniculate bodies) |
| b o w | Basal optic projection reflex extension around cerebral peduncles to nuclei of midbrain |
| L qu | Quadrigeminal plate |
| t g t | Geniculotectal tract |
| N o | Oculomotor nerve |
| C gl | Lateral geniculate body |
| gt | Temporal genu optic radiations |
| R o | Optic radiations |
| go | Occipital genu optic radiations |
| Sp c c | Splenium of corpus callosum to connect the visual centers of the two hemispheres |
| a str | Striate area |
| p o | Occipital pole |
| s c | Calcarine sulcus |
| | Vertical lines: projection area of fovea centralis |
| | Stipple: projection area of peripheral retina |
| c | Cuneus |
| spo | Parietooccipital sulcus |
| Gcs | Superior cervical ganglion |
| c c sp | Ciliospinal center $C_8$–$T_2$ Sympathetic outflow for dilation of pupil |

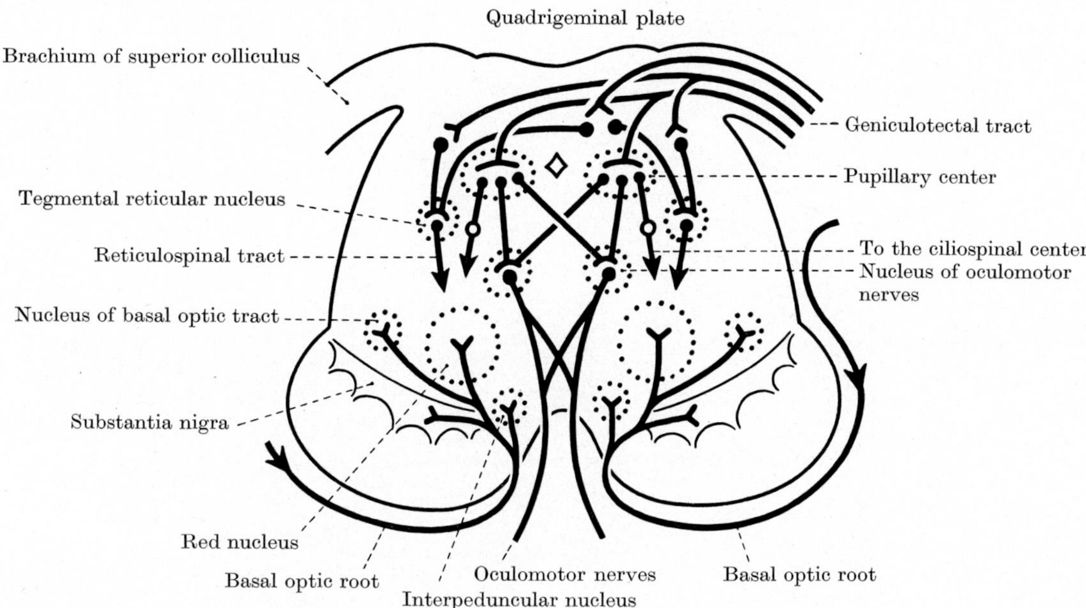

Quadrigeminal plate
Brachium of superior colliculus
Geniculotectal tract
Pupillary center
Tegmental reticular nucleus
Reticulospinal tract
To the ciliospinal center
Nucleus of oculomotor nerves
Nucleus of basal optic tract
Substantia nigra
Red nucleus
Basal optic root
Oculomotor nerves
Interpeduncular nucleus
Basal optic root


## 301 b. Oculomotor Centers, Associated Nuclei and Their Connections.

(Line diagram of midbrain in Fig. 301 a. enlarged.)

## 302. Nuclear Areas of the Oculomotor (III) and Trochlear Nerves (IV). (for the innervation of the eye muscles)

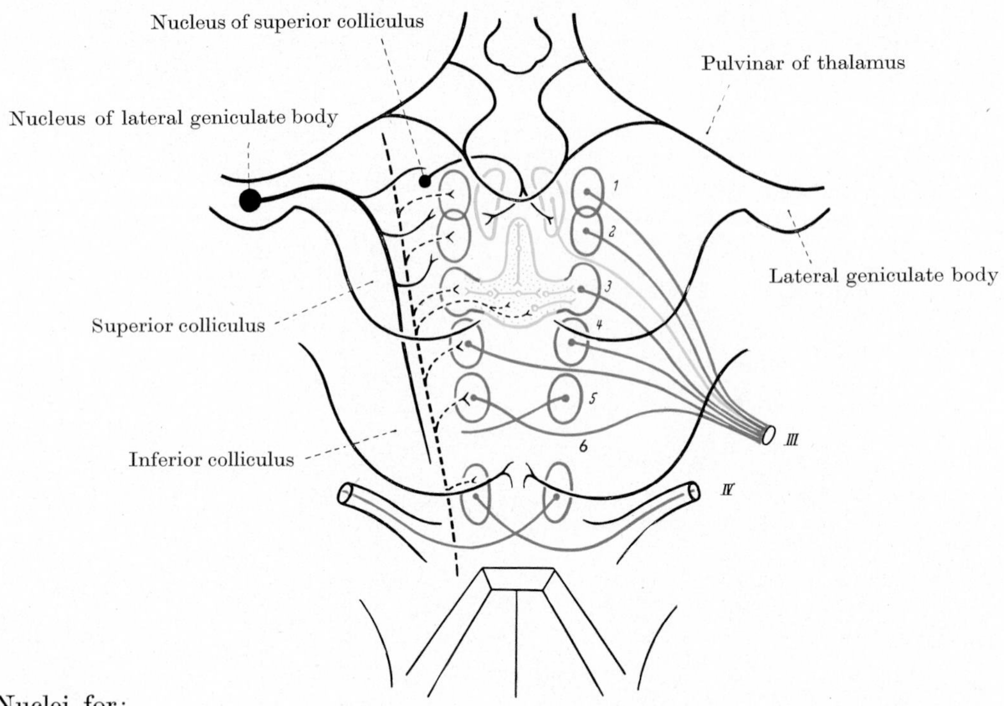
Nucleus of superior colliculus
Pulvinar of thalamus
Nucleus of lateral geniculate body
1
2
Lateral geniculate body
3
Superior colliculus
4
5
III
6
Inferior colliculus
IV

Nuclei for:

1 inferior rectus muscle
2 superior rectus muscle
3 medial rectus muscle
4 levator palpebrae superioris muscle
5 inferior oblique muscle
6 superior oblique muscle IV

**yellow:** small cell median nucleus (of Perléa)
**yellow paired:** Edinger-Westphal nucleus

**broken line:** medial longitudinal fasciculus

## 303. Visual Cortex of Occipital Pole Showing Striate Area of Calcarine Fissure.

(stria of Gennari or Vicq d'Azyr.) (Enlarged)

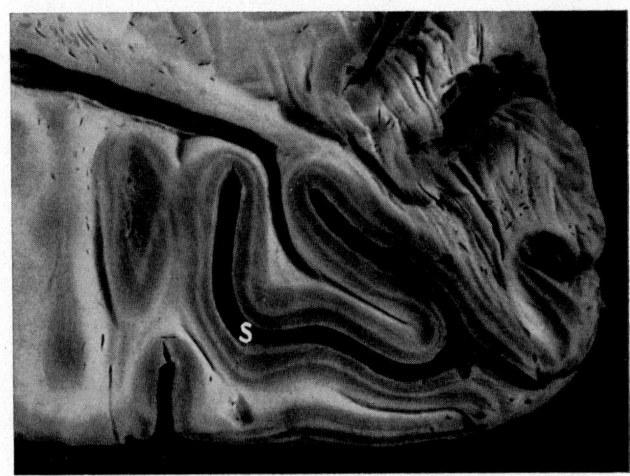
S

S = Calcarine sulcus

## 304. Diagram of Auditory Pathways and Centers.

The placement of the nuclei in the diagram does not indicate their true positions (see Figs. 324–336).

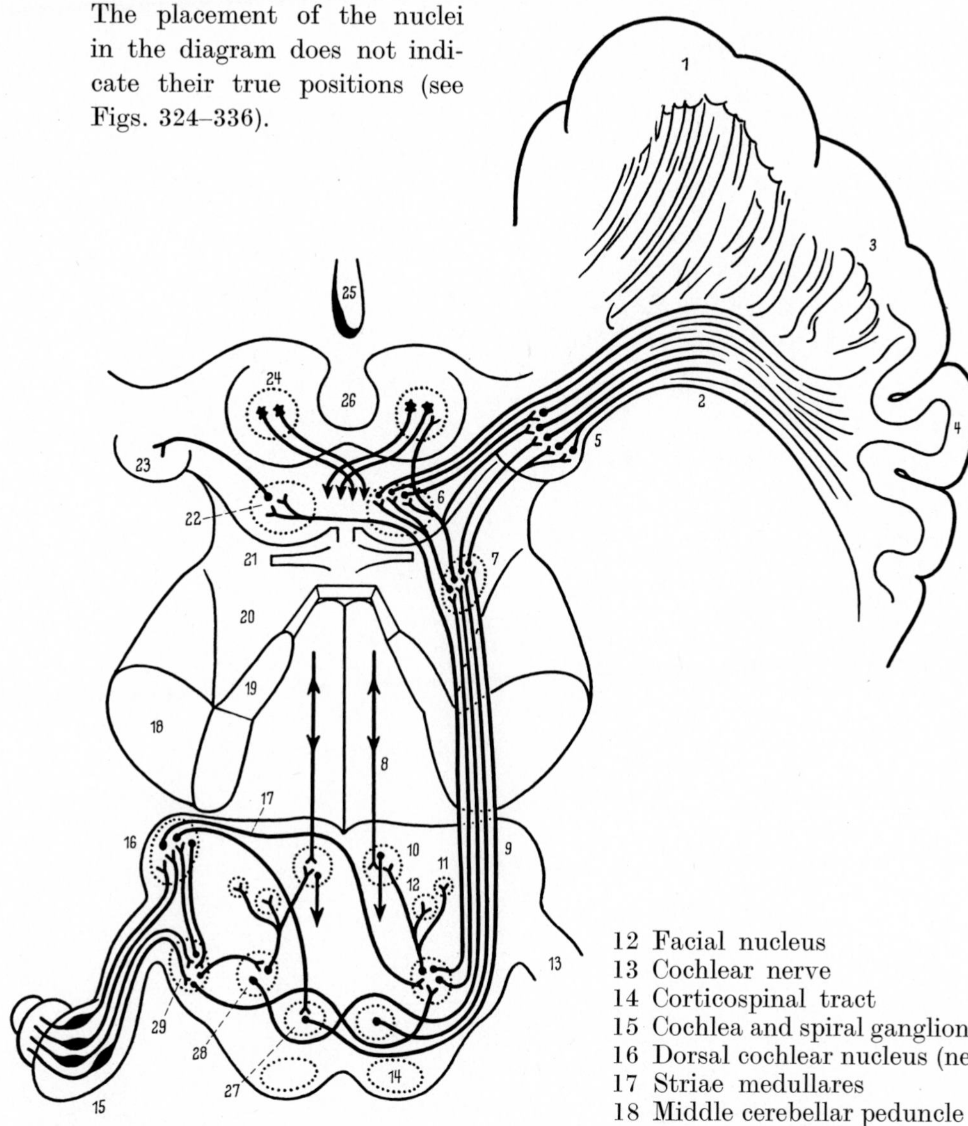
1
2
3
4
5
6
7
8
9
10
11
12
13
14
15
16
17
18
19
20
21
22
23
24
25
26
27
28
29

1 Temporal pole
2 Acoustic radiations
3 Superior temporal gyrus
4 Transverse temporal gyrus (see Fig. 206)
5 Medial geniculate body (neuron VI)
6 Inferior colliculus (neuron V)
7 Nucleus of lateral lemniscus (neuron IV)
8 Medial longitudinal fasciculus (ascending and descending fibers)
9 Lateral lemniscus
10 Nucleus of abducens nerve
11 Motor nucleus of trigeminal
12 Facial nucleus
13 Cochlear nerve
14 Corticospinal tract
15 Cochlea and spiral ganglion (neuron I)
16 Dorsal cochlear nucleus (neuron II)
17 Striae medullares
18 Middle cerebellar peduncle (Brachium pontis)
19 Superior cerebellar peduncle (Brachium conjunctivum)
20 Trigone of lemniscus
21 Trochlear nerve
22 Inferior colliculus
23 Medial geniculate body
24 Superior colliculus
25 Third ventricle
26 Pineal body
27 Trapezoid body
28 Olivary nucleus (neuron III)
29 Ventral cochlear nucleus (neuron II)

**305. Base of Brain of Two-Month Old Human Embryo.** (Rhinencephalon)

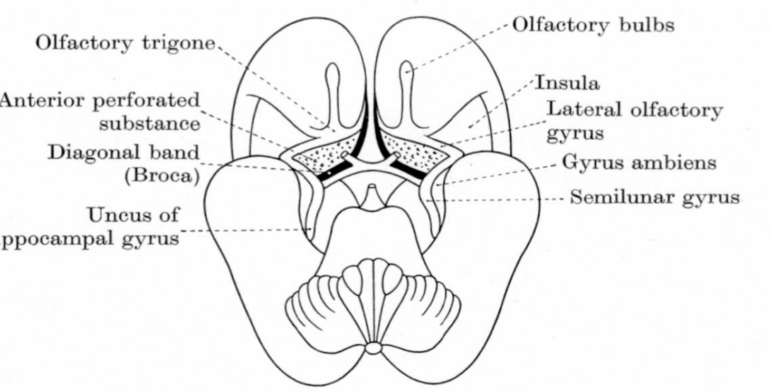
Olfactory trigone
Anterior perforated substance
Diagonal band (Broca)
Uncus of hippocampal gyrus
Olfactory bulbs
Insula
Lateral olfactory gyrus
Gyrus ambiens
Semilunar gyrus

**306. Rhinencephalic Tracts and Associated Structures.** (Olfactory pathways)

● or 0 = nerve cell bodies

≺ = synapse or nerve ending

Arrows indicate direction of impulse transmission.

**Note:** 1. A large part of the conduction system of the so-called olfactory brain and its connection to other autonomic and cortical areas has not been definitely established, either morphologically or experimentally. Observe, however, the multiplicity of circuits for automatically connecting the olfactory tracts and areas with the ascending and descending tracts of the reticular substance of the mesencephalon, pons and medulla oblongata.

**Labels for Figure 306.**

| | | | | | |
|---|---|---|---|---|---|
| c. a. | Anterior commissure | c. p. | Pineal body | n. ip. | interpeduncular nucleus |
| c. H. | Central tegmental tract | F. i. | Interventricular foramen (of Monroe) | P. | pons |
| c. n. c. | Head of caudate nucleus | Hyp. | Hypothalamus | s. r. | Reticular formation |
| c. f. | Crus of fornix | M. o. | Medulla oblongata | Th. | Thalamus |
| c. m. | Mammillary body | n. h. | Habenular nucleus | trac-olf-mes. | Olfacto-mesencephalic tract |

Fig. 306

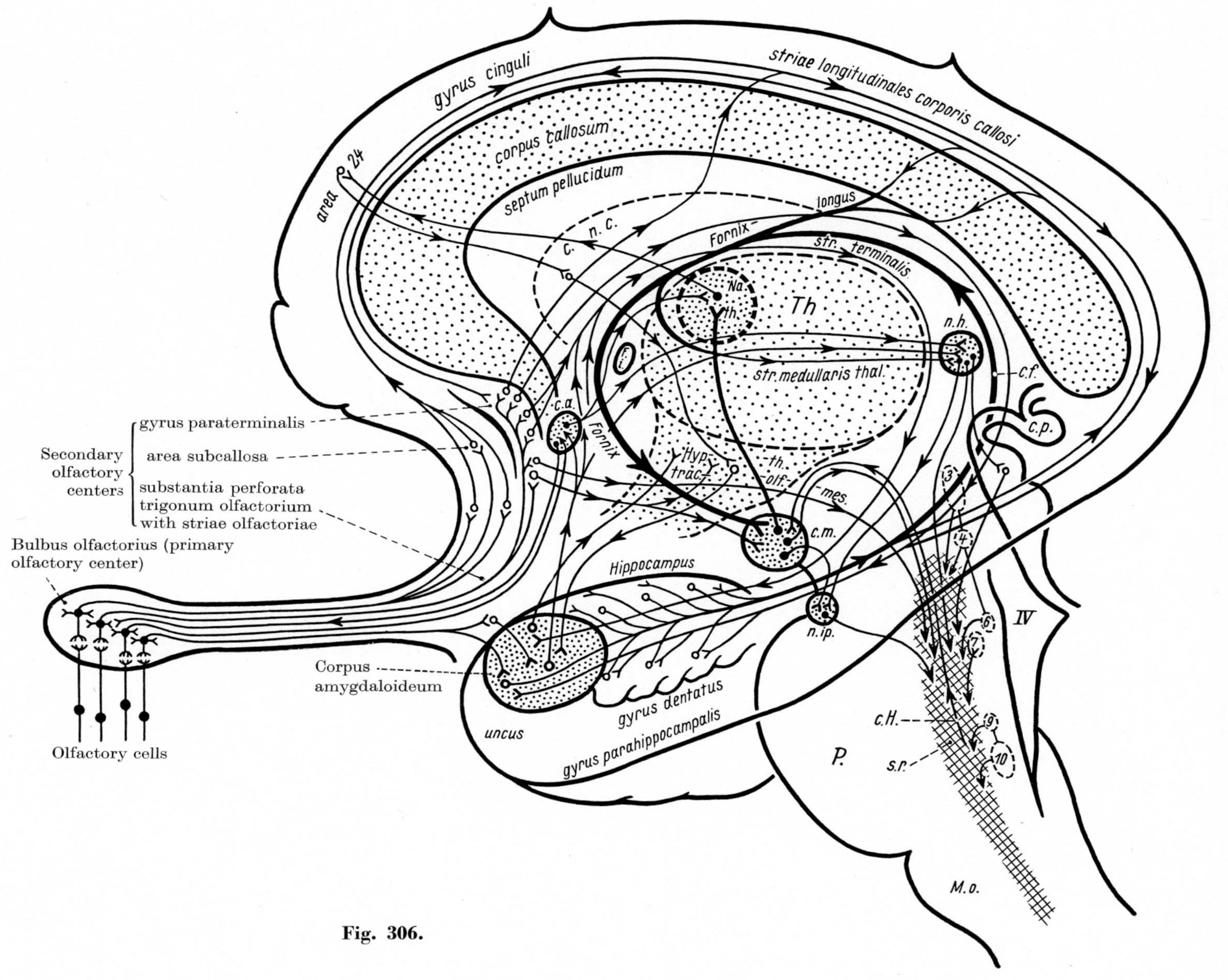

gyrus cinguli
striae longitudinales corporis callosi
area 24
corpus callosum
septum pellucidum
n. c.
c.
longus
Fornix
str. terminalis
Na.
th.
Th
n.h.
str. medullaris thal.
c.f.
c.p.
c.a.
Fornix
Hyp. trac.
th. olf.
mes.
c.m.
Hippocampus
n.ip.
IV
Secondary olfactory centers
gyrus paraterminalis
area subcallosa
substantia perforata trigonum olfactorium with striae olfactoriae
Bulbus olfactorius (primary olfactory center)
Corpus amygdaloideum
gyrus dentatus
uncus
gyrus parahippocampalis
Olfactory cells
c.H.
s.r.
P.
M.o.


Fig. 306.

Fig. 307

## 307. Left Monosynaptic Reflex and Right Polysynaptic Reflex Arcs.

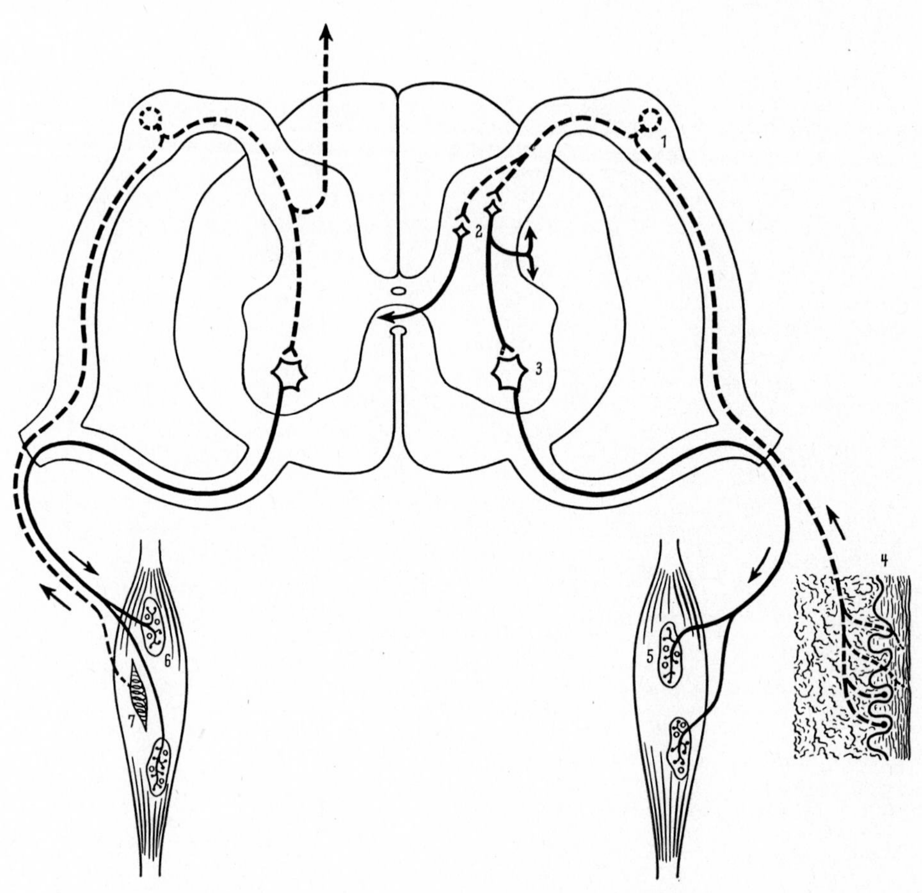
1
2
3
4
5
6
7

1 Sensory neuron
2 Intermediate neuron
3 Motor neuron, anterior horn
4 Skin
5 Motor end plate
6 Motor end plate
7 Muscle spindle

## 308. Spinal Reflex and Intersegmental Reflex Pathways.

(Four cross-sections of spinal cord viewed diagonally and from the side)

**Red:** motor (outflow) pathways

**Blue:** sensory (inflow) pathways

**Black:** association and commissural neurones

1 Monosynaptic reflex arc

2 Polysynaptic reflex arc

3 Commissural neuron

4 Funicular neuron

5 Motor neuron, anterior horn

6 Dorsal spinal ganglion cell (sensory)

7 Motor association neuron

Rd Dorsal root

Rv Ventral root

PSB Lateral pyramidal tract (corticospinal)

PVB Ventral pyramidal tract (uncrossed corticospinal)

HSB Posterior funiculus

Nsp Spinal nerve

H Skin

M Muscle

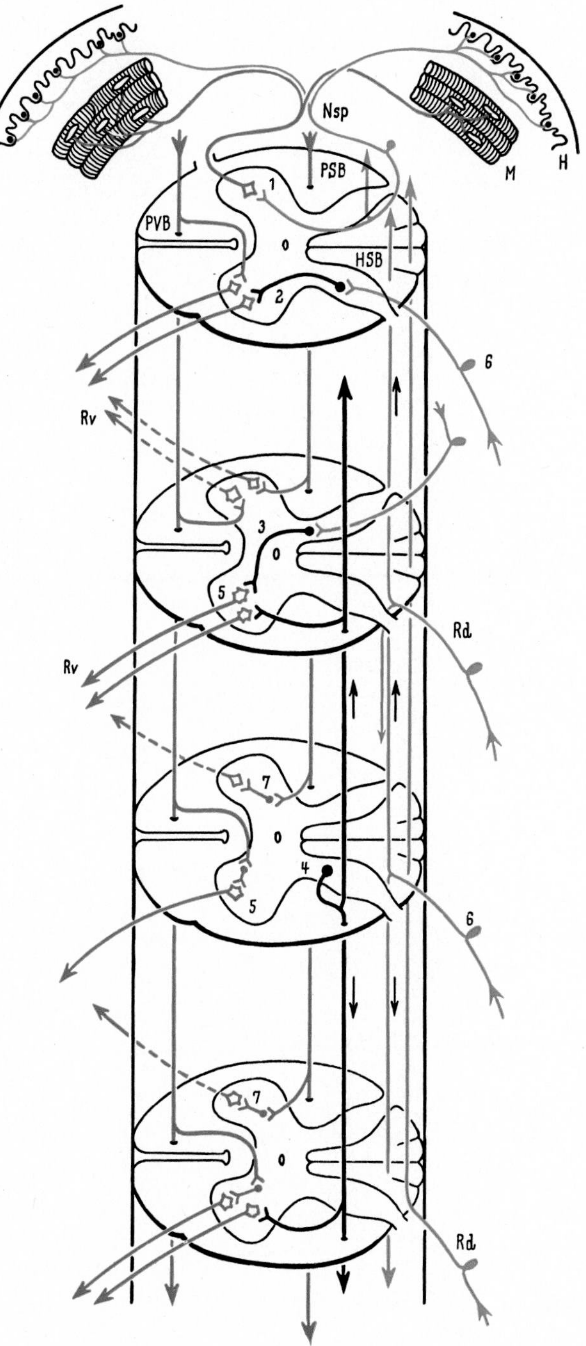
Nsp
PSB
M
H
1
PVB
0
HSB
2
6
Rv
3
0
5
Rd
Rv
7
0
4
5
6
7
0
Rd

**309. Spinal Cord Conduction Network.** Portion of Longitudinal Section. (simplified diagram) (From Benninghoff-Goerttler, Lehrbuch der Anatomie des Menschen, Vol. 3, and R. Jung, Handbuch d. inn. Medizin. Vol. V, 1953.)

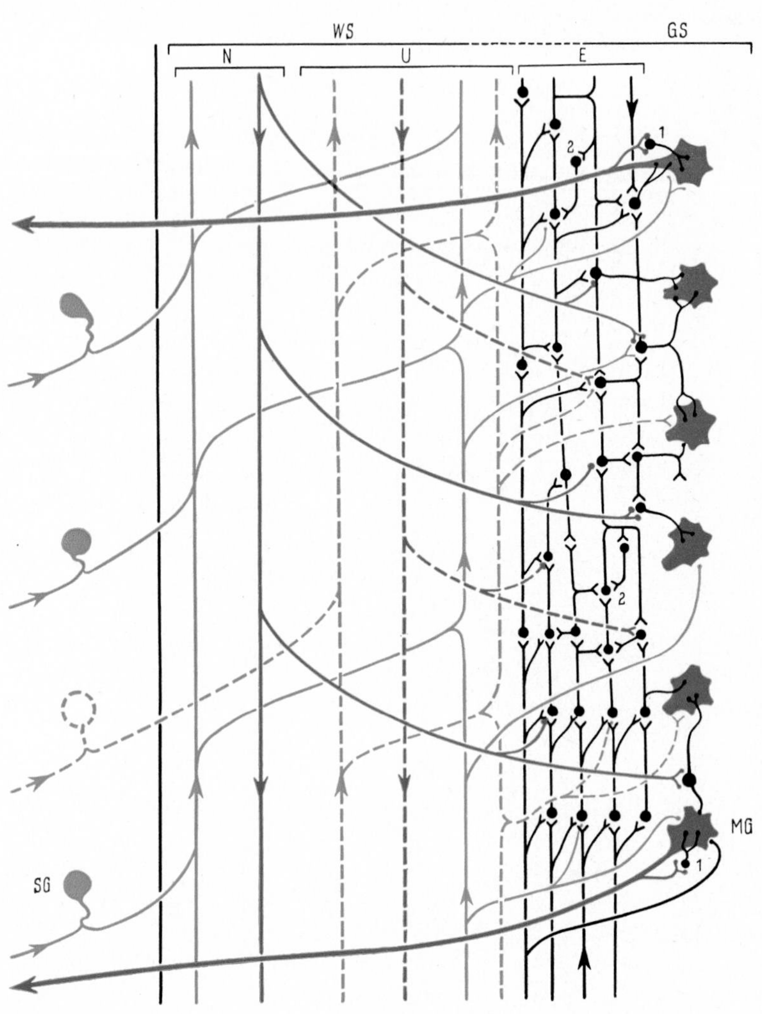
WS
GS
N
U
E
1
2
2
MG
1
SG

| | | | |
|---|---|---|---|
| WS | White matter | SG | Sensory neuron – dorsal root |
| GS | Gray matter | MG | Motor neuron – (multipolar) |

N Recent ascending and descending tracts to and from higher centers.

U Original or primitive tracts to and from medulla oblongata and other higher centers.

Ascending tracts: **interrupted blue line**
Descending tracts: **interrupted red line**

E **Black.** Primary or most primitive portion of spinal cord to medulla and midbrain.

1 Association feed-back neuron (for self-inhibition).

2 Association neuron of feed-back circuit.

## 310. Diagrammatic Cross-Section of Cervical Spinal Cord.

(Compare with Fig. 311)

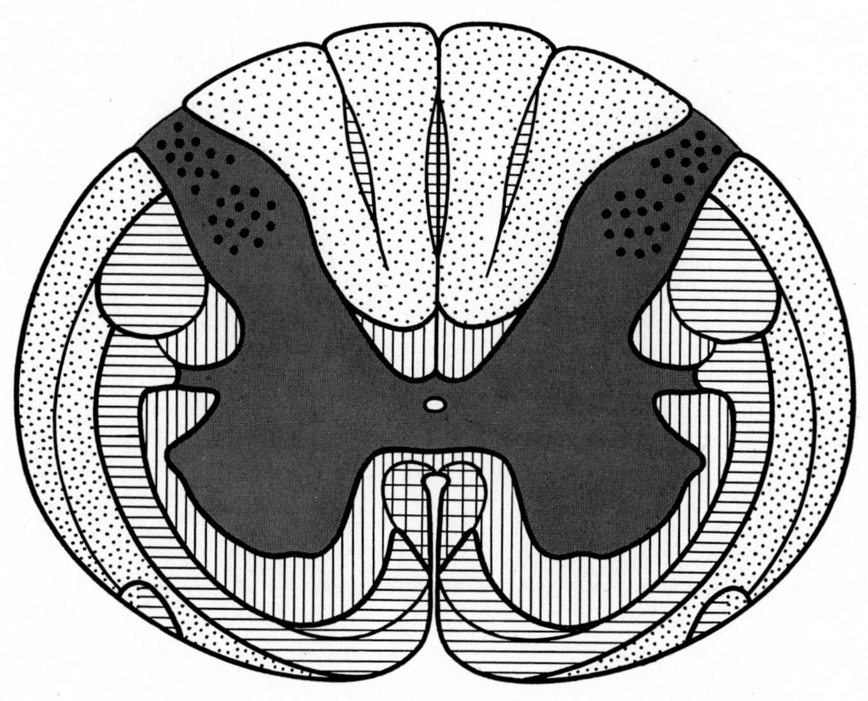

Fasciculus proprius

Descending tracts

Ascending tracts

Sulco marginal fasciculus

Tracts of dorsal horn

## 311. Composite Cross Section of Spinal Cord. (Pernkopf, Topogr. Anat.)

**Left:** Segmental lamination. (after Foerster, Handb. d. Neurologie)

**Right:** Nuclear regions, (after Benninghoff-Goertler, Lehrb. d. Anat.)

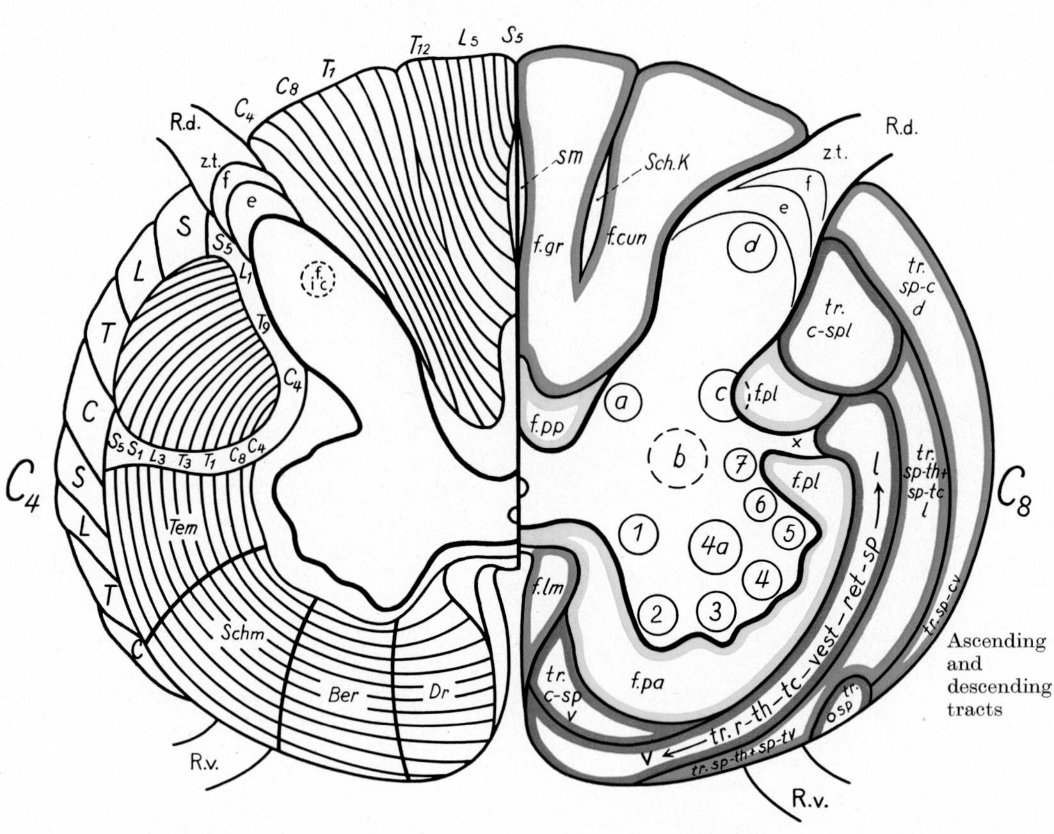
T12
L5
S5
T1
C8
C4
R.d.
z.t.
f
e
S
S5
L1
L
f. i.c.
T9
T
C4
C
S5 S1 L3 T3 T1 C8 C4
C4
S
L
Tem
T
C
Schm
Ber
Dr
R.v.
sm
Sch.K
z.t.
R.d.
f
e
d
f.gr
f.cun
tr. sp-c d
tr. c-spl
a
c
f.pl
f.pp
b
x
7
l
f.pl
tr. sp-th+ sp-tc l
C8
6
5
1
4a
4
f.lm
2
3
tr. r-th-tc-vest-ret-sp
tr. sp-cv
Ascending and descending tracts
tr. c-sp v
f.pa
tr. osp
v
tr. sp-th+sp-tv
R.v.

R. d. — Dorsal root
R. v. — Ventral root
z. t. — Terminal zone, dorsolat. fascic.
f — Zona spongiosa
e — Substantia gelatinosa
f. pp. — Fasciculus proprius (posterior)
f. pl. — Fasciculus proprius (lateral)
f. pa. — Fasciculus proprius (anterior)
f. gr. — Fasciculus gracilis
f. cun. — Fasciculus cuneatus
s. m. — Septomarginal fasciculus
Sch. K. — Interfascicular fasciculus (Schultz' comma bundle)
tr. c. spl. — Lateral corticospinal tract
tr. c. sp. v. — Anterior corticospinal tract
v←tr. r-th-tc-vest-ret-sp→l — Ant. and lat., Rubrotectovestibulo and reticulospinal tracts.
tr.-sp-th. — Lateral spinothalamic tract
sp+tc l — Lateral spinotectal tract
tr. sp+th. — Anterior spinothalamic tract
sp+tv — Anterior spinotectal tract
tr. sp–c d — Dorsal spinocerebellar tract
tr. sp. c. v. — Ventral spinocerebellar tract
tr. o. sp. — Olivospinal+spino-olivary tracts
f. lm. — Median longitudinal fasciculus

GRAY MATTER

a — Nucleus dorsalis (Clark)
b — Intermediomedial nucleus
c — Intermediolateral nucleus (Lateral horn, sympathetic presynaptic neurons)
d — Cells of posterior columns (magnocellular)

Motor Nuclei for:

1, 2 — Dorsal trunk muscles
3 — Ventral trunk muscles
4 — Trunk girdle muscles
4 a — Girdle-extremity muscles
5 — Muscles of upper arm
6 — Forearm muscles
7 — Hand (Foot) muscles

# 312. Corticospinal Pyramidal Tracts in Spinal Segment.

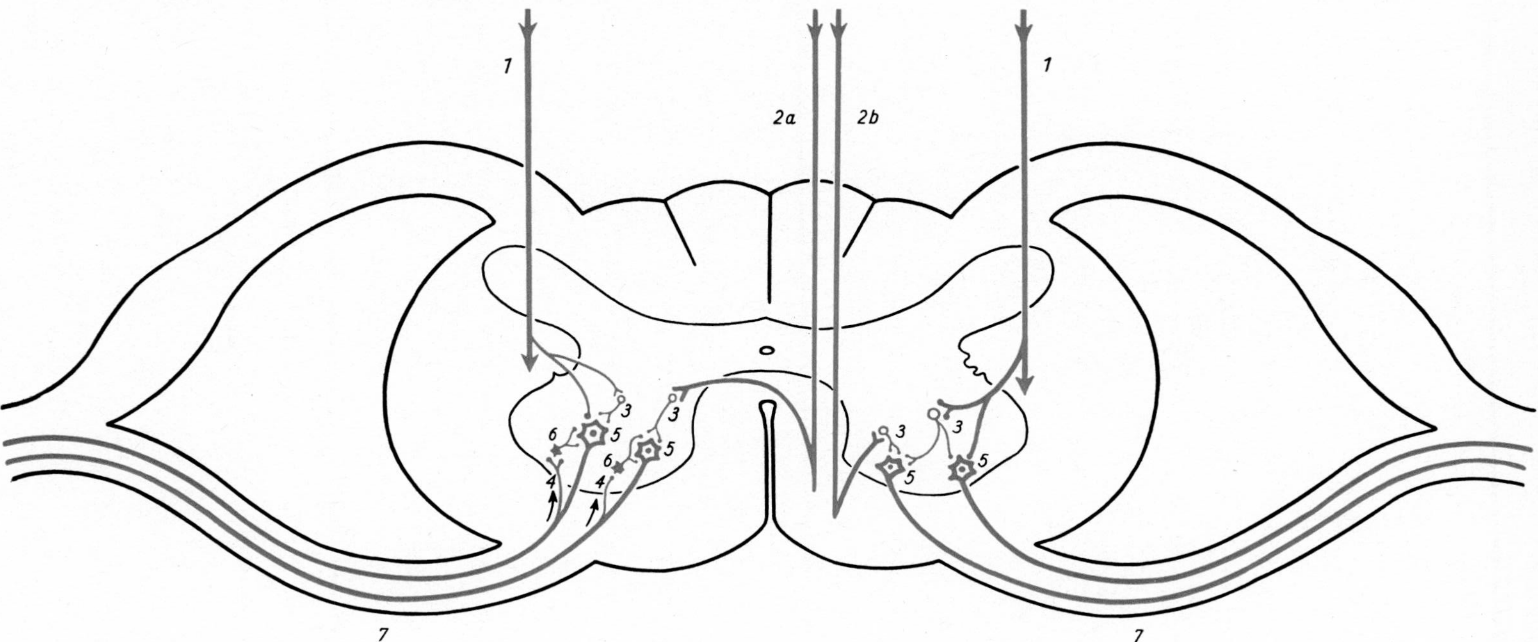
1
1
2a
2b
3
3
3
3
4
4
5
5
5
5
6
6
7
7

(1) **Lateral corticospinal tract:** Neuron-cell body (pyramidal cell) in precentral gyrus or motor cortex of cerebral hemisphere. Fibers have descended and crossed to opposite side in decussation of pyramids. (2a) and (2b) **Anterior corticospinal tract:** Cell bodies are located in motor cortex of cerebral hemisphere, but fibers have not crossed in decussation of the pyramids. Many or most of the latter do cross in the anterior commissure (2a) to synapse directly with the motor neuron (5) in the anterior horn or with

(3) An association relay neuron.

(4) Recurrent collaterals from unmyelinated portion of ventral horn motor cell.

(5) Anterior horn, multipolar motor neuron.

(6) Association neurons (Renshaw) for self-inhibition of motor neurons through a feed-back mechanism.

**Note:** 1. Recent investigations of H. G. J. M. Kuypers indicate that other more complicated feed-back circuits exist. Many motor cortical fibers synapse with the posterior horn cells, with nucleus gracilis, cuneatus, and neurons in other areas.

Fig. 313

## 313. Ascending Spinal Tracts.

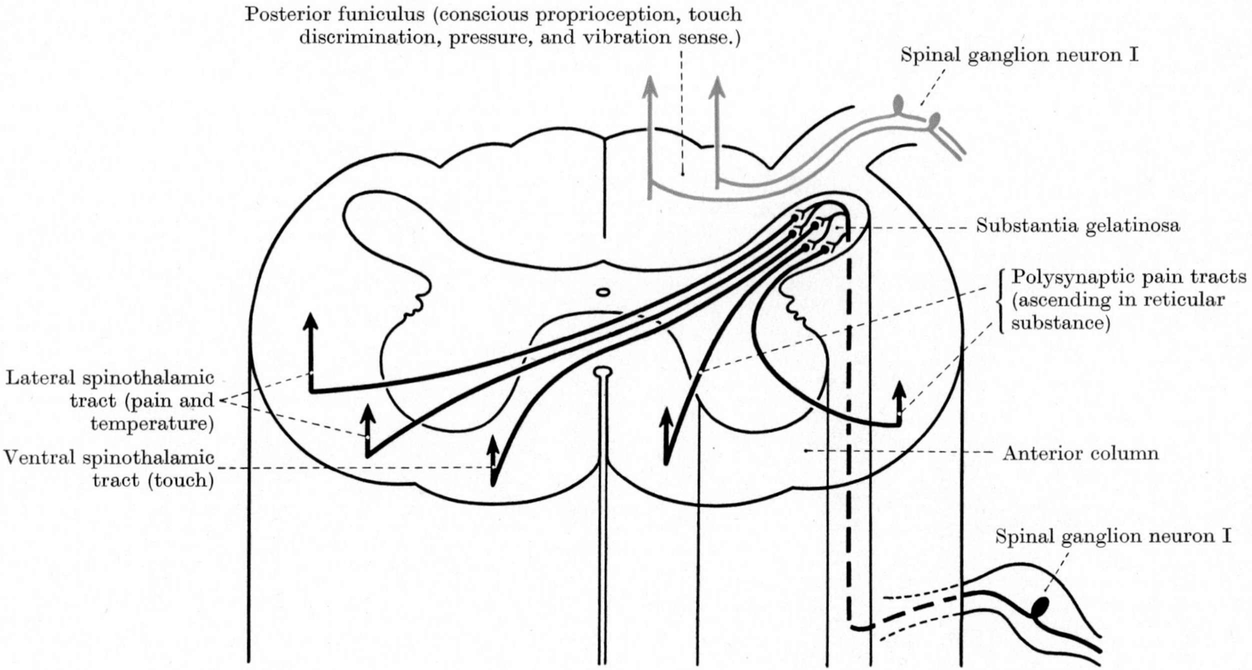
Posterior funiculus (conscious proprioception, touch discrimination, pressure, and vibration sense.)
Spinal ganglion neuron I
Substantia gelatinosa
Polysynaptic pain tracts (ascending in reticular substance)
Lateral spinothalamic tract (pain and temperature)
Ventral spinothalamic tract (touch)
Anterior column
Spinal ganglion neuron I

**Note:** 1. **Blue:** Conscious proprioception, deep touch, pressure, two-point discrimination, and vibration sensations are carried by ascending fibers in the posterior funiculus. Neuron cell body is located in dorsal spinal ganglion. These tracts are sometimes called spinobulbar tracts because they terminate in the ipsolateral nucleus gracilis or cuneatus in medulla oblongata ("bulbar" – fusiform cranial extension of spinal cord).

2. **Black:** Neurons sensitive to pain or noxious stimuli, and temperature differences are small fibers with little myelin. They segregate in the lateral division of the dorsal root and ascend or descend one or two segments in the dorsolateral fasciculus of Lissauer to synapse in the substantia gelatinosa with stellate cells in this area or dendrites of apical posterior gray column cells. Most of the second neurons cross the midline in anterior white commissure and ascend in lateral spinothalamic tract. On left side of cord, uncrossed pain pathways (schematically depicted) ascend as short multisynaptic relays in reticular substance of cord and brain stem. Little is known concerning these short neurons that ascend as crossed and uncrossed (polysynaptic pathways), but it seems likely that they carry a poorly localized deep, dull, persistent pain to the conscious level.

3. The ventral spinothalamic tract mediates light touch sensibility. The fibers take origin from cells in the posterior horn and cross to the opposite side in the anterior white commissure.

## 314. The Posterior Funiculus and the Dorsal and Ventral Spinocerebellar Tracts. (Conscious and Reflex Proprioception)

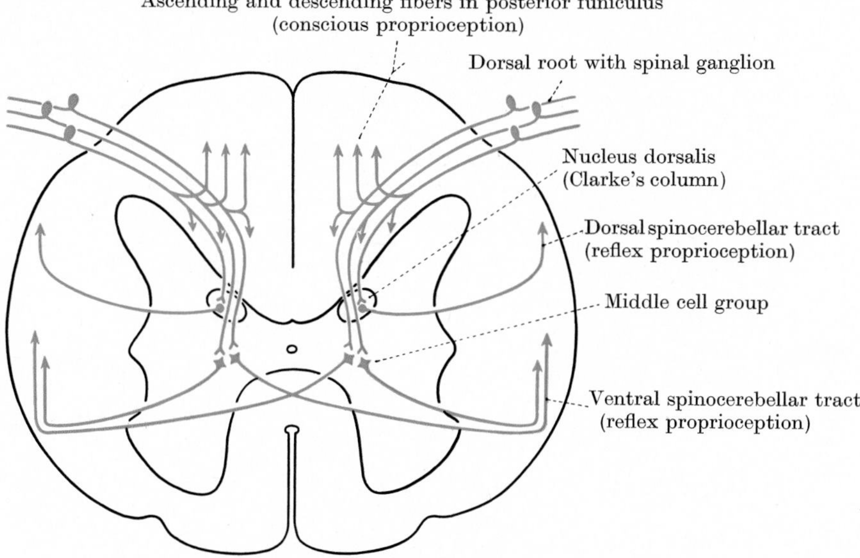
Ascending and descending fibers in posterior funiculus
(conscious proprioception)
Dorsal root with spinal ganglion
Nucleus dorsalis
(Clarke's column)
Dorsal spinocerebellar tract
(reflex proprioception)
Middle cell group
Ventral spinocerebellar tract
(reflex proprioception)

## 315. Primary Motor Neuron: The Final Common Pathway.

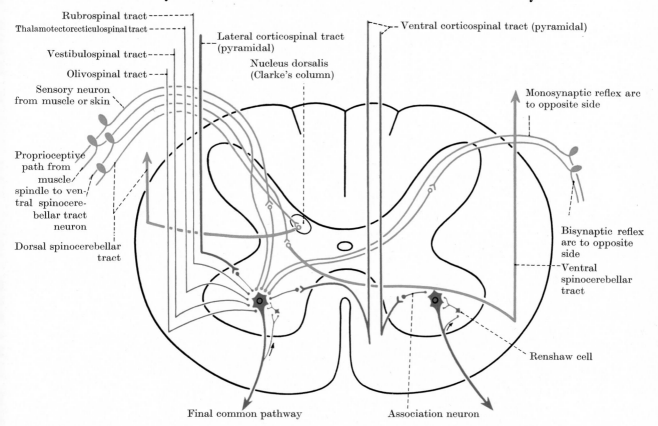

Rubrospinal tract
Thalamotectorecticulospinal tract
Vestibulospinal tract
Olivospinal tract
Sensory neuron from muscle or skin
Proprioceptive path from muscle spindle to ventral spinocerebellar tract neuron
Dorsal spinocerebellar tract
Lateral corticospinal tract (pyramidal)
Nucleus dorsalis (Clarke's column)
Ventral corticospinal tract (pyramidal)
Monosynaptic reflex arc to opposite side
Bisynaptic reflex arc to opposite side
Ventral spinocerebellar tract
Renshaw cell
Final common pathway
Association neuron

**Fig. 316**

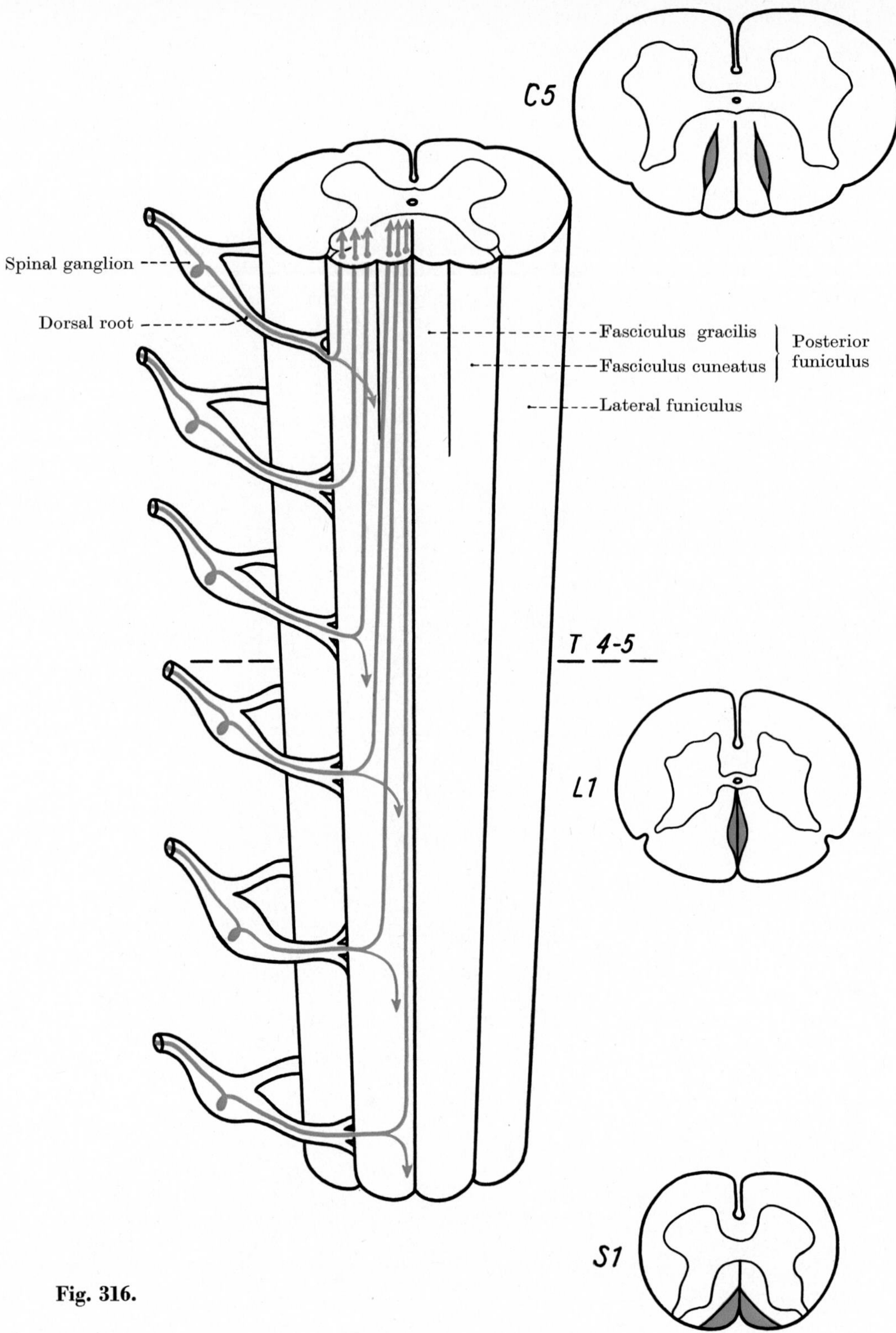

C5
Spinal ganglion
Dorsal root
Fasciculus gracilis
Fasciculus cuneatus
Posterior funiculus
Lateral funiculus
T 4-5
L1
S1


**Fig. 316.**

## 316. Posterior Funiculus; Proprioceptive Pathways. (Spinobulbar Tract).

(Seen from dorsal aspect)

Cross-sections of spinal cord at sacral (S 1), lumbar (L 1), and cervical (C 5) levels, show how fibers from dorsal spinal ganglion cells accumulate from medial to lateral. The fasciculus gracilis is from fibers entering the lower segments; and fasciculus cuneatus from thoracic and cervical segments.

Fig. 317

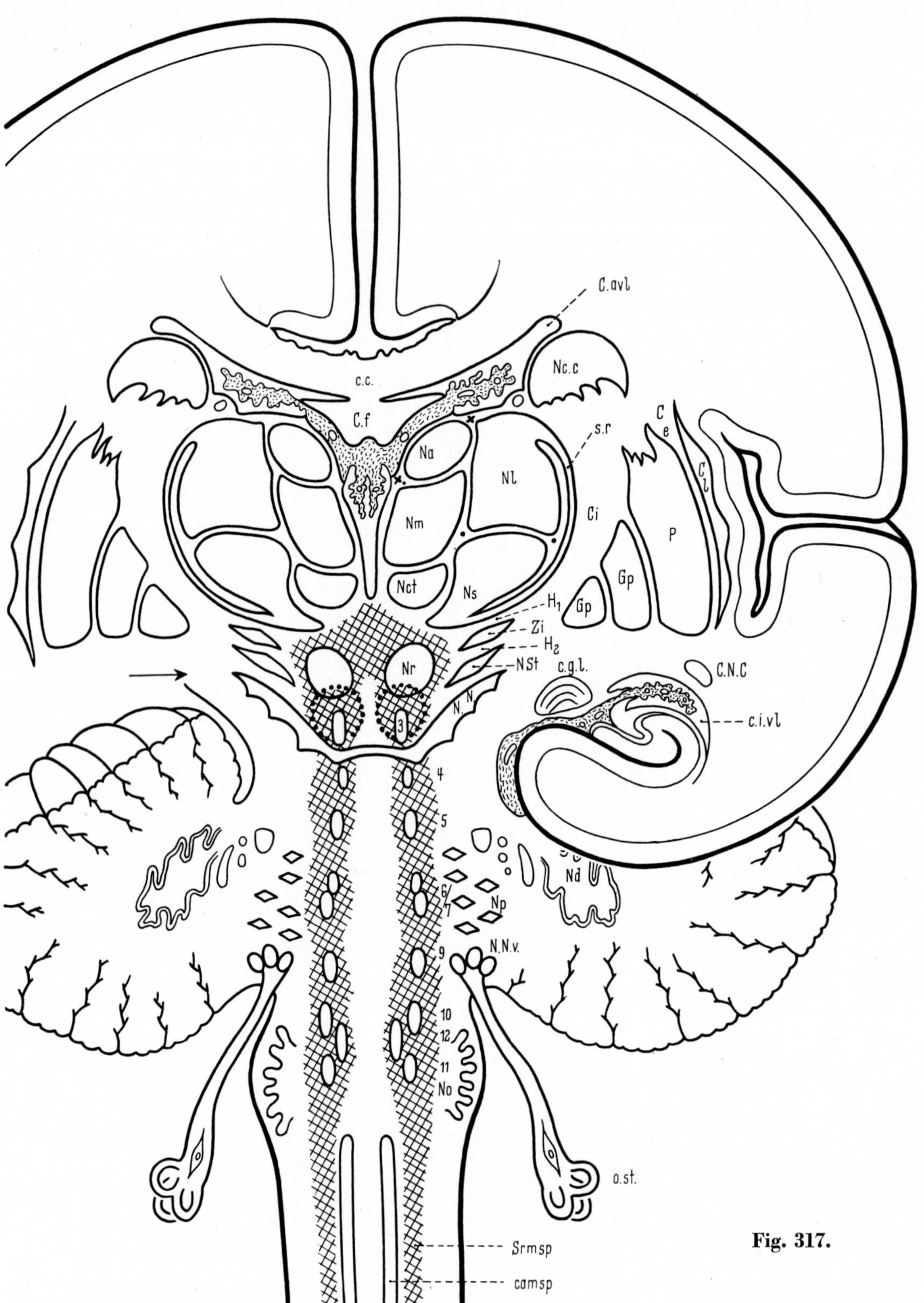

C.avl
Nc.c
c.c.
C.f
s.r
C e
C l
Na
Nl
Nm
Ci
P
Nct
Ns
Gp
Gp
H1
Zi
H2
NSt
c.g.l.
C.N.C
Nr
N.N
3
c.i.vl
4
5
6/7
Np
Nd
9
N.N.v.
10
12
11
No
o.st.
Srmsp
camsp


Fig. 317.

## 317 a. The Reticular Formation (stippled)

(modified from H. W. Magoun, Physiol. Rev. 30 : 459, 1950)

The reticular formation extends from the diencephalon through the entire brain stem and is continuous with the reticular formation of the spinal cord. It receives fibers from many descending (motor) fibers and from ascending sensory elements.

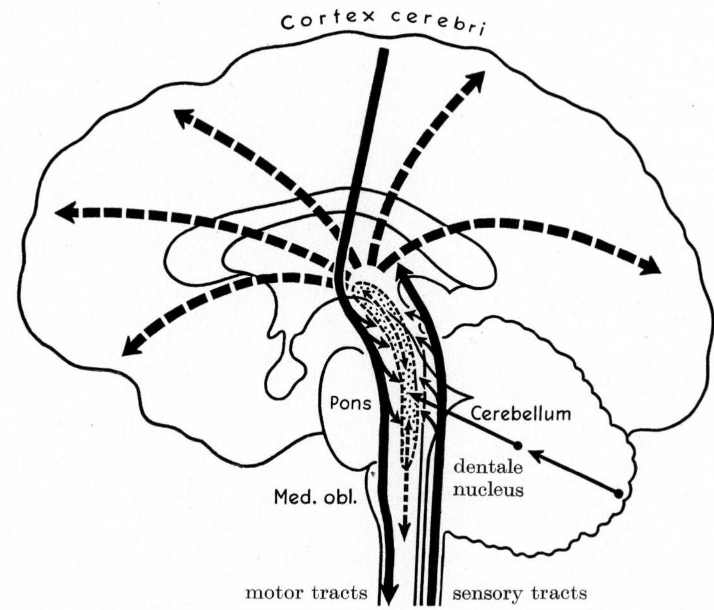

Cortex cerebri
Pons
Cerebellum
dentale nucleus
Med. obl.
motor tracts
sensory tracts


## 317. Diagrammatic Frontal Section of Brain and Brain Stem to Survey and Depict the Extrapyramidal Nuclei.

A composite illustration of Figs. 278, 279, 283, 284, 296, 335.

Cc = Corpus callosum
Cf = Body of the fornix
C avl = Anterior horn, lateral ventricle
Nc c = Head caudate nucleus
c. N. c. = Tail of caudate nucleus
P = Putamen
Gp = Globus pallidus
Cl = Claustrum
Ci = Internal capsule
Ce = External capsule
c. i. vl = Inferior horn, lateral ventricle
Na = Anterior thalamic nucleus
Nm = Medial thalamic nucleus
Ns = Semilunar nucleus of thalamus
Nl = Lateral nucleus of thalamus
Nct = Central nucleus of thalamus
Zi = Zona incerta
NSt = Subthalamic nucleus
$H_1$ = Field of Forel (ventral thalamic fasciculus)
$H_2$ = Field of Forel (fasciculus and ansa lenticularis)
c. g. l = Lateral geniculate body
Nr = Red nucleus
NN = Substantia nigra
Nd = Dentate nucleus of cerebellum
Np = Pontine nuclei
o. st. = Vestibular apparatus
NNv = Vestibular nuclei
No = Olivary nucleus
Srmsp = Reticular formation, medulla spinalis
camsp = Anterior column, medulla spinalis
3 to 12 = Nuclei of cranial nerves
. . . = Medullary lamina of thalamus
x. = Stria medullaris of thalamus
x = Stratum zonale
⟶ = Cerebral peduncle

**318. The Medial Longitudinal Fasciculus:** Coordination of ocular, vestibular, and cerebellar influence in eye and head movements. (Modified from Villiger-Ludwig)

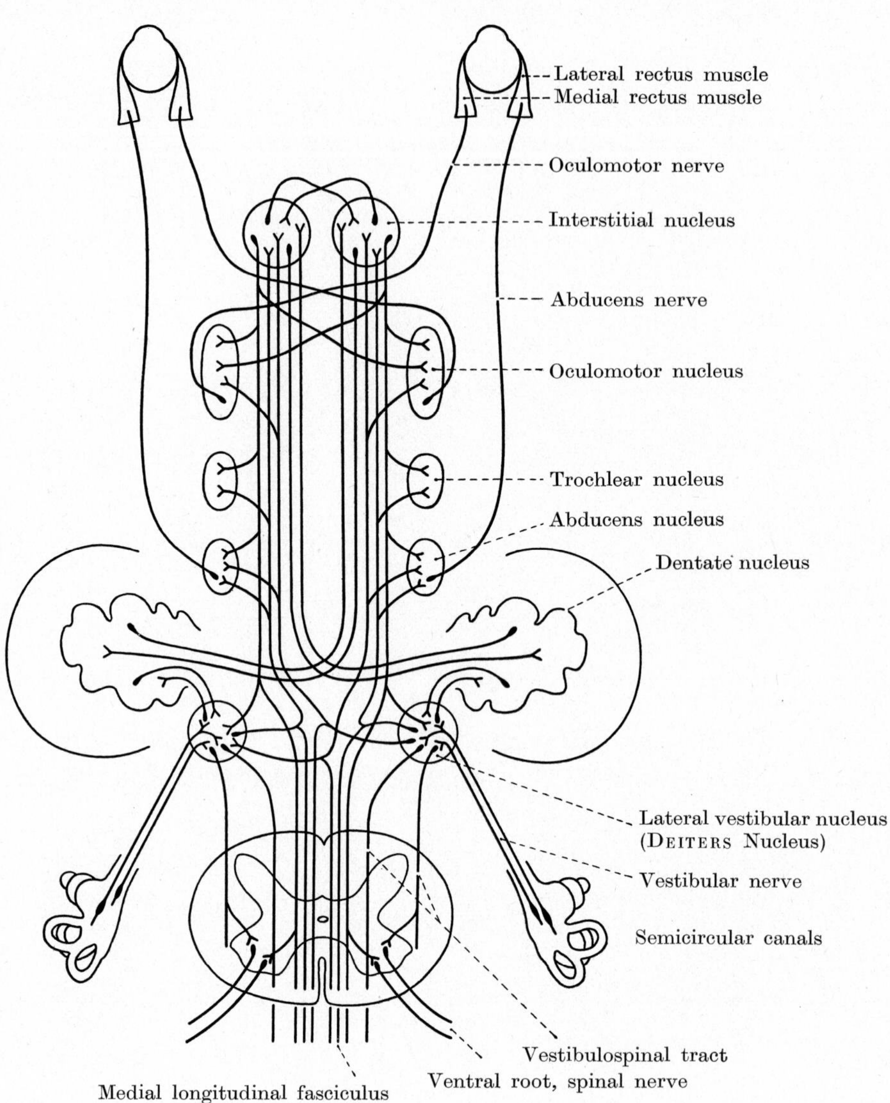
Lateral rectus muscle
Medial rectus muscle
Oculomotor nerve
Interstitial nucleus
Abducens nerve
Oculomotor nucleus
Trochlear nucleus
Abducens nucleus
Dentate nucleus
Lateral vestibular nucleus
(DEITERS Nucleus)
Vestibular nerve
Semicircular canals
Vestibulospinal tract
Ventral root, spinal nerve
Medial longitudinal fasciculus

# 319. Integrative Action of the Central Nervous System.

(Modified from Braus-Elze, Vol. III)

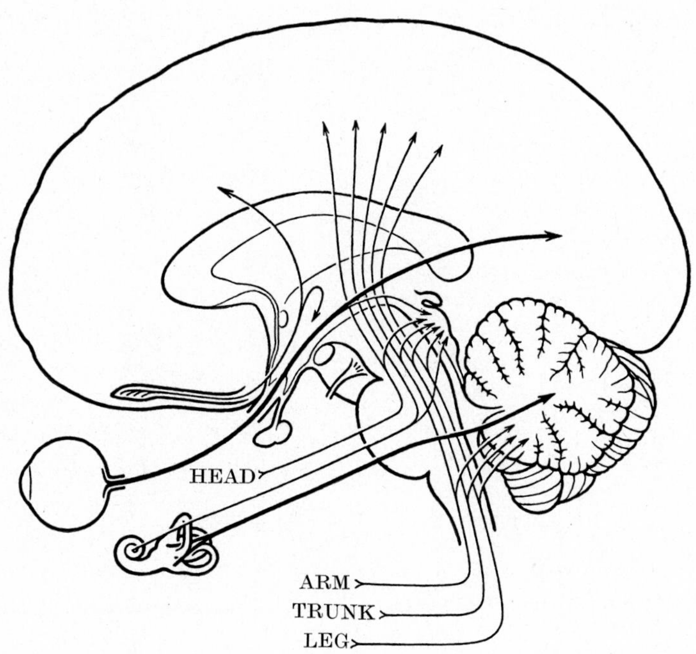
HEAD
ARM
TRUNK
LEG

Diagram illustrates pathways involved in integration of three types of information which comes to the brain before it is transmitted to the ventral horn motor cells.

a) Optic nerve impulses to diencephalon and midbrain tectum.

b) Vestibular impulses to cerebellum and midbrain tectum.

c) Spinal proprioceptive impulses from arm, trunk, and leg to cerebellum and midbrain tectum.

## 320. Brain Fiber Tracts, Right Half of Brain Dissected from Medial Side. (1/1) (Prep. Anat. Inst., Münster)

Numbers refer to numbers on Plate, not clock positions.

1 Corona radiata

2 Corpus callosum

3 Arcuate fibers

4 Internal capsule (frontal limb)

5 Internal capsule, supralentil portion

6 Internal capsule, retrolentil portion

7 Cut edge of removed thalamus

8 Internal capsule

9 Optic chiasma and optic tract

10 Cerebral crus

11 Substantia nigra

12 Quadrigeminal plate

13 Pons with transverse pontine fibers and longitudinal fasciculi

14 Medulla oblongata

15 Cerebellum

16 Fourth ventricle

17 Parietooccipital sulcus

18 Tapetum

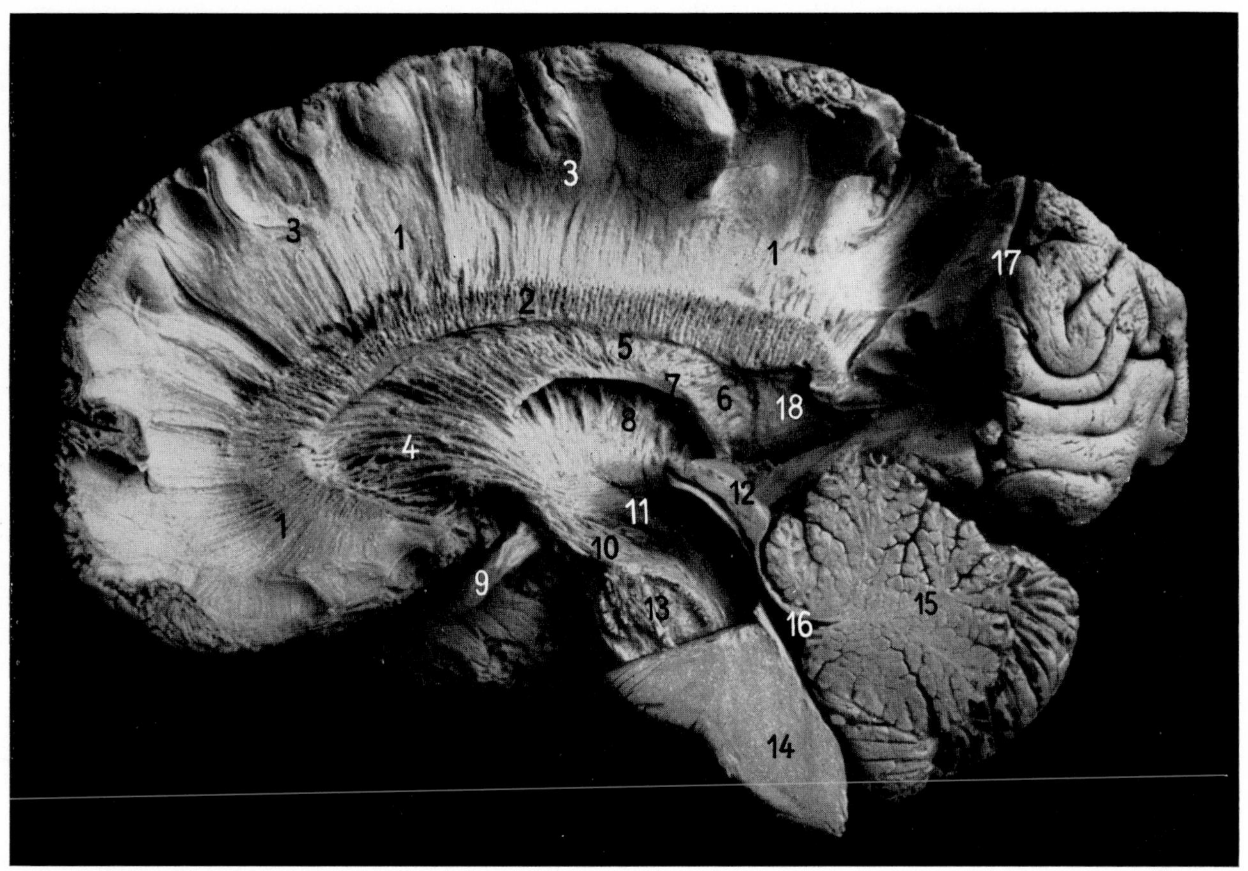
3
3
1
1
2
5
7
6
18
17
8
4
12
11
1
10
9
13
15
16
14

**Fig. 320.**

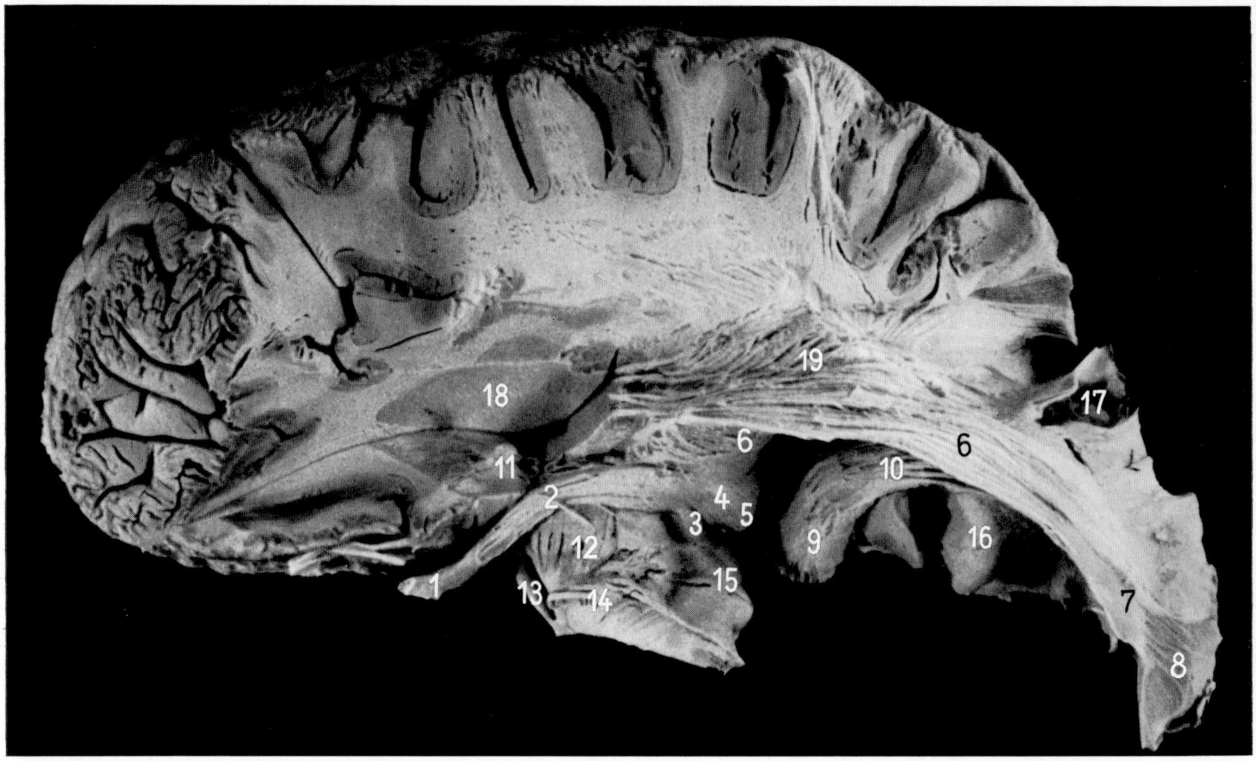

**Fig. 321.**

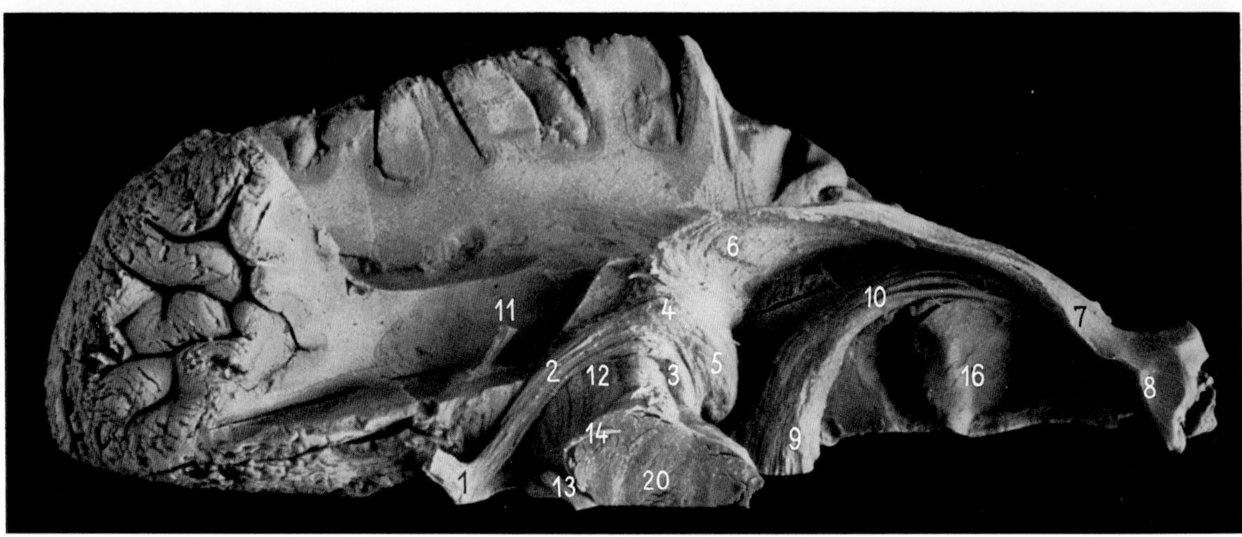
6
11
4
10
7
2
12
3
5
16
8
14
9
1
13
20

**Fig. 322.**

## 321 and 322. Visual Tracts Dissection, Left Cerebral Hemisphere and Midbrain. (1/1) (Prep. Anat. Inst., Münster)

**321.** Viewed from lateral.

**322.** Viewed from below.

Numbers refer to numbers on Plate, not clock positions.

1 Optic chiasma
2 Optic tract
3 Medial geniculate body
4 Lateral geniculate body
5 Pulvinar thalamus
6 Optic radiation, temporal genu
7 Optic radiation, occipital genu
8 Calcarine sulcus
9 Splenium corpus callosum
10 Radiations of corpus callosum (forceps major)
11 Anterior commissure
12 Cerebral crus
13 Oculomotor nerve
14 Tenia pontis
15 Quadrigeminal plate
16 Ridge in parietooccipital sulcus
17 Parietooccipital sulcus
18 Lentiform nucleus
19 Thalamic radiations (occipital limb)
20 Pons (cross-section)

## 323. Dissection of Brain to Show the Parts of the Olfactory Tracts. (1/1) (Prep. Anat. Inst., Münster)

1 **Crus of Fornix**
*crus fornicis*

2 **Splenium of Corpus Callosum**
*splenium corporis callosi*

3 **Dentate Gyrus**
*gyrus dentatus*

**Calcarine Sulcus and Calcar Avis**
*sulcus calcarinus et calcar avis*

**Lateral Ventricle, Posterior Horn**
*cornu posterius ventriculi lateralis*

5 **Fimbria of Hippocampus**
*fimbria hippocampi*

**Parahippocampal Gyrus**
*gyrus parahippocampalis*

6 **Pes Hippocampi**
*pes hippocampi*

7 **Mammillary Bodies and Mammillothalamic Tract**
*corpora mamillaria et tract. mamillothalamicus*

8 **Hippocampal Digitations**
*digitationes hippocampi*

**Amygdaloid Body**
*corpus amygdaloideum*

**Anterior Commissure**
*commissura anterior*

9 **Olfactory Bulb and Tract**
*bulbus et tractus olfactorius*

**Anterior Perforated Substance**
*substantia perforata anterior*

**Anterior Commissure, Olfactory Part**
*pars olfactoria commissurae anterioris*

**Genu of Corpus Callosum**
*genu corporis callosi*

10 **Body and Column of Fornix**
*corpus et columna fornicis*

**Septum Pellucidum**
*septum pellucidum*

11 **Triangular Recess**
*recessus triangularis*

**Lateral Longitudinal Stria of Supracallosal Gyrus**
*stria longitudinalis lateralis corporis callosi*

12 **Medial Longitudinal Stria of Supracallosal Gyrus**
*stria longitudinalis medialis corporis callosi*

Lateral ventricle was opened, but the corpus callosum-2, -9 was retained. The brain stem, diencephalon, and midbrain were removed. The fornix was dissected free and so were the mammillary bodies-7, mammillothalamic tract-7, and anterior commissure-9.

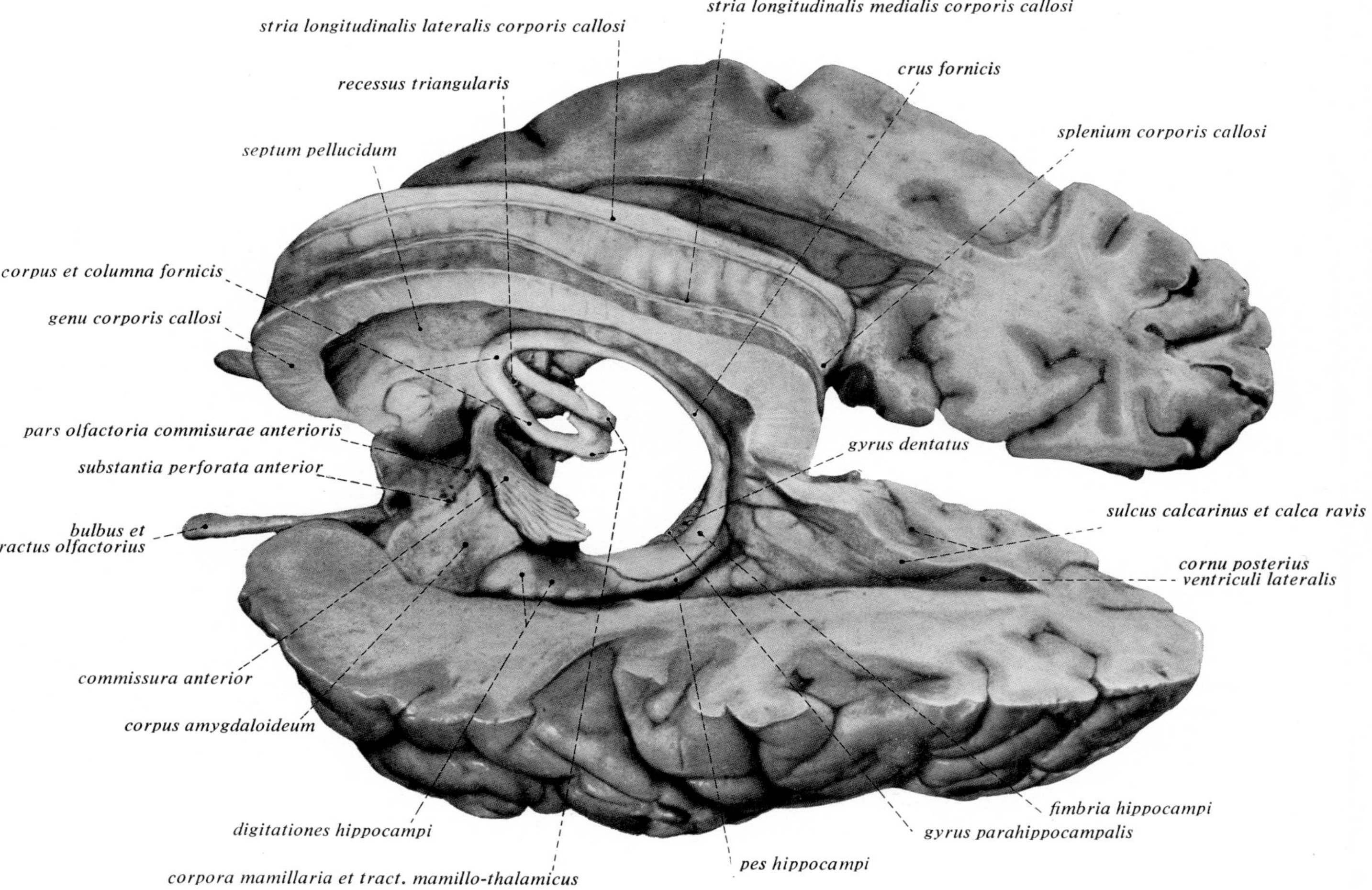

stria longitudinalis medialis corporis callosi
stria longitudinalis lateralis corporis callosi
recessus triangularis
crus fornicis
splenium corporis callosi
septum pellucidum
corpus et columna fornicis
genu corporis callosi
pars olfactoria commisurae anterioris
substantia perforata anterior
gyrus dentatus
bulbus et
tractus olfactorius
sulcus calcarinus et calca ravis
cornu posterius
ventriculi lateralis
commissura anterior
corpus amygdaloideum
fimbria hippocampi
digitationes hippocampi
gyrus parahippocampalis
pes hippocampi
corpora mamillaria et tract. mamillo-thalamicus


**Fig. 323.**

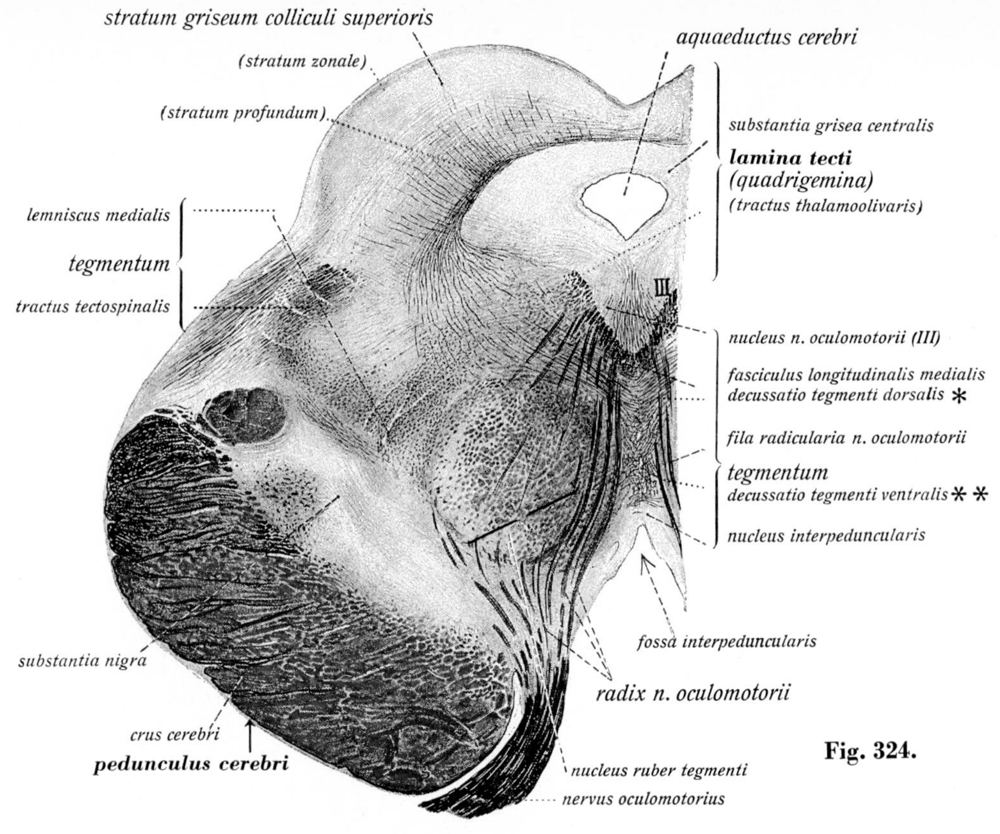
stratum griseum colliculi superioris
(stratum zonale)
(stratum profundum)
aquaeductus cerebri
substantia grisea centralis
lamina tecti
(quadrigemina)
(tractus thalamoolivaris)
lemniscus medialis
tegmentum
tractus tectospinalis
III
nucleus n. oculomotorii (III)
fasciculus longitudinalis medialis
decussatio tegmenti dorsalis *
fila radicularia n. oculomotorii
tegmentum
decussatio tegmenti ventralis * *
nucleus interpeduncularis
fossa interpeduncularis
radix n. oculomotorii
substantia nigra
crus cerebri
pedunculus cerebri
nucleus ruber tegmenti
nervus oculomotorius

**Fig. 324.**

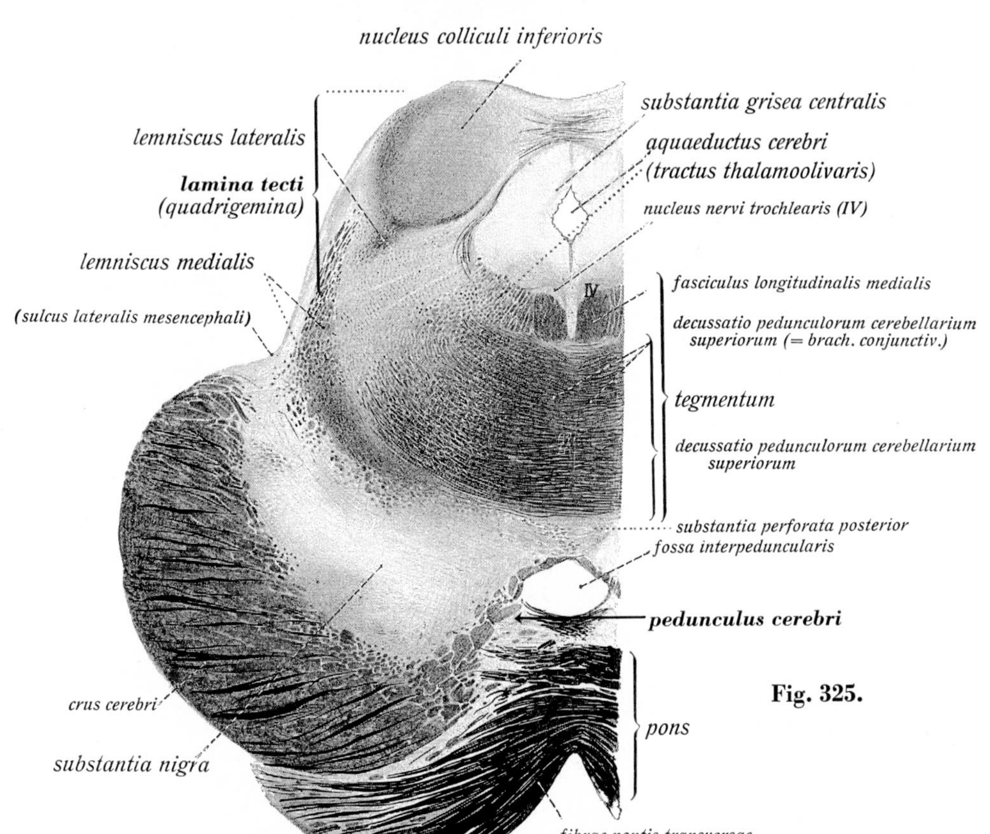
nucleus colliculi inferioris
lemniscus lateralis
lamina tecti
(quadrigemina)
substantia grisea centralis
aquaeductus cerebri
(tractus thalamoolivaris)
nucleus nervi trochlearis (IV)
lemniscus medialis
(sulcus lateralis mesencephali)
IV
fasciculus longitudinalis medialis
decussatio pedunculorum cerebellarium superiorum (= brach. conjunctiv.)
tegmentum
decussatio pedunculorum cerebellarium superiorum
substantia perforata posterior
fossa interpeduncularis
pedunculus cerebri
crus cerebri
pons
substantia nigra
fibrae pontis transversae

**Fig. 325.**

## 324. Mesencephalon at Level of Superior Colliculus. (4/1)

1 **Cerebral Aqueduct**
*aqueductus cerebri*

2 **Central Gray Substance**
*substantia grisea centralis*

**Tectal Lamina (Quadrigemina) (Thalamoolivary Tract)**
*lamina tecti (quadrigemina) (tractus thalamoolivaris)*

**Oculomotor Nucleus (III)**
*nucleus n. oculomotorii (III)*

3 **Medial Longitudinal Fasciculus**
*fascic. longitudinalis medialis*

**Dorsal Tegmental Decussation**
*decussatio tegmenti dorsalis*

**Oculomotor N., Root Filaments**
*fila radicularia n. oculomotorii*

**Ventral Tegmentum Decussation**
*decussatio tegmenti ventralis*

4 **Interpeduncular Nucleus**
*nucleus interpeduncularis*

5 **Interpeduncular Fossa**
*fossa interpeduncularis*
**Root of Oculomotor Nerve**
*radix n. oculomotorii*
**Red Nucleus**
*nucleus ruber tegmenti*

6 **Oculomotor Nerve**
*nervus oculomotorius*

7 **Cerebral Peduncle**
*pedunculus cerebri*
**Cerebral Crus**
*crus cerebri*

8 **Substantia Nigra**
*substantia nigra*

9 **Tectospinal Tract**
*tractus tectospinalis*

10 **Tegmentum**
*tegmentum*

**Medial Lemniscus**
*lemniscus medialis*

11 **Stratum Profundum**
*(stratum profundum)*

**Stratum Zonale**
*(stratum zonale)*

**Superior Colliculus, Stratum Griseum of**
*stratum griseum colliculi superioris*

**Note:** 1. Long descending cortical fiber tracts form **cerebral crus** or **peduncle**-7.

2. **Substantia nigra**-8 separates **cerebral crus** from **tegmentum.**

3. **Tegmentum**-3, -10 contains: (a) **medial lemniscus**-10 (bulbothalamic tract, proprioceptive fibers mainly); (b) **tectospinal tract**-9; (c) **medial longitudinal fasciculus**-3 (coordinates special senses, head and eye movement reflex centers); (d) **red nucleus**-5; (e) **reticulotegmental nucleus**; (f) **dorsal tegmental decussation**-3, (fibers from superior colliculus and tectum on way to tectobulbar and tectospinal tracts); (g) **ventral tegmental decussation**-3 (fibers from red nucleus, rubrobulbar, and rubrospinal tracts); (h) **decussation of superior cerebellar peduncle** (Fig. 325-3) (fibers from central cerebellar nuclei to red nucleus and thalamus, for muscle coordination.

4. **Nucleus of oculomotor nerve**-2 and filaments of oculomotor rootlets-3 streaming through mesencephalon toward interpeduncular fossa-5 emerge there as the oculomotor nerve-6 and root-5.

## 325. Mesencephalon at Level of Inferior Colliculus. (4/1)

1 **Central Gray Matter**
*substantia grisea centralis*

**Cerebral Aqueduct (Thalamoolivary Tract)**
*aqueductus cerebri (tractus thalamoolivaris)*

2 **Trochlear Nucleus (IV)**
*nucleus nervi trochlearis (IV)*

**Medial Longitudinal Fasciculus**
*fascic. longitudinalis medialis*

**Decussation of Superior Cerebellar Peduncle**
*decussatio pedunculorum cerebellarium superiorum (brach. conjunctiv.)*

3 **Tegmentum**
*tegmentum*
**Decussation of Superior Cerebellar Peduncle**
*decussatio pedunculorum cerebellarium superiorum*
**Posterior Perforated Substance**
*substantia perforata posterior*
**Interpeduncular Fossa**
*fossa interpeduncularis*

4 **Cerebral Peduncle**
*pedunculus cerebri*

5 **Pons**
*pons*
**Transverse Pontine Fibers**
*fibrae pontis transversae*

8 **Substantia Nigra**
*substantia nigra*
**Cerebral Crus**
*crus cerebri*

10 **(Lateral Mesencephalic Sulcus)**
*(sulcus lateralis mesencephali)*

**Medial Lemniscus**
*lemniscus medialis*

11 **Tectal Lamina (Quadrigemina)**
*lamina tecti (quadrigemina)*

**Lateral Lemniscus**
*lemniscus lateralis*

12 **Inferior Collicular Nucleus**
*nucleus colliculi inferioris*

**Note:** 1. **Nucleus of trochlear nerve**-2 in ventral central gray substance.

2. **Medial longitudinal fasciculus**-2 is well defined.

3. **Medial lemniscus**-10 near lateral tegmental surface.

4. **Lateral lemniscus**-11, auditory pathway to inferior colliculus.

5. **Decussation of superior cerebellar peduncle**-2, -3 (brachium conjunctivum) is extensive at this level (cerebellorubral and cerebellothalamic tracts).

## 326. Diagram of Configuration of Mesencephalon. (Müller-Spatz) (see Figs. 324, 325)

1 **Cerebral Aqueduct**
*aqueductus cerebri*

**Stratum Griseum, Superior Colliculus**
*stratum griseum colliculi superioris*

2 **Accessory Nucleus (Autonomic), Oculomotor Nerve**
*nucleus accessorius (autonomicus) n. oculomotorii*

**Dorsolateral Nucleus, Oculomotor Nerve**
*nucleus dorsolateralis n. oculomotorii*

**Trigeminal Nerve**
*n. trigem.*
**Tegmental Radiations**
*(raditio tegmenti)*
**Medial Geniculate Body**
*corpus geniculatum mediale*
**Tegmental Red Nucleus**
*nucleus ruber tegmenti*
**Tegmentum of Cerebral Peduncle**
*tegmentum pedunculi cerebri*
**Corticopontine, Occipitopontine and Temporopontine Tracts**
*tractus corticopontinus, tr. occipitopontinus + tr. temporopontinus*

4 **Corticospinal Tract and Corticonuclear Tract**
*tractus corticospinalis + tr. corticonuclearis*

5 **Corticopontine Tract and Frontopontine Tract**
*tractus corticopontinus, tr. frontopontinus*

6 **Rootlets, Oculomotor Nerve**
*fila radicularia nervi oculomotorii*

8 **Cerebral Crus**
*crus cerebri*

**Substantia Nigra (Zona Nigra) (Zona Rubra)**
*substantia nigra (zona nigra) (zona rubra)*
**Substantia Nigra**
*substantia nigra*

9 **Medial Lemniscus**
*lemniscus medialis*

10 **Nucleus of Mesencephalic Tract Trigeminal Nerve**
*nucleus tract. mesencephalici n. trigemini*
**Medial Longitudinal Fasciculus**
*fascic. longitudinalis medialis*

**Note:** 1. **Mesencephalon** consists of a ventral portion: cerebral peduncle; and a dorsal portion: the **tectum** (quadrigeminal plate). The term **tectal lamina** indicates that it is the roof of the mesencephalon.

2. **Tectum** is a mixture of gray and white matter containing four large nuclei responsible for four rounded elevations, called quadrigeminal bodies or colliculi:

(a) **Superior colliculus**-1 and **pretectal region** on each side are terminal nuclei for optic tracts and are involved in many important visual reflex activities.

(b) **Inferior colliculus** is closely associated with termination of central auditory pathways and reflexes. Both colliculi also receive fibers from spinal cord, medulla oblongata, cerebellum, and other parts of the nervous system.

(c) Cerebral aqueduct-1 connects third and fourth ventricles and is surrounded by a relatively thick layer of gray matter (stippled) called **central gray layer**. In addition to scattered neurons, there are compact groups of nerve cells associated with the central gray layer of the mesencephalon. These are the **oculomotor** and **trochlear nuclei** and the **mesencephalic nucleus of the trigeminal nerve**.

3. Large ventral part of midbrain is called the cerebral peduncle. It contains long large fiber tracts to and from cerebral hemispheres and thalamus. It is separated into the cerebral crus and **tegmentum** by the pigmented **substantia nigra.**

4. The part dorsal to the substantia nigra is called the **tegmentum** (or cover). It contains some unusual nuclei such as **red nucleus**, and extensive **reticular formation** continuous with that of the pons, and some long ascending and descending tracts. Red nucleus-3 is conspicuous at level of superior colliculus. Important tracts which stand out in this region are: (a) **medial lemniscus**-9 on its way from medulla oblongata to thalamus; (b) **medial longitudinal fasciculus**-10, connecting centers for special senses (hearing and vision) with neck muscles responsible for reflex movements of the head.

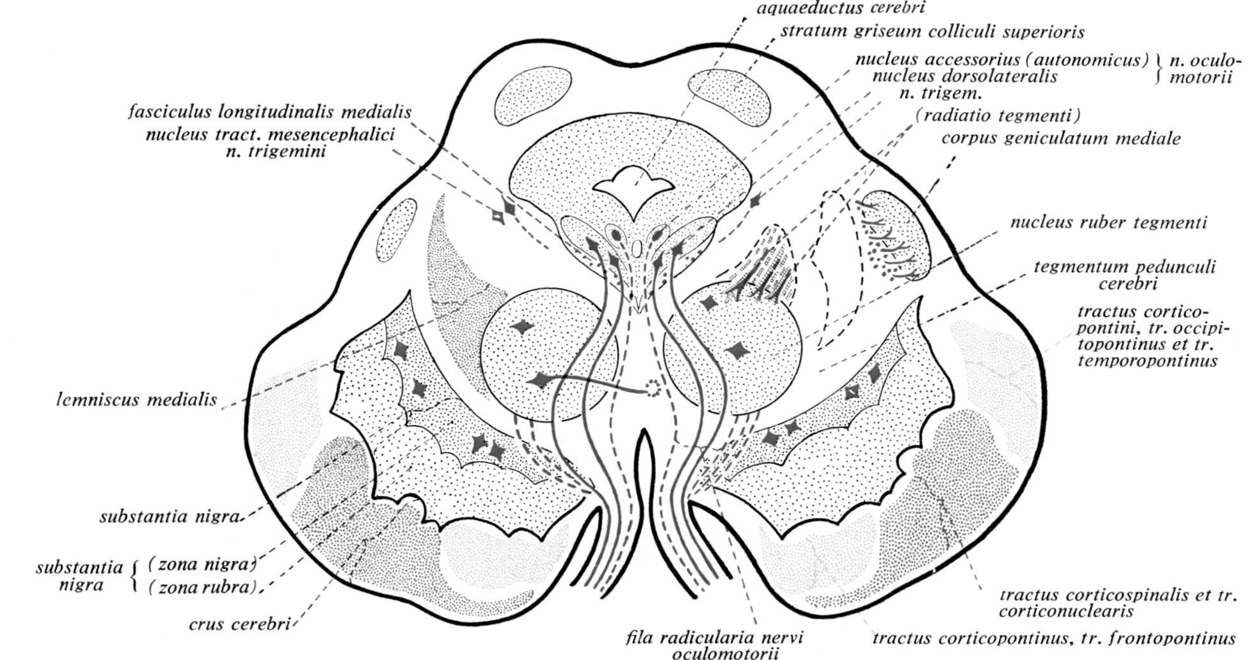
aquaeductus cerebri
stratum griseum colliculi superioris
nucleus accessorius (autonomicus)
nucleus dorsolateralis
n. oculo-motorii
n. trigem.
(radiatio tegmenti)
corpus geniculatum mediale
fasciculus longitudinalis medialis
nucleus tract. mesencephalici n. trigemini
nucleus ruber tegmenti
tegmentum pedunculi cerebri
tractus cortico-pontini, tr. occipi-topontinus et tr. temporopontinus
lemniscus medialis
substantia nigra
substantia nigra
(zona nigra)
(zona rubra)
crus cerebri
tractus corticospinalis et tr. corticonuclearis
fila radicularia nervi oculomotorii
tractus corticopontinus, tr. frontopontinus

**Fig. 326.**

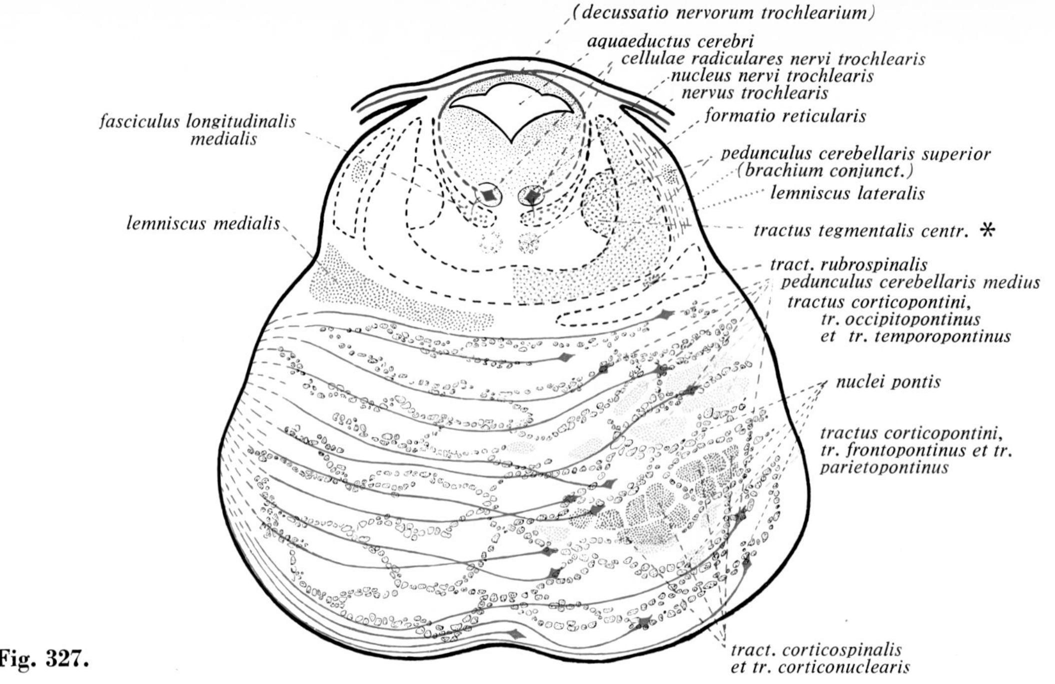
(decussatio nervorum trochlearium)
aquaeductus cerebri
cellulae radiculares nervi trochlearis
nucleus nervi trochlearis
nervus trochlearis
formatio reticularis
fasciculus longitudinalis medialis
pedunculus cerebellaris superior (brachium conjunct.)
lemniscus lateralis
lemniscus medialis
tractus tegmentalis centr. *
tract. rubrospinalis
pedunculus cerebellaris medius
tractus corticopontini, tr. occipitopontinus et tr. temporopontinus
nuclei pontis
tractus corticopontini, tr. frontopontinus et tr. parietopontinus
tract. corticospinalis et tr. corticonuclearis

Fig. 327.

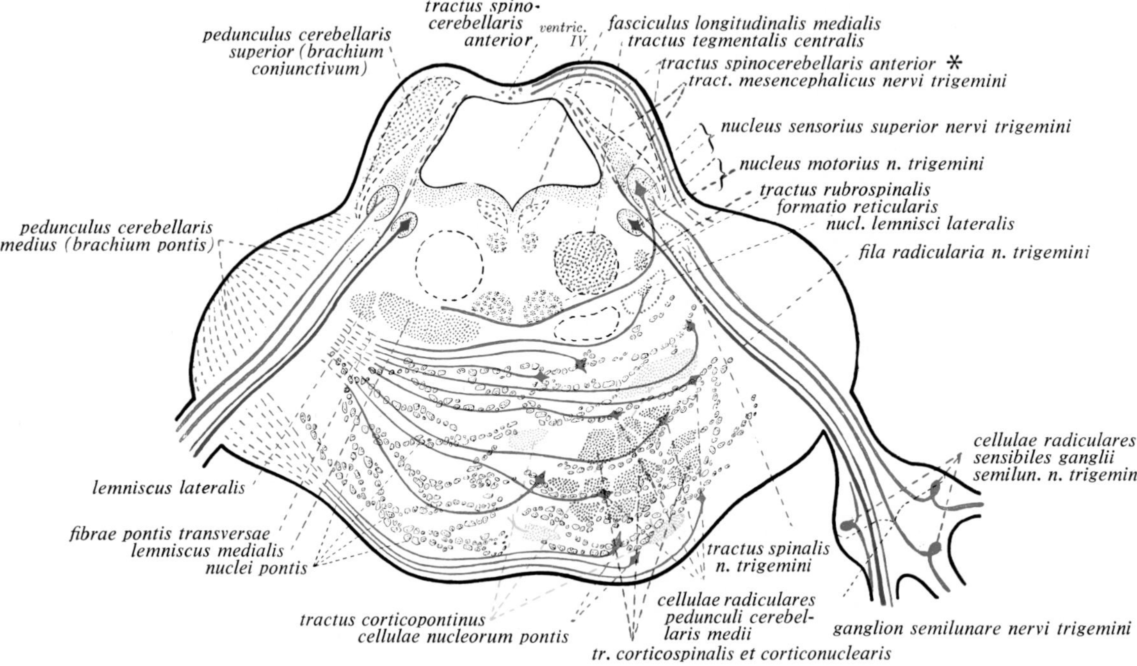
tractus spino-cerebellaris anterior
ventric. IV
fasciculus longitudinalis medialis
tractus tegmentalis centralis
pedunculus cerebellaris superior (brachium conjunctivum)
tractus spinocerebellaris anterior *
tract. mesencephalicus nervi trigemini
nucleus sensorius superior nervi trigemini
nucleus motorius n. trigemini
tractus rubrospinalis
formatio reticularis
nucl. lemnisci lateralis
pedunculus cerebellaris medius (brachium pontis)
fila radicularia n. trigemini
cellulae radiculares sensibiles ganglii semilun. n. trigemini
lemniscus lateralis
fibrae pontis transversae
lemniscus medialis
nuclei pontis
tractus spinalis n. trigemini
cellulae radiculares pedunculi cerebellaris medii
tractus corticopontinus
cellulae nucleorum pontis
ganglion semilunare nervi trigemini
tr. corticospinalis et corticonuclearis

Fig. 328.

## 327. Rostral Part of Pons. (Schematic Diagram) (Müller-Spatz)

1 **Nucleus of Trochlear Nerve**
*cellulae radiculares nervi trochlearis*
**Trochlear (Nerve) Nucleus**
*nucleus nervi trochlearis*
**Trochlear Nerve**
*nervus trochlearis*
**Reticular Formation**
*formatio reticularis*

2 **Superior Cerebellar Peduncle (Brachium Conjunctivum)**
*pedunculus cerebellaris superior (brachium conj.)*
**Lateral Lemniscus**
*lemniscus lateralis*
**Central Tegmental Tract**
*tractus tegmentalis centr.*
**Rubrospinal Tract**
*tract. rubrospinalis*
**Middle Cerebellar Peduncle**
*pedunculus cerebellaris medius*

3 **Corticopontine Tract; Occipitopontine Tract + Temporopontine Tract**
*tractus corticopontini, tr. occipitopontinus + tr. temporopontinus*
**Pontine Nuclei**
*nuclei pontis*
**Corticopontine Tract, Frontopontine + Parietopontine Tracts**
*tractus corticopontini, tr. frontopontinus, + tr. parietopontinus*

5 **Corticospinal Tract + Corticonuclear Tract**
*tract. corticospinalis + tr. corticonuclearis*

10 **Medial Lemniscus**
*lemniscus medialis*
**Medial Longitudinal Fasciculus**
*fascic. longitudinalis medialis*

12 **Decussation of Trochlear Nerves**
*(decussatio nervorum trochlearium)*
**Aqueductus Cerebri**
*aquedutus cerebri*

**Note:** Compare with Figure 329, a section just caudal to this one.
**Red:** (a) Descending tracts: **corticospinal**-5, **corticonuclear**, and **rubrospinal**-2.
(b) Trochlear nucleus-1 and its decussating fibers-12.
**Blue:** (a) Ascending tracts: **medial lemniscus**-10, central tegmental tract-2.
(b) Some of cells of **pontine nuclei**-3, their transverse fibers forming middle cerebellar peduncle-2.
(c) **Medial longitudinal fasciculus**-10.
**Green:** **Superior cerebellar peduncle**-2 (brachium conjunctivum).
**Yellow:** **Corticopontine tracts**-3.

## 328. Middle of Pons. (Schematic Diagram)

1 **Anterior Spinocerebellar Tract**
*tractus spinocerebellaris anterior*
**Trigeminal Mesencephalic Tr.**
*tr. mesencephalicus n. trigemini*
**Superior Sensory Nucleus of Trigeminal**
*nucleus sensorius sup. n. trigem.*
**Trigeminal Motor Nucleus**
*nucleus motorius n. trigemini*

2 **Rubrospinal Tract**
*tractus rubrospinalis*
**Reticular Formation**
*formatio reticularis*
**Lateral Lemniscus Nucleus**
*nucl. lemnisci lateralis*

3 **Filaments of Trigeminal Nerve**
*fila radicularia n. trigemini*

4 **Cells of Sensory Root Ganglion of Trigeminal Nerve**
*cellulae radiculares sensibiles ganglii [trigem.] semilun. n. trigemini*

5 **Trigeminal Nerve, Semilunare Ganglion [Trigeminal Ganglion]**
*ganglion semilunare nervi trigemini [ganglion trigeminale]*
**Trigeminal Nerve, Spinal Tract**
*tractus spinalis n. trigemini*
**Cells of Origin of Middle Cerebellar Peduncle**
*cellulae radiculares pedunculi cerebellaris medii*
**Corticospinal Tract + Corticonuclear**
*tr. corticospinalis + corticonuclearis*

6 **Cells of Pontine Nucleus**
*cellulae nucleorum pontis*

7 **Corticopontine Tract**
*tractus corticopontinus*

8 **Pontine Nuclei**
*nuclei pontis*
**Medial Lemniscus**
*lemniscus medialis*
**Transverse Pontine Fibers**
*fibrae pontis transversae*
**Lateral Lemniscus**
*lemniscus lateralis*

9 **Middle Cerebellar Peduncle (Brachium Pontis)**
*pedunculus cerebellaris medius (brachium pontis)*

11 **Superior Cerebellar Peduncle (Brachium Conjunctivum)**
*pedunculus cerebellaris superior (brachium conjunctivum)*

12 **Anterior Spinocerebellar Tract**
*tractus spinocerebellaris anterior*
**Fourth Ventricle**
*Ventric. IV*
**Medial Longitudinal Fasciculus**
*fascic. longitudinalis medialis*
**Central Tegmental Tract**
*tractus tegmentalis centralis*

**Note:** 1. Colors indicate same structures as in Figure 327, with these additions:
**Red:** (a) **Motor nucleus of trigeminal and efferent fibers.**
**Blue:** (a) **Anterior spinocerebellar fibers**-1.
(b) Area (blue broken lines) where **middle cerebellar peduncle**-9 was removed.
2. **Reticular formation**-2, depicted as a small circumscribed area, is much larger and boundaries are indefinite.

## 329. Brain Stem at Level of Pons. (5/1) (Tracts, dark; gray matter, light)

1 **Trigeminal Nerve, Mesencephalic Tract**
*tractus mesencephalicus n. trigemini*
**Locus Coruleus**
*locus coruleus*
**Central Gray Matter**
*substantia grisea centralis*
**Superior Medullary Velum**
*velum medullare anterius [superius]*
**Fourth Ventricle**
*ventriculus quartus*
**Medial Eminence**
*eminentia medialis*
**Medial Longitudinal Fasciculi**
*fasciculi longitudinales mediales*

2 **Pons, Dorsal Portion**
*pars dorsalis pontis*
**Reticular Formation**
*formatio reticularis*
**Tegmental Nucleus**
*nucleus tegmenti*

3 **Transverse Pontine Fibers**
*fibrae pontis transversae*
**Raphe Pontis**
*raphe pontis*

4 **Pons, Basilar Portion**
*pars basilaris pontis*
**Pontine Nuclei**
*nuclei pontis*

7 **Transverse Pontine Fibers**
*fibrae pontis transversae*

8 **Longitudinal Fasciculi of Pons (Corticospinal Tract)**
*fasciculi longitudinales (tractus corticospinalis) pontis*

10 **Medial Lemniscus**
*lemniscus medialis*
**Lateral Lemniscus (Acoustic)**
*lemniscus lateralis (acusticus)*

11 **Thalamoolivary Tract**
*tractus thalamoolivaris*
**Nucleus of Lateral Lemniscus**
*nucleus lemnisci lateralis*
**Anterior Spinocerebellar Tract**
*tractus spinocerebellaris anterior*
**Superior Cerebellar Peduncle (Brachium Conjunctivum)**
*pedunculus cerebellaris superior (brachium conjunctivum)*

**Note:** 1. Fibers of **cerebral crus** pass through **basilar portion of pons**-4. These long cortical fiber tract bundles (**longitudinal pontine fasciculi**-8) are split up in basilar part of pons by scattered **pontine nuclei**-4 and their **transverse pontine fibers**-3, on their way to middle cerebellar peduncles.

2. In **dorsal portion of pons**-2:
(a) **reticular formations**-2;
(b) **medial lemniscus**-10 (flattened horizontally);
(c) **medial longitudinal fasciculus**-1;
(d) **superior cerebellar peduncle**-11 decussates in mesencephalon and distributes fibers to red nucleus and thalamus;
(e) **lateral lemniscus**-10 (auditory pathway to inferior colliculus).

## 330. Caudal Part of Pons, at Level of Abducens Nucleus. (5/1)

1 **Abducens Nucleus VI**
*nucleus n. abducentis (VI)*
**Facial Colliculus**
*colliculus facialis*
**Genu of Facial Nerve**
*genu n. facialis*
**Medial Longitudinal Fasciculus**
*fascic. longitudinalis medialis*
**Root Filaments of Abducens Nerve**
*fila radicularia n. abducentis*

2 **Pons, Dorsal Portion**
*pars dorsalis pontis*
**Reticular Formation**
*formatio reticularis*

3 **Medial Lemniscus**
*lemniscus medialis*
**Trapezoid Body**
*corpus trapezoideum*

4 **Raphe of Pons**
*raphe pontis*
**Pontine Nuclei**
*nuclei pontis*
**Basilar Portion of Pons**
*pars basilaris pontis*

5 **Basilar Sulcus of Pons**
*sulcus basilaris pontis*

7 **Longitudinal Fasciculi of Pons (Corticospinal Tract)**
*fasciculi longitudinales (tractus corticospinalis) pontis*
**Transverse Pontine Fibers**
*fibrae pontis transversae*
**Middle Cerebellar Peduncle (Brachium Pontis)**
*pedunculus cerebellaris medius (brachium pontis)*

9 **Ventral Nucleus of Trapezoid Body**
*nucleus [ventralis] anterior corporis trapezoidei*

10 **Nucleus of Facial Nerve**
*nucleus nervi facialis*
**Nucleus of Spinal Tract (5th)**
*nucl. tract. spinalis n. trigem.*
**Inferior Cerebellar Peduncle (Restiform Body)**
*pedunculus cerebellaris inferior (corpus restiforme)*
**Root of Facial Nerve**
*radix n. facialis*

11 **Superior Vestibular Nucleus**
*nucleus vestibularis superior*

12 **Fourth Ventricle**
*ventriculus quartus*
**Rhomboid Fossa**
*fossa rhomboidea*

**Note:** 1. Root fibers-10 of facial nerve make a bend around **abducens nucleus**-1. Only **genu of facial nerve**-1 is clearly visible.

2. **Middle cerebellar peduncle**-8 where cerebellum was attached.

3. VI denotes **abducens nucleus**-1. Root filaments of abducens nerve-1 sweep ventrally to exit near pontomedullary junction.

4. At this level, transverse pontine fibers-8 are less numerous and tend to form bundles (**trapezoid body**-3). Longitudinal corticospinal fasciculi of the pons-7 (corticonuclear tracts) become aggregated and more conspicuous, but they remain separated by pontine nuclei-4 and a few bundles of transverse fibers.

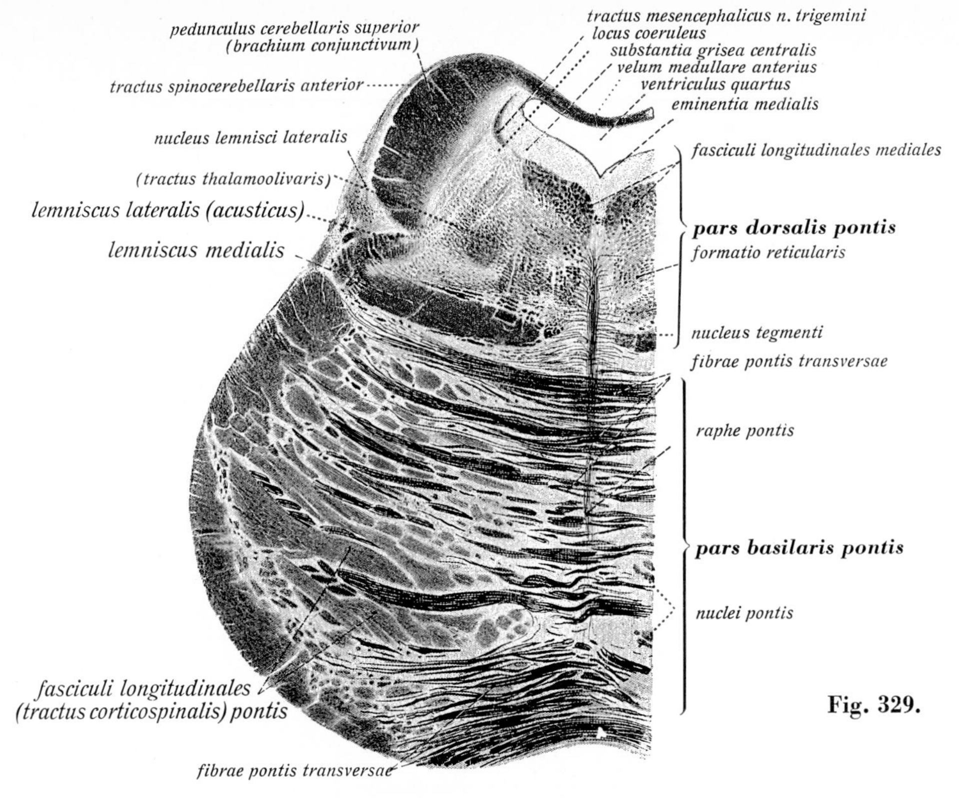

pedunculus cerebellaris superior
(brachium conjunctivum)
tractus spinocerebellaris anterior
nucleus lemnisci lateralis
(tractus thalamoolivaris)
lemniscus lateralis (acusticus)
lemniscus medialis
tractus mesencephalicus n. trigemini
locus coeruleus
substantia grisea centralis
velum medullare anterius
ventriculus quartus
eminentia medialis
fasciculi longitudinales mediales
pars dorsalis pontis
formatio reticularis
nucleus tegmenti
fibrae pontis transversae
raphe pontis
pars basilaris pontis
nuclei pontis
fasciculi longitudinales
(tractus corticospinalis) pontis
fibrae pontis transversae


**Fig. 329.**

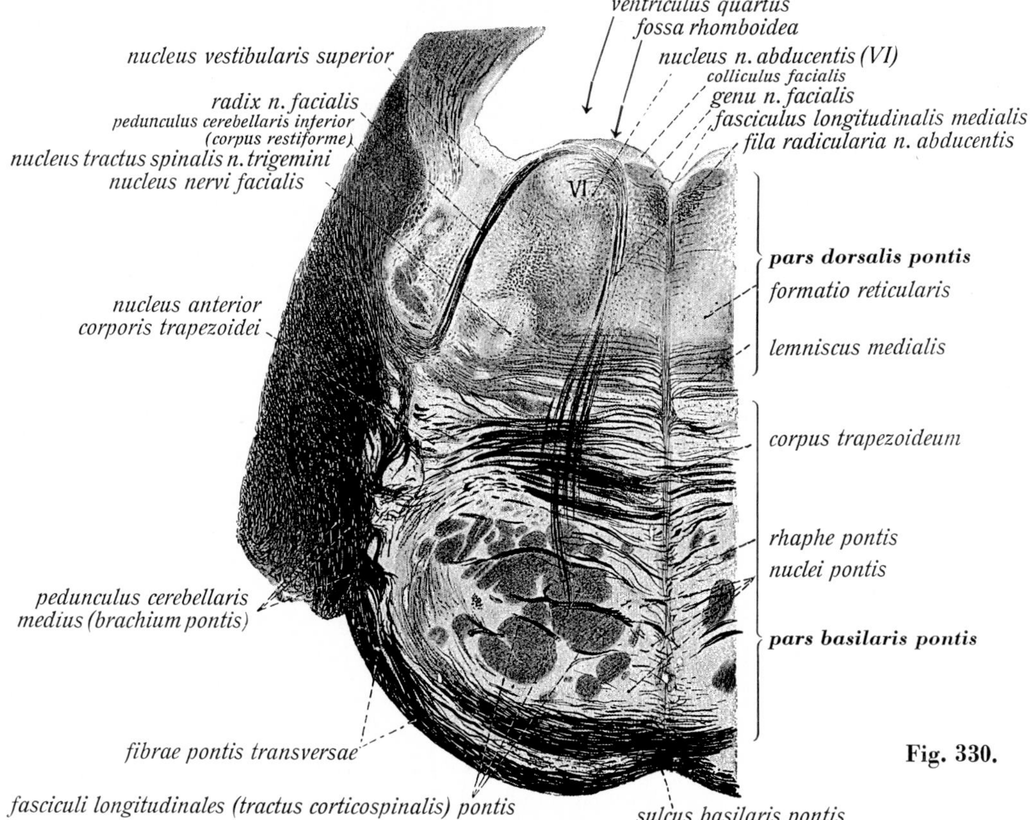

ventriculus quartus
fossa rhomboidea
nucleus vestibularis superior
radix n. facialis
pedunculus cerebellaris inferior
(corpus restiforme)
nucleus tractus spinalis n. trigemini
nucleus nervi facialis
nucleus n. abducentis (VI)
colliculus facialis
genu n. facialis
fasciculus longitudinalis medialis
fila radicularia n. abducentis
VI
pars dorsalis pontis
formatio reticularis
lemniscus medialis
nucleus anterior
corporis trapezoidei
corpus trapezoideum
rhaphe pontis
nuclei pontis
pars basilaris pontis
pedunculus cerebellaris
medius (brachium pontis)
fibrae pontis transversae
fasciculi longitudinales (tractus corticospinalis) pontis
sulcus basilaris pontis


**Fig. 330.**

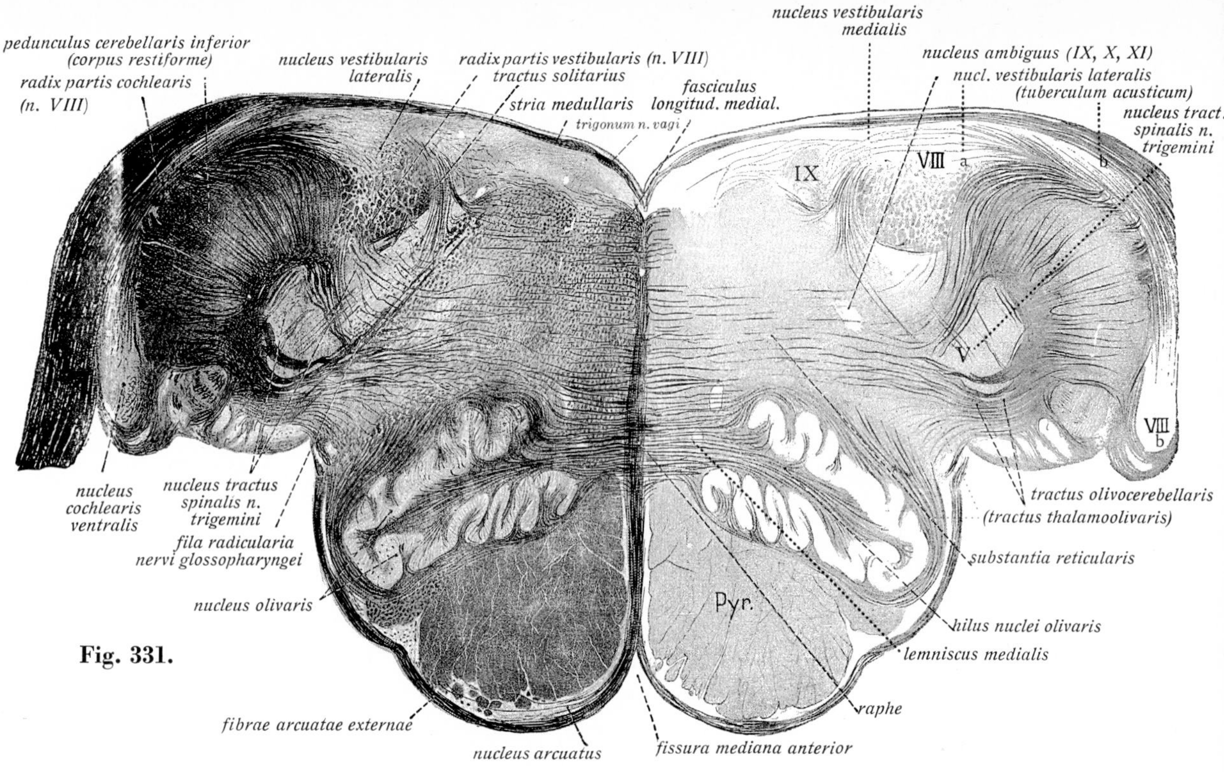

pedunculus cerebellaris inferior (corpus restiforme)
radix partis cochlearis (n. VIII)
nucleus vestibularis lateralis
radix partis vestibularis (n. VIII)
tractus solitarius
stria medullaris
trigonum n. vagi
fasciculus longitud. medial.
nucleus vestibularis medialis
nucleus ambiguus (IX, X, XI)
nucl. vestibularis lateralis (tuberculum acusticum)
nucleus tract. spinalis n. trigemini
IX
VIII a
b
V
VIII b
nucleus cochlearis ventralis
nucleus tractus spinalis n. trigemini
fila radicularia nervi glossopharyngei
nucleus olivaris
Pyr.
tractus olivocerebellaris (tractus thalamoolivaris)
substantia reticularis
hilus nuclei olivaris
lemniscus medialis
raphe
fibrae arcuatae externae
nucleus arcuatus
fissura mediana anterior

**Fig. 331.**

nucleus intercalatus
nucleus dorsalis n. vagi
nucleus vestibularis medialis
radix partis vestibularis
substantia reticularis
ala cinerea
raphe
fasciculus longitudin. medialis
tractus solitarius
nucleus tractus solitarii
nucleus cochlearis dorsalis
pedunculus cerebellaris inferior (corpus restiforme)
IX
VIII a
b
XII
X
X
XI
V
nucleus tractus spinalis nervi trigemini
fila radicularia nervi accessorii
fila radicularia n. vagi
tractus olivocerebellaris
fila radicularia nervi vagi
fila radicularia n. accessorii
nucleus olivaris accessorius dorsalis
nucleus olivaris
substantia reticularis
XII
hilus nuclei olivaris
nucleus ambiguus
nucleus olivaris [oliva inferior]
fila radicularia nervi hypoglossi
nucleus olivaris accessorius medialis
pyramis
ibrae arcuatae externae
lemniscus medialis
nucleus arcuatus

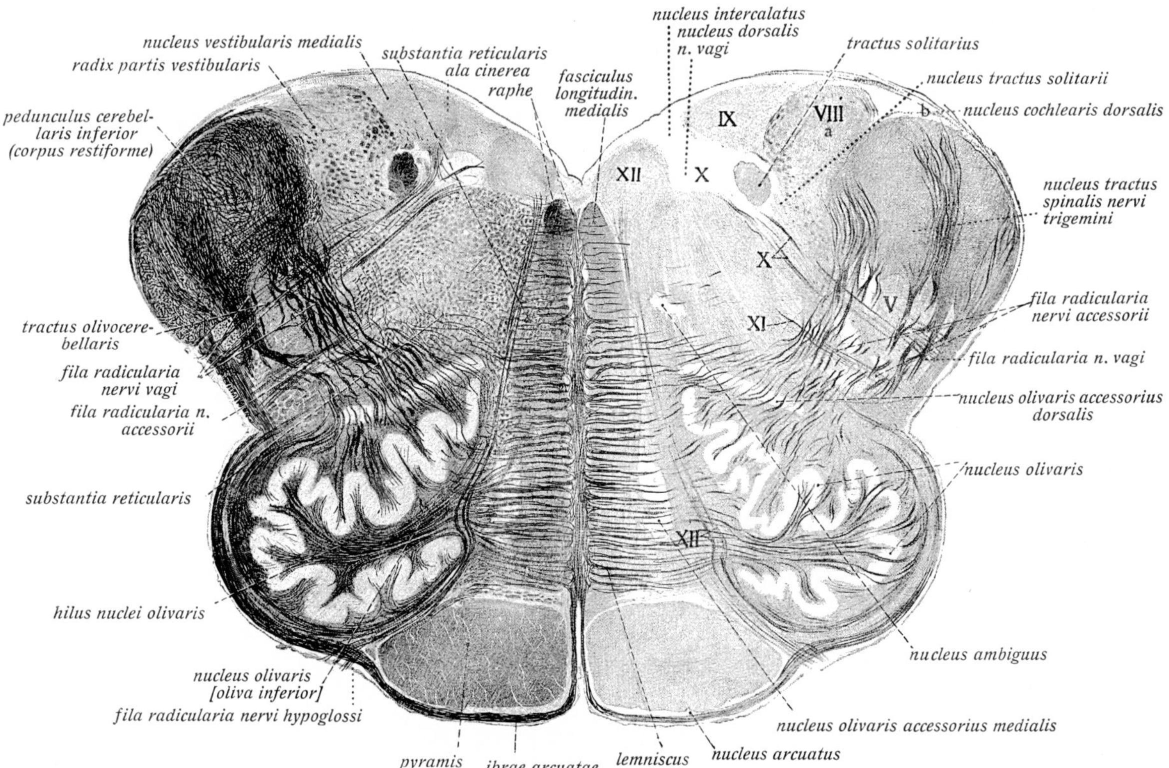

**Fig. 332.**

## 331. Section Through Rostral Part of Medulla Oblongata. (7/1)

Roman numbers indicate nuclei of corresponding cerebral nerves.

1 **Medial Vestibular Nucleus**
*nucleus vestibularis medialis*
**Nucleus Ambiguus IX, X, XI**
*nucleus ambiguus (IX, X, XI)*

2 **Lateral Vestibular Nucleus**
*nucl. vestibularis lateralis*
**Tuberculum Acusticum**
*(tuberculum acusticum)*
**Nucleus of Spinal Tract of V**
*nucleus tr. spinalis n. trigemini*

3 **Olivocerebellar Tract**
*tractus olivocerebellaris*
**Thalamoolivary Tract**
*(tractus thalamoolivaris)*

4 **Reticular Substance**
*substantia reticularis*
**Hilus of Olivary Nucleus**
*hilus nuclei olivaris*
**Medial Lemniscus**
*lemniscus medialis*

5 **Raphe**
*raphe*
**Pyramid**
*pyramis*

6 **Anterior Median Fissure**
*fissura mediana anterior*

7 **Arcuate Nucleus**
*nucleus arcuatus*

8 **External Arcuate Fibers**
*fibrae arcuatae externae*
**Olivary Nucleus**
*nucleus olivaris*
**Root Filaments of Glosso-pharyngeal Nerve**
*fila radicularia nervi glosso-pharyngei*

9 **Nucleus of Spinal Tract of V**
*nucleus tr. spinalis n. trigemini*
**Ventral Cochlear Nucleus**
*nucleus cochlearis ventralis*

10 **Root of Cochlear Part (VIII N.)**
*radix partis cochlearis*
**Inferior Cerebellar Peduncle (Restiform Body)**
*pedunculus cerebellaris inferior (corpus restiforme)*
**Lateral Vestibular Nucleus**
*nucleus vestibularis lateralis*

11 **Root Fibers of Vestibular Nerve**
*radix partis vestibularis (n. VIII)*
**Solitary Tract**
*tractus solitarius*
**Stria Medullaris**
*stria medullaris*

12 **Trigone of Vagus Nerve**
*trigonum n. vagi*
**Medial Longitudinal Fasciculus**
*fasciculus longitud. medial.*

**Note:** 1. Long descending tracts in pons collect to form the **pyramids** (pyr.)-5.
2. **Medial lemniscus**-4 and **medial longitudinal fasciculus**-12 near midline.
3. Diffuse ill-defined **reticular substance**-4.
4. **Nucleus ambiguus**-1 medial to **nucleus of spinal tract** of V-2, -9.

## 332. Section Through Medulla Oblongata at Middle of Olive. (7/1)

1 **Dorsal Nucleus of Vagus Nerve**
*nucleus dorsalis n. vagi*
**Solitary Tract**
*tractus solitarius*

2 **Nucleus of Solitary Tract**
*nucleus tractus solitarii*
**Dorsal Cochlear Nucleus**
*nucleus cochlearis dorsalis*
**Nucleus, Spinal Tract of V**
*nucleus tractus spinalis nervi trigemini*

3 **Rootlet Fibers of Accessory N.**
*fila radicularia nervi accessorii*
**Rootlet Fibers of Vagus Nerve**
*fila radicularia n. vagi*
**Dorsal Accessory, Olivary Nuc.**
*nucleus olivaris accessorius dorsalis*
**Olivary Nucleus**
*nucleus olivaris*

4 **Nucleus Ambiguus**
*nucleus ambiguus*

5 **Medial Accessory Olivary Nuc.**
*nucleus olivaris accessorius medialis*
**Arcuate Nucleus**
*nucleus arcuatus*

6 **Medial Lemniscus**
*lemniscus medialis*
**External Arcuate Fibers**
*fibrae arcuatae externae*

7 **Pyramid**
*pyramis*

8 **Root Filaments, Hypoglossal N.**
*fila radicularia nervi hypoglossi*
**Inferior Olivary Nucleus**
*nucleus olivaris (oliva inferior)*
**Hilus of Olivary Nucleus**
*hilus nuclei olivaris*

9 **Reticular Substance**
*substantia reticularis*
**Root Filaments, Accessory N.**
*fila radicularia n. accessorii*
**Root Filaments of Vagus Nerve**
*fila radicularia nervi vagi*
**Olivocerebellar Tract**
*tractus olivocerebellaris*

10 **Inferior Cerebellar Peduncle (Restiform Body)**
*pedunculus cerebellaris inferior (corpus restiforme)*
**Root of Vestibular Part**
*radix partis vestibularis*

11 **Medial Vestibular Nucleus**
*nucleus vestibularis medialis*
**Reticular Substance**
*substantia reticularis*
**Ala Cinerea**
*ala cinerea*

12 **Raphe**
*rhaphe*
**Medial Longitudinal Fasciculus**
*fasciculus longitudin. medialis*
**Nucleus Intercalatus**
*nucleus intercalatus*

**Note:** 1. **Pyramids**-7, (corticospinal tract) **medial lemniscus**-6, prominent **medial longitudinal fasciculus**-12 and **hypoglossal nucleus** XII occupy region of entire medial sagittal plane.

2. **Rootlets of hypoglossal nerve** pass from nucleus XII through medulla to exit between pyramids and olive (somatic motor to all tongue muscles).

3. **Nucleus of solitary tract**-2 (terminal nucleus of vagus sensory fibers).

4. More ventral but indefinite **nucleus ambiguus**-4 (motor to branchiomeric muscles) in proximity of root filaments of 11th cranial or accessory nerve-9.

## 333. Caudal Part of Pons near Pontomedullary Junction. (Müller-Spatz)

1 **Dentate Nucleus (of Cerebellum)**
*nucleus dentatus cerebelli*
**Superior Cerebellar Peduncle**
*
**Facial Genu**
*genu nerv. facial.*
**Cerebellar Cortex**
*cortex cerebelli*

2 **Spinal Tract of Trigeminal Nerve**
*tractus spinalis nervi trigemini*
**Nucleus of Spinal Tract of V**
*nucleus tractus spin. n. trigemini*
**Middle Cerebellar Peduncle (Brachium Pontis)**
*pedunculus cerebellaris medius (brachium pontis)*

3 **Central Tegmental Tract**
*tractus tegmentalis centralis*
**Rubrospinal Tract**
*tract. rubrospinalis*
**Spinothalamic Tract**
*tractus spinothalamicus*

4 **Cerebellar Flocculus**
*flocculus cerebelli*

5 **Pontine Nuclei**
*nuclei pontis*
**Abducens Nerve**
*nervus abducens*
**Fiber from Cerebellar Cortex to Pontine Nuclei**
+

6 **Corticopontine Tract**
*tract. corticopont.*
**Corticospinal and Corticonuclear Tracts**
*tractus corticospinalis + cort.-nuclearis*

8 **Reticular Formation**
*formatio reticularis*
**Trapezoid Body**
*corpus trapezoideum*
**Dorsal Nucleus of Trapezoid Body**
*nucleus dorsalis corporis trapezoidei*
**Nucleus of Abducens Nerve**
*nucleus n. abducentis*

9 **Transverse Fibers of Pons**
*fibrae pontis transversae*
**Medial Vestibular Nucleus**
*nucl. vestibularis medialis*

12 **Vermis of Cerebellum**
*vermis cerebelli*
**Anterior Spinocerebellar Tract**
*tractus spinocerebellaris anterior*
**Fourth Ventricle**
*ventriculus quartus*

## 334. Rostral Part of Medulla Oblongata. (Müller-Spatz)

1 **Emboliform Nucleus**
*nucleus emboliformis*
**Fourth Ventricle**
*ventric. IV*
**Chorioid Plexus of 4th Ventricle**
*plexus chorioideus ventriculi IV*

2 **Dentate Nucleus**
*nucleus dentatus*
**Superior Cerebellar Peduncle (Brachium Conjunctivum)**
*pedunculus cerebellaris superior (brachium conjunctivum)*
**Cerebellar Tonsil**
*tonsilla cerebelli*

3 **Medial Vestibular Nucleus**
*nucl. vestibularis medialis*
**Posterior Spinocerebellar Tract**
*tract. spinocerebellaris posterior*
**Spinal Tract of Trigeminal (V)**
*tractus spinalis n. V*
**Rubrospinal Tract**
*tract. rubrospinalis*
**Cerebellar Flocculus**
*flocculus cerebelli*

4 **Cochlea**
*cochlea*
**Spiral Cochlear Ganglion**
*ganglion spirale cochleae*

5 **Ventral Spinocerebellar Tract**
*tract. spinocer. anterior*
**Central Tegmental Tract**
*tr. tegmentalis centralis*

6 **Corticospinal Tract**
*tractus corticospinalis*

7 **Medial Lemniscus**
*lemniscus medialis*
**Olivary Nucleus**
*nucleus olivaris*
**Spinothalamic Tract**
*tractus spinothalamicus*
**Reticular Formation**
*formatio retic.*

8 **Fiber from Dorsal Cochlear Nucleus to Trapezoid Body**
*
**Superior Ganglion of Glosso-pharyngeal Nerve**
*ganglion superius nervi glosso-pharyngei*
**Ganglion Cell of Nerve IX**
*cellula ganglii nervi IX*
**Spinal Nucleus of Trigeminal N.**
*nucleus tr. spinalis nervi trigemini*
**Chorioid Plexus of 4th Ventricle**
*plexus chorioideus ventriculi IV*
**Ventral Cochlear Nucleus**
*nucl. cochlearis ventralis*

9 **Lateral Recess of 4th Ventricle**
*recessus lateralis ventriculi IV*
**Nucleus of Solitary Tract**
*nucleus tractus solitarii*
**Dorsal Cochlear Nucleus**
*nucleus cochlearis dorsalis*

11 **Inferior Medullary Velum**
*velum medullare posterius [inferius]*

12 **Cortex of Vermis**
*cortex vermis*

**RED:** a) **Corticospinal**, **corticonuclear**, and **rubrospinal tracts.**
b) **Abducens nucleus**-8 and nerve-5 **(root filaments).**
c) **Genu** and **rootlets** of **facial nerve**-1.

**YELLOW:** Small portion of **corticopontine tract**-6.

**GREEN:** **Superior cerebellar peduncle**-1.

**BLACK:** (stippled area) **Reticular formation** arbitrarily outlined for simplicity.

**MIXED COLORS:** **Central tegmental tract**-3

**BLUE: (333) Pontine nuclei**-5, **trapezoid body**-8, **nucleus and tract of trigeminal nerve**-2, **middle cerebellar peduncle** (brachium pontis)-2, medial vestibular nucleus-9, **spinothalamic tract**-3 (pain and temperature), **dentate nucleus**-1 and fibers to superior cerebellar peduncle-1.

**BLUE: (334) Cochlear ganglion** neurons-5, **spinal nucleus** and **tract of trigeminal**-3, **posterior spinocerebellar tract**-3, **medial lemniscus**-7, **spinothalamic tract**-7, **glosso-pharyngeal nucleus of solitary tract**-9.

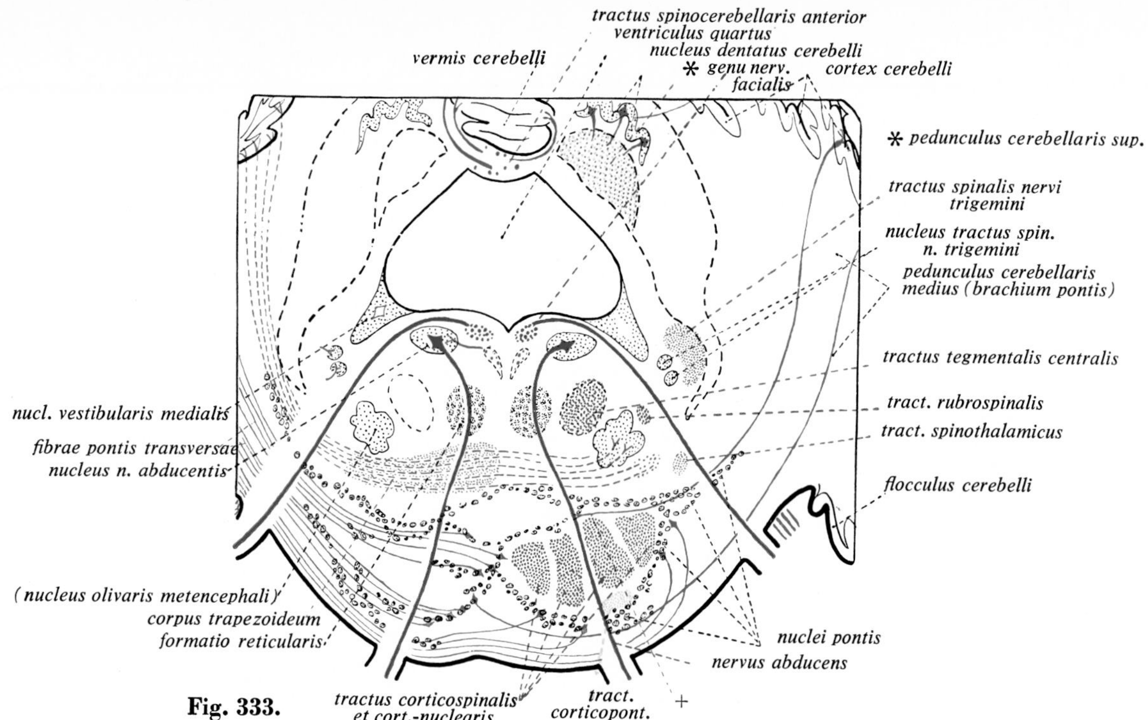
tractus spinocerebellaris anterior
ventriculus quartus
nucleus dentatus cerebelli
vermis cerebelli
* genu nerv. facialis
cortex cerebelli
* pedunculus cerebellaris sup.
tractus spinalis nervi trigemini
nucleus tractus spin. n. trigemini
pedunculus cerebellaris medius (brachium pontis)
tractus tegmentalis centralis
nucl. vestibularis medialis
tract. rubrospinalis
fibrae pontis transversae
tract. spinothalamicus
nucleus n. abducentis
flocculus cerebelli
(nucleus olivaris metencephali)
corpus trapezoideum
formatio reticularis
nuclei pontis
nervus abducens
tractus corticospinalis et cort.-nuclearis
tract. corticopont.
+

**Fig. 333.**

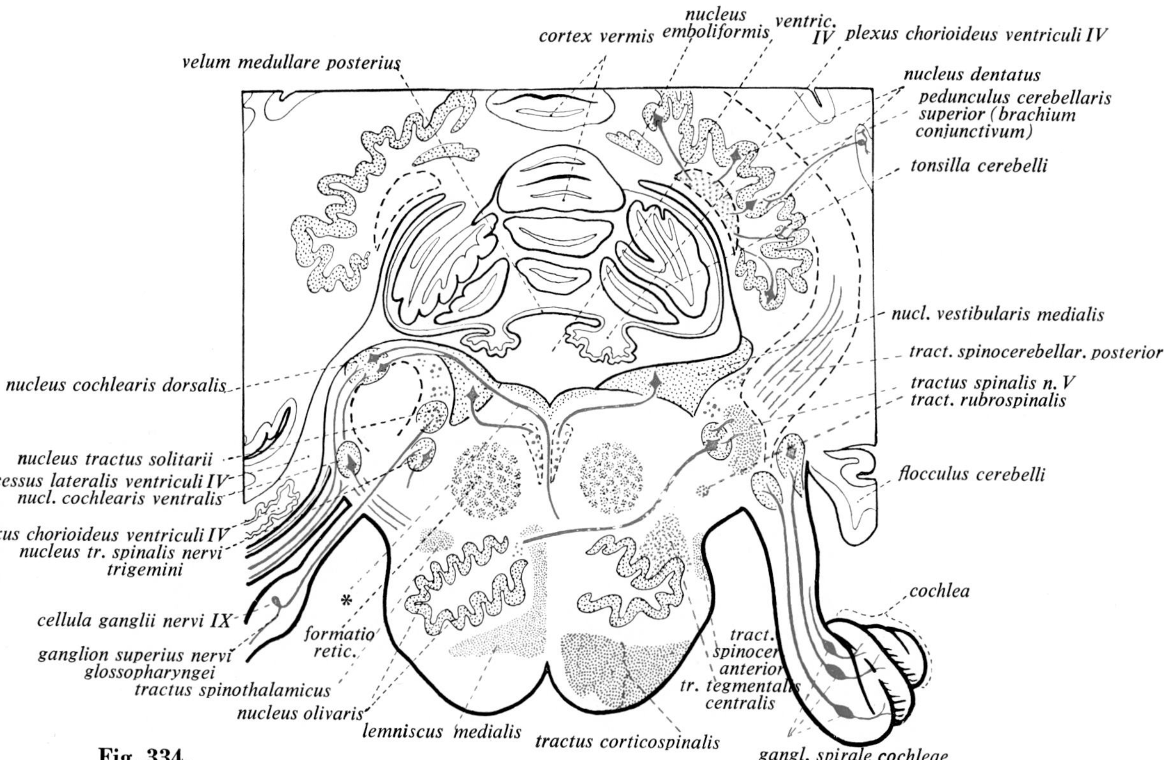
nucleus emboliformis
ventric. IV
plexus chorioideus ventriculi IV
cortex vermis
velum medullare posterius
nucleus dentatus
pedunculus cerebellaris superior (brachium conjunctivum)
tonsilla cerebelli
nucl. vestibularis medialis
tract. spinocerebellar. posterior
nucleus cochlearis dorsalis
tractus spinalis n. V
tract. rubrospinalis
nucleus tractus solitarii
ecessus lateralis ventriculi IV
nucl. cochlearis ventralis
flocculus cerebelli
exus chorioideus ventriculi IV
nucleus tr. spinalis nervi trigemini
cochlea
*
cellula ganglii nervi IX
formatio retic.
tract. spinocer anterior
ganglion superius nervi glossopharyngei
tr. tegmentalis centralis
tractus spinothalamicus
nucleus olivaris
lemniscus medialis
tractus corticospinalis
gangl. spirale cochleae

**Fig. 334.**

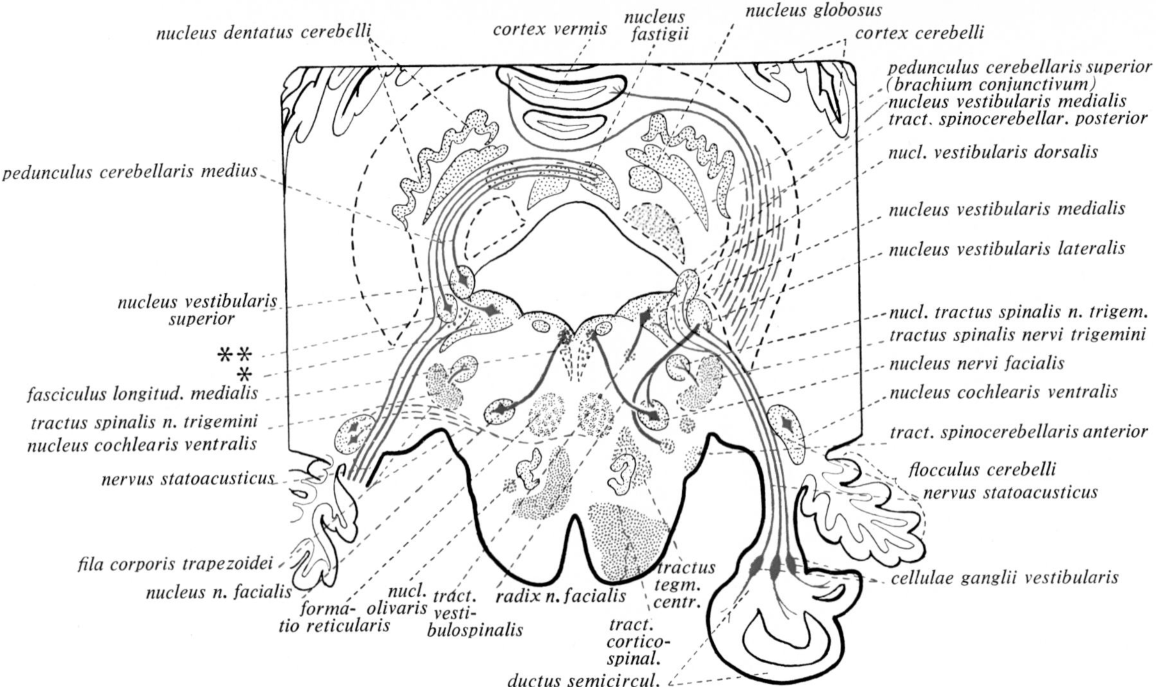
nucleus dentatus cerebelli
cortex vermis
nucleus fastigii
nucleus globosus
cortex cerebelli
pedunculus cerebellaris superior (brachium conjunctivum)
nucleus vestibularis medialis
tract. spinocerebellar. posterior
nucl. vestibularis dorsalis
pedunculus cerebellaris medius
nucleus vestibularis medialis
nucleus vestibularis lateralis
nucleus vestibularis superior
nucl. tractus spinalis n. trigem.
tractus spinalis nervi trigemini
**
*
nucleus nervi facialis
fasciculus longitud. medialis
nucleus cochlearis ventralis
tractus spinalis n. trigemini
nucleus cochlearis ventralis
tract. spinocerebellaris anterior
nervus statoacusticus
flocculus cerebelli
nervus statoacusticus
fila corporis trapezoidei
tractus tegm. centr.
cellulae ganglii vestibularis
nucleus n. facialis
nucl. olivaris
forma- tio reticularis
tract. vesti- bulospinalis
radix n. facialis
tract. cortico- spinal.
ductus semicircul.

**Fig. 335.**

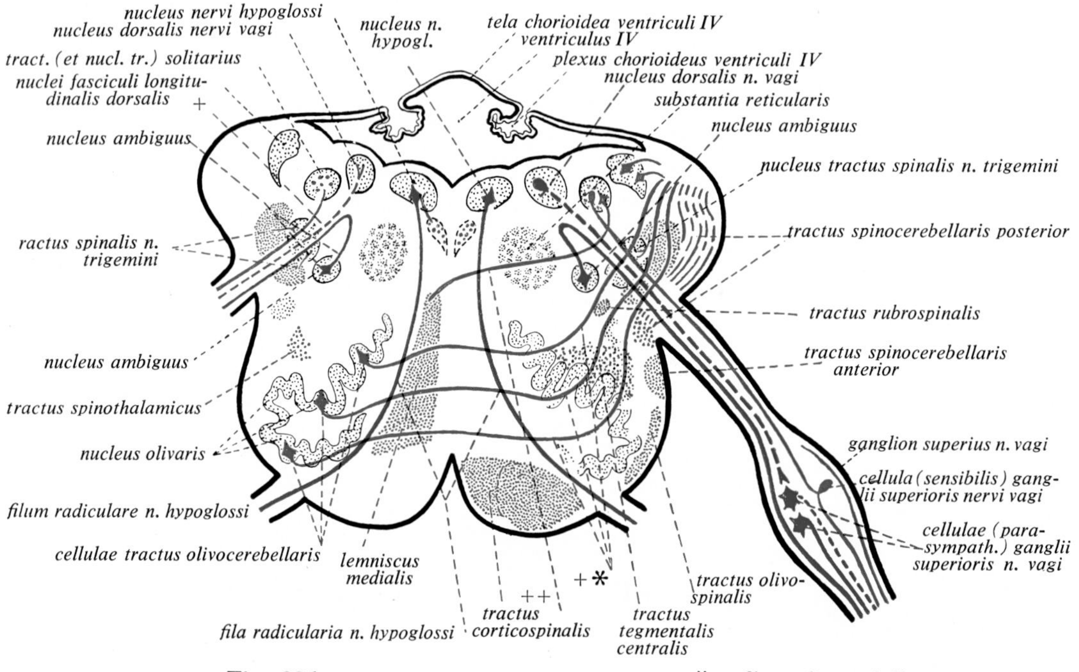
nucleus nervi hypoglossi
nucleus dorsalis nervi vagi
nucleus n. hypogl.
tela chorioidea ventriculi IV
ventriculus IV
tract. (et nucl. tr.) solitarius
plexus chorioideus ventriculi IV
nuclei fasciculi longitu- dinalis dorsalis
+
nucleus dorsalis n. vagi
substantia reticularis
nucleus ambiguus
nucleus ambiguus
nucleus tractus spinalis n. trigemini
ractus spinalis n. trigemini
tractus spinocerebellaris posterior
tractus rubrospinalis
nucleus ambiguus
tractus spinocerebellaris anterior
tractus spinothalamicus
ganglion superius n. vagi
nucleus olivaris
cellula (sensibilis) ganglii superioris nervi vagi
filum radiculare n. hypoglossi
cellulae (para- sympath.) ganglii superioris n. vagi
cellulae tractus olivocerebellaris
lemniscus medialis
+*
++
tractus olivo- spinalis
tractus corticospinalis
tractus tegmentalis centralis
fila radicularia n. hypoglossi

**Fig. 336.**

+ * = fibrae olivocerebellares

## 335. Medulla Oblongata at Level of Vestibular Nuclei. (Müller-Spatz)

1 **Globose Nucleus**
*nucleus globosus*
**Cerebellar Cortex**
*cortex cerebelli*

2 **Superior Cerebellar Peduncle (Brachium Conjunctivum)**
*pedunculus cerebellaris superior (brachium conjunctivum)*
**Medial Vestibular Nucleus**
*nucleus vestibularis medialis*
**Posterior Spinocerebellar Tract**
*tract. spinocerebellar. posterior*
**Superior Vestibular Nucleus**
*nucleus vestibularis dorsalis [superior]*
**Medial Vestibular Nucleus**
*nucleus vestibularis medialis*
**Lateral Vestibular Nucleus**
*nucleus vestibularis lateralis*
**Nucleus of Spinal Tract V**
*nucl. tractus spinalis n. trigem.*

3 **Spinal Tract of Trigeminal N.**
*tractus spinalis nervi trigemini*
**Nucleus of Facial Nerve**
*nucleus nervi facialis*
**Ventral Cochlear Nucleus**
*nucleus cochlearis ventralis*
**Anterior Spinocerebellar Tract**
*tract. spinocerebellaris anterior*
**Cerebellar Flocculus**
*flocculus cerebelli*

4 **Statoacoustic Nerve [Vestibulocochlear Nerve]**
*nervus statoacusticus [n. vestibulocochlearis]*
**Cells of Vestibular Ganglion**
*cellulae ganglii vestibularis*

5 **Semicircular Duct**
*ductus semicircul.*
**Corticospinal Tract**
*tract. corticospinalis*
**Central Tegmental Tract**
*tractus tegm. centr.*

6 **Rootlets of Facial Nerve**
*radix n. facialis*

7 **Vestibulospinal Tract**
*tract. vestibulospinalis*
**Olivary Nucleus**
*nucl. olivaris*
**Reticular Formation**
*formatio reticularis*
**Facial Nerve Nucleus**
*nucleus n. facialis*

8 **Filaments of Trapezoid Body**
*fila corporis trapezoidei*
**Statoacoustic Nerve [Vestibulocochlear Nerve]**
*nervus statoacusticus [n. vestibulocochlearis]*

9 **Spinal Tract of Trigeminal N.**
*tractus spinalis n. trigemini*
**Medial Longitudinal Fasciculus**
*fasciculus longitud. medialis*
**Fiber from Vestibular Nerve**
*
**Fiber from Vestibular Nerve (Lateral Nucleus)**
**
**Superior Vestibular Nucleus**
*nucleus vestibularis superior*

10 **Middle Cerebellar Peduncle**
*pedunculus cerebellaris medius*
**Dentate Nucleus**
*nucleus dentatus cerebelli*

12 **Cortex Vermis**
*cortex vermis*
**Fastigial Nucleus**
*nucleus fastigii*

**Note:** Sensory fibers from vestibular portion of eighth nerve to vestibular nuclei-3, -9.

## 336. (see next page)

## 336. Olivary Region of Medulla; Nuclei of Cranial Nerves IX–XII.

Composite of Figures 227–229. (Müller-Spatz)

1 **Dorsal [Motor] Nucl., Vagus N.**
*nucleus dorsalis n. vagi*
**Gray Reticular Formation**
*formatio reticularis grisea*

2 **Ambiguus Nucleus**
*nucleus ambiguus*
**Nucleus of Spinal Tract V**
*nucleus tractus spinalis n. trigemini*

3 **Posterior Spinocerebellar Tract**
*tractus spinocerebellaris post.*
**Rubrospinal Tract**
*tractus rubrospinalis*
**Anterior Spinocerebellar Tract**
*tractus spinocerebellaris anterior*

4 **Superior Ganglion, Vagus N.**
*ganglion superius n. vagi*
**Sensory Cell of Superior Ganglion of Vagus**
*cellula (sensibilis) ganglii superioris nervi vagi*

5 **Olivospinal Tract**
*tractus olivospinalis*
**Central Tegmental Tract**
*tractus tegmentalis centralis*
**Olivocerebellar**
+*

6 **Fiber from Solitary Nucleus Tract to Medial Lemniscus**
++
**Corticospinal Tract**
*tractus corticospinalis*

7 **Root Fibers of Hypoglossal N.**
*fila radicularia n. hypoglossi*
**Medial Lemniscus**
*lemniscus medialis*

8 **Cells of Olivocerebellar Tract**
*cellulae tractus olivocerebellaris*
**Root Fiber of Hypoglossal N.**
*filum radiculare n. hypoglossi*
**Olivary Nucleus**
*nucleus olivaris*

9 **Spinothalamic Tract**
*tractus spinothalamicus*
**Ambiguus Nucleus**
*nucleus ambiguus*
**Spinal Tract of Trigeminal N.**
*tractus spinalis n. trigemini*

10 **Ambiguus Nucleus**
*nucleus ambiguus*
**Afferent Fiber to Dorsal Nucleus of Vagus Nerve**
+
**Solitary Tract (and Nucleus of Tract)**
*tract. (et nucl. tr.) solitarius*
**Dorsal [Motor] Nucl. of Vagus**
*nucleus dorsalis nervi vagi*
**Hypoglossal Nucleus**
*nucleus nervi hypoglossi*

11 **Hypoglossal Nucleus**
*nucleus nervi hypogl.*

12 **Chorioid Tela of 4th Ventricle**
*tela chorioidea ventriculi IV*
**Fourth Ventricle**
*ventriculus IV*
**Chorioid Plexus, 4th Ventricle**
*plexus chorioideus ventriculi IV*

**Note:** 1. +* Olivocerebellar fibers-5, and their nucleus-8.

2. ++ Fiber from **nucleus of solitary tract**-10 to medial lemniscus-6.

3. Synapse between presynaptic neuron, located in **dorsal motor nucleus**-1 **of vagus** and the postsynaptic neuron does **not** occur in the superior ganglion-4 of the vagus nerve, as indicated in this diagram, but normally takes place more distally with the cells scattered through the viscera supplied by vagus nerve.

# 337. Medulla Oblongata at Caudal End of the Olive. (7/1)

Roman numerals indicate nuclei of corresponding cranial nerves. Tracts, dark; gray matter, light.

1 **Solitary Tract**
*tractus solitarius*
**Nucleus of Solitary Tract**
*nucleus tractus solitarii*

2 **Raphe**
*raphe*

3 **Internal Arcuate Fibers**
*fibrae arcuatae internae*
**Ambiguus Nucleus IX, X, XI**
*nucleus ambiguus (IX, X, XI)*
**Thalamoolivary Tract**
*tractus thalamoolivaris*

4 **Hilus of Olivary Nucleus**
*hilus nuclei olivaris*

5 **Medial Accessory Olivary Nucleus**
*nucleus olivaris accessorius medialis*
**Decussation of Lemniscus**
*decussatio lemniscorum*

6 **Pyramid**
*pyramis*

7 **Root of Hypoglossal Nerve**
*radix n. hypoglossi*

8 **External Arcuate Fibers**
*fibrae arcuatae externae*

**Inferior Olivary Nucleus**
*nucleus olivaris (oliva inferior)*

9 **Lateral Reticular Nucleus**
*nucleus reticularis lateralis*

**Olivocerebellar Tract**
*tractus olivocerebellaris*

**Rootlet Filaments of Vagus N.**
*fila radicularia nervi vagi*

**Spinal Tract, Trigeminal Nerve + Nucleus of Tract**
*tractus spinalis n. trigemini (+ nucleus tractus)*

10 **Reticular Substance + Internal Arcuate Fibers**
*[formatio reticularis] substantia reticularis + fibrae arcuatae int.*
**Inferior Cerebellar Peduncle (Restiform Body)**
*pedunculus cerebellaris inferior (corpus restiforme)*
**Cuneate Nucleus**
*nucleus cuneatus*

11 **Reticular Substance**
*substantia reticularis [formatio reticularis]*
**Tenia of Fourth Ventricle**
*tenia ventriculi quarti*

12 **Dorsal Nucleus of Vagus**
*nucl. dorsalis nervi vagi*
**Rhomboid Fossa**
*fossa rhomboidea*
**Median Sulcus - Rhomboid Fossa**
*sulcus medianus foss. rhomb.*

**Note:** 1. Same features as in Figure 336.

2. In midsagittal plane, fibers from gracile and cuneate nuclei-10 form **decussation of medial lemniscus**-5.

3. **Nuclei-XII of hypoglossal nerves**-7 are conspicuous ventral to **fourth ventricle** (rhomboid fossa-12), which is becoming narrower as it approaches central canal in spinal cord. (Fig. 338-1)

4. **Dorsal (motor) nucleus of vagus**-12 (parasympathetic presynaptic neurons).

Fig. 338

## 338. Medulla Oblongata at Decussation of Lemniscus. (7/1)

1 **Tubercle of Nucleus Gracilis**
*tuberculum nuclei gracilis*

**Tubercle of Cuneate Nucleus**
*tuberculum nuclei cuneati*

**Central Intermediate Substance + Central Canal**
*substantia intermedia centralis + canal. central.*

2 **Dorsal [Motor] Nucleus of Vagus Nerve** (IX, X)
*nucleus dorsalis nervi vagi* (IX, X)

**Decussation of Lemniscus**
*decussatio lemniscorum*

**Posterior Column**
*(columna posterior)*

3 **Nucleus of Spinal Tract V**
*nucleus tractus spinalis nervi trigemini*

**Posterior Spinocerebellar Tract**
*tract. spinocerebellaris posterior*

**Medial Longitudinal Fasciculus**
*fasciculus longitud. medialis*

4 **Anterior Spinocerebellar Tract**
*tractus spinocerebellaris anterior*

**Medial Accessory Olivary Nucl.**
*nucl. olivaris accessorius med.*

5 **Pyramid**
*pyramis*

6 **Anterior Median Fissure**
*fissura mediana anterior*

7 **Arcuate nucleus**
*nucleus arcuatus*

8 **Anterior Column**
*(columna anterior)*

**Reticular Formation (Gray)**
*formatio reticularis (substantia reticularis grisea)*

10 **Spinal Tract, Trigeminal**
*tractus spinalis n. trigemini*

11 **Spinal Tract Nucleus, V**
*nucleus tractus spinalis n. trigemini*

**Cuneate Nucleus**
*nucleus cuneatus*

**Nucleus Gracilis**
*nucleus gracilis*

12 **Posterior Median Sulcus**
*sulcus medianus posterior*

**Note:** 1. Fibers from nerve cell bodies in **nucleus gracilis**-11 and **nucleus cuneatus**-11 sweep around central gray matter-1 as internal arcuate fibers and decussate in mid-line to form **medial lemniscus** (Fig. 337-5).

2. **Reticular formation**-8 and the **pyramids**-5 in ventral portion.

**337.** (see preceding page)

## 339. Medulla Oblongata at Rostral Part of Pyramidal Decussation.
(7/1)

1 **Central Canal**
*canalis centralis*

2 **Spinal Accessory Nucleus**
*nucleus spinalis nervi accessorii*

3 **Nucleus Ambiguus**
*nucleus ambiguus*

5 **Anterior Column**
*columna anterior*

6 **Pyramidal Decussation**
*decussatio pyramidum*

**Pyramid**
*pyramis*

9 **Root Fibers of Accessory Nerve**
*fila radicularia n. accessorii*

**Reticular Formation**
*formatio reticularis*

**Tuberculum Cinereum**
*(tuberculum cinereum)*

**Spinal Tract, Trigeminal Nerve**
*tractus spinalis n. trigemini*

10 **Nucleus of Spinal Tract, Trigeminal Nerve**
*nucl. tract. spin. n. trigemini*

**Nucleus Cuneatus**
*nucleus cuneatus*

11 **Nucleus Gracilis**
*nucleus gracilis*

12 **Posterior Median Sulcus**
*sulcus medianus posterior*

**Note:** 1. At this level pyramidal fibers begin to cross midline and pass from a ventral to a dorsolateral position. This crossing is called the **decussation of the pyramids**-6. These fibers then descend in the lateral funiculus of the spinal cord as the lateral corticospinal tract. (Fig. 340-9; Fig. 342-6)

2. Large nuclear masses in cranial ends of **fasciculus gracilis**-11 and **fasciculus cuneatus**-10 in dorsal funiculus are called the **nuclei of these fasciculi.** They represent the second neuron in the sensory chain. Fibers from these neurons, after decussating, become the medial lemniscus (Fig. 341-7), which travels through the brain stem to the thalamus.

## 340. Medulla Oblongata at Level of the More Caudal Part of Pyramidal Decussation.

2 **Spinal Nucleus, Accessory Nerve**
*nucleus spinalis nervi accessorii*

**Nucleus of Spinal Tract of Trigeminal**
*nucleus tractus spinalis nervi trigemini*

**Spinal Tract, Trigeminal Nerve**
*tractus spinalis nervi trigemini*

3 **Posterior Spinocerebellar Tract**
*tractus spinocerebellaris posterior*

4 **Anterior Spinocerebellar Tract**
*tractus spinocerebellaris anterior*

**Olivospinal Tract (Helweg)**
*(tractus olivospinalis (Helweg)*

5 **Pyramidal Decussation**
*decussatio pyramidum*

6 **Anterior Funiculus**
*funiculus anterior*

7 **Anterior Median Fissure**
*fissura mediana anterior*

8 **Anterior Column**
*columna anterior*

9 **Nucleus Ambiguus**
*nucleus ambiguus*

**Lateral Corticospinal Tract**
*tractus corticospinalis lateralis*

10 **Posterior Column**
*columna posterior*

**Nucleus of Spinal Tract, Trigeminal Nerve**
*nucleus tractus spinalis nervi trigemini*

12 **Fasciculus Gracilis** / **Fasciculus Cuneatus** } **Posterior Funiculi**
*fasciculus gracilis* / *fasciculus cuneatus* } *funiculi posterioris*

**Note:** 1. At this level, the **pyramids**-5 or **corticospinal tracts**-9 which form them are still in process of changing position from the ventral part of the central nervous system to the dorsolateral position in the lateral funiculus of the spinal cord. Fibers that do not decussate at this point are called the ventral or uncrossed corticospinal tract. (Fig. 299)

2. Gray matter at this level is not conspicuous, partly because it is cut up by decussating pyramidal fibers.

## 341. Diagram of Section of Medulla Oblongata at Level of Decussation of Medial Lemniscus. (after Müller-Spatz)

Near the section shown in Figure 338.

1 **Posterior Funiculus**
*funiculus posterior*

2 **Cells of Nuclei of Posterior Funiculus**
*cellulae nucleorum funiculi posterioris*

**Nucleus of Spinal Trigeminal Tract (Posterior Column)**
*nucleus tractus spinalis nervi V (columna posterior)*

3 **Spinal Tract Trigeminal Nerve**
*tractus spinalis n. trigemini*
**Rubrospinal Tract**
*tractus rubrospinalis*

**Posterior Spinocerebellar Tract**
*tr. spinocerebellaris posterior*
**Anterior Spinocerebellar Tract**
*tr. spinocerebellaris anterior*
**Olivary Nucleus**
*nucleus olivaris*

5 **Corticospinal Tract**
*tractus corticospinalis*

7 **Medial Lemniscus**
*lemniscus medialis*

8 **Decussation of Lemniscus**
*decussatio lemniscorum*

**Olivospinal Tract**
*(tractus olivospinalis)*
**Anterior Column**
*columna anterior*

9 **Lateral Spinothalamic Tract**
*tractus spinothalamicus lateralis*

**Filaments of Accessory Nerve**
*filum radiculare nervi accessorii*

10 **Nucleus Cuneatus**
*nucleus cuneatus*
**Nucleus Gracilis**
*nucleus gracilis*

12 **Central Canal**
*canalis centralis*

## 342. Diagram of Section of Medulla at Level of Pyramidal Decussation. (7/1) (after Müller-Spatz)

Compare with Figures 339 and 340.

1 **Fasciculus Gracilis**
*fasciculus gracilis*

2 **Fasciculus Cuneatus**
*fasciculus cuneatus*

**Nucleus of Spinal Tract of Trigeminal (Posterior Column)**
*nucl. tractus spinalis n. trigemini (columna posterior)*

**Spinal Tract, Trigeminal**
*tractus spinalis n. trigemini*

3 **Posterior Spinocerebellar Tract**
*tr. spinocerebellaris posterior*
**Rubrospinal Tract**
*tractus rubrospinalis*
**Anterior Spinocerebellar Tract**
*tr. spinocerebellaris anterior*

4 **Anterior Column**
*columna anterior*
**1st Cervical Nerve, Ventral Root Filaments**
*nerv. cervicalis I (filum radicul. ventrale)*

6 **Decussation of Pyramid**
*decussatio pyramidum*

8 **Spinothalamic Tract**
*tractus spinothalamicus*

**Olivospinal Tract**
*(tractus olivospinalis)*

10 **Central Canal**
*canalis centralis*

11 **Nucleus Gracilis**
*nucleus gracilis*

### Etymology:

cuneatus = L. *cuneus*, a wedge
gracilis = L. slender
decussation = L. *decussare*, to intersect or cross each other; from *decussis*, then written X.

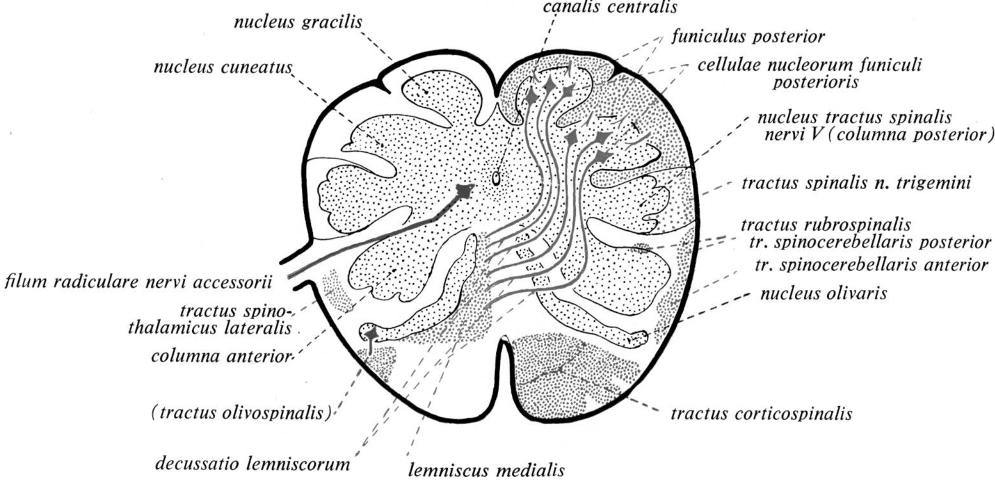

canalis centralis
nucleus gracilis
funiculus posterior
nucleus cuneatus
cellulae nucleorum funiculi posterioris
nucleus tractus spinalis nervi V (columna posterior)
tractus spinalis n. trigemini
tractus rubrospinalis
tr. spinocerebellaris posterior
tr. spinocerebellaris anterior
filum radiculare nervi accessorii
nucleus olivaris
tractus spino-thalamicus lateralis
columna anterior
(tractus olivospinalis)
tractus corticospinalis
decussatio lemniscorum
lemniscus medialis


**Fig. 341.**

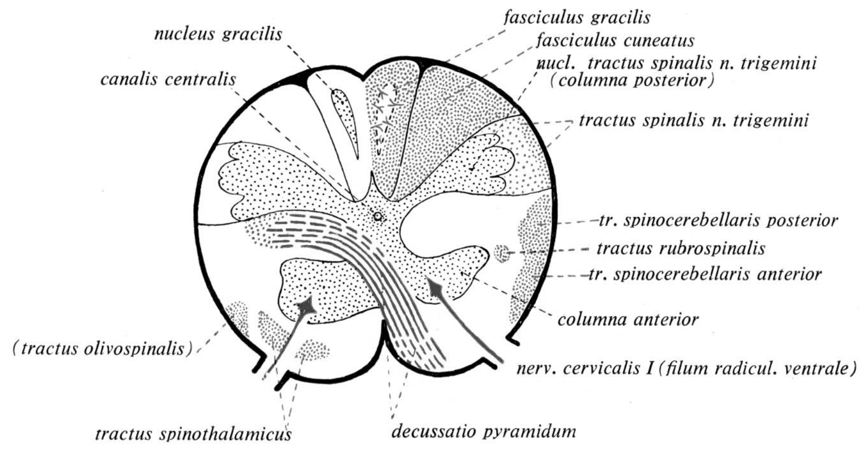

fasciculus gracilis
nucleus gracilis
fasciculus cuneatus
nucl. tractus spinalis n. trigemini (columna posterior)
canalis centralis
tractus spinalis n. trigemini
tr. spinocerebellaris posterior
tractus rubrospinalis
tr. spinocerebellaris anterior
columna anterior
(tractus olivospinalis)
nerv. cervicalis I (filum radicul. ventrale)
tractus spinothalamicus
decussatio pyramidum


**Fig. 342.**

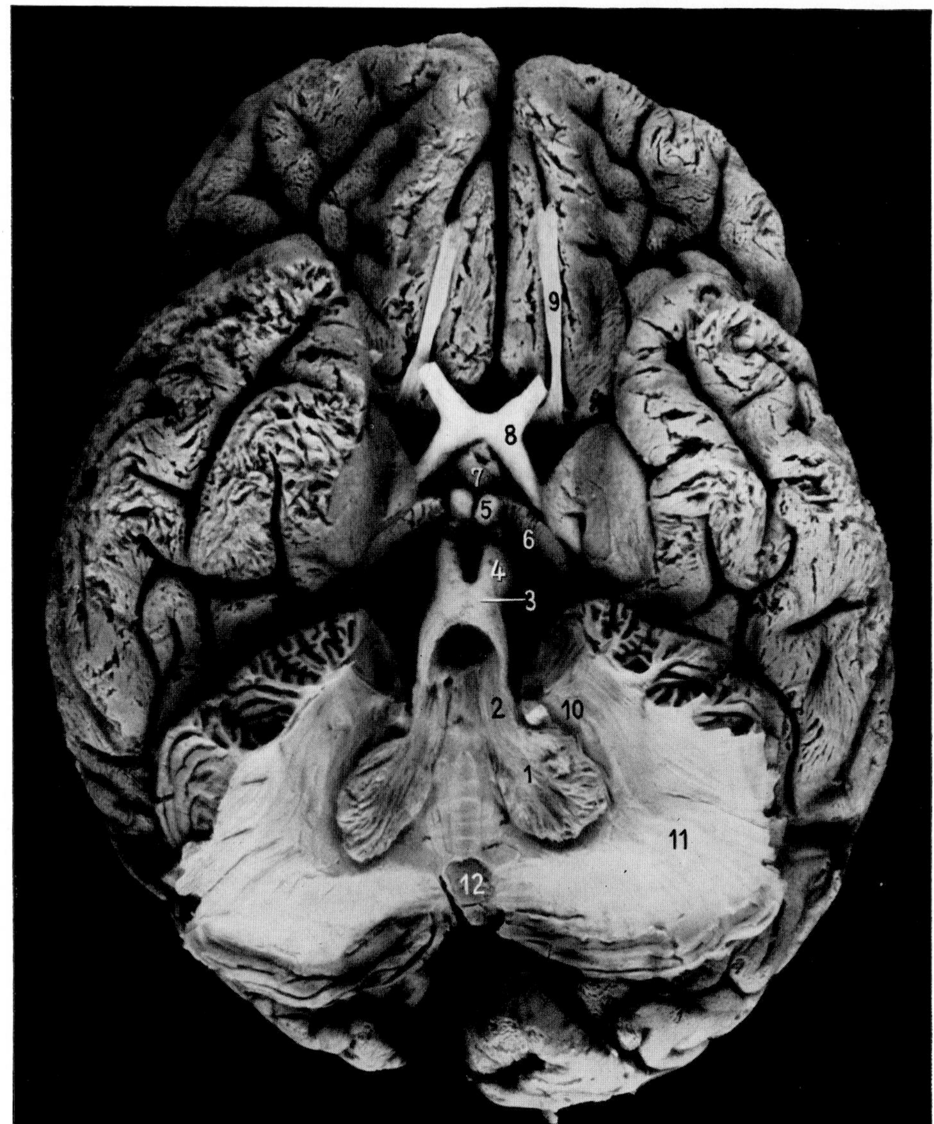

9
8
7
5
6
4
3
2
10
1
11
12


**Fig. 343.**

*1* *nucleus dentatus*
*2* *tractus cerebellorubralis*
*3* *decussatio pedunculorum cerebellarium superior.*
*4* *nucleus ruber*
*5* *corpus mamillare*
*6* *pedunculus cerebri*
*7* *tuber cinereum und infundibulum*
*8* *chiasma opticum*
*9* *tractus olfactorius*
*10* *pedunculus cerebellaris inferior*
*11* *substantia medullaris hemispherii cerebelli*
*12* *vermis inferior*

## 343. Connection of Dentate Nucleus of Cerebellum to Red Nucleus

(cerebellorubral tracts). Dissection of Fiber Pathway – Basal Aspect of Brain (Prep. Anat. Inst., Münster)

**Note:** 1. The superior cerebellar peduncle (brachium conjunctivum) is the chief cerebellar outflow pathway. It contains fibers not only from the dentate nucleus-1 but also from the globose and emboliform nuclei.

2. The superior cerebellar peduncles decussate just ventral to the inferior colliculus. Many of these fibers then pass to the red nuclei and are relayed rostrally to the thalamus or caudally along rubroreticular and rubrospinal tracts to bulbar and spinal motor neurons. Some fibers of the superior cerebellar peduncle are also carried directly to the thalamus and globus pallidus by way of the ansa lenticularis.

1 Dentate nucleus
2 Cerebellorubral tract
3 Decussation superior cerebellar peduncle (Brachium conjunctivum)
4 Red nucleus
5 Mammillary body
6 Cerebral peduncle
7 Tuber cinereum and infundibulum
8 Optic chiasma
9 Olfactory tract
10 Inferior cerebellar peduncle (Restiform body)
11 Cerebellum medullary substance
12 Inferior vermis

(Above numbers are not clock key numbers)

# AUTONOMIC NERVOUS SYSTEM

## 344. Diagrammatic Comparison of the Cerebrospinal or Somatic (Left) and Autonomic Reflex Arcs and Outflow Patterns (Right).

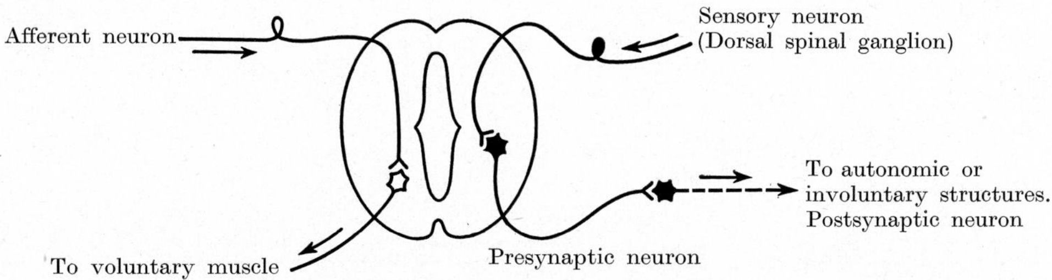
Afferent neuron
Sensory neuron
(Dorsal spinal ganglion)
To autonomic or
involuntary structures.
Postsynaptic neuron
To voluntary muscle
Presynaptic neuron

**Note:** 1. The **autonomic outflow** pattern always involves a second relay (postsynaptic) neuron whose cell body is outside the central nervous system.

2. One **presynaptic neuron** makes synapse with approximately 32 **postsynaptic neurons**; often in different segments of the body.

3. The autonomic outflow pattern thus makes possible the stimulation of a widespread or generalized involuntary response of a large number of small effectors in multiple areas of the body. (Example: Large numbers of sweat glands, arrector pili muscles, smooth muscle cells in intestinal tract in different areas may be activated by a relatively small number of presynaptic neurons.) Another set of structures in which such an arrangement would be required is in the widespread simultaneous involuntary regulation of the smooth muscle cells that control blood pressure by regulating the peripheral resistance to blood flow.

**Etymology:**

autonomic = Gr. *autos,* self + *nomos,* law.
sympathetic = Gr. *syn,* with + *pathos,* suffering
parasympathetic = Gr. *para,* beside

# 345. Diagram of the Origin, General Distribution, and Relationship of the Autonomic Nervous System to the Central Nervous System.

Presynaptic neurons – unbroken lines Postsynaptic neurons – broken lines

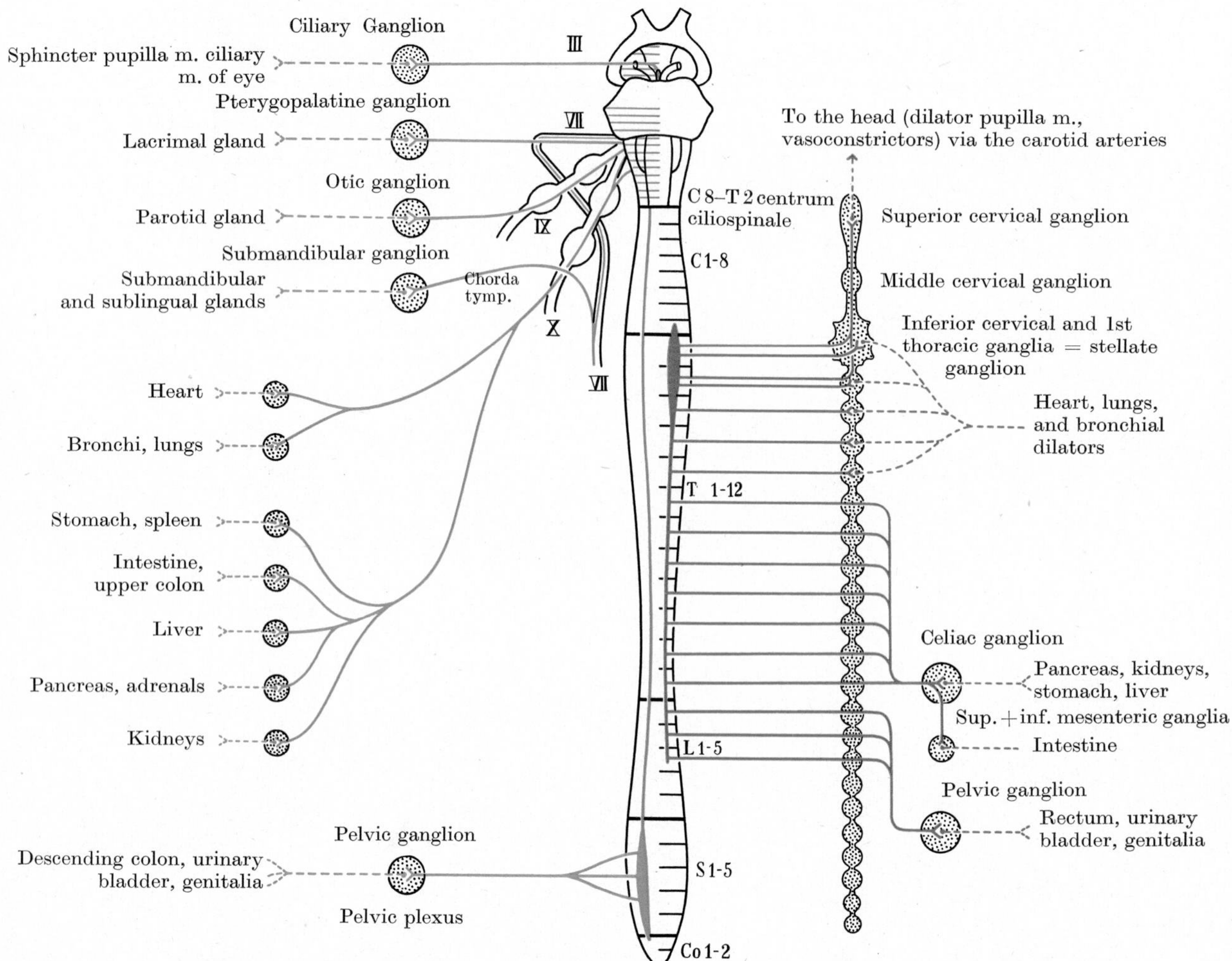
Ciliary Ganglion
Sphincter pupilla m. ciliary m. of eye
III
Pterygopalatine ganglion
VII
Lacrimal gland
Otic ganglion
Parotid gland
IX
Submandibular ganglion
Submandibular and sublingual glands
Chorda tymp.
X
VII
To the head (dilator pupilla m., vasoconstrictors) via the carotid arteries
C 8–T 2 centrum ciliospinale
Superior cervical ganglion
C 1-8
Middle cervical ganglion
Inferior cervical and 1st thoracic ganglia = stellate ganglion
Heart
Bronchi, lungs
Heart, lungs, and bronchial dilators
T 1-12
Stomach, spleen
Intestine, upper colon
Liver
Pancreas, adrenals
Kidneys
Celiac ganglion
Pancreas, kidneys, stomach, liver
Sup. + inf. mesenteric ganglia
Intestine
L 1-5
Pelvic ganglion
Rectum, urinary bladder, genitalia
Pelvic ganglion
Descending colon, urinary bladder, genitalia
S 1-5
Pelvic plexus
Co 1-2

**Note:** 1. The **autonomic nervous system** comprises all nerves that supply glands, cardiac, and smooth muscle of viscera and blood vessels. These structures function automatically and are primarily involuntary. While this part of the nervous system supplies visceral structures, it is intimately associated with the somatic or voluntary portion of the nervous system.

2. In order to regulate visceral or autonomic structures, it is usually necessary to exert dualistic control (i. e. dilate vs constrict the pupil; accelerate vs decelerate heart; stimulate vs inhibit activity of intestines or glands). The **autonomic nervous system** is thus divided into two parts, **sympathetic and parasympathetic,**

that appear to have opposite or antagonistic effects but, in reality, they cooperate to regulate function of visceral structures by their simultaneous integrated dualistic influence.

3. While both sympathetic and parasympathetic systems enervate many of the same structures, they are not strictly speaking beside each other and their presynaptic neurons are located in different parts of the central nervous system.

**RED – Sympathetic Outflow.** Presynaptic neuron cell bodies are located in lateral horn (intermediolateral cell column) of thoracic and upper lumbar segments. The presynaptic nerve fibers pass through ventral roots and trunks of all thoracic and upper two lumbar spinal nerves and join ganglionated sympathetic chain by way of white rami communicantes in these segments (Fig. 346 b). Each presynaptic neuron synapses with approximately 32–40 postsynaptic neurons. The cell bodies of postsynaptic neurons are aggregated to form the 24–25 ganglia of the sympathetic chain.

Fibers of the presynaptic neuron may synapse with several postsynaptic neurons in the ganglion of its segment of origin. It may also pass cranially or caudally to other ganglia in the sympathetic chain to synapse with one or more postsynaptic neurons in ganglia of other segments. Presynaptic neurons may, in addition, pass through sympathetic trunk and ganglion to splanchnic nerves to synapse in collateral ganglion (i. e., celiac, mesenteric and pelvic). Postsynaptic nerve fibers are thus distributed to all glands and smooth muscle in viscera and blood vessels of all segments caudal to and including the first cervical. Distribution to head regions involves plexuses of postsynaptic nerve fibers that follow external and internal carotid arteries, their branches, and other structures in the head. Sympathetic outflow is sometimes called the thoracolumbar outflow of the autonomic nervous system.

**BLUE – Parasympathetic outflow** takes place through 4 cranial nerves (III Oculomotor, VII Facial [intermedius], IX Glossopharyngeal and X Vagus) and three sacral nerves (2, 3, 4). This is therefore called the craniosacral outflow of the autonomic nervous system. The postsynaptic neurons of the more rostral parasympathetic outflow are aggregated to form ganglia.

| | | |
|---|---|---|
| III Oculomotor N. | **ciliary ganglion** | iris circular M. ciliary body |
| VII Facial N. | **pterygopalatine ganglion** | lacrimal and nasal glands |
| (intermedius) | **submandibular ganglion** | submandibular and sublingual glands |
| IX Glossopharyngeal N. | **otic ganglion** | parotid salivary gland |

The vagus (blue) supplies most thoracic and abdominal viscera with presynaptic parasympathetic fibers from dorsal motor nucleus of the vagus. Pelvic sacral nerves supply the remaining lower abdominal and pelvic structures. In the thorax and abdomen, postsynaptic neurons are not generally aggregated to form ganglia, but are scattered in walls of the visceral structures (i. e., myenteric and submucous plexuses).

## 346. Schematic Diagram of Autonomic Sympathetic and Parasympathetic Neurons (their relation to the gray matter of spinal cord, spinal nerve, dorsal spinal ganglion, and sympathetic chain ganglion).

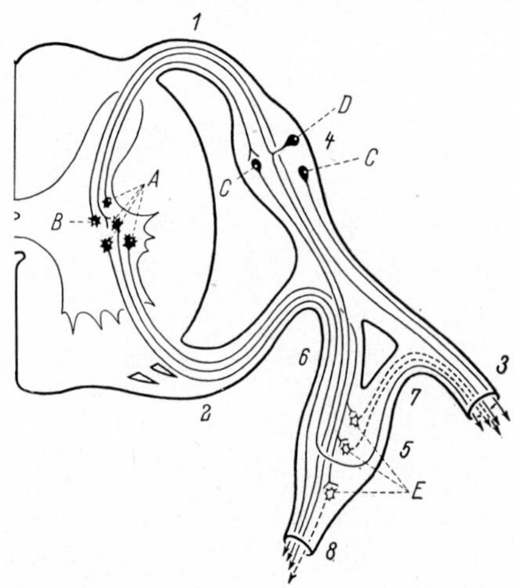
1
D
4
C
A
C
B
6
3
7
2
5
E
8

1 Dorsal root of spinal nerve
2 Ventral root of spinal nerve
3 Spinal nerve
4 Spinal ganglion
5 Sympathetic chain ganglion
6 White ramus communicans
7 Gray ramus communicans
8 Branch of sympathetic ganglion to to viscus

A Intermediolateral nucleus or column. (Presynaptic neuron cell bodies – black)
B Hypothetical parasympathetic neuron
C Unipolar antidromic vasomotor neuron
D Bipolar antidromic vasomotor neuron
E Postsynaptic sympathetic neurons of sympathetic ganglion

**Note:** 1. **Black:** Presynaptic neuron cell bodies in intermediolateral cell column or nucleus (A). Fibers pass through ventral root (2), white ramus communicans (6), and synapse with three postsynaptic neurons (E) in sympathetic ganglion (5).

2. Two postsynaptic unmyelinated neurons (E) send fibers through gray ramus communicans (7) to spinal nerve for peripheral distribution to sweat glands, blood vessels, and arrector pili muscles. Another postsynaptic neuron sends fibers to visceral branch of ganglion.

3. The parasympathetic neurons in the spinal cord (B) involve antidromic conduction of impulses (i. e., motor impulses traveling to periphery through the dorsal root). These are shown here but will not be further discussed because they are too hypothetical.

## 347. Referred Pain. Segmental Exteroceptive Referral of Visceral Irritation and Pain. (Förster Hdbch. der Neurologie, Vol. 5, 1936.)

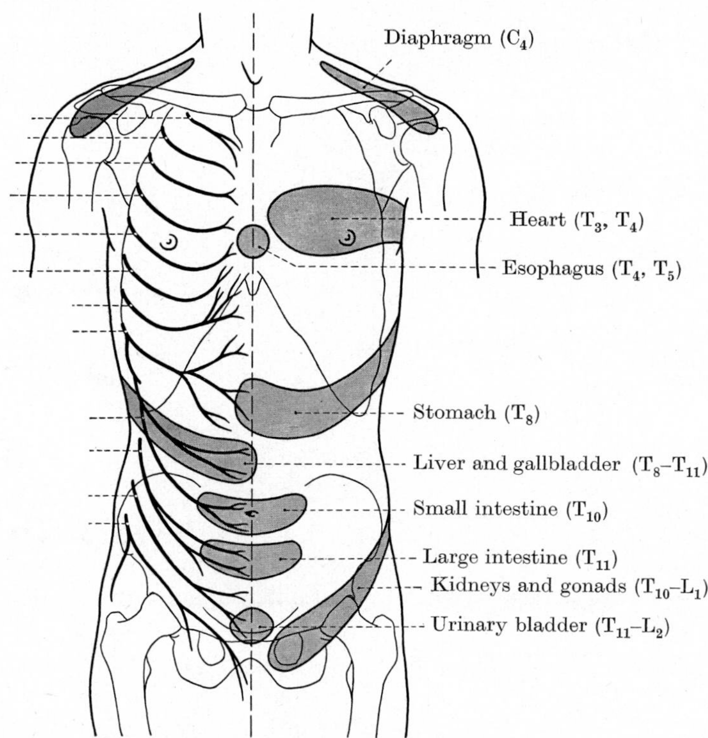
Diaphragm ($C_4$)
Heart ($T_3$, $T_4$)
Esophagus ($T_4$, $T_5$)
Stomach ($T_8$)
Liver and gallbladder ($T_8$–$T_{11}$)
Small intestine ($T_{10}$)
Large intestine ($T_{11}$)
Kidneys and gonads ($T_{10}$–$L_1$)
Urinary bladder ($T_{11}$–$L_2$)

The sensory fibers from viscera follow the autonomic nerves to the sympathetic trunk. From here they pass through white ramus communicans and the dorsal root, where the cell bodies are located. They enter the central nervous system and terminate in close association with, and in the same manner as, sensory fibers from peripheral structures in that segment. Frequently, the pain associated with certain visceral irritative diseases is referred to the corresponding skin segment or dermatome. The above diagram, which depicts the main referred pain areas for many of the viscera and deeper organs, is of great practical value in the diagnosis of diseases that involve visceral structures.

## 348 and 349. Ganglionated Sympathetic Trunk of Newborn.

**348.** Labelled.

**349.** Photograph lightly retouched.

Brachial and lumbosacral plexuses.

Sympathetic trunk and its ganglia (1–5) in lumbar region.

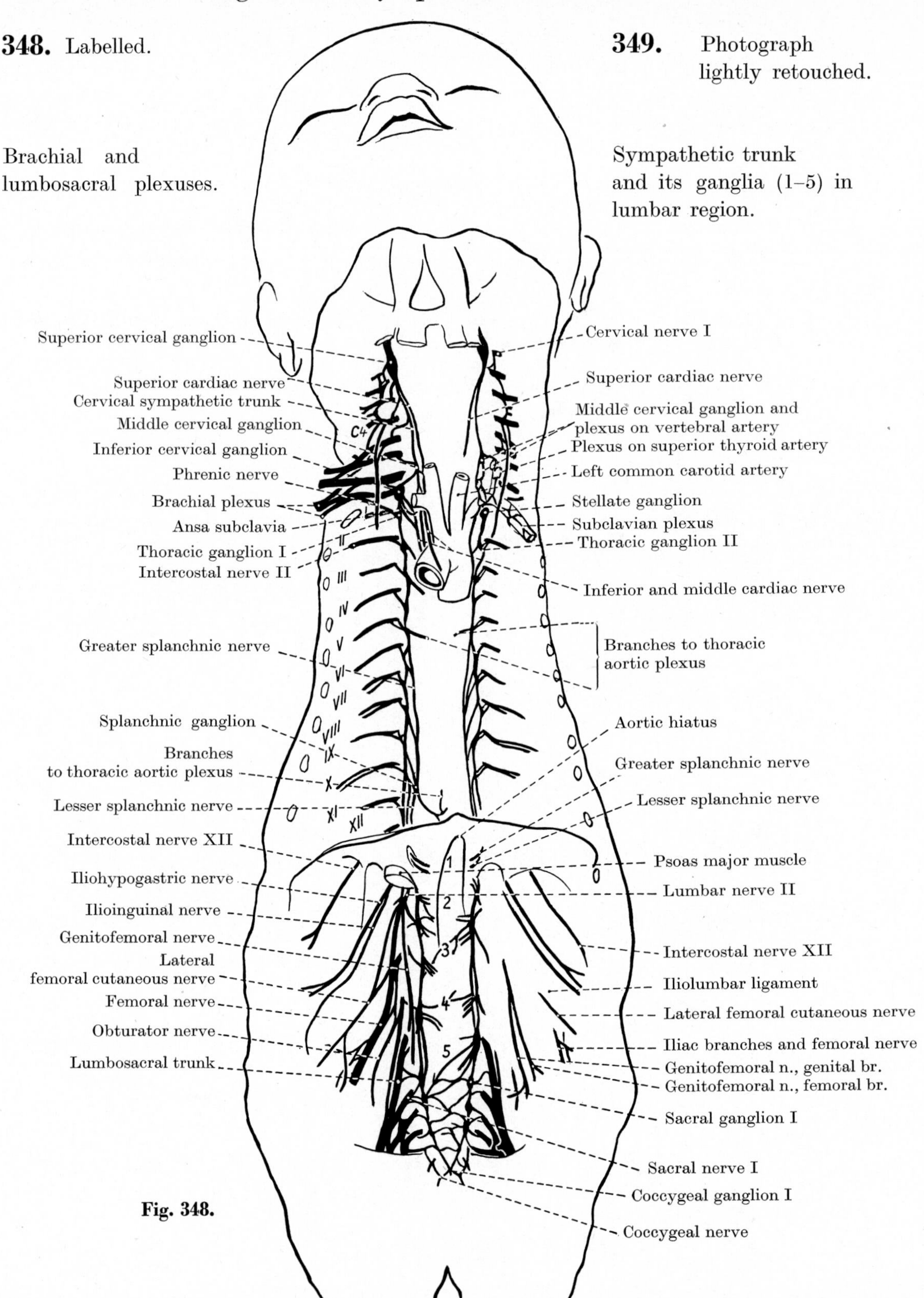
Superior cervical ganglion
Superior cardiac nerve
Cervical sympathetic trunk
Middle cervical ganglion
Inferior cervical ganglion
Phrenic nerve
Brachial plexus
Ansa subclavia
Thoracic ganglion I
Intercostal nerve II
Greater splanchnic nerve
Splanchnic ganglion
Branches to thoracic aortic plexus
Lesser splanchnic nerve
Intercostal nerve XII
Iliohypogastric nerve
Ilioinguinal nerve
Genitofemoral nerve
Lateral femoral cutaneous nerve
Femoral nerve
Obturator nerve
Lumbosacral trunk
Cervical nerve I
Superior cardiac nerve
Middle cervical ganglion and plexus on vertebral artery
Plexus on superior thyroid artery
Left common carotid artery
Stellate ganglion
Subclavian plexus
Thoracic ganglion II
Inferior and middle cardiac nerve
Branches to thoracic aortic plexus
Aortic hiatus
Greater splanchnic nerve
Lesser splanchnic nerve
Psoas major muscle
Lumbar nerve II
Intercostal nerve XII
Iliolumbar ligament
Lateral femoral cutaneous nerve
Iliac branches and femoral nerve
Genitofemoral n., genital br.
Genitofemoral n., femoral br.
Sacral ganglion I
Sacral nerve I
Coccygeal ganglion I
Coccygeal nerve
C4
II
III
IV
V
VI
VII
VIII
IX
X
XI
XII
1
2
3
4
5

**Fig. 348.**

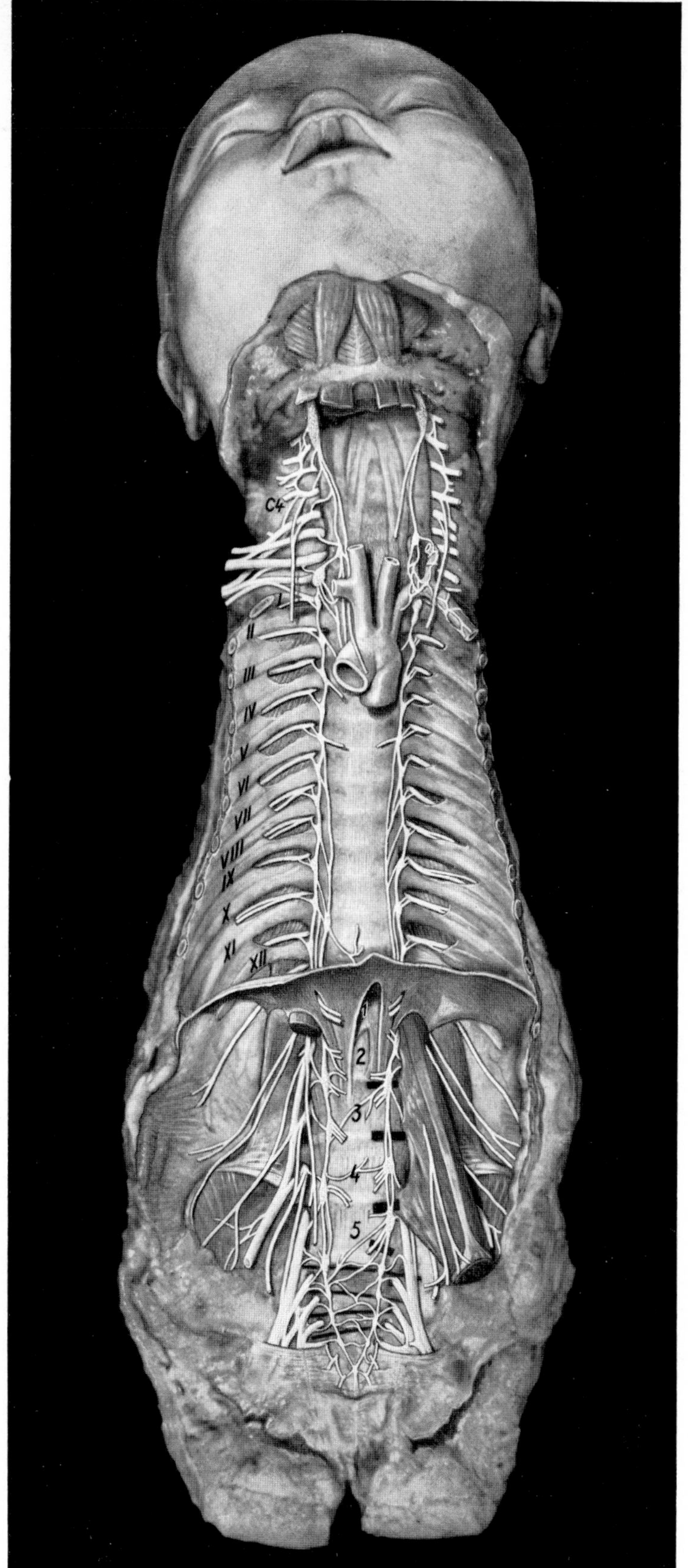
C4
II
III
IV
V
VI
VII
VIII
IX
X
XI
XII
1
2
3
4
5

Fig. 349.

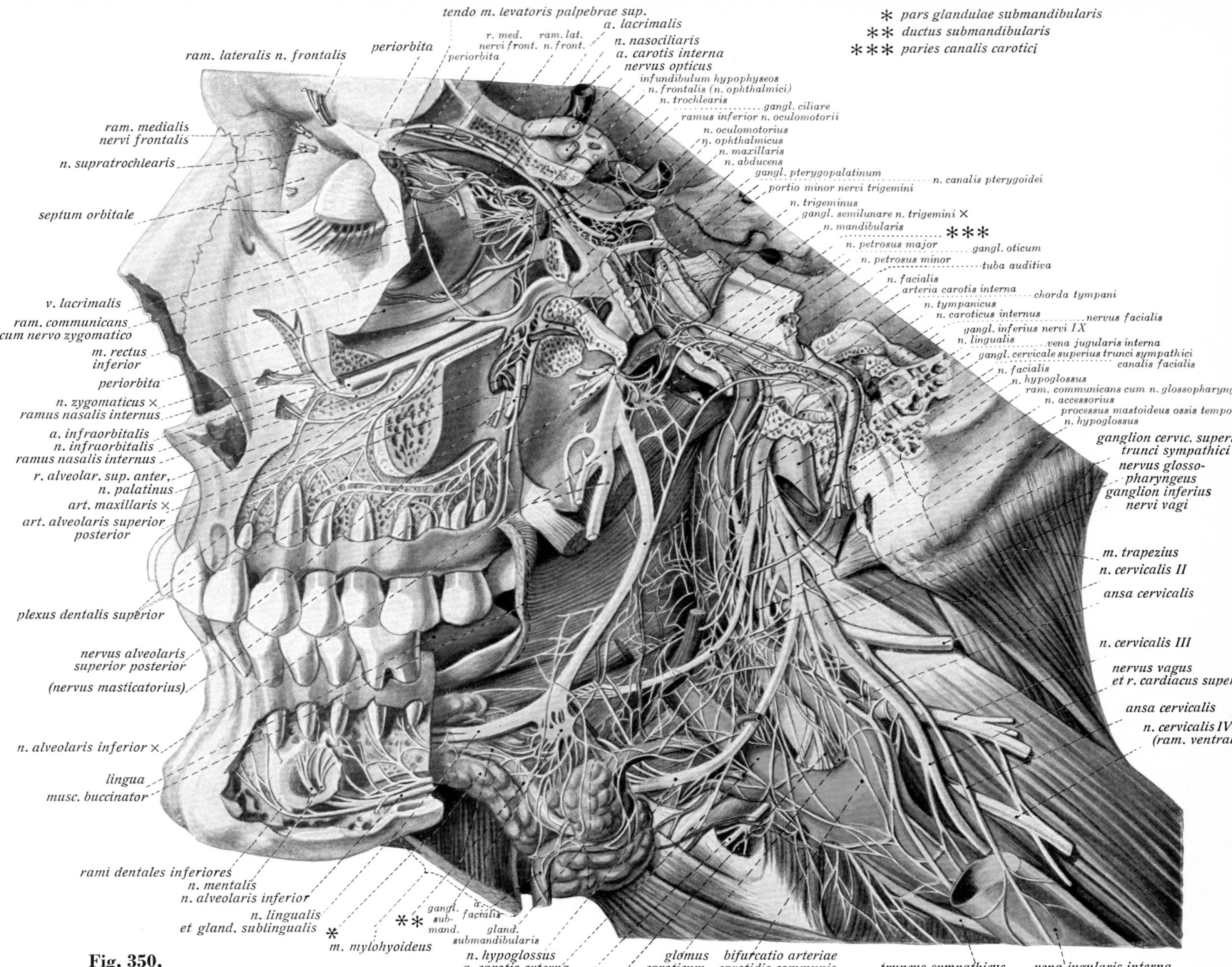
tendo m. levatoris palpebrae sup.
a. lacrimalis
r. med. nervi front.
ram. lat. n. front.
n. nasociliaris
a. carotis interna
nervus opticus
infundibulum hypophyseos
n. frontalis (n. ophthalmici)
n. trochlearis
gangl. ciliare
ramus inferior n. oculomotorii
n. oculomotorius
n. ophthalmicus
n. maxillaris
n. abducens
gangl. pterygopalatinum
n. canalis pterygoidei
portio minor nervi trigemini
n. trigeminus
gangl. semilunare n. trigemini ×
n. mandibularis
***
n. petrosus major
gangl. oticum
n. petrosus minor
tuba auditiva
n. facialis
arteria carotis interna
chorda tympani
n. tympanicus
n. caroticus internus
nervus facialis
gangl. inferius nervi IX
n. lingualis
vena jugularis interna
gangl. cervicale superius trunci sympathici
canalis facialis
n. facialis
n. hypoglossus
ram. communicans cum n. glossopharyngeo
n. accessorius
processus mastoideus ossis temporalis
n. hypoglossus
ganglion cervic. superius trunci sympathici
nervus glosso-pharyngeus
ganglion inferius nervi vagi
m. trapezius
n. cervicalis II
ansa cervicalis
n. cervicalis III
nervus vagus et r. cardiacus superior
ansa cervicalis
n. cervicalis IV (ram. ventralis)
* pars glandulae submandibularis
** ductus submandibularis
*** paries canalis carotici
ram. lateralis n. frontalis
periorbita
periorbita
ram. medialis nervi frontalis
n. supratrochlearis
septum orbitale
v. lacrimalis
ram. communicans cum nervo zygomatico
m. rectus inferior
periorbita
n. zygomaticus ×
ramus nasalis internus
a. infraorbitalis
n. infraorbitalis
ramus nasalis internus
r. alveolar. sup. anter.
n. palatinus
art. maxillaris ×
art. alveolaris superior posterior
plexus dentalis superior
nervus alveolaris superior posterior
(nervus masticatorius)
n. alveolaris inferior ×
lingua
musc. buccinator
rami dentales inferiores
n. mentalis
n. alveolaris inferior
n. lingualis
et gland. sublingualis
*
m. mylohyoideus
**
gangl. sub-mand.
a. facialis
gland. submandibularis
n. hypoglossus
a. carotis externa
ram. int. n. laryngei superioris
glomus caroticum
ram. ext. n. laryngei superioris
bifurcatio arteriae carotidis communis
truncus sympathicus
vena jugularis interna
Fig. 350.

# 350. Cranial Portion of Autonomic Nervous System. (after Braeucker).

1 **Pterygopalatine Ganglion**
*gangl. pterygopalatinum*
**Nerve of Pterygoid Canal**
*n. canalis pterygoidei*
**Motor Root of Trigeminal**
*portio minor nervi trigemini [radix motoria]*
**Trigeminal Nerve**
*n. trigeminus*
**[Trigeminal Ggl.], Trigeminal N.**
*gangl. semilunare [gangl. trigeminale] n. trigemini*
**Mandibular Nerve**
*n. mandibularis*
**Wall of Carotid Canal**
***
**Greater Petrosal Nerve**
*n. petrosus major*
**Otic Ganglion**
*gangl. oticum*
**Lesser Petrosal Nerve**
*n. petrosus minor*

2 **Auditory Tube**
*tuba auditiva*
**Facial Nerve**
*n. facialis*
**Internal Carotid Artery**
*arteria carotis interna*
**Chorda Tympani**
*chorda tympani*
**Tympanic Nerve**
*n. tympanicus*
**Internal Carotid Nerve**
*n. caroticus internus*
**Facial Nerve**
*nervus facialis*
**Inf. Ggl. of Glossopharyngeal N.**
*gangl. inferius nervi IX*
**Lingual Nerve**
*n. lingualis*
**Internal Jugular Vein**
*vena jugularis interna*
**Superior Cervical Ganglion, Sympathetic Trunk**
*gangl. cervicale superius trunci sympathici*
**Facial Canal**
*canalis facialis*
**Facial Nerve**
*n. facialis*
**Hypoglossal Nerve**
*n. hypoglossus*
**Connection with Glossopharyngeal Nerve**
*ram. communicans cum n. glossopharyngeo*

3 **Accessory Nerve**
*n. accessorius*
**Mastoid Process of Temporal Bone**
*processus mastoideus ossis temporalis*
**Hypoglossal Nerve**
*n. hypoglossus*
**Superior Cervical Ganglion, Sympathetic Trunk**
*ganglion cervic. superius trunci sympathici*
**Glossopharyngeal Nerve**
*nervus glossopharyngeus*
**Inferior Ganglion, Vagus Nerve**
*ganglion inferius nervi vagi*
**Trapezius Muscle**
*m. trapezius*
**2nd Cervical Nerve**
*n. cervicalis II*
**Ansa Cervicalis**
*ansa cervicalis*

4 **3rd Cervical Nerve**
*n. cervicalis III*
**Vagus Nerve + Sup. Cardiac Br.**
*nervus vagus + r. cardiacus superior*
**Ansa Cervicalis**
*ansa cervicalis*
**4th Cervical Nerve (Ventral Ramus)**
*n. cervicalis IV (ram. ventralis)*

5 **Internal Jugular Vein**
*vena jugularis interna*
**Sympathetic Trunk** (displaced ventrally)
*truncus sympathicus*

6 **Bifurcation of Common Carotid Artery**
*bifurcatio arteriae carotidis communis*
**Carotid Body**
*glomus caroticum*
**Sup. Laryngeal N., Ext. Br.**
*ram. ext. n. laryngei superioris*

7 **Sup. Laryngeal N., Int. Br.**
*ram. int. n. laryngei superioris*
**External Carotid Artery**
*a. carotis externa*
**Hypoglossal Nerve**
*n. hypoglossus*
**Submandibular Gland**
*gland. submandibularis*
**Facial Artery**
*a. facialis*
**Submandibular Ganglion and Duct**
*gangl. submand.* **
**Mylohyoid Muscle**
*m. mylohyoideus*
**Submandibular Gland**
*
**Lingual Nerve + Sublingual Gland**
*n. lingualis + gland. sublingualis*

8 **Inferior Alveolar Nerve**
*n. alveolaris inferior*
**Mental Nerve**
*n. mentalis*
**Inferior Dental Branches**
*rami dentales inferiores*
**Buccinator Muscle**
*musc. buccinator*
**Tongue**
*lingua*
**Inferior Alveolar Nerve**
*n. alveolaris inferior*
**(Masticator Nerve)**
*(nervus masticatorius)*
**Superior Posterior Alveolar Nerve**
*nervus alveolaris superior posterior*

9 **Superior Dental Plexus**
*plexus dentalis superior*
**Superior Posterior Alveolar Artery**
*art. alveolaris superior posterior*
**Maxillary Artery**
*art. maxillaris*
**Palatine Nerve**
*n. palatinus*
**Superior Anterior Alveolar Branch**
*r. alveolar. sup. anter.*
**Int. Nasal Br. [of Maxillary N.]**
*ramus basalis internus*
**Infraorbital Artery + Nerve**
*a. + n. infraorbitalis*
**Internal Nasal Branch**
*ramus nasalis internus*
**Zygomatic Nerve**
*n. zygomaticus*

10 **Periorbita**
*periorbita*
**Inferior Rectus Muscle**
*m. rectus inferior*
**Zygomaticolacrimal Communication**
*ram. communicans cum nervo zygomatico*
**Lacrimal Vein**
*v. lacrimalis*
**Orbital Septum**
*septum orbitale*
**Supratrochlear Nerve**
*n. supratrochlearis*
**Frontal Nerve, Medial Branch**
*ram. medialis nervi frontalis*

11 **Frontal Nerve, Lateral Branch**
*ram. lateralis n. frontalis*
**Periorbita**
*periorbita*
**Levator Palpebrae Sup. Muscle, Tendon**
*tendo m. levatoris palpebrae sup.*
**Frontal Nerve, Medial Branch**
*r. med. nervi front.*

12 **Frontal Nerve, Lateral Branch**
*ram. lat. n. front.*
**Lacrimal Artery**
*arteria lacrimalis*
**Nasociliary Nerve**
*n. nasociliaris*
**Internal Carotid Artery**
*a. carotis interna*
**Optic Nerve**
*nervus opticus*
**Hypophyseal Infundibulum**
*infundibulum hypophyseos*
**Frontal Nerve (Ophthalmic Nerve)**
*n. frontalis (n. ophthalmici)*
**Trochlear Nerve**
*n. trochlearis*
**Ciliary Ganglion**
*gangl. ciliare*
**Oculomotor N., Inf. Br.**
*ramus inferior n. oculomotorii*
**Oculomotor Nerve**
*n. oculomotorius*
**Ophthalmic Nerve**
*n. ophthalmicus*
**Maxillary Nerve**
*n. maxillaris*
**Abducens Nerve**
*n. abducens*

## 350 and 351. Cranial Portion of Autonomic Nervous System. (after Braeucker).

The four **cranial autonomic ganglia** and their connections with most of the cranial nerves were displayed by removal of soft parts and opening osseous canals.

**Note:** 1. **Ciliary ganglion**-12 in orbital cavity, lateral to optic nerve. Presynaptic neurons from **accessory (automomic) oculomotor nucleus** (Edinger-Westphal) via oculomotor nerve, inferior ramus-12. Postsynaptic fibers pass to bulbus oculi by **short ciliary nerves.** They supply the ciliary muscle, which regulates the shape of the lens (focal distance) and the circular muscle of the iris, which constricts the pupil.

2. **Pterygopalatine ganglion**-1 lies in fossa of same name. Axons from presynaptic neurons in **superior salivatory nucleus,** pass by way of **intermedius portion of facial nerve** and its **greater petrosal branch**-1 and **nerve of pterygoid canal**-1 to pterygopalatine ganglion-1. Postsynaptic fibers join branches of **maxillary nerve**-12 that pass to nasal cavity and palate. Some fibers also follow zygomatic branch of **maxillary nerve** to its communication with lacrimal nerve-10 to supply **lacrimal gland** with parasympathetic fibers.

3. **Otic ganglion**-1 in infratemporal fossa, medial to mandibular division of trigeminal nerve-1 receives presynaptic fibers from **inferior salivatory nucleus** via **glossopharyngeal**-3. Fibers leave 9th nerve-2 as the **tympanic nerve**-2, which passes through a groove on tympanic bulla (tympanic plexus) to middle cranial fossa, to become the **lesser petrosal nerve**-1, which then enters infratemporal fossa to supply **otic ganglion**-1 with presynaptic fibers. Postsynaptic nerve fibers join the **auriculotemporal** nerve to supply the **parotid gland.**

4. **Submandibular ganglion**-7 is attached to lingual nerve-7. It receives presynaptic fibers from **superior salivatory nucleus,** via **facial nerve** (intermedius portion VII) and its **chorda tympani** branch-2. The latter curves through the tympanic cavity and infratemporal fossa to join the **lingual nerve**-2, which transmits the fibers to the **submandibular ganglion**-7. The postsynaptic nerve fibers pass directly to the **submandibular** and **sublingual glands** to regulate the process of salivary secretion.

5. Since there is no **sympathetic outflow** in any of the cranial or cervical nerves, the glands and smooth muscles of the **head and neck** must receive **sympathetic innervation** indirectly from the **presynaptic outflow in upper thoracic region.** The presynaptic sympathetic neuron fibers join sympathetic trunk in thorax and pass up the **cervical sympathetic trunk to a cervical sympathetic ganglion.** The apex of the superior cervical ganglion-2 is shown near the internal carotid artery-2 just before the artery enters the carotid canal in the temporal bone. The postsynaptic nerve fibers from cells that form the superior cervical ganglion-2 pass to the internal carotid plexus by way of the **internal carotid nerve**-2. From the internal **carotid plexus,** sympathetic twigs are supplied to all the divisions of the **trigeminal** nerves and **other cranial nerves** which then distribute the postsynaptic sympathetic nerve fibers to the parts of the head that they supply. For example, some of the postsynaptic sympathetic fibers on carotid plexus join the greater petrosal nerve-1 as the deep petrosal nerve to form the nerve of the pterygoid canal-1. This nerve thus conveys presynaptic parasympathetic fibers of VII plus postsynaptic sympathetic fibers to the pterygopalatine ganglion. The postsynaptic sympathetic fibers merely pass through the ganglion into all its branches to be distributed.

6. The **superior cervical ganglion** also supplies nerve twigs of postsynaptic neurons to the external carotid artery-7 as **external carotid nerve and plexus.** These fibers form a plexus on this artery and follow it to all the parts of the head which it supplies. In addition, the superior cervical ganglion supplies postsynaptic sympathetic fibers to the vagus, glossopharyngeal, and hypoglossal nerves-3, for distribution. The connections of sympathetic ganglia with the cervical nerves are called **rami communicantes** and are depicted in other illustrations.

## 351. Cranial Portion of Autonomic Nervous System. A simplified version of Fig. 250. (Nerves, **black**)

1 **Oculomotor Nerve**
*n. oculomotorius*

**Semilunar Ganglion of Trigeminal Nerve** [Trigeminal Ganglion]
*gangl. semilunare n. trigemini [gang. trigeminale]*

**Trigeminal Nerve, Motor Portion**
*portio minor nervi trigemini*

**Trigeminal Nerve**
*n. trigeminus*

**Mandibular Nerve**
*n. mandibularis*

**Greater Petrosal Nerve**
*n. petrosus major*

**Otic Ganglion**
*gangl. oticum*

2 **Lesser Petrosal Nerve**
*n. petrosus minor*

**Facial Nerve**
*n. facialis*

**Chorda Tympani**
*chorda tympani*

**Tympanic Nerve**
*n. tympanicus*

**Facial Nerve**
*nervus facialis*

**Inferior Ganglion Nerve IX**
*gangl. inferius nervi IX*

**Superior Cervical Ganglion Sympathetic Trunk**
*gangl. cervicale superior trunci sympathici*

**Facial Nerve**
*n. facialis*

3 **Hypoglossal Nerve**
*n. hypoglossus*

**Anastomosis with Glossopharyngeal Nerve**
*anastomosis ad. n. glossopharyngeum*

**Accessory Nerve**
*n. accessorius.*

**Hypoglossal Nerve**
*n. hypoglossus*

**Superior Cervical Ganglion, Sympathetic Trunk**
*ganglion cervic. superius trunci sympathici*

**Glossopharyngeal Nerve**
*nervus glossopharyngeus*

**Vagus Nerve, Inferior Ganglion**
*ganglion inferius nervi vagi*

**Cervical Nerve II**
*n. cervicalis II*

**Ansa Cervicalis**
*ansa cervicalis*

4 **Cervical Nerve III**
*n. cervicalis III*

5 **Cervical Nerve IV (Ventral Branch)**
*n. cervicalis IV (ram. ventralis)*

**Ansa Cervicalis**
*ansa cervicalis*

**Sympathetic Trunk**
*truncus sympathicus*

**Vagus Nerve and Superior Cardiac Branch**
*nervus vagus et r. cardiacus superior*

6 **Carotid Body**
*glomus caroticum*

7 **Superior Laryngeal Nerve, External Branch**
*ram. ext. n. laryngei superioris*

**Superior Laryngeal Nerve, Internal Branch**
*ram. int. n. laryngei superioris*

**Hypoglossal Nerve**
*n. hypoglossus*

**Submandibular Ganglion**
*gangl. submand.*

**Lingual Nerve**
*n. lingualis*

8 **Inferior Alveolar Nerve**
*n. alveolaris inferior*

**Inferior Dental Branches**
*rami dentales inferiores*

**Mental Nerve**
*n. mentalis*

**Lingual Nerve**
*n. lingualis*

**Internal Carotid Nerve**
*n. caroticus internus*

9 **Inferior Alveolar Nerve**
*n. alveolaris inferior*

**(Masticator Nerve) (Motor Trigeminal)**
*(nervus masticatorius)*

**Superior Dental Plexus**
*plexus dentalis superior*

**Posterior Superior Alveolar Nerve**
*nervus alveolaris superior posterior*

**Superior Anterior Alveolar Branch**
*r. alveol. sup. anter.*

**Internal Nasal Branch**
*ramus nasalis internus*

**Infraorbital Nerve**
*n. infraorbitalis*

10 **Nerve of Pterygoid Canal**
*n. canalis pterygoidei*

**Palatine Nerve**
*n. palatinus*

**Pterygopalatine Ganglion**
*gangl. pterygopalatinum*

**Zygomatic Nerve**
*n. zygomaticus*

**Maxillary Nerve**
*n. maxillaris*

**Ophthalmic Nerve**
*n. ophthalmicus*

**Communicating Branch with Zygomatic Nerve**
*ram. communicans cum nervo zygomatico*

**Supratrochlear Nerve**
*n. supratrochlearis*

**Medial Branch**
*ram. medialis*

**Frontal Nerve, Lateral Branch**
*ram. lateralis n. frontalis*

11 **Frontal Nerve, Medial Branch**
*r. med. nervi frontalis*

**Nasociliary Nerve**
*n. nasociliaris*

12 **Optic Nerve**
*nervus opticus*

**Frontal Nerve (Ophthalmic Nerve)**
*n. frontalis (n. ophthalmici)*

**Trochlear Nerve**
*n. trochlearis*

**Ciliary Ganglion**
*gangl. ciliare*

**Oculomotor Nerve, Inferior Division**
*ramus inferior n. oculomotorii*

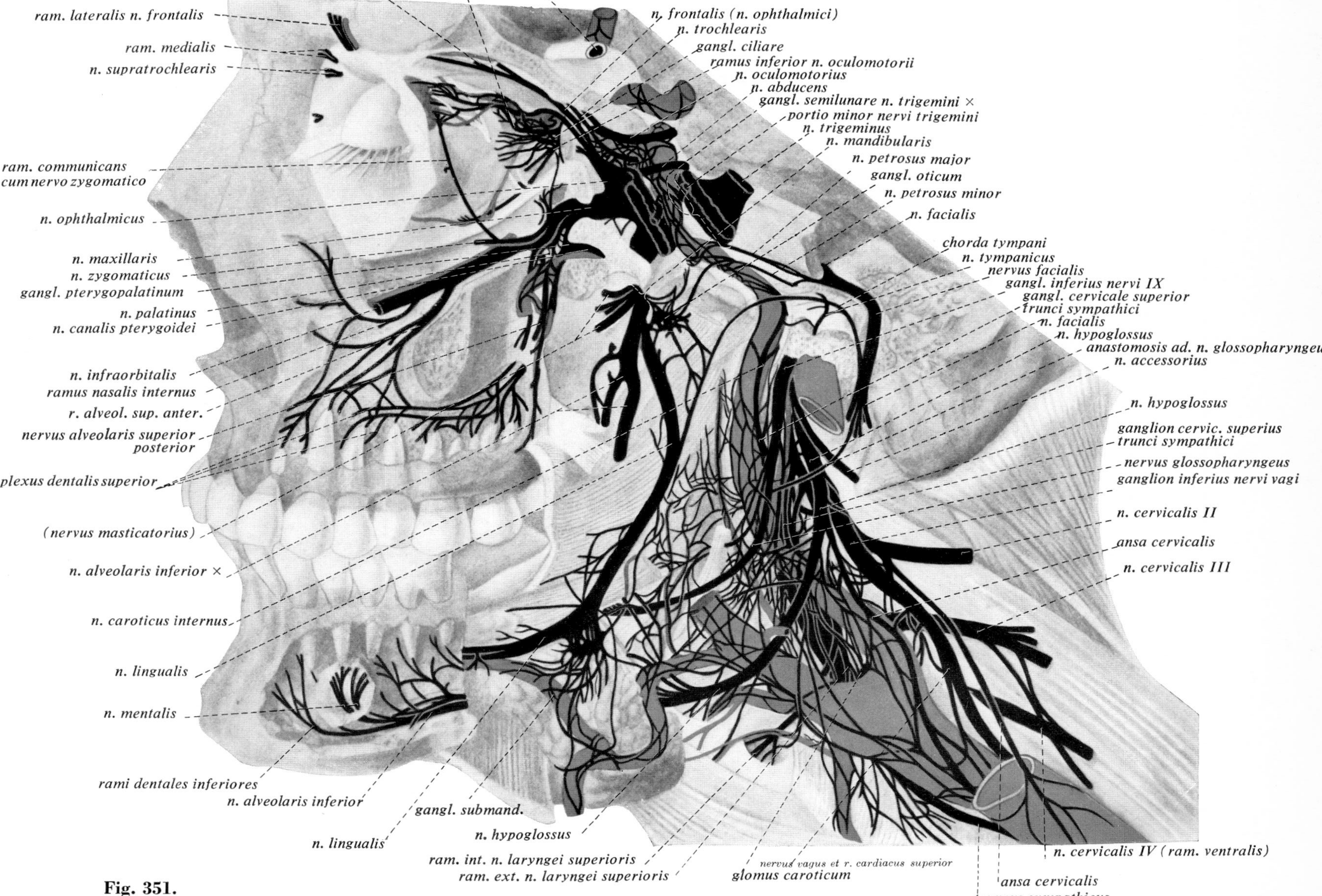
r. med. nervi frontalis
n. nasociliaris
nervus opticus
ram. lateralis n. frontalis
ram. medialis
n. supratrochlearis
n. frontalis (n. ophthalmici)
n. trochlearis
gangl. ciliare
ramus inferior n. oculomotorii
n. oculomotorius
n. abducens
gangl. semilunare n. trigemini ×
portio minor nervi trigemini
n. trigeminus
n. mandibularis
ram. communicans
cum nervo zygomatico
n. petrosus major
gangl. oticum
n. petrosus minor
n. ophthalmicus
n. facialis
chorda tympani
n. tympanicus
nervus facialis
gangl. inferius nervi IX
gangl. cervicale superior
trunci sympathici
n. facialis
n. hypoglossus
anastomosis ad. n. glossopharyngeum
n. accessorius
n. maxillaris
n. zygomaticus
gangl. pterygopalatinum
n. palatinus
n. canalis pterygoidei
n. infraorbitalis
ramus nasalis internus
r. alveol. sup. anter.
nervus alveolaris superior
posterior
n. hypoglossus
ganglion cervic. superius
trunci sympathici
nervus glossopharyngeus
ganglion inferius nervi vagi
plexus dentalis superior
(nervus masticatorius)
n. cervicalis II
ansa cervicalis
n. alveolaris inferior ×
n. cervicalis III
n. caroticus internus
n. lingualis
n. mentalis
rami dentales inferiores
n. alveolaris inferior
gangl. submand.
n. hypoglossus
n. lingualis
ram. int. n. laryngei superioris
ram. ext. n. laryngei superioris
nervus vagus et r. cardiacus superior
glomus caroticum
n. cervicalis IV (ram. ventralis)
ansa cervicalis
truncus sympathicus

**Fig. 351.**

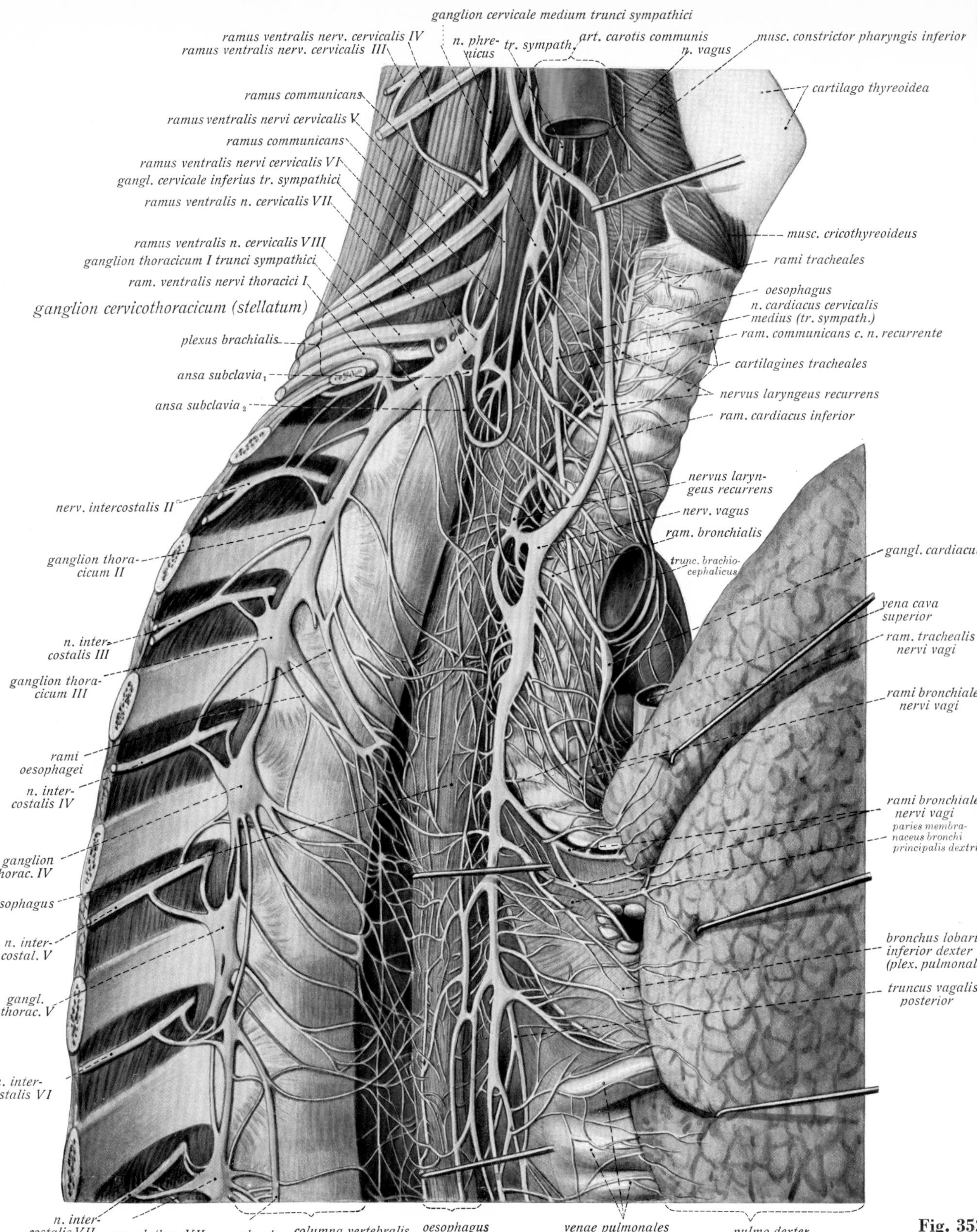
ganglion cervicale medium trunci sympathici
ramus ventralis nerv. cervicalis IV
ramus ventralis nerv. cervicalis III
n. phrenicus
tr. sympath.
art. carotis communis
n. vagus
musc. constrictor pharyngis inferior
cartilago thyreoidea
ramus communicans
ramus ventralis nervi cervicalis V
ramus communicans
ramus ventralis nervi cervicalis VI
gangl. cervicale inferius tr. sympathici
ramus ventralis n. cervicalis VII
musc. cricothyreoideus
ramus ventralis n. cervicalis VIII
ganglion thoracicum I trunci sympathici
rami tracheales
ram. ventralis nervi thoracici I
oesophagus
n. cardiacus cervicalis medius (tr. sympath.)
ganglion cervicothoracicum (stellatum)
ram. communicans c. n. recurrente
plexus brachialis
cartilagines tracheales
ansa subclavia 1
ansa subclavia 2
nervus laryngeus recurrens
ram. cardiacus inferior
nervus laryngeus recurrens
nerv. intercostalis II
nerv. vagus
ram. bronchialis
ganglion thoracicum II
trunc. brachiocephalicus
gangl. cardiacu
vena cava superior
n. intercostalis III
ram. trachealis nervi vagi
ganglion thoracicum III
rami bronchiale nervi vagi
rami oesophagei
n. intercostalis IV
rami bronchiale nervi vagi
paries membranaceus bronchi principalis dextri
ganglion thorac. IV
oesophagus
n. intercostal. V
bronchus lobari inferior dexter (plex. pulmonal.
gangl. thorac. V
truncus vagalis posterior
n. intercostalis VI
n. intercostalis VII
gangl. thor. VII
n. splanchnicus major (radix prima)
columna vertebralis
oesophagus
venae pulmonales
pulmo dexter

Fig. 35

## 352. Upper Thoracic and Lower Cervical Portion of Autonomic Nervous System. (1/1) (after Braeucker)

The autonomic nerves were exposed by removing most of the other structures. The trunk of the vagus-12 has been pulled forward with a hook. The right lung-5 was pulled forward to the left and the esophagus-8 and autonomic plexuses exposed.

1 **Inferior Pharyngeal Constrictor Muscle**
*musc. constrictor pharyngis inferior*

**Thyroid Cartilage**
*cartilago thyreoidea*

**Cricothyroid Muscle**
*musc. cricothyreoideus*

**Tracheal Rami**
*rami tracheales*

**Esophagus**
*esophagus*

**Middle Cervical Cardiac Nerve, (Sympathetic Trunk)**
*n. cardiacus cervicalis medius (tr. sympath.)*

**Ramus Communicans to Recurrent Nerve**
*ram. communicans c. n. recurrente*

**Tracheal Cartilages**
*cartilagines tracheales*

**Recurrent Laryngeal Nerve**
*nervue laryngeus recurrens*

**Inferior Cardiac Branch**
*ram. cardiacus inferior*

2 **Recurrent Laryngeal Nerve**
*nervus laryngeus recurrens*

**Vagus Nerve**
*nerv. vagus*

**Bronchial Branch**
*ram. bronchialis*

**Brachiocephalic Trunk**
*trunc. brachiocephalicus*

3 **Cardiac Ganglion**
*gangl. cardiacum*

**Superior Vena Cava**
*vena cava superior*

**Vagus Nerve, Tracheal Branch**
*ram. trachealis nervi vagi*

**Vagus Nerve, Bronchial Br.**
*rami bronchiales nervi vagi*

4 **Vagus Nerve, Bronchial Br.**
*rami bronchiales nervi vagi*

**Membranous Wall of Right Main Bronchus**
*paries membranaceus bronchi principalis dextri*

**Right Inferior Lobar Bronchus, (Pulmonary Plexus)**
*bronchus lobaris inferior dexter (plex. pulmonal.)*

**Posterior Vagal Trunk**
*truncus vagalis posterior*

5 **Right Lung**
*pulmo dexter*

6 **Pulmonary Veins**
*venae pulmonales*

**Esophagus**
*esophagus*

7 **Vertebral Column**
*columna vertebralis*

**Greater Splanchnic Nerve, 1st Root**
*n. splanchnicus major (radix prima)*

**Thoracic Ganglion, 7th**
*gangl. thor. VII*

**Intercostal Nerve, 7th**
*n. intercostalis VII*

**Intercostal Nerve, 6th**
*n. intercostalis VI*

8 **Thoracic Ganglion, 5th**
*gangl. thorac. V*

**Intercostal Nerve, 5th**
*n. intercostal. V*

**Esophagus**
*esophagus*

**Thoracic Ganglion, 4th**
*ganglion thorac. IV*

**Intercostal Nerve, 4th**
*n. intercostalis IV*

**Esophageal Branches**
*rami esophagei*

9 **Thoracic ganglion, 3rd**
*ganglion thoracicum III*

**Intercostal Nerve, 3rd**
*n. intercostalis III*

**Thoracic Ganglion, 2nd**
*ganglion thorcacicum II*

10 **Intercostal Nerve, 2nd**
*nerv. intercostalis II*

**Ansa Subclavia, Ventral Limb**
*ansa subclavia*

**Ansa Subclavia, Dorsal Limb**
*ansa subclavia*

11 **Brachial Plexus**
*plexus brachialis*

**Cervicothoracic Ganglion (Stellate)**
*ganglion cervicothoracicum (stellatum)*

**1st Thoracic Nerve, Ventral Ramus**
*ram. ventralis nervi thoracici I*

**1st Thoracic Ganglion, Sympathetic Trunk**
*ganglion thoracicum I trunci sympathici*

**8th Cervical Nerve, Ventral Ramus**
*ramus ventralis n. cervicalis VIII*

**7th Cervical Nerve, Ventral Ramus**
*ramus ventralis n. cervicalis VII*

**Inferior Cervical Ganglion, Sympathetic Trunk**
*gangl. cervicale inferius tr. sympathici*

**6th Cervical Nerve, Ventral Ramus**
*ramus ventralis nervi cervicalis VI*

**Ramus Communicans**
*ramus communicans*

**5th Cervical Nerve, Ventral Ramus**
*ramus ventralis nervi cervicalis V*

**Ramus Communicans**
*ramus communicans*

**3rd Cervical Nerve, Ventral Ramus**
*ramus ventralis nerv. cervicalis III*

**4th Cervical Nerve, Ventral Ramus**
*ramus ventralis nerv. cervicalis IV*

12 **Sympathetic Trunk, Middle Cervical Ganglion**
*ganglion cervicale medium trunci sympathici*

**Phrenic Nerve**
*n. phrenicus*

**Sympathetic Trunk**
*tr. sympath.*

**Common Carotid Artery**
*art. carotis communis*

**Vagus Nerve**
*n. vagus*

(Notes on following page)

## 352. Upper Thoracic and Lower Cervical Portion of Autonomic Nervous System. (1/1) (after Braeucker)

**Note:** 1. **Thoracic sympathetic chain**-7 to -10 with a ganglion in each costal or intercostal space.

2. Each thoracic ganglion-9 has two or more communications with an intercostal nerve, called **rami communicantes** (singular, **ramus communicans**).

3. Since one of these communicating rami is composed mainly of myelinated axons from neurons in intermediolateral column, it has a white appearance in the fresh state. It is, therefore, usually called the **white ramus communicans** (sympathetic outflow). The other communicating ramus is composed primarily of postsynaptic unmyelinated nerve fibers that are passing from the ganglion to the spinal nerve to be distributed peripherally. This connection is conventionally called a **gray ramus communicans.**

4. The **sympathetic trunk** extends upwards in neck, as the **cervical sympathetic trunk**-12 dorsal to carotid artery, but some of the originally segmented ganglia have fused. There are, likewise, connections with spinal nerves (ramus communicans-11), but these connections in the cervical region are made up of postsynaptic sympathetic fibers that are unmyelinated **(gray rami communicantes).** In the lower cervical region, they pass to the ventral rami of the cervical nerves that form the brachial plexus-11 to be distributed to the superior extremities. In the upper cervical region, they pass to the upper cervical nerves to be distributed to the parts of the head and neck supplied by these nerves. The superior cervical ganglion also contributes postsynaptic nerve fibers to both internal and external carotid arteries for distribution peripherally.

5. The **vagus nerve**-12 as it "wanders" through the neck, gives off branches such as the recurrent laryngeal nerve-2, branches to the esophagus, pharynx, larynx, trachea and cardiac branches-2, -3. In the thorax, it supplies branches to the pulmonary-4 and esophageal-6 plexuses. This nerve carries the **presynaptic parasympathetic fibers** from cells in **dorsal motor nucleus of vagus** which will synapse with neurons located in the wall of the organs which they supply. The name of this nerve indicates its extensive distribution, *vagus* = wanderer.

# 353. Lower Thoracic Portion of the Autonomic Nervous System.

(1/1) (after Braeucker)

**Note:** 1. Relation of **intercostal arteries**-7, **veins**-7, **nerves**-7, and **gray and white rami communicantes** (connections between sympathetic ganglia and intercostal nerves).

2. **Splanchnic nerves** take origin from 6th to 11th thoracic ganglia and pass caudally through diaphragm to abdominal ganglia and viscera. They are called the splanchnics because they supply the abdominal viscera (Gr. splanchna = viscera). These nerves are composed mainly of **myelinated presynaptic fibers** that pass from intercostal nerves through thoracic ganglia without synapse. They **synapse in collateral ganglia,** such as the **celiac ganglion** (See Fig. 355-10). Postsynaptic neurons then follow arteries to the abdominal viscera. Splanchnic nerves also **convey myelinated sensory nerve fibers (pain) from abdominal viscera** to sympathetic trunk where they pass from ganglia to intercostal nerves through white rami communicantes and, through the dorsal root (cell bodies in dorsal spinal ganglion), to central nervous system.

3. Right and left vagus nerves form a plexus on the esophagus (Fig. 354–3, -8). As the vagus nerves follow the esophagus through the diaphragm, fibers from vagal plexus form two main cords called the anterior and posterior vagal trunks-3. The posterior vagal trunk contains fibers from both right and left vagus nerves and so does the anterior vagal trunk.

4. Position of **thoracic duct**-7.

# 353. Lower Thoracic Portion of the Autonomic Nervous System.
(1/1) (after Braeucker)

This is a continuation of Figure 352, but more veins and arteries were left intact, and the thoracic duct is shown as it passes through the thorax.

1 **Membranous Wall of Right Inferior and Middle Bronchial Lobes**
*paries membranaceus bronchi lobaris medii et inferioris dextri*

**Lung**
*pulmo*

**Right Vagus Nerve, Esophageal Branch**
*ramus esophageus n. vagi dextri*

**Right Vagus Nerve Branch**
*ram. n. vagi dextri*

2 **Bronchial Branches of Vagus Nerve (Pulmonary Plexus)**
*rami bronchiales nervi vagi (plexus pulmonal)*

**Right Pulmonary Veins**
*venae pulmonales dextrae*

3 **Pericardium**
*pericardium*

**Vagus Nerve, Esophageal Plexus**
*plexus esophageus n. vagi*

**Posterior Vagal Trunk**
*truncus vagalis posterior*

**Esophagus**
*esophagus*

4 **Inferior Vena Cava**
*vena cava inferior*

**Phrenic Nerve**
*nervus phrenicus*

**Vena Caval Foramen**
*foramen venae cavae*

5 **Diaphragm**
*diaphragma*

6 **Thoracic Aorta + Plexus of Thoracic Aorta**
*aorta thoracica + plexus aorticus thoracicus*

**Thoracic Duct**
*ductus thoracicus*

**Lesser Splanchnic Nerve**
*n. splanchnicus minor*

7 **Greater Splanchnic Nerve**
*nervus splanchnicus major*

**11th Thoracic Ganglion, Sympathetic Trunk**
*ganglion thoracicum XI*

**Quadratus Lumborum Muscle**
*m. quadratus lumborum*

**Branch of Intercostal Artery**
*ram. art. intercostalis*

**Intercostal Nerve**
*nervus intercostalis*

**Intercostal Artery**
*art. intercostalis*

**Intercostal Vein**
*vena intercostalis*

**Thoracic Duct**
*ductus thoracicus*

8 **10th Thoracic Ganglion**
*ganglion thoracicum X*

**10th Intercostal Nerve**
*n. intercost. X*

**9th Thoracic Ganglion**
*gangl. thoracicum IX*

**9th Intercostal Nerve**
*n. intercostalis IX*

**Interganglionic Branch**
*ramus interganglionaris*

9 **7th Thoracic Ganglion**
*ganglion thorac. VII*

10 **Interganglionic Branches**
*rami interganglionares*

**6th Thoracic Ganglion**
*ganglion thorac. VI*

11 **5th Thoracic Ganglion, Sympathetic Trunk**
*ganglion thoracicum V trunci sympathici*

12 **Azygos Vein**
*vena azygos*

**Esophagus**
*esophagus*

**Vagus Nerve**
*nervus vagus*

**Bronchial Artery Branch**
*ramus bronchialis*

(Notes on preceding page)

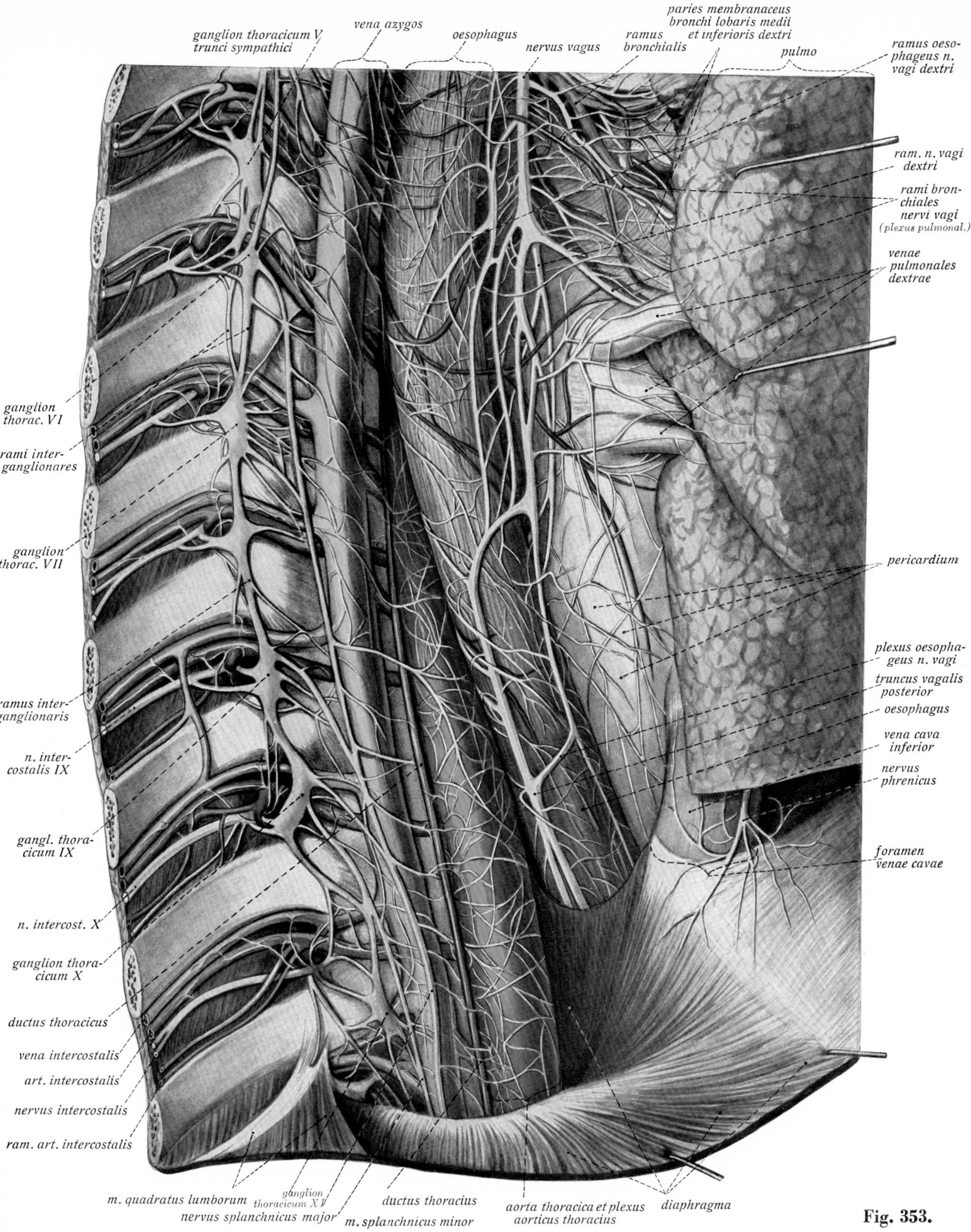
ganglion thoracicum V
trunci sympathici
vena azygos
oesophagus
nervus vagus
ramus
bronchialis
paries membranaceus
bronchi lobaris medii
et inferioris dextri
pulmo
ramus oeso-
phageus n.
vagi dextri
ram. n. vagi
dextri
rami bron-
chiales
nervi vagi
(plexus pulmonal.)
venae
pulmonales
dextrae
pericardium
plexus oesopha-
geus n. vagi
truncus vagalis
posterior
oesophagus
vena cava
inferior
nervus
phrenicus
foramen
venae cavae
ganglion
thorac. VI
rami inter-
ganglionares
ganglion
thorac. VII
ramus inter-
ganglionaris
n. inter-
costalis IX
gangl. thora-
cicum IX
n. intercost. X
ganglion thora-
cicum X
ductus thoracicus
vena intercostalis
art. intercostalis
nervus intercostalis
ram. art. intercostalis
m. quadratus lumborum
ganglion
thoracicum XI
nervus splanchnicus major
ductus thoracius
m. splanchnicus minor
aorta thoracica et plexus
aorticus thoracius
diaphragma

Fig. 353.

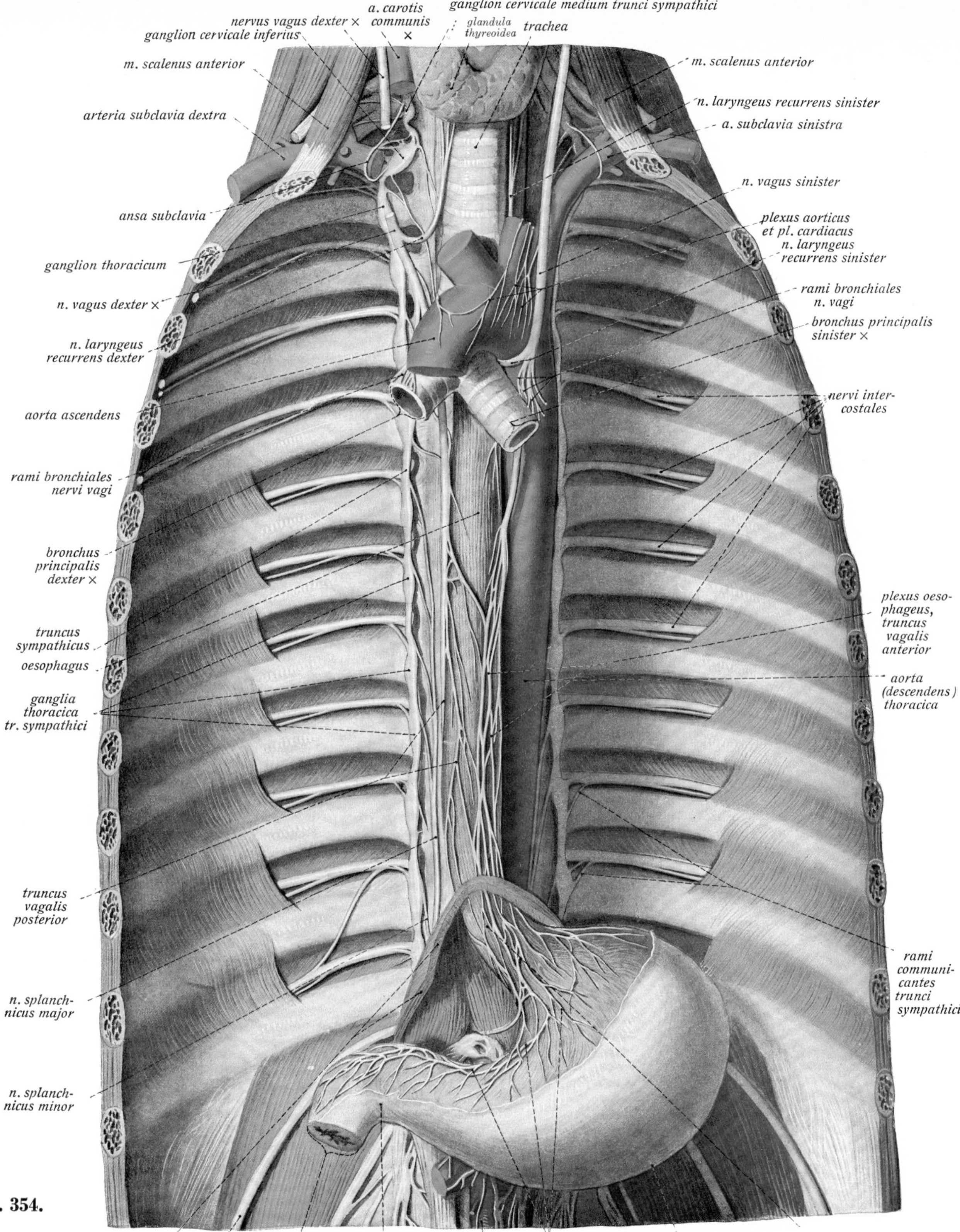

a. carotis communis ×
ganglion cervicale medium trunci sympathici
nervus vagus dexter ×
ganglion cervicale inferius
glandula thyreoidea
trachea
m. scalenus anterior
m. scalenus anterior
n. laryngeus recurrens sinister
arteria subclavia dextra
a. subclavia sinistra
n. vagus sinister
ansa subclavia
plexus aorticus et pl. cardiacus
n. laryngeus recurrens sinister
ganglion thoracicum
rami bronchiales n. vagi
n. vagus dexter ×
bronchus principalis sinister ×
n. laryngeus recurrens dexter
nervi intercostales
aorta ascendens
rami bronchiales nervi vagi
bronchus principalis dexter ×
plexus oesophageus, truncus vagalis anterior
truncus sympathicus
oesophagus
aorta (descendens) thoracica
ganglia thoracica tr. sympathici
truncus vagalis posterior
rami communicantes trunci sympathici
n. splanchnicus major
n. splanchnicus minor
diaphragma ×
n. intercostalis XII
duodenum ×
pylorus
aorta (descendens) abdominalis
plexus gastricus
ventriculus
pars abdominalis oesophagi


**Fig. 354.**

# 354. Sympathetic Trunk and Vagus Nerve in Thorax and Upper Abdominal Region. (1/3)

Ventral wall of thorax and abdomen removed. Veins and viscera removed except for stomach-5, esophagus-9, and trachea-12.

1 **Scalenus Anterior Muscle**
*m. scalenus anterior*

**Recurrent Laryngeal Nerve** (Left)
*n. laryngeus recurrens sinister*

**Subclavian Artery** (Left)
*a. subclavia sinistra*

**Vagus Nerve** (Left)
*n. vagus sinister*

**Aortic Plexus and Cardiac Plexus**
*plexus aorticus + pl. cardiacus*

**Recurrent Laryngeal Nerve** (Left)
*n. laryngeus recurrens sinister*

**Vagus Nerve, Bronchial Branches**
*rami bronchiales n. vagi*

2 **Main Bronchus** (Left)
*bronchus principalis sinister*

**Intercostal Nerves**
*nervi intercostales*

3 **Anterior Vagal Trunk, Esophageal Plexus**
*plexus esophageus*
*truncus vagalis anterior*

**Descending Thoracic Aorta**
*aorta (descendens) thoracica*

4 **Sympathetic Trunk, Rami Communicantes**
*rami communicantes trunci sympathici*

5 **Esophagus, Abdominal Portion**
*pars abdominalis esophagi*

**Stomach**
*ventriculus*

6 **Gastric Plexus**
*plexus gastricus*

**Descending Abdominal Aorta**
*aorta (descendens) abdominalis*

**Pylorus**
*pylorus*

7 **Duodenum**
*duodenum*

**12th Intercostal Nerve**
*n. intercostalis XII*

**Diaphragm**
*diaphragma*

**Lesser Splanchnic Nerve**
*n. splanchnicus minor*

8 **Greater Splanchnic Nerve**
*n. splanchnicus major*

**Posterior Vagal Trunk**
*truncus vagalis posterior*

9 **Thoracic Ganglia, Sympathetic Trunk**
*ganglia thoracica tr. sympathica*

**Esophagus**
*esophagus*

**Sympathetic Trunk**
*truncus sympathicus*

**Main Bronchus** (Right)
*bronchus principalis dexter*

10 **Vagus Nerve, Bronchial Branches**
*rami bronchiales nervi vagi*

**Ascending Aorta**
*aorta ascendens*

**Recurrent Laryngeal Nerve** (Right)
*n. laryngeus recurrens dexter*

**Vagus Nerve** (Right)
*n. vagus dexter*

**1st Thoracic Ganglion**
*ganglion thoracicum I*

11 **Ansa Subclavia**
*ansa subclavia*

**Subclavian Artery** (Right)
*arteria subclavia dextra*

**Anterior Scalenus Muscle**
*m. scalenus anterior*

**Inferior Cervical Ganglion**
*ganglion cervicale inferius*

**Vagus Nerve** (Right)
*nervus vagus dexter*

12 **Common Carotid Artery**
*a. carotis communis*

**Middle Cervical Ganglion of Sympathetic Trunk**
*ganglion cervicale medium trunci sympathici*

**Thyroid Gland**
*glandula thyreoidea*

**Trachea**
*trachea*

**Note:** 1. **Thoracic sympathetic trunk**-9, its ganglia and **ansa subclavia**-11.

2. **Greater splanchnic nerve**-8 takes origin from 6th to 9th thoracic ganglia, with occasional connections with 5th and 10th-9.

3. **Recurrent laryngeal nerve**-10, on right, passes caudal to subclavian artery; on left-1, it passes caudal to the arch of aorta and ligamentum arteriosus.

4. As **vagus nerve** passes dorsal to root of lung, it approaches the esophagus, breaks up into an **esophageal plexus** in which the right and left vagus nerves thus lose their identity, but many of the branches collect as a **dorsal** and a **ventral vagus cord.** These cords pass through the diaphragm with the esophagus and continue to the abdominal viscera.

5. **Subclavian arteries** pass dorsal to scalenus anterior muscles.

# 355. Abdominal and Pelvic Portions of Autonomic Nervous System. (2/3)

Ventral walls of the body and all viscera were removed. Psoas muscles, kidneys, and suprarenals were removed in order to expose the abdominal and pelvic sympathetic trunk, abdominal aorta, vascular plexuses, and visceral branches of the pudendal plexus.

1 **Ramus Communicans**
*ramus communicans*
**12th Intercostal Nerve**
*nerv. intercostalis XII*
**Rib, XI**
*costa XI*

2 **Celiac Trunk**
*truncus celiacus*
**12th Intercostal Nerve**
*n. intercostalis XII*
**1st Lumbar Nerve**
*n. lumbalis I*
**Superior Mesenteric Artery**
*a. mesenterica superior*
**2nd Lumbar Nerve**
*nerv. lumbalis II*
**Quadratus Lumborum Muscle**
*m. quadratus lumborum*
**Abdominal Aortic Plexus**
*plexus aorticus abdominalis*
**3rd Lumbar Nerve, Ventral Ramus**
*n. lumbalis III (ram. ventralis)*

3 **4th Lumbar Nerve, Ventral Ramus**
*n. lumbalis IV (ram. ventralis)*

4 **5th Lumbar Nerve**
*nervus lumbalis V*
**Lumbosacral Trunk**
*truncus lumbosacralis*
**1st Sacral Nerve, Ventral Ramus**
*nervus sacralis I (ram. ventralis)*
**2nd Sacral N., Ventral Ramus**
*nervus sacralis II (ram. ventralis)*
**3rd Sacral Nerve**
*nervus sacralis III*

5 **4th Sacral Nerve, Ventral Ramus**
*nervus sacralis IV (ram. ventralis)*
**Acetabulum**
*acetabulum*
**Sacral Plexus**
*plexus sacralis*
**Pudendal Plexus**
*plexus pudendus*

6 **Visceral Branches of Pudendal Nerve**
*
**5th Sacral Nerve**
*n. sacralis V*
**Coccygeal Nerve**
*n. coccygeus*
**Rectum**
*rectum*
**Ganglion Impar**
*ganglion impar*

7 **Levator Ani Muscle**
*m. levator ani*
**Coccygeus Muscle**
*m. coccygeus*
**Sacral Ganglion**
*ganglia sacralia*

8 **Rami Communicantes**
*rami communicantes*
**Lumbar Ganglion**
*ganglion lumbale*
**Iliac Plexus**
*plexus iliacus*
**Iliac Muscle**
*m. iliacus*

9 **Iliac Crest**
*crista iliaca*
**Inferior Mesenteric Plexus**
*plexus mesentericus inferior*
**Quadratus Lumborum Muscle**
*m. quadratus lumborum*
**Sympathetic Trunk**
*truncus sympathicus*
**Superior Mesenteric Ganglion**
*ganglion mesentericum superius*

10 **Renal Artery**
*a. renalis*
**Renal Ganglion and Plexus**
*ganglion + plexus renal.*
**Celiac Ganglion (Celiac Plexus)**
*ganglia celiaca (plexus celiacus)*
**12th Rib**
*costa XII*
**Lumbar Portion of Diaphragm, Right Crus**
*crus dextrum partis lumbalis diaphragmatis*
**Thoracic Ganglia**
*ganglia thoracica*

11 **11th Rib**
*costa XI*
**Lesser Splanchnic Nerve**
*nervus splanchnicus minor*

12 **Greater Splanchnic Nerve**
*n. splanchnicus major*
**Diaphragm**
*diaphragma*
**Cardia**
*cardia*
**11th Intercostal Nerve**
*n. intercostalis XI*

**Note:** 1. **Celiac**-10, **superior mesenteric**-9, **inferior mesenteric**-9, **renal**-10, and **aortic**-2 **plexuses** with their associated ganglia.

2. **Splanchnic nerves**-11, -12, entering the abdominal complex, convey fibers from neurons in lateral column which emerge from 5th to 11th thoracic sympathetic ganglia.

3. **The sympathetic chain of ganglia**-9 passing through abdomen and into pelvis to end in coccygeal region.

4. **Rami communicantes**-8 are connections between sympathetic ganglia and nerves of lumbar and sacral plexuses. In the lower lumbar and sacral region, these are designated gray rami communicantes because they consist of postsynaptic fibers on their way to join the spinal nerves to be distributed peripherally to smooth muscles, sweat glands, arrector pili muscles, and similar autonomic structures.

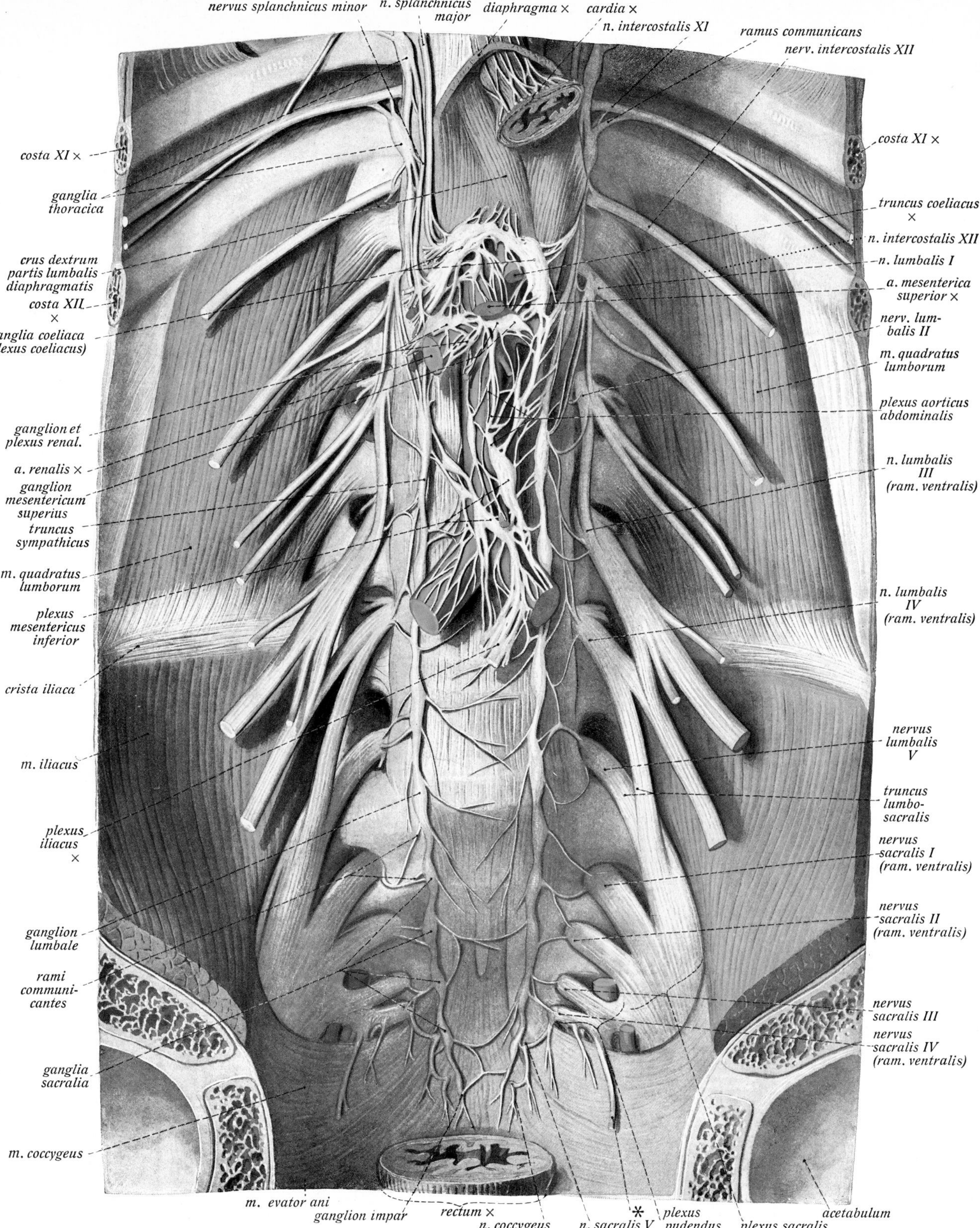

nervus splanchnicus minor
n. splanchnicus major
diaphragma ×
cardia ×
n. intercostalis XI
ramus communicans
nerv. intercostalis XII
costa XI ×
ganglia thoracica
costa XI ×
truncus coeliacus ×
n. intercostalis XII
crus dextrum partis lumbalis diaphragmatis
n. lumbalis I
costa XII ×
a. mesenterica superior ×
ganglia coeliaca (plexus coeliacus)
nerv. lumbalis II
m. quadratus lumborum
plexus aorticus abdominalis
ganglion et plexus renal.
a. renalis ×
n. lumbalis III (ram. ventralis)
ganglion mesentericum superius
truncus sympathicus
m. quadratus lumborum
n. lumbalis IV (ram. ventralis)
plexus mesentericus inferior
crista iliaca
m. iliacus
nervus lumbalis V
truncus lumbo-sacralis
plexus iliacus ×
nervus sacralis I (ram. ventralis)
nervus sacralis II (ram. ventralis)
ganglion lumbale
rami communicantes
nervus sacralis III
nervus sacralis IV (ram. ventralis)
ganglia sacralia
m. coccygeus
m. evator ani
ganglion impar
rectum ×
n. coccygeus
n. sacralis V
* plexus pudendus
plexus sacralis
acetabulum
* rami viscerales plex. pud.


Fig. 355.

# SPECIAL SENSE ORGANS

## Ear – Eye

Fig. 356

# 356. Diagrammatic Horizontal Section of Human Bulbus Oculi Through Optic Nerve.

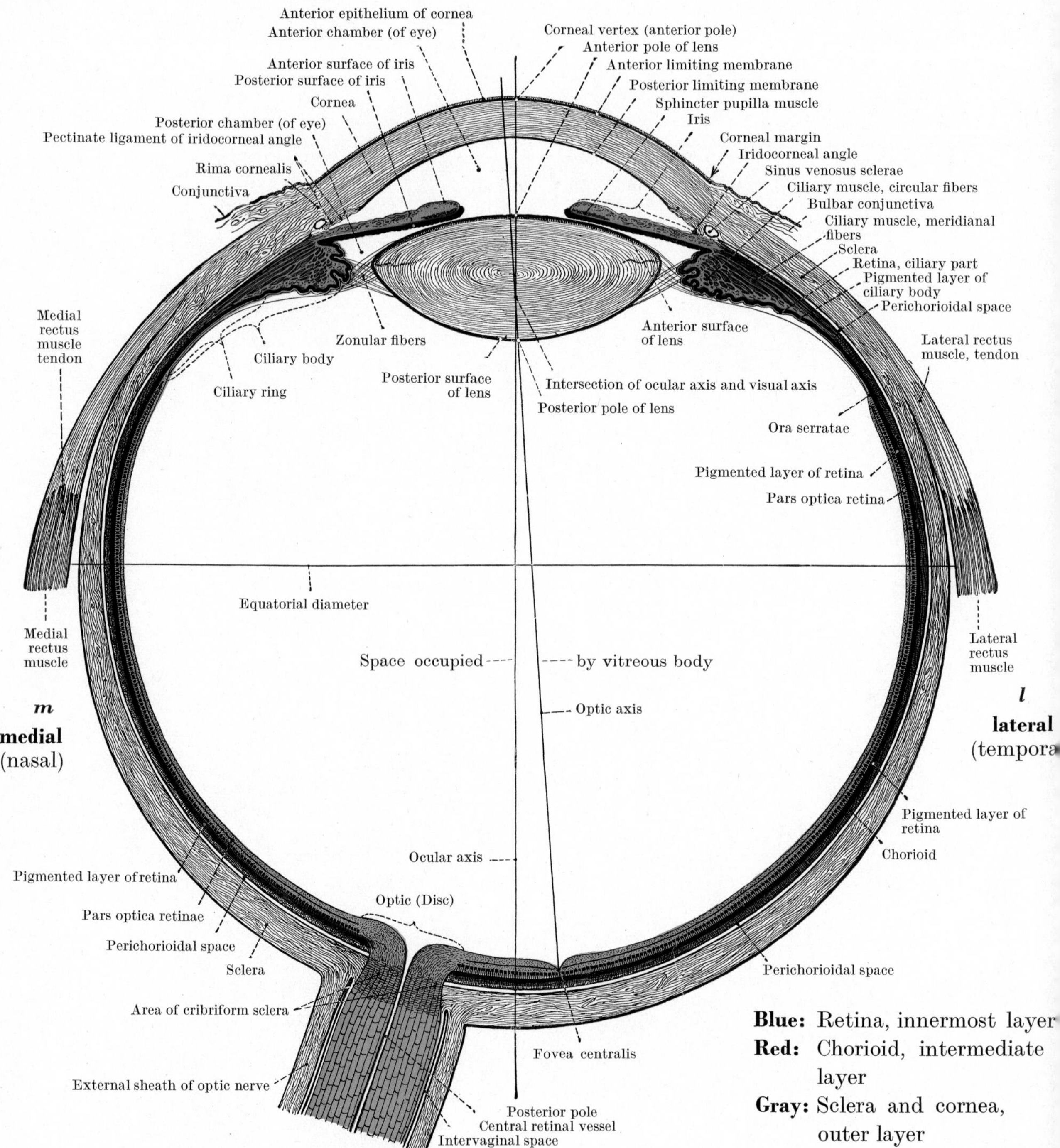

Anterior epithelium of cornea
Anterior chamber (of eye)
Anterior surface of iris
Posterior surface of iris
Cornea
Posterior chamber (of eye)
Pectinate ligament of iridocorneal angle
Rima cornealis
Conjunctiva
Corneal vertex (anterior pole)
Anterior pole of lens
Anterior limiting membrane
Posterior limiting membrane
Sphincter pupilla muscle
Iris
Corneal margin
Iridocorneal angle
Sinus venosus sclerae
Ciliary muscle, circular fibers
Bulbar conjunctiva
Ciliary muscle, meridianal fibers
Sclera
Retina, ciliary part
Pigmented layer of ciliary body
Perichorioidal space
Medial rectus muscle tendon
Zonular fibers
Ciliary body
Ciliary ring
Anterior surface of lens
Posterior surface of lens
Lateral rectus muscle, tendon
Intersection of ocular axis and visual axis
Posterior pole of lens
Ora serratae
Pigmented layer of retina
Pars optica retina
Equatorial diameter
Medial rectus muscle
Space occupied by vitreous body
Lateral rectus muscle
Optic axis
m
medial
(nasal)
l
lateral
(tempora
Pigmented layer of retina
Chorioid
Ocular axis
Pigmented layer of retina
Optic (Disc)
Pars optica retinae
Perichorioidal space
Sclera
Perichorioidal space
Area of cribriform sclera
Fovea centralis
External sheath of optic nerve
Posterior pole
Central retinal vessel
Intervaginal space


**Blue:** Retina, innermost layer
**Red:** Chorioid, intermediate layer
**Gray:** Sclera and cornea, outer layer

# 356. Diagrammatic Horizontal Section of Human Bulbus Oculi Through Optic Nerve.

**Note:** 1. **Cornea**-11 has a greater curvature than the rest of the eyeball. It thus acts as a lens to decrease the focal distance of the bulbus oculi.

2. The bulbus oculi is composed of three concentric layers or coats:

a) The **sclera**-7 and **cornea**-11 constitute the **outer fibrous tunic** which is mainly protective.

b) The **chorioid coat**-4 or **vascular tunic** is **nutritive,** and **muscular**.

c) The **retina**-3C, or nerve layer is the **light sensitive** portion of the eye.

3. The space in front of the lens, occupied by aqueous humor, is divided into two compartments by the iris-11:

a) The space in front of the iris is the **anterior chamber**-11.

b) The **posterior chamber**-11 is the narrow interval between the iris and lens and its suspensory ligaments.

4. The extensive compartment between the lens-12 and retina is occupied by the **vitreous body**, a very transparent relatively noncellular body, firmly adherent to the ora serrata-2C of the retina. The vitreous body is partly hyaluronic acid, exhibiting the proper degree of polymerization to maintain the gel-like consistency necessary for its function.

5. The **lens**-12 is a cellular transparent biconvex body, held in place by the suspensory ligament of the lens or the zonular fibers-11 C.

6. The **zonular fibers** attach to the epithelium of the ciliary body as far dorsally as the ora serrata-2C.

7. When the ciliary muscle-1 is relaxed, the maximum tension of the zonular fibers-11 C is maintained by the semi-rigid sclera and the pressure of the vitreous body. In this state, the tense zonular fibers or suspensory ligament tend to flatten the lens and increase the focal distance of the lens for far vision. When the ciliary muscle-1 contracts, the attachments of the zonular fibers are pulled toward the lens. The zonular fibers (suspensory ligament) then become less tense and the elastic lens (at least in young individuals) assumes a more spherical shape, giving it a shorter focal distance for close vision and reading.

Fig. 357

**357. Structural Diagram of the Sclera.** **Right:** superficial; **Left:** deep layers.

Schematic representation of the course of the main collagen elastic fiber bundles in the sclera. In the anterior part, circular girdling rings occur that blend with the eye-muscle tendons to form the strong corneoscleral ring. In the dorsal part of the bulbus oculi, the arrangement of the fiber bundles is designed to facilitate accommodation for changes in intraocular pressure. (From investigations on ox eyes.)

## 358. Diagram of Chorioidal Blood Vessels of Eye.

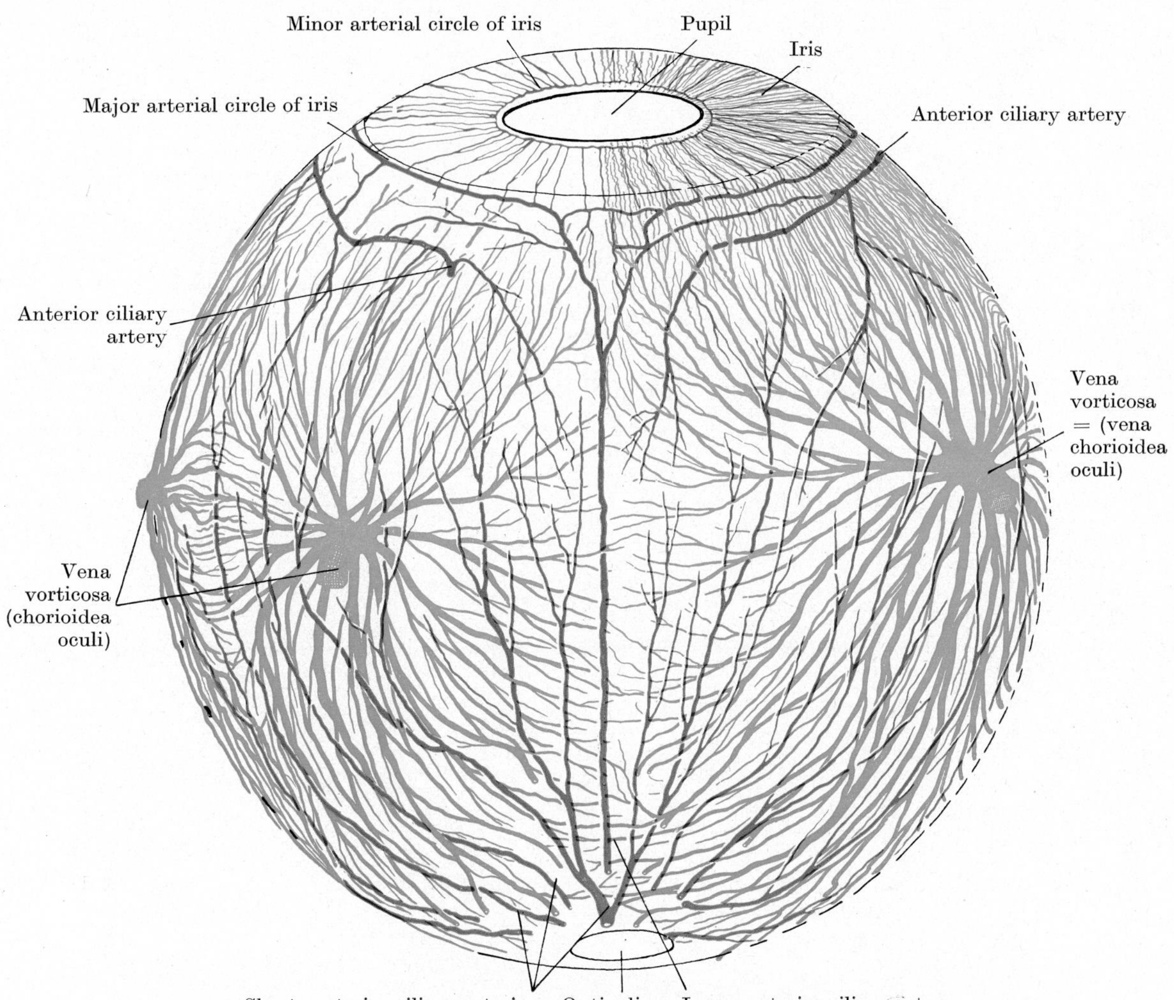
Minor arterial circle of iris
Pupil
Iris
Major arterial circle of iris
Anterior ciliary artery
Anterior ciliary artery
Vena vorticosa = (vena chorioidea oculi)
Vena vorticosa (chorioidea oculi)
Short posterior ciliary arteries
Optic disc
Long posterior ciliary artery

**359. Diagram of the Blood Vessels of the Bulbus Oculi.** (after the investigations of Th. Leber)

Compare with Figure 358 which is a phantom view of the blood vessels of the chorioid coat.

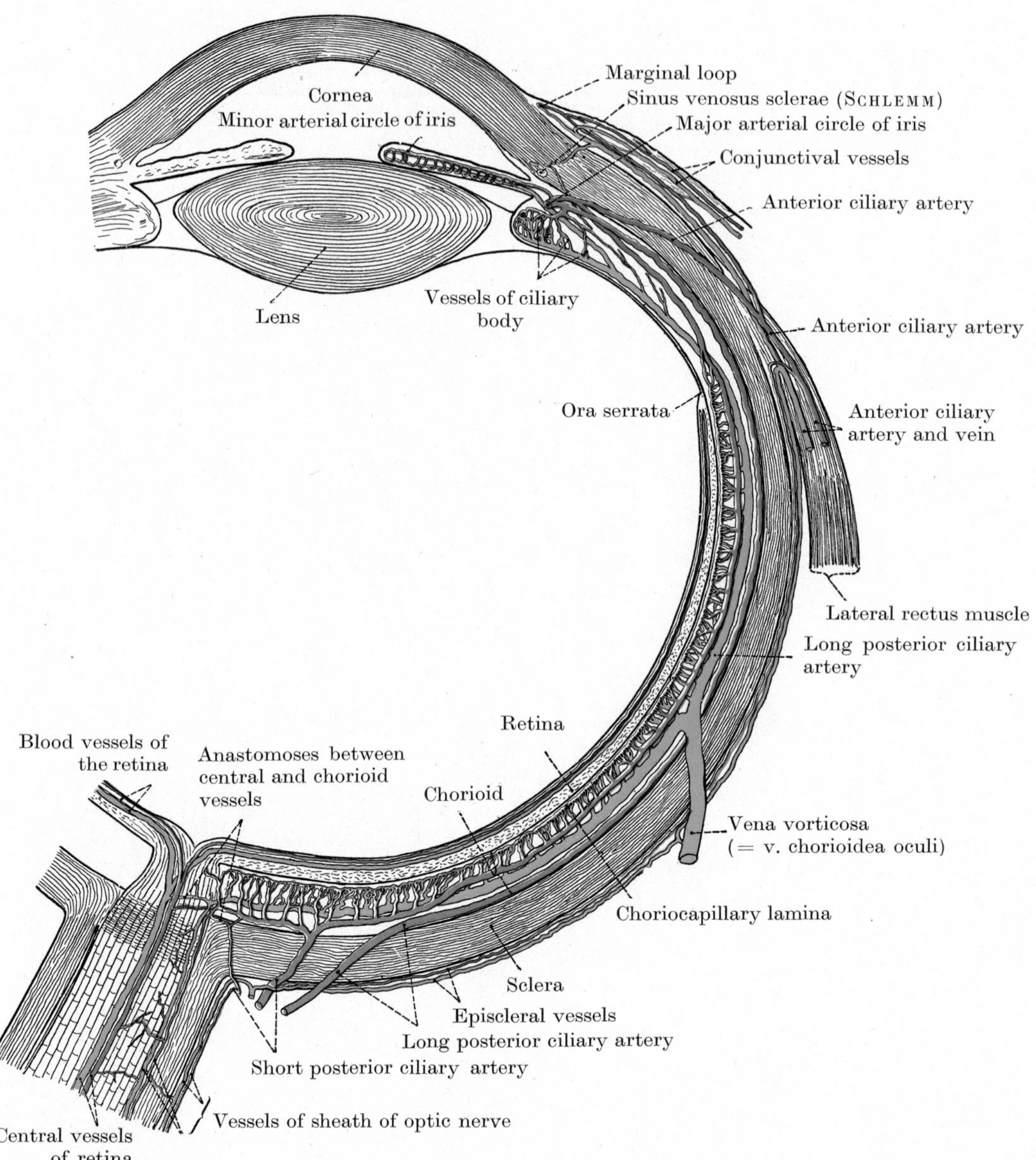
Cornea
Minor arterial circle of iris
Marginal loop
Sinus venosus sclerae (SCHLEMM)
Major arterial circle of iris
Conjunctival vessels
Anterior ciliary artery
Lens
Vessels of ciliary body
Anterior ciliary artery
Ora serrata
Anterior ciliary artery and vein
Lateral rectus muscle
Long posterior ciliary artery
Retina
Blood vessels of the retina
Anastomoses between central and chorioid vessels
Chorioid
Vena vorticosa (= v. chorioidea oculi)
Choriocapillary lamina
Sclera
Episcleral vessels
Long posterior ciliary artery
Short posterior ciliary artery
Vessels of sheath of optic nerve
Central vessels of retina

## 360. Diagram of Fundus of Right Eye: The Retinal Vessels and Structures as seen through Ophthalmoscope. (See Figures 373–375)

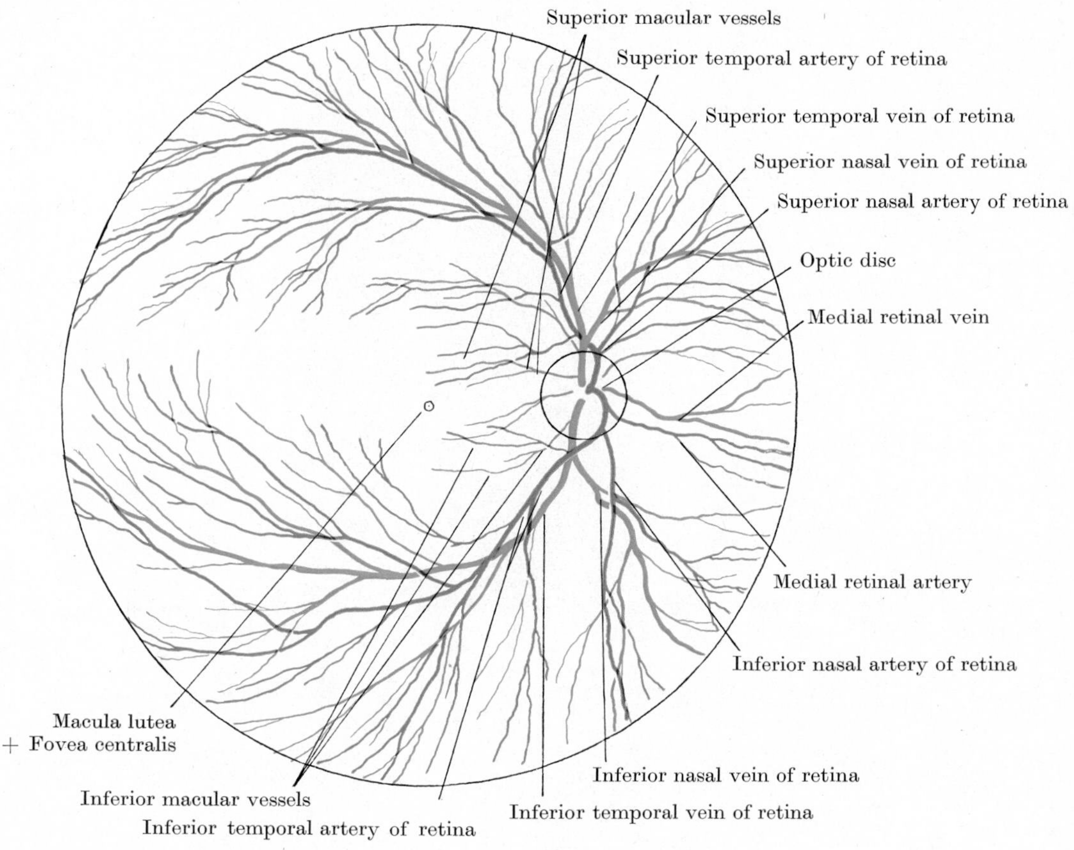
Superior macular vessels
Superior temporal artery of retina
Superior temporal vein of retina
Superior nasal vein of retina
Superior nasal artery of retina
Optic disc
Medial retinal vein
Medial retinal artery
Inferior nasal artery of retina
Inferior nasal vein of retina
Inferior temporal vein of retina
Inferior temporal artery of retina
Inferior macular vessels
Macula lutea
+ Fovea centralis

**Note:** 1. The names of blood vessels indicate the directions taken by the vessels (or the area of the retina supplied by the vessels) as they radiate from the optic disc or **optic papilla**-2.

2. The **macula lutea** and the **fovea centralis**-8, which represent the part of the retina with the greatest visual acuity, are devoid of larger blood vessels.

### Etymology:

*macula lutea* is the yellow spot on the retina.

*macula* = L. a spot

*luteus* = L. yellow

*fovea centralis* refers to central depression in *macula lutea*.

*fovea* = L. a pit

## 361. Lens of Newborn. (15/1)

The direction of lens fibers and their insertion on lens stars. (side view, modified from Blechschmidt)

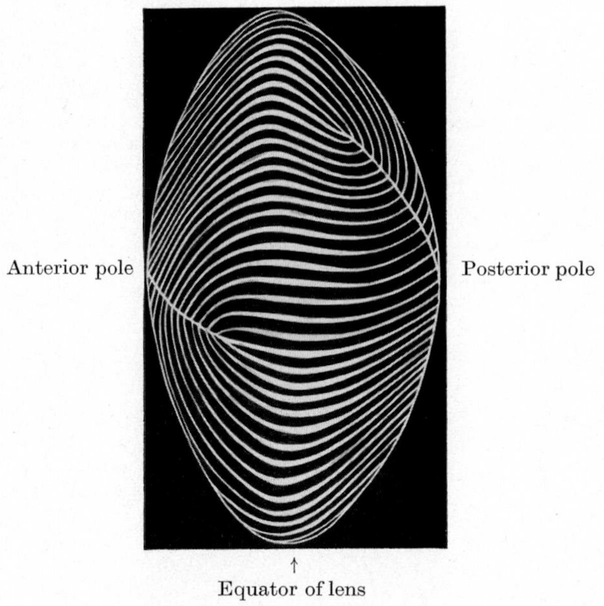
Anterior pole
Posterior pole
Equator of lens

## 362. Cross-Section of Optic Nerve. (enlarged about 12×)

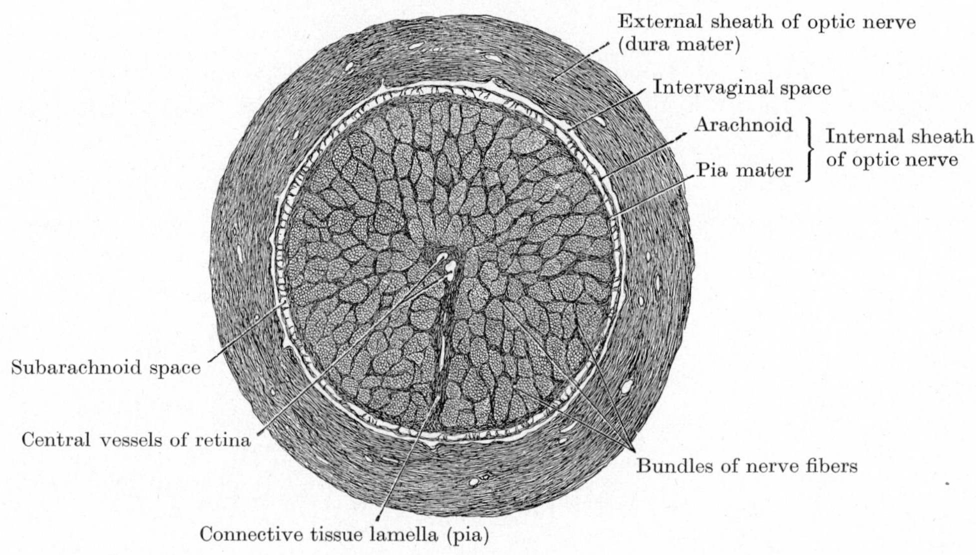
External sheath of optic nerve (dura mater)
Intervaginal space
Arachnoid
Pia mater
Internal sheath of optic nerve
Subarachnoid space
Central vessels of retina
Bundles of nerve fibers
Connective tissue lamella (pia)

## 363. Vertical Section Through the Upper Eyelid. (15/1)

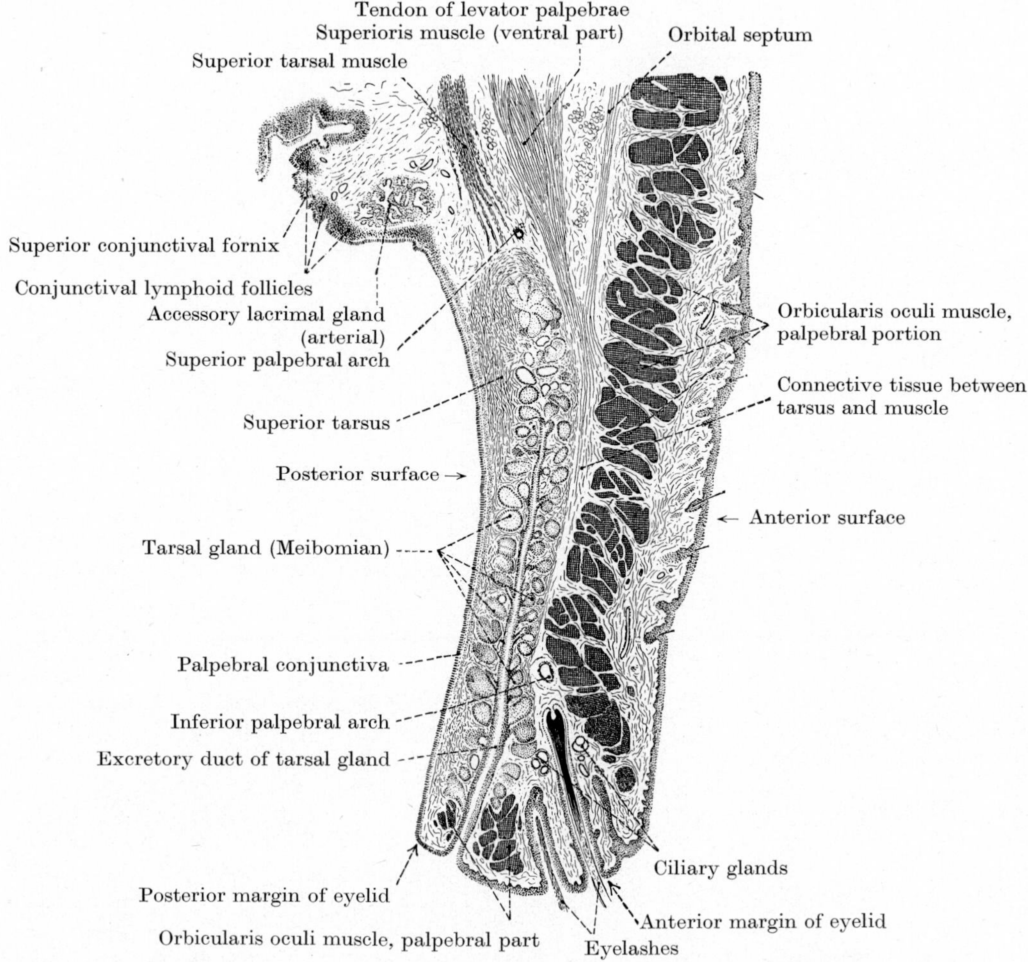
Tendon of levator palpebrae
Superioris muscle (ventral part)
Orbital septum
Superior tarsal muscle
Superior conjunctival fornix
Conjunctival lymphoid follicles
Accessory lacrimal gland
(arterial)
Superior palpebral arch
Orbicularis oculi muscle, palpebral portion
Connective tissue between tarsus and muscle
Superior tarsus
Posterior surface
Anterior surface
Tarsal gland (Meibomian)
Palpebral conjunctiva
Inferior palpebral arch
Excretory duct of tarsal gland
Ciliary glands
Posterior margin of eyelid
Anterior margin of eyelid
Orbicularis oculi muscle, palpebral part
Eyelashes

**Note:** 1. **The five layers of eyelid:**

a) Very thin skin on anterior surface-3 continuous with conjunctiva-8.

b) Superficial fascia, loose connective tissue-2 with little or no fat.

c) Relatively thin orbicularis oculi muscle-2 for closing and blinking eyes. (supplied by facial nerve)

d) Tarsofascial layer, includes tarsus-10, orbital septum-12, and palpebral fascia to which the levator palpebrae superioris muscle tendon attaches-12.

e) Conjunctiva-8 on posterior surface.

# 364. Diagrams of Insertions of Six Eye Muscles of Right Eye.

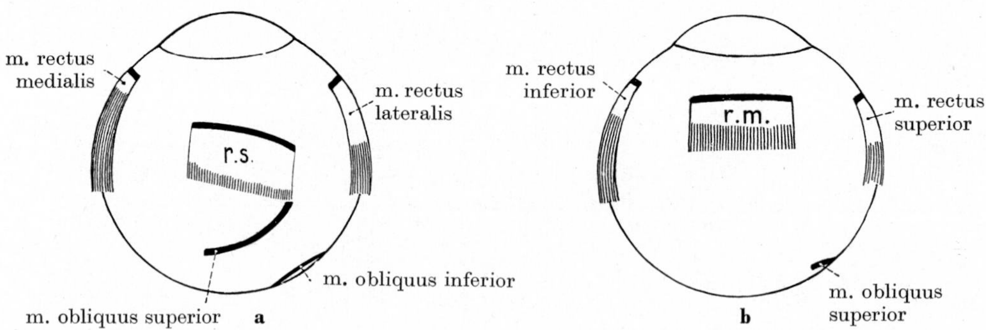
m. rectus
medialis
m. rectus
lateralis
r.s.
m. obliquus inferior
m. obliquus superior
a
m. rectus
inferior
r.m.
m. rectus
superior
m. obliquus
superior
b

Fig. 364.

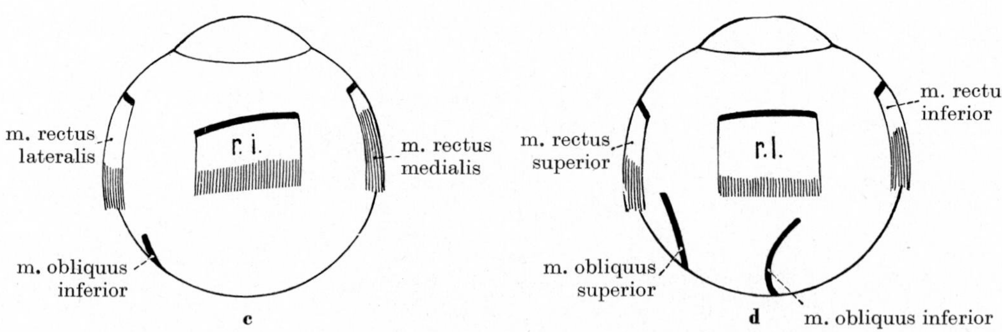
m. rectus
lateralis
r. i.
m. rectus
medialis
m. obliquus
inferior
c
m. rectus
superior
r.l.
m. rectus
inferior
m. obliquus
superior
d
m. obliquus inferior

a) From above
c) From below

b) From medial
d) From lateral

r. i. = inferior rectus m.
r. l. = lateral rectus m.

r. m. = medial rectus m.
r. s. = superior rectus m.

## 365. Diagram of Insertions of Rectus Muscles of Right Eye.

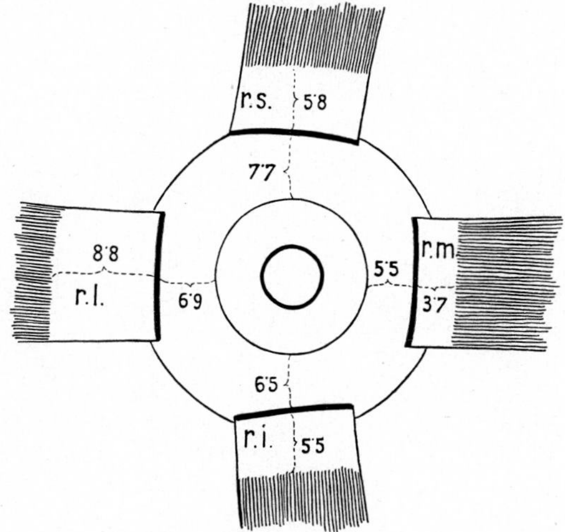
r.s.
5·8
7·7
8·8
r.l.
6·9
5·5
r.m.
3·7
6·5
r.i.
5·5

Measurements of tendon and distances from corneal margin (in mm) (after Merkel-Kallius in Graefe-Saemisch Handbook). Fleshy parts of muscles shaded.

## 366. Diagram of Force Components of Eye Muscles of Right Eye.

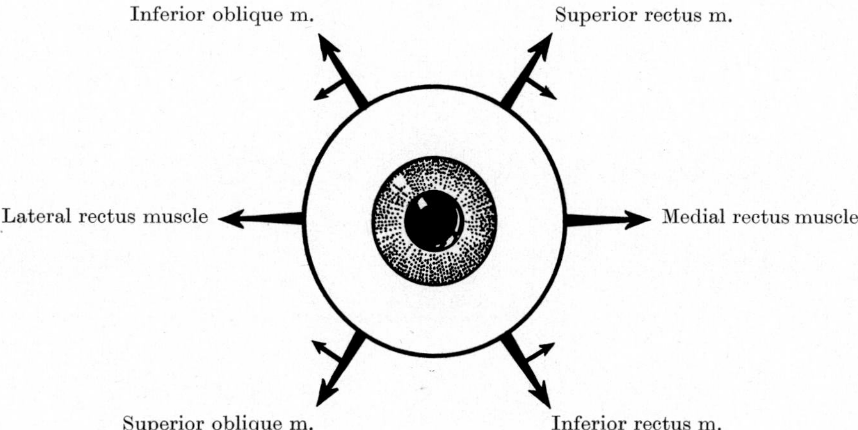
Inferior oblique m.
Superior rectus m.
Lateral rectus muscle
Medial rectus muscle
Superior oblique m.
Inferior rectus m.

Fig. 367

## 367. Base of the Brain with Right and Left Eyeballs and Their Eye Muscles. (about 1/1)

1 Eyeball
2 Optic nerve
3 Medial rectus muscle
4 Lateral rectus muscle
5 Fibrous ring (entrance point of ophthalmic artery)
6 Optic chiasma
7 Olfactory bulbs and tract
8 Oculomotor nerve
9 Hypophysis (pituitary gland)
10 Internal carotid artery
11 Vertebral artery
12 Basilar artery
13 Medulla oblongata
14 Frontal pole
15 Temporal pole
16 Cerebellum

Numbers refer to numbers on Plate, not to clock positions.

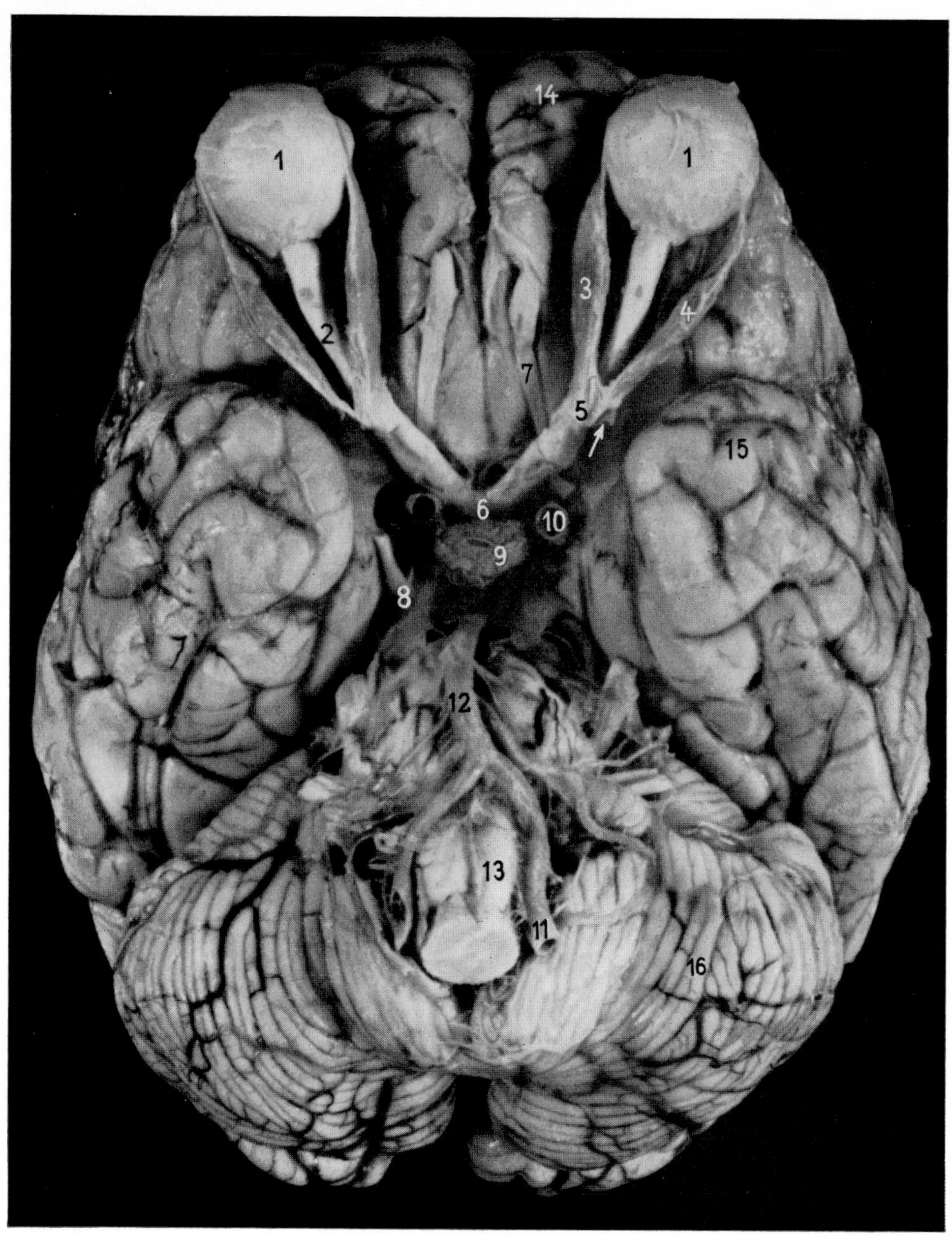
14
1
1
3
2
4
7
5
15
6
10
9
8
7
12
13
11
16

Fig. 367.

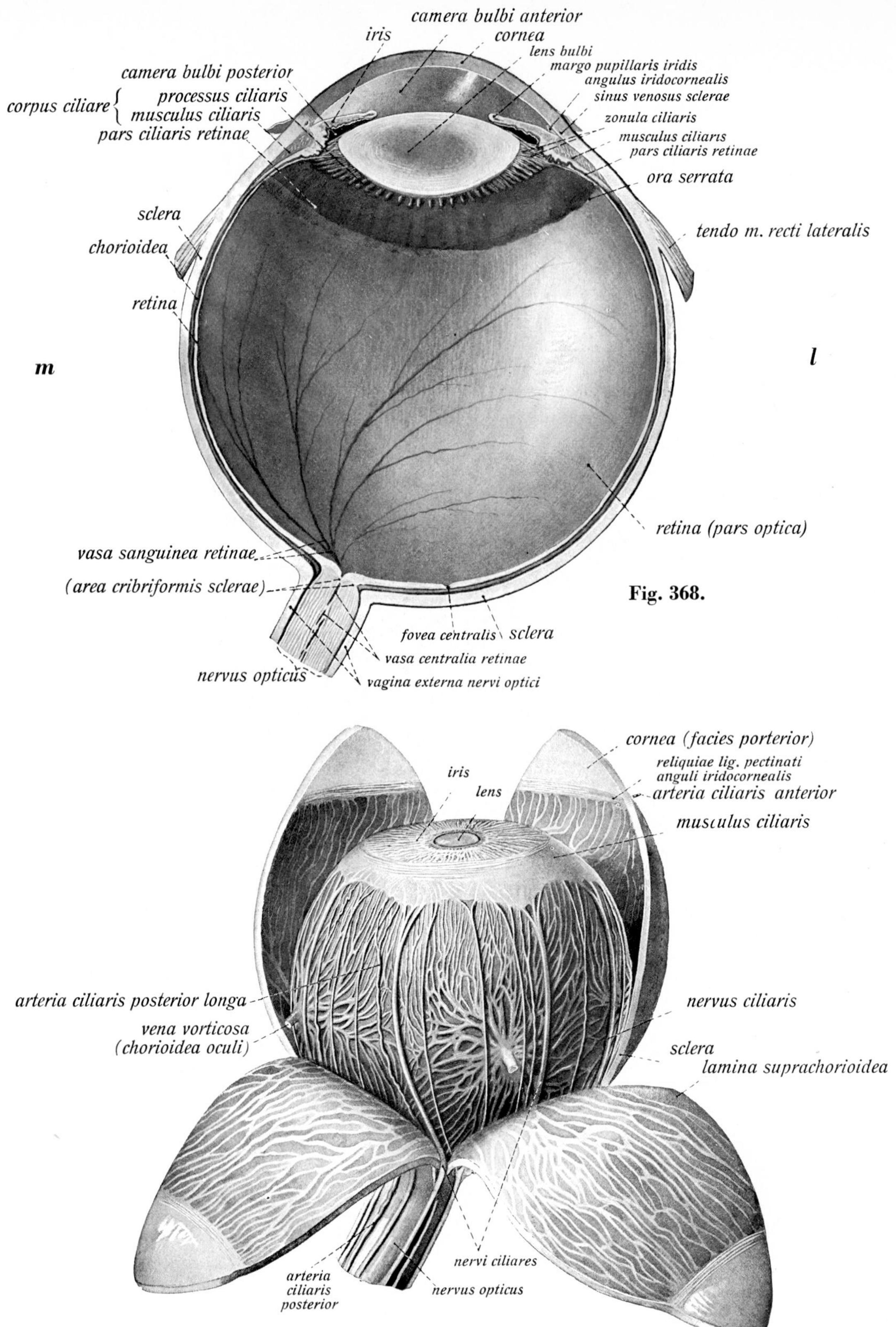

camera bulbi anterior
iris
cornea
lens bulbi
margo pupillaris iridis
angulus iridocornealis
sinus venosus sclerae
camera bulbi posterior
corpus ciliare
processus ciliaris
musculus ciliaris
pars ciliaris retinae
zonula ciliaris
musculus ciliaris
pars ciliaris retinae
ora serrata
sclera
tendo m. recti lateralis
chorioidea
retina
m
l
retina (pars optica)
vasa sanguinea retinae
(area cribriformis sclerae)
fovea centralis
sclera
vasa centralia retinae
nervus opticus
vagina externa nervi optici
cornea (facies porterior)
iris
reliquiae lig. pectinati
anguli iridocornealis
lens
arteria ciliaris anterior
musculus ciliaris
arteria ciliaris posterior longa
nervus ciliaris
vena vorticosa
(chorioidea oculi)
sclera
lamina suprachorioidea
nervi ciliares
arteria
ciliaris
posterior
nervus opticus


Fig. 368.

Fig. 369.

## 368. Right Bulbus Oculi of a Human Subject. (5/1)

The bulbus oculi was sectioned in horizontal or meridian plane. The vitreous body was removed. (Compare with Figure 356)

m = medial or nasal                l = lateral or temporal

1 **Lens (of Eye)**
*lens bulbi*

**Pupillary Margin of the Iris**
*margo pupillaris iridis*

**Iridocorneal Angle**
*angulus iridocornealis*

**Sinus Venosus Sclerae**
*sinus venosus sclerae*

**Zonula Ciliaris**
*zonula ciliaris*

**Ciliary Muscle**
*musculus ciliaris*

**Pars Ciliaris Retinae**
*pars ciliaris retinae*

2 **Ora Serrata**
*ora serrata*
**Tendon of Lateral Rectus Muscle**
*tendo m. recti lateralis*

4 **Retina, Optical Part**
*retina (pars optica)*
5 **Sclera**
*sclera*
6 **Fovea Centralis**
*fovea centralis*
**Central Retinal Vessels**
*vasa centralia retinae*
**External Sheath of Optic Nerve**
*vagina externa nervi optici*
7 **Optic Nerve**
*nervus opticus*
8 **(Scleral Cribriform Area)**
*(area cribriformis sclerae)*
**Blood Vessels of Retina**
*vasa sanguinea retinae*
9 **Retina**
*retina*
10 **Chorioid**
*chorioidea*

**Sclera**
*sclera*

**Ciliary Part of Retina**
*pars ciliaris retinae*

**Ciliary Body** { **Ciliary Process**, **Ciliary Muscle** }
*corpus ciliare* { *processus ciliaris*, *musculus ciliaris* }

**Posterior Chamber (of Eye)**
*camera bulbi posterior*
*[camera posterior bulbi]*

12 **Iris**
*iris*

**Anterior Chamber (of Eye)**
*camera bulbi anterior [camera anterior bulbi]*

**Cornea**
*cornea*

## 369. Intermediate Tunic or Chorioid Vascular Coat of the Eye. (4/1)

Chorioid was exposed by splitting sclera along meridian lines and reflecting the flaps.

1 **Cornea, Posterior Surface**
*cornea (facies posterior)*
**Remnants of Pectinate Ligament of Iridocorneal Angle**
*reliquiae lig. pectinati anguli iridocornealis*
2 **Anterior Ciliary Artery**
*arteria ciliaris anterior*

**Ciliary Muscle**
*musculus ciliaris*

3 **Ciliary Nerve**
*nervus ciliaris*

4 **Sclera**
*sclera*

**Suprachorioid Plate**
*lamina suprachorioidea*

6 **Ciliary Nerves**
*nervi ciliares*

**Optic Nerve**
*nervus opticus*

7 **Posterior Ciliary Artery**
*arteria ciliaris posterior*

9 **Vorticose Vein**
**Chorioid of Eye**
*vena vorticosa*
*(chorioidea oculi)*

**Long Posterior Ciliary Artery**
*arteria ciliaris posterior longa*

12 **Iris**
*iris*

**Lens**
*lens*

### Etymology:

*iris* = Gr. rainbow. Used by Greeks for any bright colored circle, such as the eyes of a peacock's tail.

cornea = L. *corneus*, horny

sclera = Gr. *skleros*, hard. The tough outer layer of eye.

vortex = L. *vertex* (sometimes spelled vortex), whirl or whirlpool. (*vertere* = to turn) *vena vorticosa* (veins that form a whorl as they converge to form larger veins)

chorioid = Gr. *chorion*, skin + *eidos*, resemblance. Middle tunic of bulbus oculi.

## 370. Intermediate or Chorioid Coat of Eye. (seen from front) (5/1)

The cornea and sclera have been removed.

**1 Lens (Anterior Surface)**
*lens (facies anterior)*

**2 Iris, Pupillary Margin**
*margo pupillaris iridis*

**3 Pectinate Ligament at Iridocorneal Angle**
*lig. pectinatum anguli iridocornealis*

**4 Iris, Anterior Surface**
*facies anterior iridis*

**5 Chorioid**
*chorioidea*

**7 Iris, Lesser Ring**
*anulus iridis minor*

**8 Iris, Ciliary Margin**
*margo ciliaris iridis*

**Iris Greater Ring + Contraction Folds of Iris**
*anulus iridis major + plicae iridis*

**9 Blood Vessels, Chorioid**
*vasa sanguinea chorioidea*

**Ciliary Nerve**
*nervus ciliaris*

**10 Ciliary Muscle**
*musculus ciliaris*

**11 Anterior Pole of Lens**
*polus anterior lentis*

**12 Ciliary Nerves**
*nervi ciliares*

**Note:** 1. **Ciliary nerves**-12 and blood vessels-9 converge toward the **ciliary muscle**-10 and **iris**-4.

## 371. Ventral Surface of Human Iris. (8/1)

The cornea has been removed.

**1 Circular Folds**
*plicae circulares*

**Pupillary Zone of Iris**
*anulus iridis minor*

**2 Ciliary Zone of Iris**
*anulus iridis major*

**4 Ciliary Margin + Pectinate Ligament of Iridocorneal Angle**
*margo ciliaris et lig. pectinatum anguli iridocornealis*

**5 Pupillary Margin + Pars Iridica Retinae**
*margo pupillaris et pars iridica retinae*

**8 Anterior Surface of Lens**
*lens, facies anterior*

**11 Contraction Folds of Iris**
*plicae iridis*

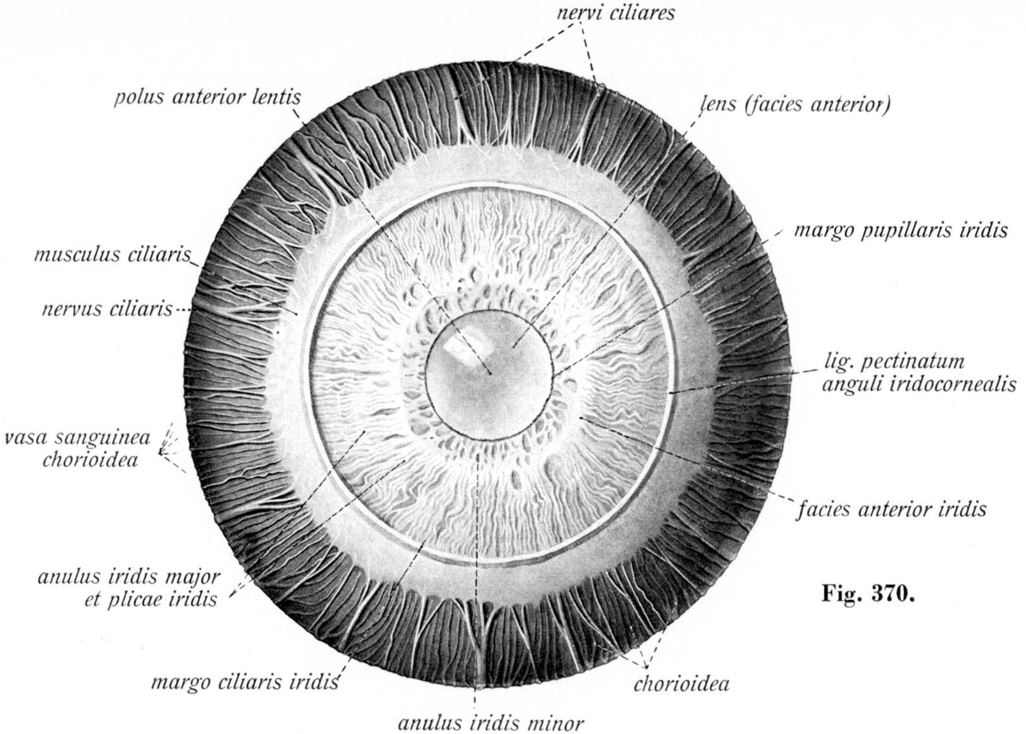
nervi ciliares
polus anterior lentis
lens (facies anterior)
margo pupillaris iridis
musculus ciliaris
nervus ciliaris
lig. pectinatum
anguli iridocornealis
vasa sanguinea
chorioidea
facies anterior iridis
anulus iridis major
et plicae iridis
margo ciliaris iridis
chorioidea
anulus iridis minor

**Fig. 370.**

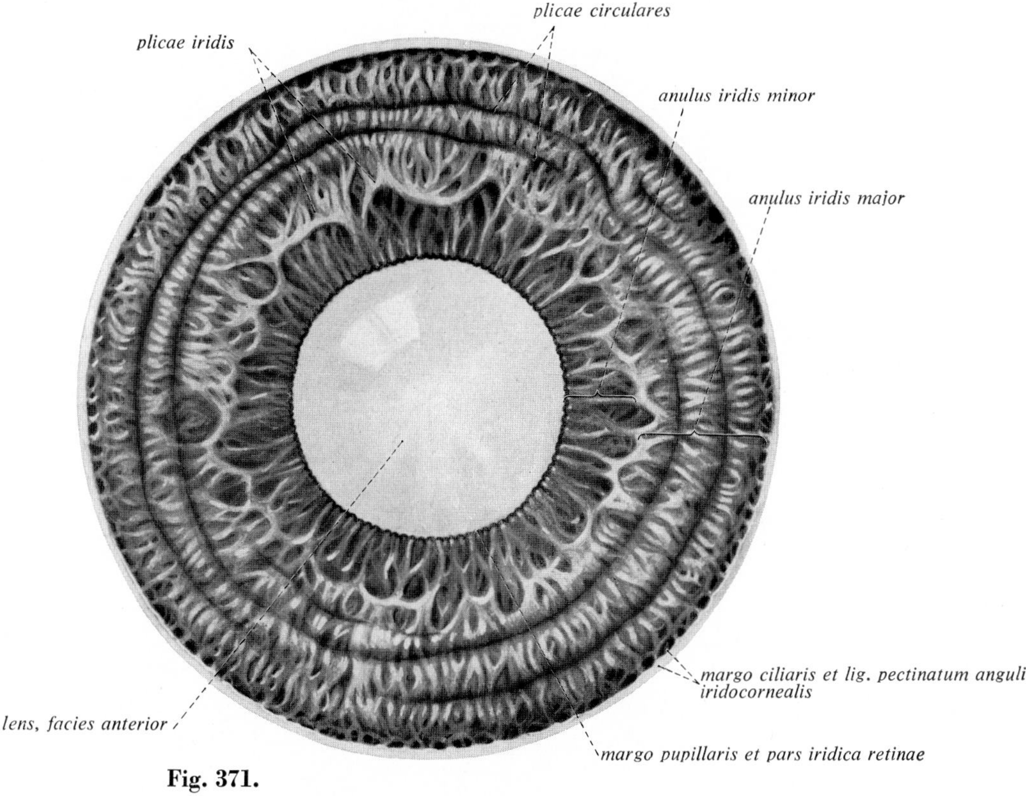
plicae circulares
plicae iridis
anulus iridis minor
anulus iridis major
margo ciliaris et lig. pectinatum anguli
iridocornealis
lens, facies anterior
margo pupillaris et pars iridica retinae
0 1 2 3mm

**Fig. 371.**

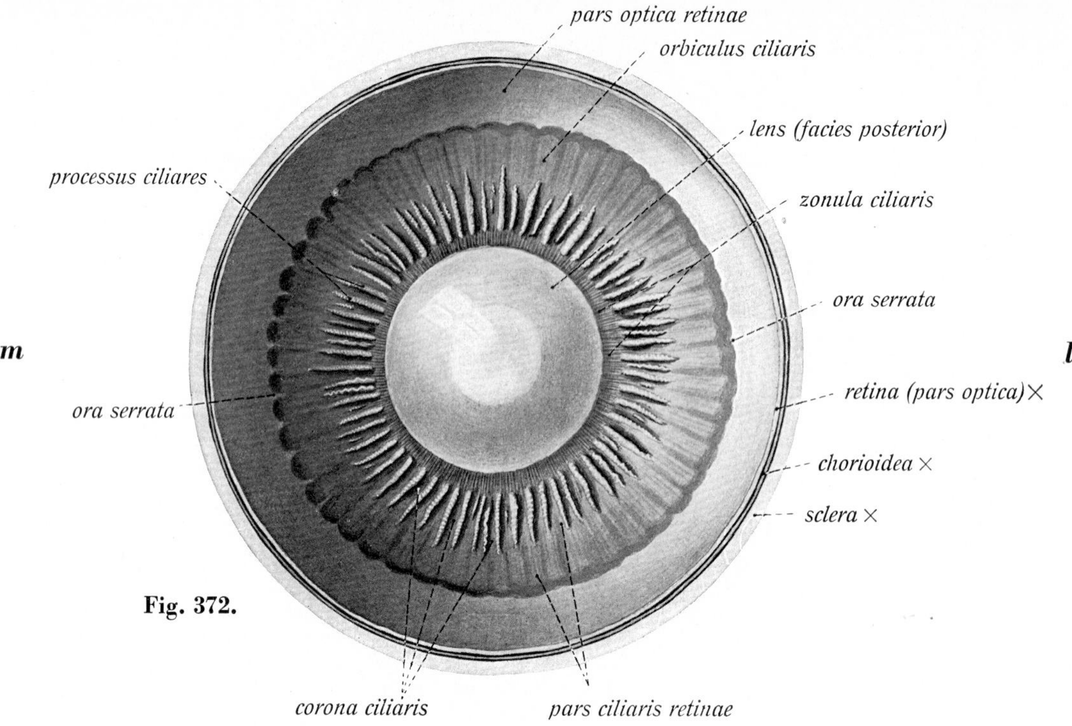
pars optica retinae
orbiculus ciliaris
lens (facies posterior)
processus ciliares
zonula ciliaris
ora serrata
m
l
ora serrata
retina (pars optica)×
chorioidea ×
sclera ×
corona ciliaris
pars ciliaris retinae

**Fig. 372.**

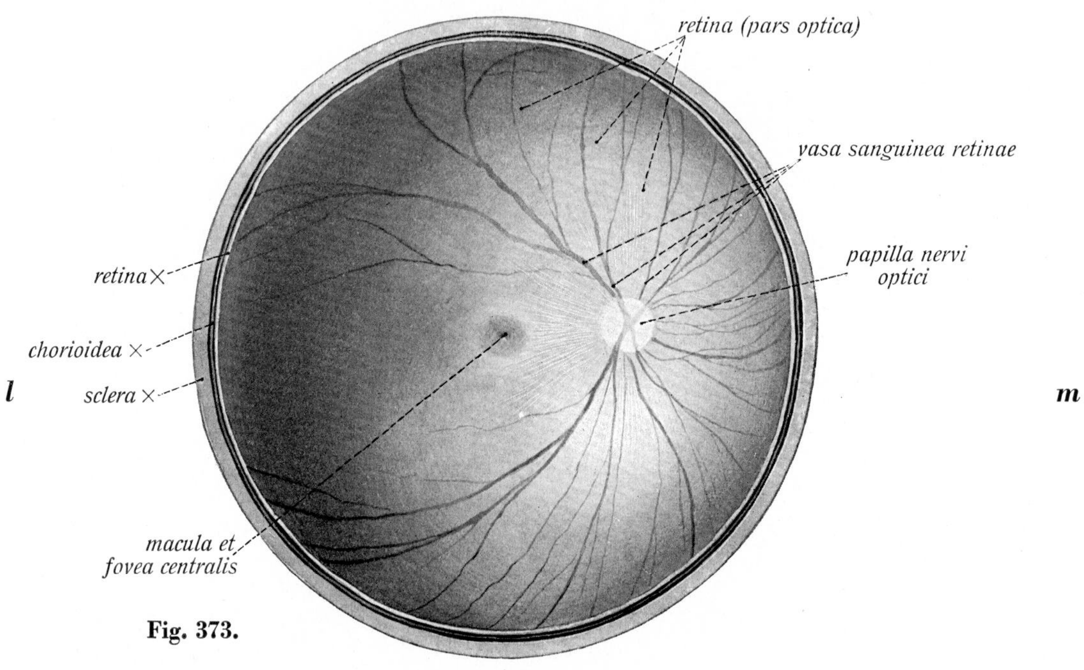
retina (pars optica)
vasa sanguinea retinae
papilla nervi
optici
retina×
chorioidea ×
l
sclera ×
m
macula et
fovea centralis

**Fig. 373.**

## 372. Right Bulbus Oculi Sectioned in Equatorial Plane.
(see Fig. 376) (5/1)

Ventral half seen from the dorsal aspect. The vitreous body removed. m = medial. l = lateral.

1 **Ciliary Ring**
*orbiculus ciliaris*

2 **Lens, Posterior Surface**
*lens (facies posterior)*

**Zonula Ciliaris**
*zonula ciliaris*

3 **Ora Serrata**
*ora serrata*

**Retina (Optic Portion)**
*retina (pars optica)*

4 **Chorioid**
*chorioidea*

**Sclera**
*sclera*

6 **Pars Ciliaris Retinae**
*pars ciliaris retinae*

7 **Ciliary Corona**
*corona ciliaris*

9 **Ora Serrata**
*ora serrata*

10 **Ciliary Processes**
*processus ciliares*

12 **Optic Part of Retina**
*pars optica retinae*

**Note:** 1. **Ora serrata**-3 where pars optica retina-3 becomes the ciliary part of retina-6.

## 373. Right Bulbus Oculi Sectioned in Equatorial Plane. (5/1)

Dorsal half seen from ventral aspect. Vitreous body removed.

1 **Retina, Pars Optica**
*retina (pars optica)*

2 **Blood Vessels of Retina**
*vasa sanguinea retinae*

**Disc of Optic Nerve**
*papilla nervi optici [discus nervi optic]*

8 **Macula and Fovea Centralis**
*macula + fovea centralis*

9 **Sclera**
*sclera*
**Chorioid**
*chorioidea*
**Retina**
*retina*

**Note:** 1. Layers of wall of bulbus oculi:

a) **sclera**-9
b) **chorioid**-9
c) **retina**-9

2. Ramification of central vessels of retina which enter bulbus oculi at optic disc.

3. Large retinal vessels do not cross **fovea centralis** of **macula**-8, which are **areas of maximum visual acuity.**

### Etymology:

*fovea* = L. a pit (in anatomy, a depression of small diameter)
*serratus* = L. *serra*, saw (serrated like a saw)
*macula* = L. a spot (on retina at posterior pole of eyeball)

## 374. Retina: Normal Fundus of an Eye of Medium Pigmentation.

(as it appears through the ophthalmoscope) (after Haab, Atlas der Ophthalmoskopie)

| | | | | | |
|---|---|---|---|---|---|
| p n o | = | Optic papilla<br>*papilla nervi optici* | f c | = | Fovea centralis<br>*fovea centralis* |
| v s r | = | Blood vessels of retina<br>*vasa sanguinea retinae* | * | = | Veins of retina |
| ** | = | Chorioidal ring | + | = | Arteries of retina |

**Note:** 1. Retinal vessels show distinct reflex striae. Around papilla of optic nerve, the scleral ring is easily seen, but the chorioidal ring is indistinct. (see Fig. 375).

2. Vessels of chorioid coat are not apparent because of pigment in retina.

## 375. Retina: Normal Fundus of Eye with Slight Pigmentation.

(as it appears through the ophthalmoscope) (after Haab, Atlas der Ophthalmoskopie).

**Note:** 1. In light-complected or fair individuals, there is correspondingly less pigment in the retina, therefore blood vessels even in the chorioid coat may be faintly seen, while those of the retina and optic disc are plainly and clearly seen. In highly pigmented individuals, the retina appears dark red, and in Chinese subjects it is gray.

2. The above variations are responsible for the partial or complete obliteration of some rings observed at margin of the optic disc. (Fig. 374). Other variations include a complete or partial scleral ring within a pigmented chorioidal ring.

3. Retinal arteries are usually narrower and a more bright red than veins. They reflect a bright streak of light (highlight) along their length.

4. The central depression of optic disc may be accentuated by chronically increased intraocular tension. This condition causes the reflected streak of light along the length of the artery to appear broken where the vessel bends over elevated rim of the optic disc.

(Confinued)

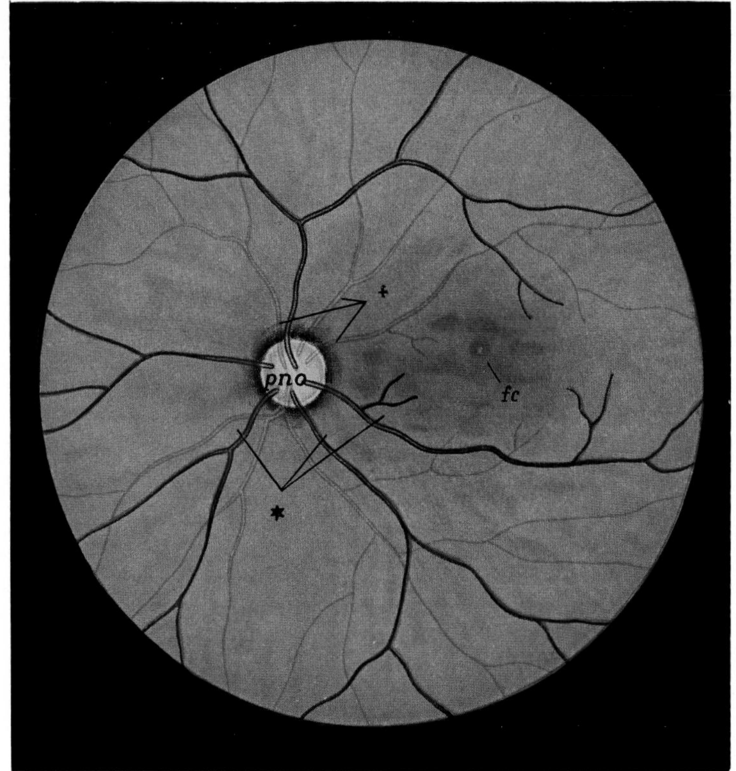

+
pno
fc
*


Fig. 374.

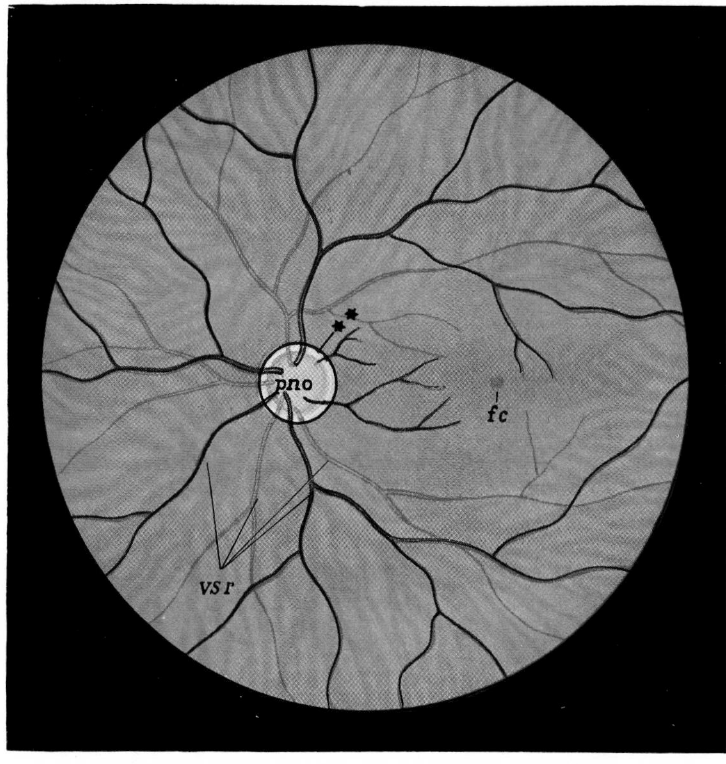

*
*
pno
fc
vsr


Fig. 375.

5. Retinal arteries normally cross in front of the veins, but retinal veins are usually visible through them. When the artery is sclerotic, however, the vein may appear to be interrupted.

6. In many mammals, there is an iridescent reflecting area associated with the retina, called the **tapetum**. This is responsible for the reflection of the green-yellow light which causes the shine in eyes of cats, dogs and other animals when they are illuminated by a beam of light at night. Since the human eye has no reflecting tapetum, the reflected light is not observed in the human subject.

**Etymology:**

*tapetum* = L. carpet, curtain, tapestry

## 376. Enlarged Segment of Ciliary Portion or Retina. (10/1)

Enlargement of specimen shown in Figure 372.

1 **Ciliary Folds**
*plicae ciliares*

2 **Ciliary Processes**
*processus ciliares*

**Zonula Ciliaris**
*zonula ciliaris*

**Lens, Posterior Surface**
*lens (facies posterior)*

5 **Ciliary Corona**
*corona ciliaris*

8 **Orbiculus Ciliaris** (non-visual area of retina)
*orbiculus ciliaris (pars ceca retinae)*
**Retina**
*retina*
**Chorioid**
*chorioidea*

**Sclera**
*sclera*

9 **Pars Optica Retinae**
*pars optica retinae*

**Ora Serrata**
*ora serrata*

**Pars Ciliaris Retinae**
*pars ciliaris retinae*

## 377. Posterior Surface of Iris and Ciliary Body. (10/1)

After excision of lens, the cornea is visible through the pupil, and the dorsal surface of the iris is seen more clearly. On the left side, the zonular fibers were removed.

1 **Pars Ciliaris Retinae**
*pars ciliaris retinae*

**Zonular Fibers**
*fibrae zonulares*

2 **Pupil (Cornea)**
*pupilla (cornea)*

5 **Folds of Iris**
*plicae iridis*

7 **Posterior Surface of Iris**
*facies posterior iridis*

8 **Orbiculus Ciliaris**
*orbiculus ciliaris*

**Ciliary Body**
*corpus ciliare*

9 **Pupillary Margin**
*margo pupillaris*

10 **Ciliary Folds**
*plicae ciliares*
**Ciliary Processes**
*processus ciliares*

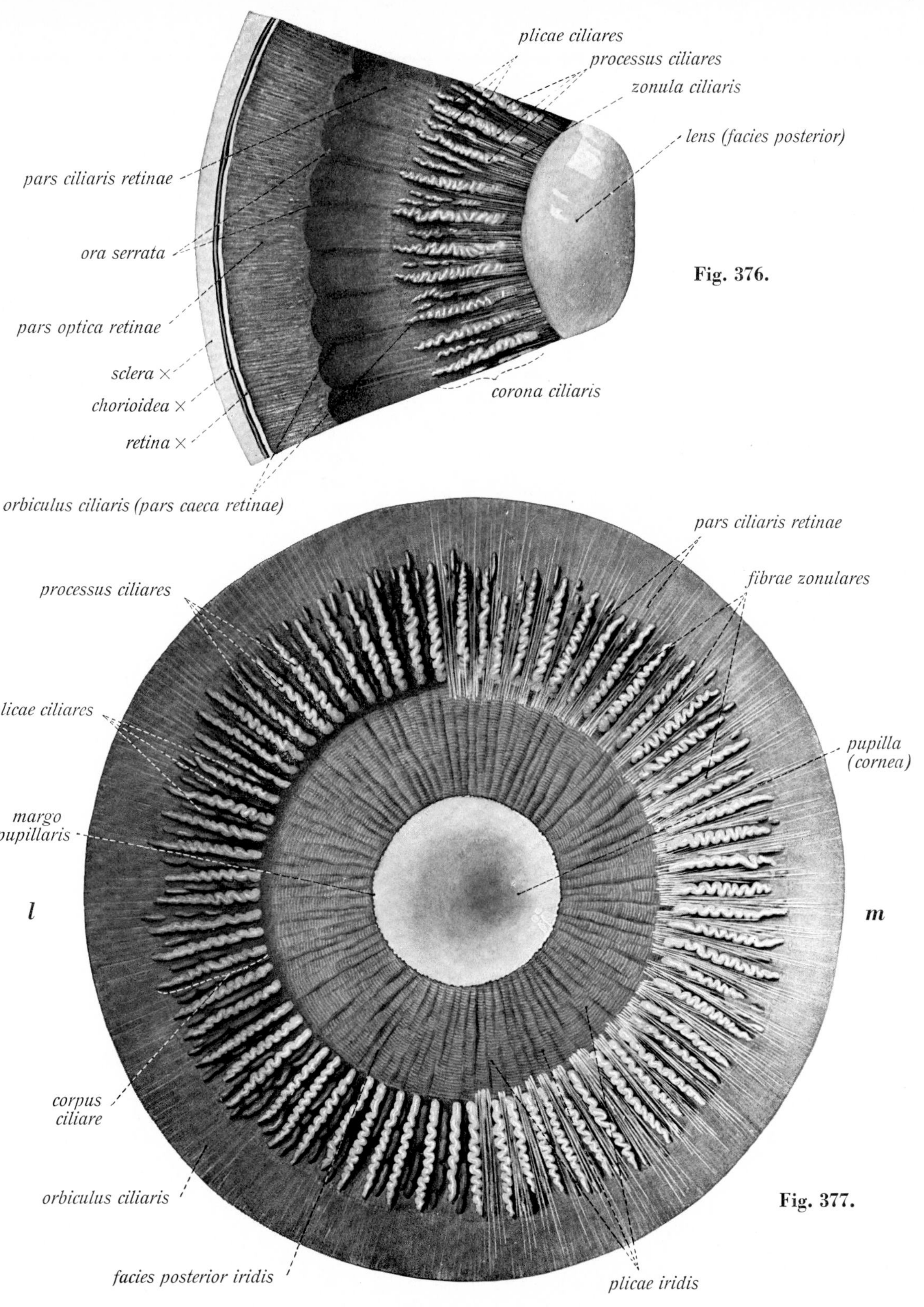
plicae ciliares
processus ciliares
zonula ciliaris
lens (facies posterior)
pars ciliaris retinae
ora serrata
pars optica retinae
sclera ×
chorioidea ×
retina ×
corona ciliaris
orbiculus ciliaris (pars caeca retinae)

**Fig. 376.**

pars ciliaris retinae
processus ciliares
fibrae zonulares
plicae ciliares
pupilla
(cornea)
margo
pupillaris
l
m
corpus
ciliare
orbiculus ciliaris
facies posterior iridis
plicae iridis

**Fig. 377.**

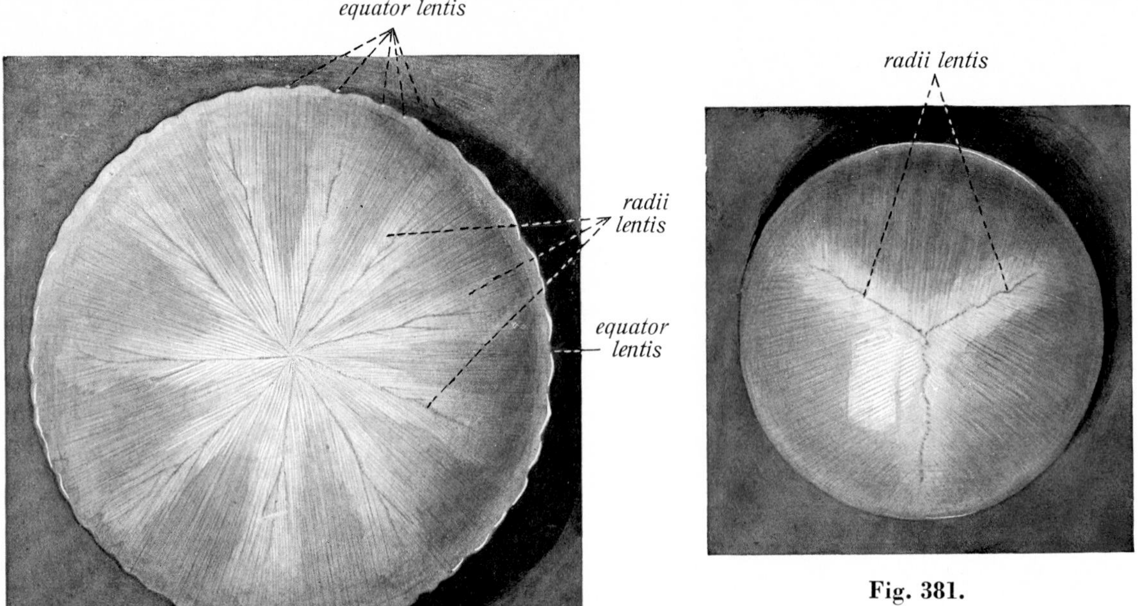
equator lentis
radii lentis
equator lentis
radii lentis

Fig. 378.

Fig. 381.

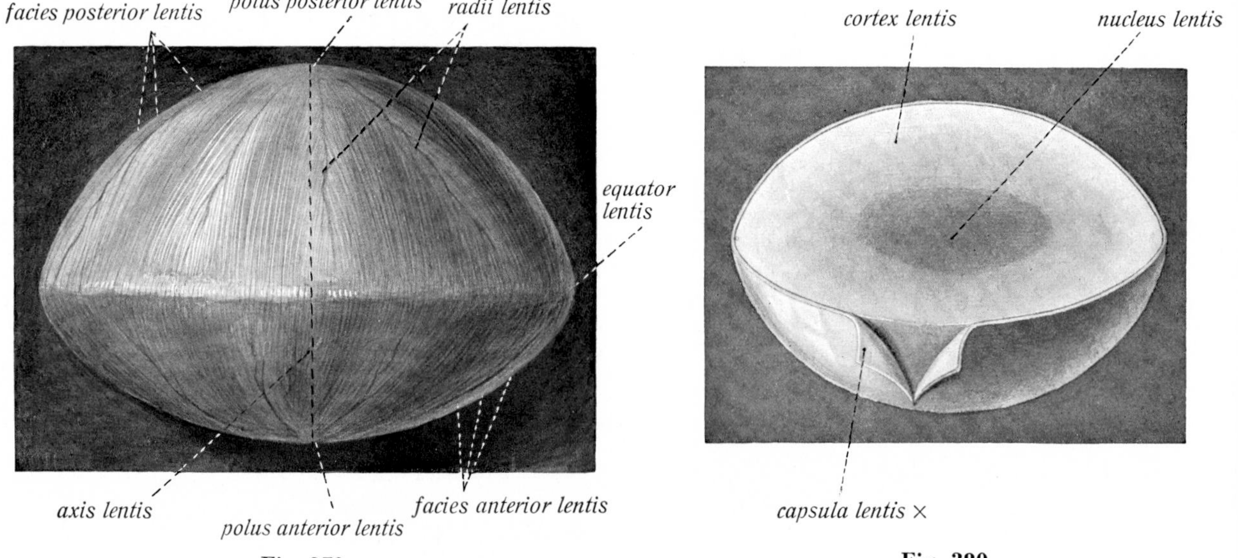
facies posterior lentis
polus posterior lentis
radii lentis
equator lentis
axis lentis
polus anterior lentis
facies anterior lentis
cortex lentis
nucleus lentis
capsula lentis ×

Fig. 379.

Fig. 380.

## 378. Lens of an Adult. (from in front; lens star with multiple rays) (10/1)

## 379. Lens, Equatorial View. (10/1)

1 **Rays of the Lens**
*radii lentis*

2 **Equator of Lens**
*equator lentis*

5 **Anterior Surface of Lens**
*facies anterior lentis*

6 **Anterior Pole of Lens**
*polus anterior lentis*

8 **Axis of Lens**
*axis lentis*

10 **Posterior Surface of Lens**
*facies posterior lentis*

11 **Posterior Pole of Lens**
*polus posterior lentis*

## 380. Lens Halved in Equatorial Plane. (capsule cut and partially reflected) (6/1)

## 381. Lens of Child. (ventral aspect; lens star with three rays) (10/1)

**Note:** 1. In the fetus, the lens is nearly spherical. It retains this shape in the child, but as the individual grows older, the lens continues to produce lenticular cells at the equator. This results in a somewhat oblong-shaped lens in middle age. In old age, it becomes flattened on both surfaces. This gradual flattening results in farsightedness or hypermetropia.

2. As the equatorial diameter of the lens increases, it also becomes more dense and less plastic. The flattened, more rigid lens of old age is responsible for its inability to accommodate for short distances.

## 382. Sector of Iris and Ciliary Body. (from dorsal aspect) (15/1)

Same as Figure 377, but at higher magnification.

2 **Posterior Surface of Iris**
*facies posterior iridis*

4 **Finer, More Closely Placed Central Radial Folds**
*plicae iridis radiales centrales*

**Radial Folds of Iris**
*plicae iridis radiales*

5 **Ciliary Processes**
*processus ciliares*

6 **Ciliary Folds**
*plicae ciliares*

7 **Orbiculus Ciliaris**
*orbiculus ciliaris*

11 **Ora Serrata**
*ora serrata*

12 **Ciliary Process**
*processus ciliaris*

**Note:** The radial folds of the iris-4 and the finer more closely placed central radial folds-4 of the posterior surface of the iris-2.

## 383. Fibers of Suspensory Apparatus (Zonular Fibers) of the Lens. (seen from in front) (10/1)

The sclera and cornea have been removed, as well as the iris, except its narrow outer margin-4, -8. This exposed the lens-2 and ventral ends of the ciliary processes-2. The zonular fibers-4 form the suspensory ligament of the lens, to pass between the ciliary processes on their way to their insertion into the margin of the lens. The lens star and lens fibers are also illustrated.

2 **Orbiculus Ciliaris**
*orbiculus ciliaris*
**Ciliary Processes**
*processus ciliares*
**Lens, Anterior Pole**
*polus anterior lentis*

3 **Remnants of Pectinate Lig.**
*reliquiae lig. pectinati anguli iridocornealis*

4 **Iris, Anterior Surface, Ciliary Margin**
*facies anterior iridis, margo ciliaris*

**Zonular Fibers**
*fibrae zonulares*

5 **Ciliary Body**
*corpus ciliare*
**Zonular Ciliaris**
*zonula ciliaris*
**Radii of Lens**
*radii lentis*

8 **Iris, Anterior Surface, Ciliary Margin**
*facies anterior iridis, margo ciliaris*

**Lens, Anterior Surface**
*facies anterior lentis*

**Anterior Chamber (of Eye)**
*camera oculi anterior [camera anterior bulbi]*

9 **Ciliary Nerves**
*nervi ciliares*

10 **Ciliary Nerves**
*nervi ciliares*
**Blood Vessels**
*vasa sanguinea*

**Note:** Remnants of the pectinate ligament at the iridocorneal angle-3.

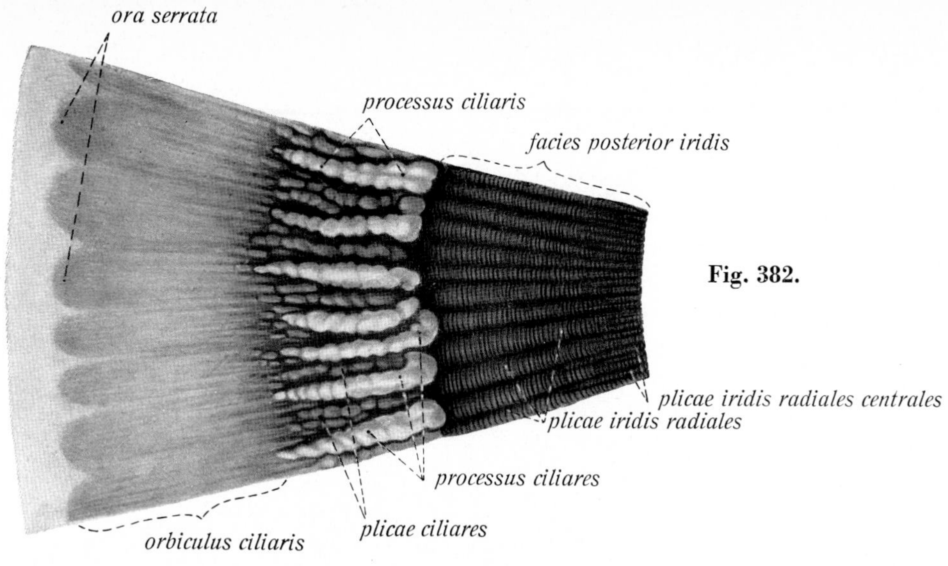
ora serrata
processus ciliaris
facies posterior iridis
plicae iridis radiales centrales
plicae iridis radiales
processus ciliares
plicae ciliares
orbiculus ciliaris

**Fig. 382.**

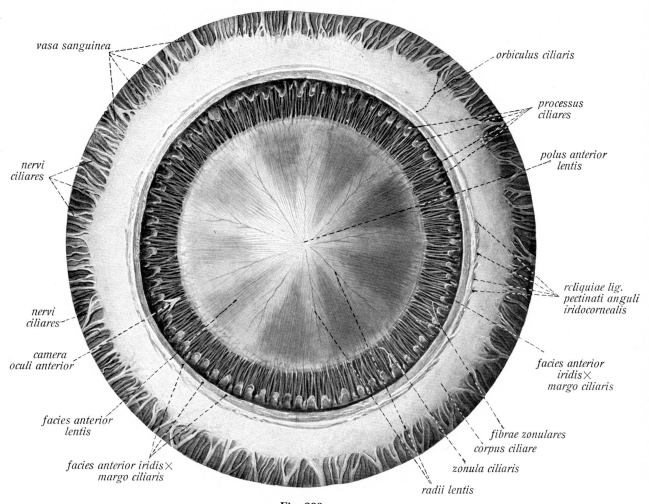

*vasa sanguinea*
*orbiculus ciliaris*
*processus ciliares*
*nervi ciliares*
*polus anterior lentis*
*rcliquiae lig. pectinati anguli iridocornealis*
*nervi ciliares*
*camera oculi anterior*
*facies anterior iridis× margo ciliaris*
*facies anterior lentis*
*fibrae zonulares*
*corpus ciliare*
*facies anterior iridis× margo ciliaris*
*zonula ciliaris*
*radii lentis*

**Fig. 383.**

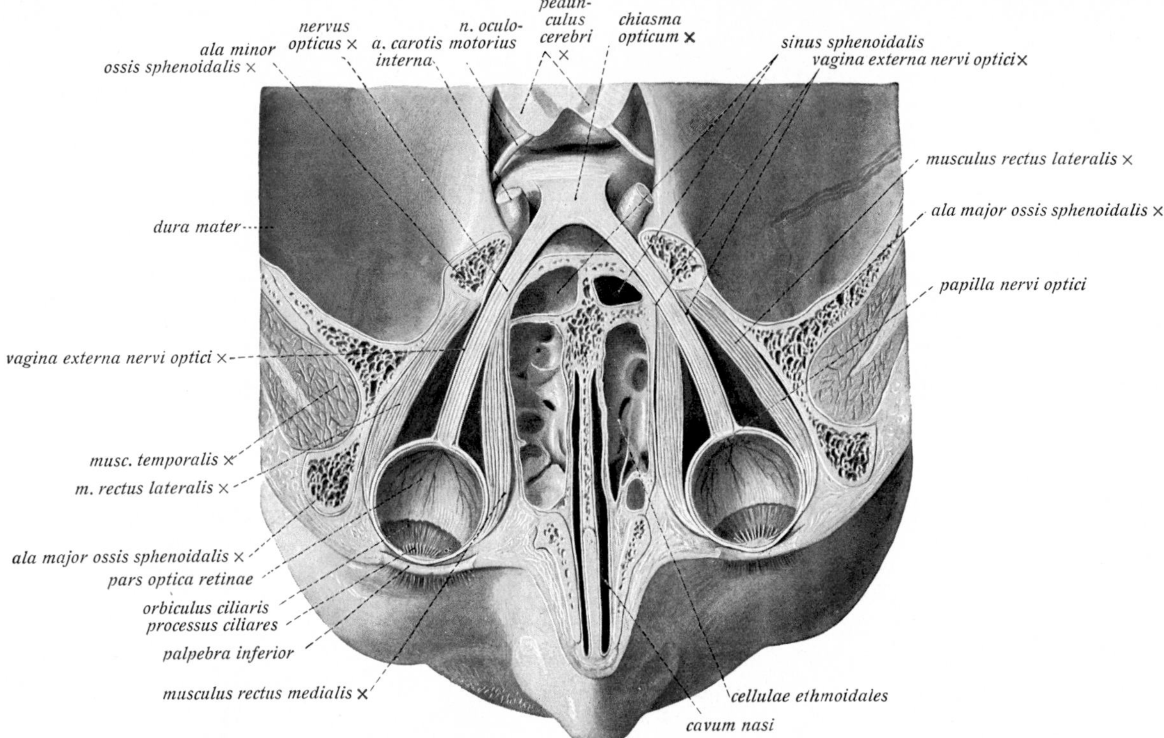

ala minor
ossis sphenoidalis ×
nervus
opticus ×
a. carotis
interna
n. oculo-
motorius
pedun-
culus
cerebri
×
chiasma
opticum ×
sinus sphenoidalis
vagina externa nervi optici×
musculus rectus lateralis ×
ala major ossis sphenoidalis ×
papilla nervi optici
dura mater
vagina externa nervi optici ×
musc. temporalis ×
m. rectus lateralis ×
ala major ossis sphenoidalis ×
pars optica retinae
orbiculus ciliaris
processus ciliares
palpebra inferior
musculus rectus medialis ×
cellulae ethmoidales
cavum nasi


**Fig. 384.**

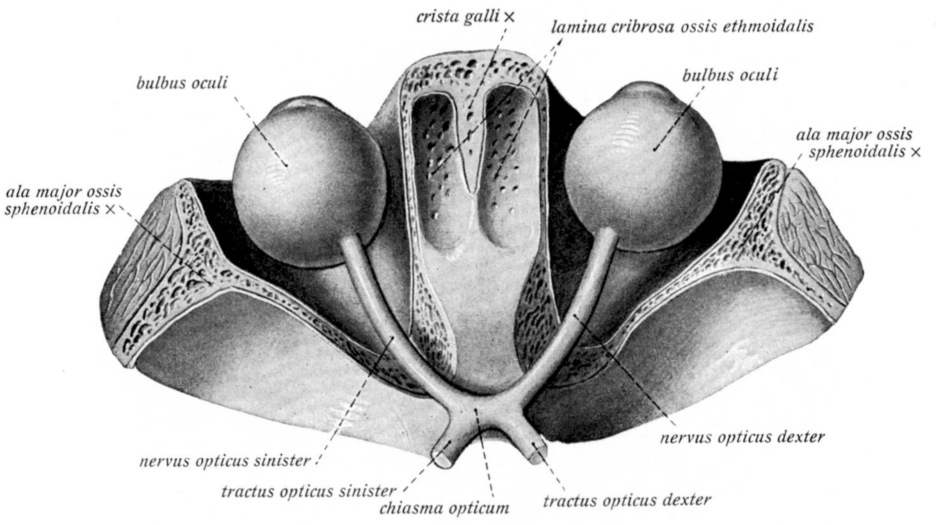

crista galli ×
lamina cribrosa ossis ethmoidalis
bulbus oculi
bulbus oculi
ala major ossis
sphenoidalis ×
ala major ossis
sphenoidalis ×
nervus opticus dexter
nervus opticus sinister
tractus opticus sinister
chiasma opticum
tractus opticus dexter


**Fig. 385.**

## 384. Horizontal Section Through Both Orbital Cavities and the Optic Nerves. (2/3)

1 **Sphenoidal Sinus**
*sinus sphenoidalis*
**External Sheath of Optic Nerve**
*vagina externa nervi optici*

2 **Lateral Rectus Muscle**
*musculus rectus lateralis*
**Greater Wing of Sphenoid**
*ala major ossis sphenoidalis*

3 **Optic Disc**
*papilla [discus] nervi optici*

5 **Ethmoidal Cells**
*cellulae ethmoidales*
**Nasal Cavity**
*cavum nasi*

8 **Medial Rectus Muscle**
*musculus rectus medialis*
**Lower Eyelid**
*palpebra inferior*
**Ciliary Processes**
*processus ciliares*
**Orbiculus Ciliaris**
*orbiculus ciliaris*
**Retina, Pars Optica**
*pars optica retinae*
**Greater Wing of Sphenoid**
*ala major ossis sphenoidalis*

9 **Lateral Rectus Muscle**
*m. rectus lateralis*
**Temporal Muscle**
*musc. temporalis*
**External Sheath of Optic Nerve**
*vagina externa nervi optici*

10 **Dura Mater**
*dura mater*
**Sphenoid Bone, Lesser Wing**
*ala minor ossis sphenoidalis*

11 **Optic Nerve**
*nervus opticus*
**Internal Carotid Artery**
*a. carotis interna*
**Oculomotor Nerve**
*n. oculomotorius*

12 **Cerebral Peduncle**
*pedunculus cerebri*
**Optic Chiasma**
*chiasma opticum*

**Note:** 1. The optic nerve is a brain tract, composed of approximately a million axons from ganglion cells in retina. The ganglion cells collect impulses that bipolar cells receive from approximately 7 million cones and 125 million rods and carry this information to the visual centers in the brain.

2. Meningeal coverings of optic nerve are similar to those on the brain and spinal cord. (See Fig. 362).

## 385. The Two Ocular Bulbs and Optic Nerves of a Child. (1/1)

All other contents of orbital cavities were removed.

1 **Cribriform Plate of Ethmoid**
*lamina cribrosa ossis ethmoidalis*

2 **Eyeball**
*bulbus oculi*
**Greater Wing of Sphenoid Bone**
*ala major ossis sphenoidalis*

4 **Optic Nerve, Right**
*nervus opticus dexter*

5 **Optic Tract, Right**
*tractus opticus dexter*

7 **Optic Chiasma**
*chiasma opticum*

8 **Optic Tract, Left**
*tractus opticus sinister*
**Optic Nerve, Left**
*nervus opticus sinister*

9 **Greater Wing of Sphenoid Bone**
*ala major ossis sphenoidalis*

10 **Eyeball**
*bulbus oculi*

12 **Crista Galli**
*crista galli*

## 386. Right Palpebral Cleft. (Rima palpebrarum open) (1/1)

1 **Upper Eyelid**
*palpebra superior*

2 **Pupil**
*pupilla*

3 **Caruncula Lacrimalis**
*caruncula lacrimalis*

4 **Medial Angle of Eye**
*angulus oculi medialis*

5 **Inferior Palpebral Sulcus**
*sulcus palpebromalaris*
**Bulbar Conjunctiva**
*tunica conjunctiva bulbi*

6 **Posterior Border of Eyelid**
*limbus palpebralis posterior*
**Anterior Border of Eyelid**
*limbus palpebralis anterior*

7 **Iris**
*iris*

**Lower Eyelid**
*palpebra inferior*

**Lateral Commissure of Eyelids**
*commissura palpebrarum lat.*

8 **Lateral Angle of Eye**
*angulus oculi lateralis*

11 **Superior Palpebral Sulcus**
*sulcus palpebralis superior*

## 387. Right Palpebral Cleft. (Eye closed) (1/1)

1 **Superior Palpebral Sulcus**
*sulcus palpebralis superior*

5 **Medial Angle of Eye**
*angulus oculi medialis*
**Inferior Palpebral Sulcus**
*(sulcus palpebromalaris)*

6 **Lower Eyelid**
*palpebra inferior*

7 **Eyelashes**
*cilia*

8 **Lateral Angle of Eye**
*angulus oculi lateralis*

10 **Upper Eyelid**
*palpebra superior*

12 **Eyebrow**
*supercilium*

## 388. Eyelids Pulled Apart to Increase Size of Opening. (1/1)

2 **Papilla + Punctum Lacrimale**
*papilla + punctum lacrimale*
**Lacrimal Reservoir**
*lacus lacrimalis*
**Caruncula Lacrimalis**
*caruncula lacrimalis*

3 **Medial Angle of Eye**
*angulus oculi medialis*

5 **Plica Semilunaris of Conjunctiva**
*plica semilunaris conjunctivae*

**Anterior Border of Eyelid**
*limbus palpebralis anterior*

6 **Posterior Border of Eyelid**
*limbus palpebralis posterior*

7 **Conjunctiva of Eyelid (Tarsal Glands)**
*tunica conjunctiva palpebrae (glandulae tarsales)*
**Inferior Fornix of Conjunctiva**
*fornix conjunctivae inferior*

8 **Bulbar Conjunctiva**
*tunica conjunctiva bulbi*

**Note:** 1. **Palpebral conjunctiva**-7 and **bulbar conjunctiva**-8 meet at the **inferior conjunctival fornix**-7.

2. Palpebral conjunctiva is continuous with the skin at the rima palpebrarum (anterior palpebral border-5).

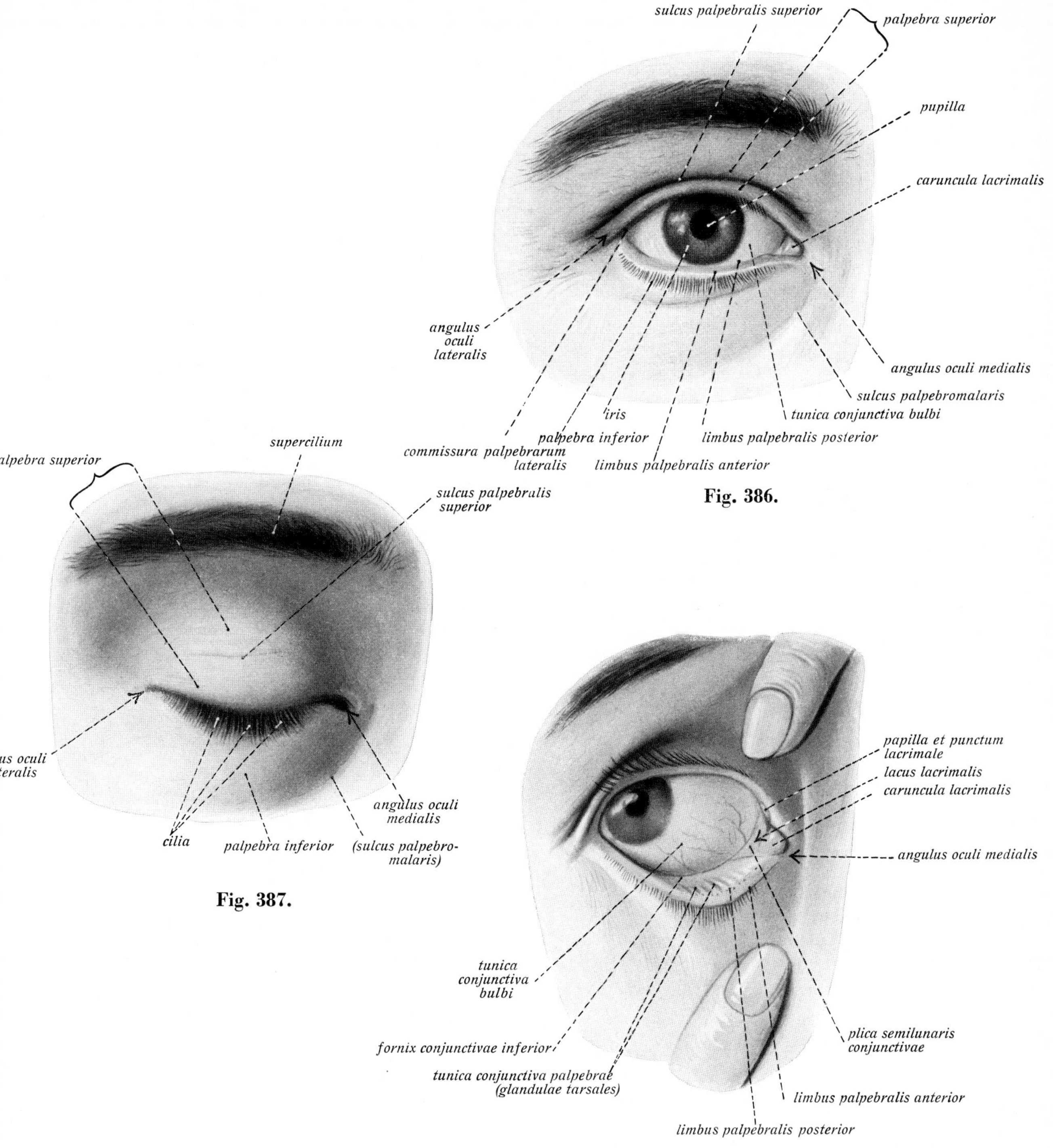

sulcus palpebralis superior
palpebra superior
pupilla
caruncula lacrimalis
angulus oculi lateralis
angulus oculi medialis
sulcus palpebromalaris
tunica conjunctiva bulbi
iris
palpebra inferior
limbus palpebralis posterior
commissura palpebrarum lateralis
limbus palpebralis anterior
alpebra superior
supercilium
sulcus palpebralis superior
lus oculi
teralis
angulus oculi medialis
cilia
palpebra inferior
(sulcus palpebromalaris)
papilla et punctum lacrimale
lacus lacrimalis
caruncula lacrimalis
angulus oculi medialis
tunica conjunctiva bulbi
plica semilunaris conjunctivae
fornix conjunctivae inferior
tunica conjunctiva palpebrae (glandulae tarsales)
limbus palpebralis anterior
limbus palpebralis posterior


**Fig. 386.**

**Fig. 387.**

**Fig. 388.**

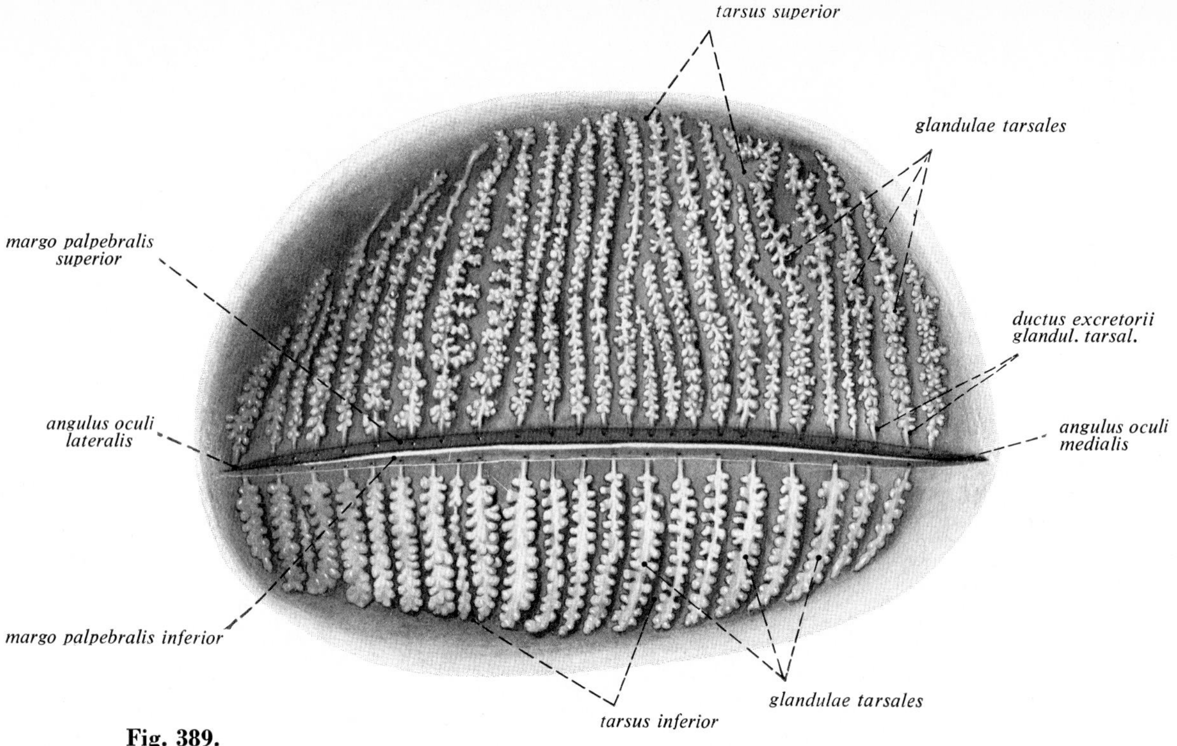

tarsus superior
glandulae tarsales
margo palpebralis superior
ductus excretorii glandul. tarsal.
angulus oculi lateralis
angulus oculi medialis
margo palpebralis inferior
glandulae tarsales
tarsus inferior


**Fig. 389.**

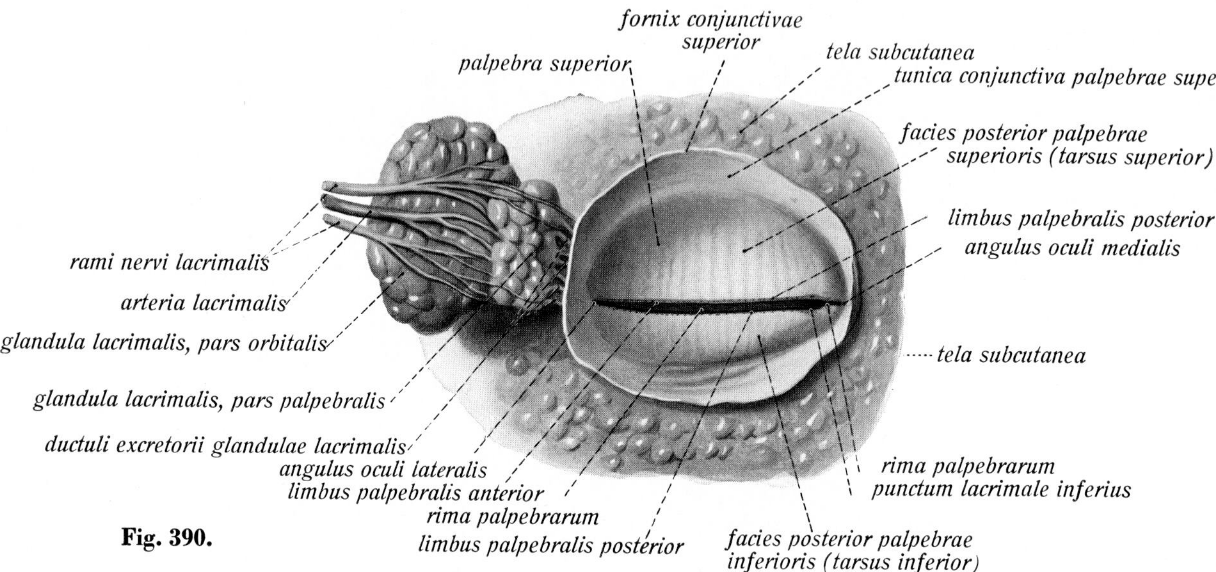

fornix conjunctivae superior
palpebra superior
tela subcutanea
tunica conjunctiva palpebrae superi
facies posterior palpebrae superioris (tarsus superior)
limbus palpebralis posterior
angulus oculi medialis
rami nervi lacrimalis
arteria lacrimalis
glandula lacrimalis, pars orbitalis
tela subcutanea
glandula lacrimalis, pars palpebralis
ductuli excretorii glandulae lacrimalis
angulus oculi lateralis
limbus palpebralis anterior
rima palpebrarum
limbus palpebralis posterior
rima palpebrarum
punctum lacrimale inferius
facies posterior palpebrae inferioris (tarsus inferior)


**Fig. 390.**

## 389. Eyelids Viewed From the Dorsal Side. (4/1)

The eyelids were cleared in sodium hydroxide glycerine, to demonstrate the tarsal glands (of Meibom).

2 **Tarsal Glands**
*glandulae tarsales*

3 **Excretory Duct, Tarsal Gland**
*ductus excretorii glandul. tarsal.*
**Medial Ocular Angle**
*angulus oculi medialis*

5 **Tarsal Glands**
*glandulae tarsales*

6 **Inferior Tarsus**
*tarsus inferior*

7 **Inferior Palpebral Margin**
*margo palpebralis inferior*

9 **Lateral Ocular Angle**
*angulus oculi lateralis*

10 **Superior Palpebral Margin**
*margo palpebralis superior*

12 **Superior Tarsus**
*tarsus superior*

## 390. Eyelids and Lacrimal Glands. (dorsal aspect) (1/1)

The conjunctiva was cut at the fornices.

1 **Subcutaneous Layer**
*tela subcutanea*
**Superior Palpebral Conjunctiva**
*tuncia conjunctiva palpebrae superioris*

2 **Posterior Surface of Upper Eyelid (Superior Tarsus)**
*facies posterior palpebrae superioris (tarsus superior)*

3 **Posterior Palpebral Border**
*limbus palpebralis posterior*
**Medial Angle of Eye**
*angulus oculi medialis*

4 **Subcutaneous Layer**
*tela subcutanea*

**Rima Palpebrarum**
*rima palpebrarum*

**Inferior Lacrimal Puncta**
*punctum lacrimale inferius*

5 **Posterior Surface Lower Eyelid (Inferior Tarsus)**
*facies posterior palpebrae inferioris (tarsus inferior)*

7 **Posterior Palpebral Border**
*limbus palpebralis posterior*

8 **Rima Palpebrarum**
*rima palpebrarum*
**Anterior Palpebral Border**
*limbus palpebralis anterior*
**Lateral Angle of Eye**
*angulus oculi lateralis*

9 **Lacrimal Gl., Excretory Ducts**
*ductuli excretorii glandulae lacrimalis*

**Lacrimal Gland, Palpebral Portion**
*glandula lacrimalis, pars palpebralis*

**Orbital Portion of Lacrimal Gland**
*glandula lacrimalis, pars orbitalis*

**Lacrimal Artery**
*arteria lacrimalis*

**Lacrimal Nerve, Branches**
*rami nervi lacrimalis*

11 **Superior Eyelid**
*palpebra superior*

12 **Superior Fornix of Conjunctiva**
*fornix conjunctivae superior*

## 391. The Palpebral Fascia or Orbital Septum. (Right eye) (1/1)

The skin, superficial fascia, and orbicularis oculi muscle were removed. In the lateral part of the upper lid, the orbital septum was incised and pulled up so that the orbital and palpebral parts of the lacrimal gland could be seen. The tendon of the levator palpebrae superioris muscle separates the two parts of the lacrimal gland.

1 **Orbital Septum**
*septum orbitale*

**Superior Tarsus**
*tarsus superior*

2 **Medial Palpebral Ligament**
*lig. palpebrale mediale*

3 **Nasal Bone**
*os nasale*

4 **Frontal Process of Maxilla**
*processus frontalis maxillae*

6 **Inferior Tarsus**
*tarsus inferior*

7 **Zygomatic Bone**
*os zygomaticum*

8 **Orbital Septum, Orbital Fat Body** (Shining Through)
*septum orbitale, corpus adiposum orbitae***

9 **Lateral Palpebral Raphe**
*raphe palpebralis lateralis*

**Excretory Ductules of Lacrimal Gland**
*ductuli excretorii glandulae lacrimalis*

10 **Lacrimal Gland, Palpebral Portion**
*glandula lacrimalis, pars palpebralis*
**Lacrimal Gland, Orbital Portion**
*glandula lacrimalis, pars orbitalis*

11 **Tendon of Levator Palpebrae Superioris**
*tendo m. levatoris palpebralis superioris*

12 **Orbital Septum** (cut and pulled up)
*septum orbitale**

**Note:** 1. **Orbital septum**-1, is continuous with the periosteum of the orbital cavity and margin of orbit.

## 392. The Lacrimal Apparatus and Ducts (1/1) (Prep: Anat. Inst., Münster)

The eyelids were pulled away from the bulbus oculi so the conjunctival sac is visible. Part of the outer nose was removed to display the nasolacrimal duct.

1 **Superior Lacrimal Canaliculus**
*canaliculus lacrimalis superior*
**Orbicularis Oculi Muscle**
*m. orbicularis oculi*
**Lacrimal Caruncle**
*caruncula lacrimalis*

2 **Fornix of Lacrimal Sac**
*fornix sacci lacrimalis*
**Orifice of Lacrimal Canaliculi**
*orificium canaliculi lacrimalis*

3 **Inferior Lacrimal Canaliculus**
*canaliculus lacrimalis inferior*
**Lacrimal Papilla + Punctum Lacrimale**
*papilla lacrimalis et punctum lacrimale*

**Middle Nasal Concha**
*concha nasalis media*

4 **Orifice of Nasolacrimal Duct and Inferior Nasal Meatus**
*orificium ductus nasolacrimalis et meatus nasi inferior*
**Inferior Nasal Concha**
*concha nasalis inferior*

7 **Mucosa of Maxillary Sinus**
*mucosa sinus maxillaris*
**Infraorbital Nerve**
*n. infraorbitalis*

8 **Palpebral Conjunctiva**
*tunica conjunctiva palpebrae*

9 **Inferior Fornix of Conjunctiva**
*fornix conjunctivae inferior*

**Ocular Conjunctiva**
*tunica conjunctiva bulbi*

10 **Excretory Ducts, Lacrimal Gland**
*ductuli excretorii glandulae lacrimalis*

11 **Fornix of Superior Conjunctiva**
*fornix conjunctivae superior*

12 **Lacrimal Papilla + Punctum Lacrimale**
*papilla lacrimalis et punctum lacrimale*
**Plica Semilunaris of Conjunctiva**
*plica semilunaris conjunctivae*

**Note:** 1. On the medial palpebral angle, the lacrimal ducts converge toward the lacrimal sac.

2. The muscle bundles that separate from the orbicularis oculi muscle to pass around the lacrimal canals and sac. By contraction, they press the tear fluid out of the tear ducts.

3. The nasolacrimal duct has its opening caudal to the inferior nasal concha.

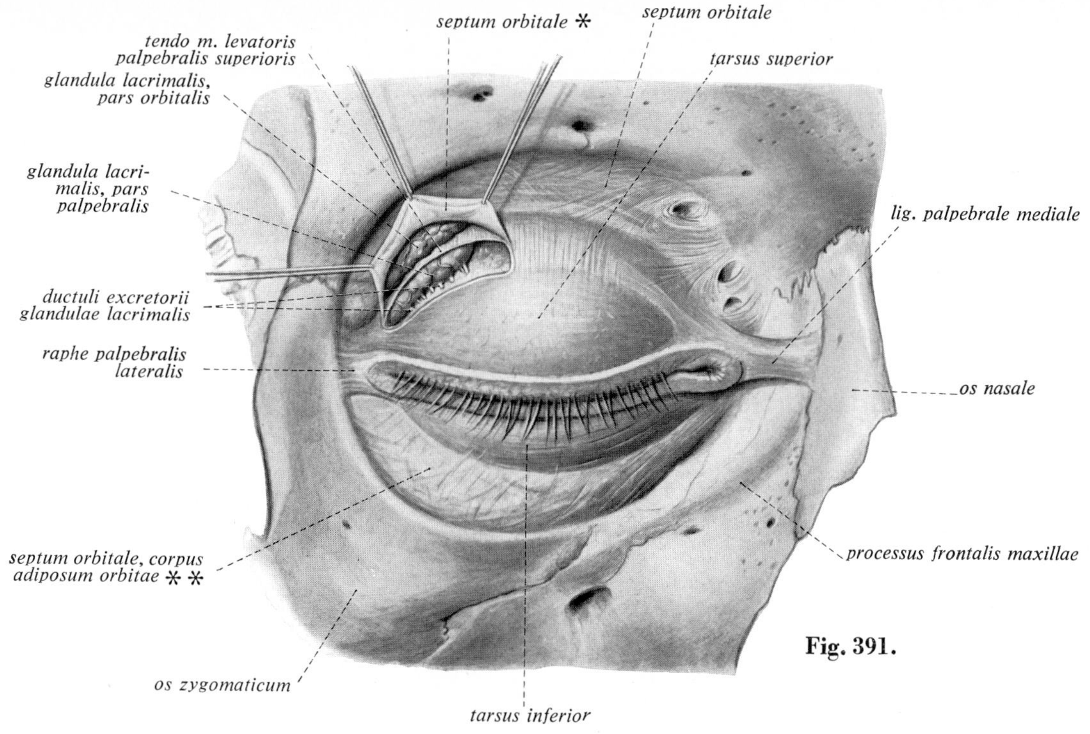
septum orbitale *
septum orbitale
tendo m. levatoris palpebralis superioris
tarsus superior
glandula lacrimalis, pars orbitalis
glandula lacrimalis, pars palpebralis
lig. palpebrale mediale
ductuli excretorii glandulae lacrimalis
raphe palpebralis lateralis
os nasale
septum orbitale, corpus adiposum orbitae **
processus frontalis maxillae
os zygomaticum
tarsus inferior

Fig. 391.

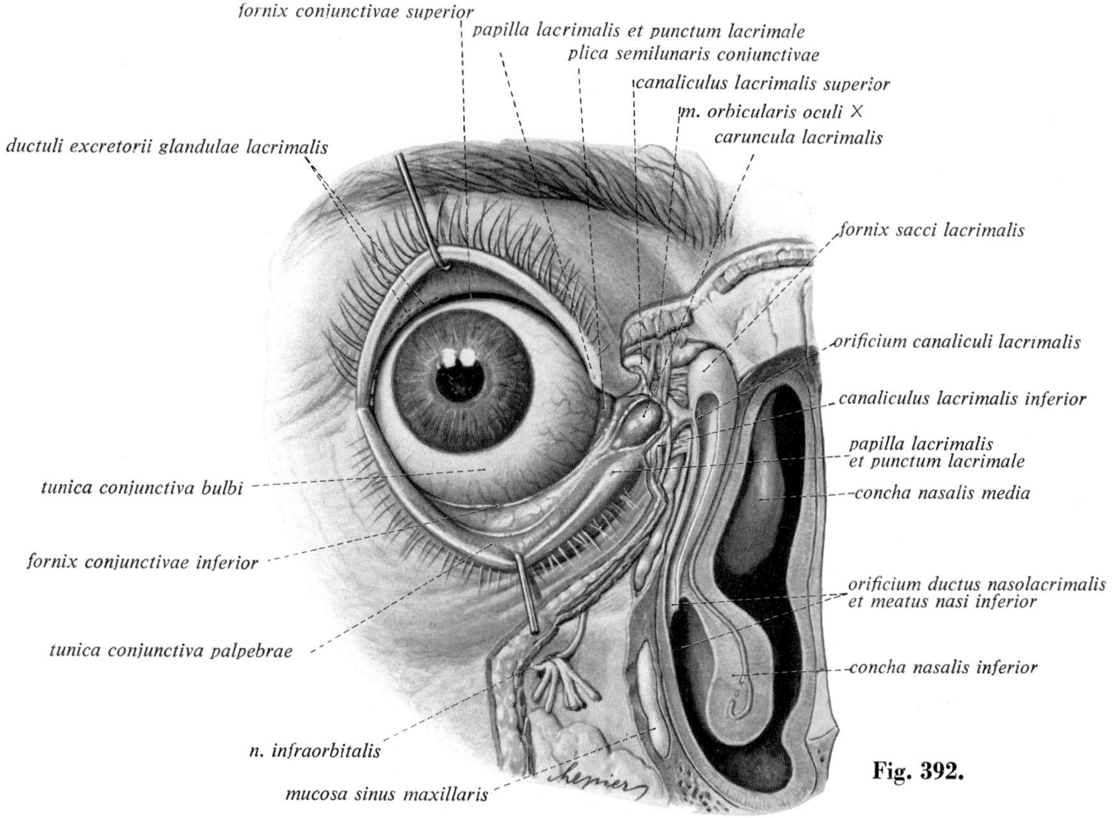
fornix conjunctivae superior
papilla lacrimalis et punctum lacrimale
plica semilunaris conjunctivae
canaliculus lacrimalis superior
m. orbicularis oculi ×
caruncula lacrimalis
ductuli excretorii glandulae lacrimalis
fornix sacci lacrimalis
orificium canaliculi lacrimalis
canaliculus lacrimalis inferior
papilla lacrimalis et punctum lacrimale
tunica conjunctiva bulbi
concha nasalis media
fornix conjunctivae inferior
orificium ductus nasolacrimalis et meatus nasi inferior
tunica conjunctiva palpebrae
concha nasalis inferior
n. infraorbitalis
mucosa sinus maxillaris

Fig. 392.

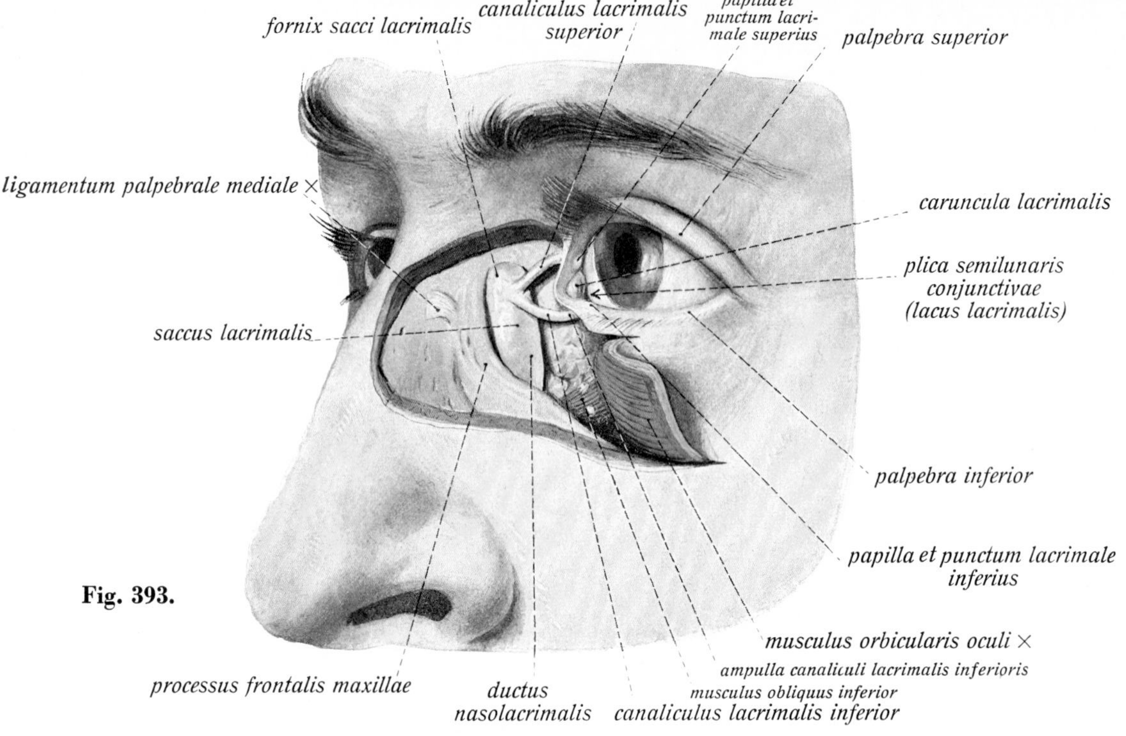
fornix sacci lacrimalis
canaliculus lacrimalis superior
papilla et punctum lacrimale superius
palpebra superior
ligamentum palpebrale mediale ×
caruncula lacrimalis
plica semilunaris conjunctivae (lacus lacrimalis)
saccus lacrimalis
palpebra inferior
papilla et punctum lacrimale inferius
musculus orbicularis oculi ×
ampulla canaliculi lacrimalis inferioris
musculus obliquus inferior
processus frontalis maxillae
ductus nasolacrimalis
canaliculus lacrimalis inferior

**Fig. 393.**

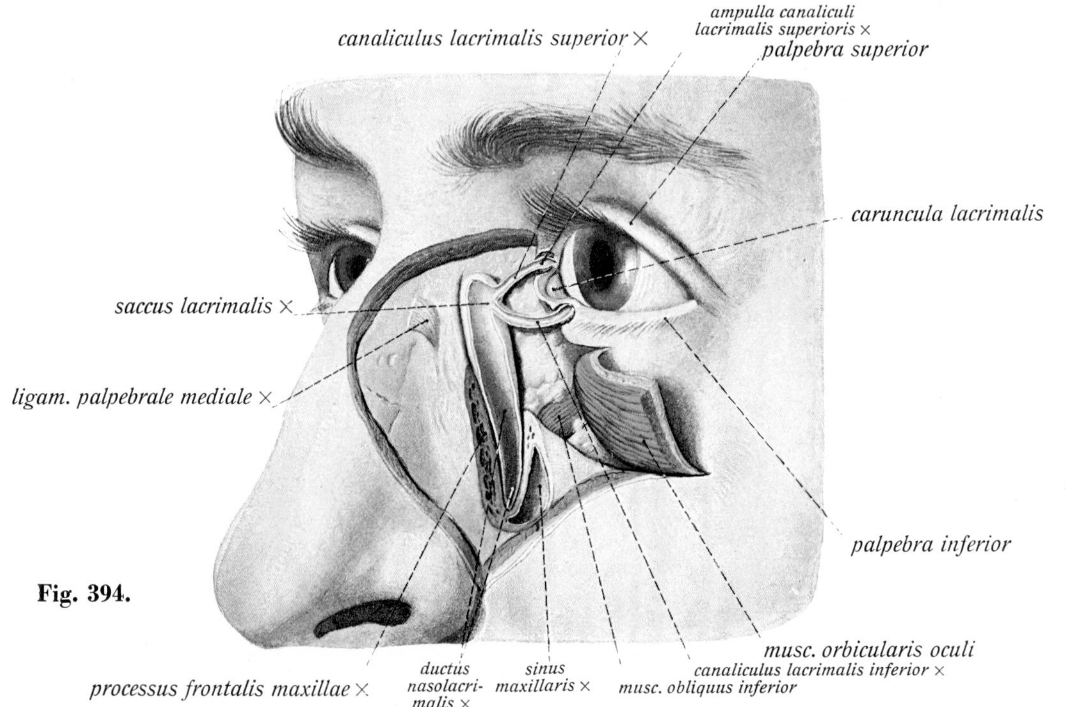
canaliculus lacrimalis superior ×
ampulla canaliculi lacrimalis superioris ×
palpebra superior
caruncula lacrimalis
saccus lacrimalis ×
ligam. palpebrale mediale ×
palpebra inferior
musc. orbicularis oculi
canaliculus lacrimalis inferior ×
processus frontalis maxillae ×
ductus nasolacrimalis ×
sinus maxillaris ×
musc. obliquus inferior

**Fig. 394.**

## 393. Lacrimal Sac and Canaliculi. (lateral front view) (1/1)

Skin, superficial fascia, and some of the muscles were partly removed or reflected. The medial palpebral ligament-10 was divided.

1 **Superior Lacrimal Papilla + Superior Lacrimal Punctum**
*papilla + punctum lacrimale superius*
**Upper Eyelid**
*palpebra superior*

2 **Caruncula Lacrimalis**
*caruncula lacrimalis*
**Plica Semilunaris of Conjunctiva (Lacus Lacrimalis)**
*plica semilunaris conjunctivae (lacus lacrimalis)*

4 **Lower Eyelid**
*palpebra inferior*

**Inferior Lacrimal Papilla + Punctum**
*papilla + punctum lacrimale inferius*

5 **Orbicularis Oculi Muscle**
*musculus orbicularis oculi*
**Ampulla of Inferior Lacrimal Canaliculus**
*ampulla canaliculi lacrimalis inferioris*
**Inferior Oblique Muscle**
*musculus obliquus inferior*

6 **Inferior Lacrimal Canaliculus**
*canaliculus lacrimalis inferior*

**Nasolacrimal Duct**
*ductus nasolacrimalis*

8 **Frontal Process of Maxilla**
*processus frontalis maxillae*

9 **Lacrimal Sac**
*saccus lacrimalis*

10 **Medial Palpebral Ligament**
*ligamentum palpebrale mediale*

12 **Fornix, Lacrimal Sac**
*fornix sacci lacrimalis*
**Superior Lacrimal Canaliculus**
*canaliculus lacrimalis superior*

## 394. The Lacrimal Canaliculi, Lacrimal Sac, and Nasolacrimal Duct.

(1/1) (Opened by removal of the ventrolateral side of these canals.)

The section is the same as Figure 393 but, in addition, a piece of the frontal process of the maxilla was chiseled away in order to expose the lower part of the **nasolacrimal duct**-7.

1 **Ampulla of Superior Lacrimal Canaliculus**
*ampulla canaliculi lacrimalis superioris*
**Upper Eyelid**
*palpebra superior*

2 **Caruncula Lacrimalis**
*caruncula lacrimalis*

4 **Lower Eyelid**
*palpebra inferior*

5 **Orbicularis Oculi Muscle**
*musc. orbicularis oculi*
**Inferior Lacrimal Canaliculus**
*canaliculus lacrimalis inferior*
**Inferior Oblique Muscle**
*musc. obliquus inferior*

6 **Maxillary Sinus**
*sinus maxillaris*

7 **Nasolacrimal Duct**
*ductus nasolacrimalis*

8 **Maxilla, Frontal Process**
*processus frontalis maxillae*

9 **Medial Palpebral Ligament**
*ligam. palpebrale mediale*

**Lacrimal Sac**
*saccus lacrimalis*

11 **Superior Lacrimal Canaliculus**
*canaliculus lacrimalis superior*

## 395. The Eye Muscles. (viewed from the lateral side) (slightly enlarged)

The lateral wall of the orbit and most of the contents of the orbital cavity including the fascia, the eyelids, and the ventral end of the levator palpebrae superioris-12 were removed. The **bulbus oculi**, **optic nerve**, and **extrinsic muscles** of the eye were left intact.

1 **Superior Rectus Muscle**
*musc. rectus superior*
**Bulbus Oculi**
*bulbus oculi*

2 **Lateral Rectus Muscle**
*m. rectus lateralis*
**Common Tendinous Ring**
*anulus tendineus communis*

3 **Optic Nerve**
*nervus opticus*
**Sphenoid Bone**
*os sphenoidale*

4 **Inferior Rectus Muscle**
*musc. rectus inferior*

5 **Infratemporal Fossa**
*fossa infratemporalis*

6 **Inferior Orbital Fissure**
*fissura orbitalis inferior*
**Maxillary Sinus**
*sinus maxillaris*

7 **Maxilla**
*maxilla*

8 **Inferior Oblique Muscle**
*m. obliquus inferior*

9 **Infraorbital Margin**
*margo infraorbitalis*
**Cornea**
*cornea*

11 **Frontal Bone**
*os frontale*

12 **Periorbita**
*periorbita*
**Levator Palpebrae Superioris Muscle**
*m. levator palpebrae superioris*

**Note:** 1. Six of the seven ocular muscles control the movements and position of the eyeball.

2. Five of the eye muscles (all except the inferior oblique) take origin from the **common tendinous ring**-2 which surrounds the optic nerve-3 at the apex of the orbital cavity.

## 396. Eye Muscles. (seen from the lateral side) (slightly enlarged)

Same dissection as in Figure 395 but, in addition, the rectus lateralis muscle and the optic nerve were divided. The bulbus oculi was rotated in order to expose its dorsal pole with the stump of the optic nerve. Most of the levator palpebrae superioris muscle was removed.

1 **Tendon of Superior Oblique Muscle**
*tendo musc. obliqui superioris*
**Superior Oblique Muscle**
*musc. obliquus superior*
**Superior Rectus Muscle**
*m. rectus superior*

2 **Levator Palpebrae Superioris Muscle**
*m. levator palpebrae superioris*
**Lateral Rectus Muscle**
*m. rectus lateralis*

3 **Optic Nerve**
*nervus opticus*
**Sphenoid Bone**
*os sphenoidale*

4 **Medial Rectus Muscle**
*m. rectus medialis*
**Inferior Orbital Fissure**
*fissura orbitalis inferior*

5 **Inferior Rectus Muscle**
*m. rectus inferior*

6 **Maxillary Sinus**
*sinus maxillaris*

7 **Periorbita**
*periorbita*

8 **Inferior Oblique Muscle**
*m. obliquus inferior*
**Maxilla**
*maxilla*
**Optic Nerve**
*nervus opticus*

9 **Lateral Rectus Muscle**
*m. rectus lateralis*
**Bulbus Oculi**
*bulbus oculi*

10 **Supraorbital Margin**
*margo supraorbitalis*

12 **Frontal Bone**
*os frontale*
**Trochlea (Superior Oblique Muscle)**
*trochlea (musculi obliqui superioris)*

**Note:** 1. The **trochlea**-12 and **tendon of the superior oblique muscle**.

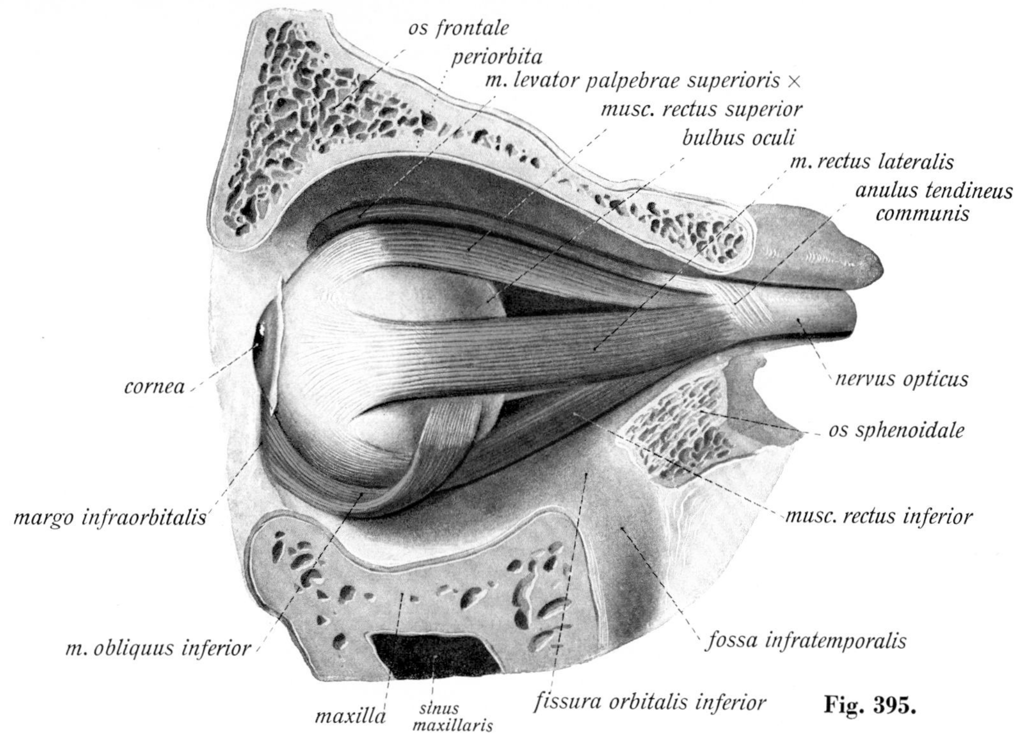
os frontale
periorbita
m. levator palpebrae superioris ×
musc. rectus superior
bulbus oculi
m. rectus lateralis
anulus tendineus communis
cornea
nervus opticus
os sphenoidale
margo infraorbitalis
musc. rectus inferior
m. obliquus inferior
fossa infratemporalis
maxilla
sinus maxillaris
fissura orbitalis inferior

**Fig. 395.**

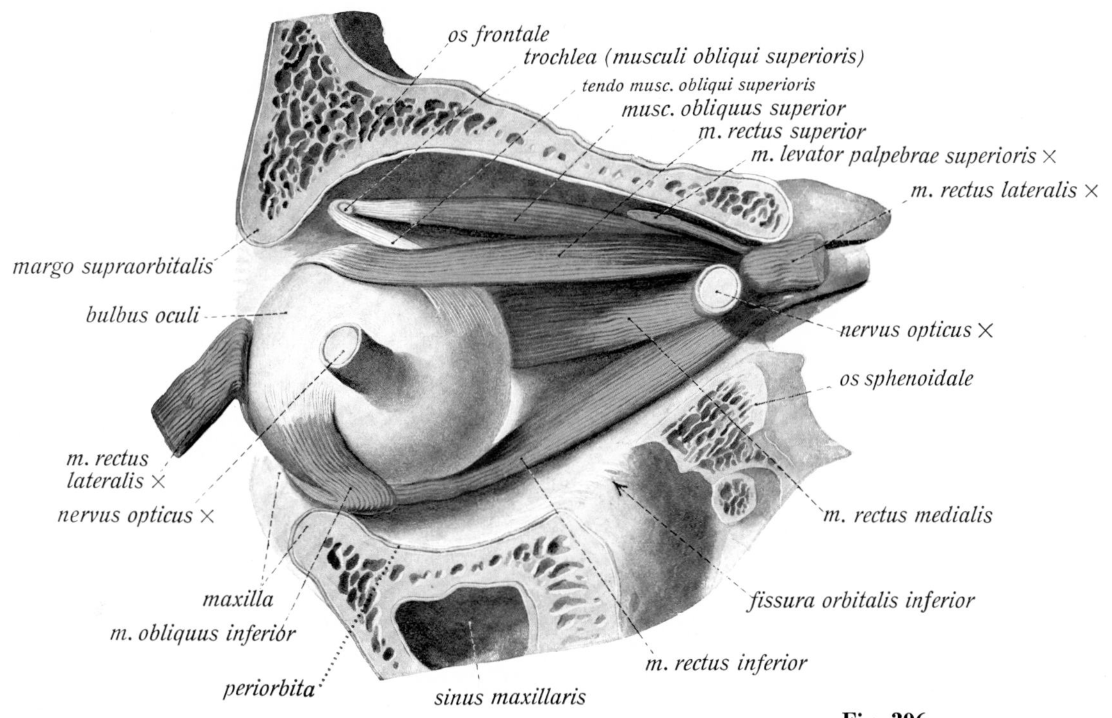
os frontale
trochlea (musculi obliqui superioris)
tendo musc. obliqui superioris
musc. obliquus superior
m. rectus superior
m. levator palpebrae superioris ×
m. rectus lateralis ×
margo supraorbitalis
bulbus oculi
nervus opticus ×
os sphenoidale
m. rectus lateralis ×
nervus opticus ×
m. rectus medialis
maxilla
fissura orbitalis inferior
m. obliquus inferior
m. rectus inferior
periorbita
sinus maxillaris

**Fig. 396.**

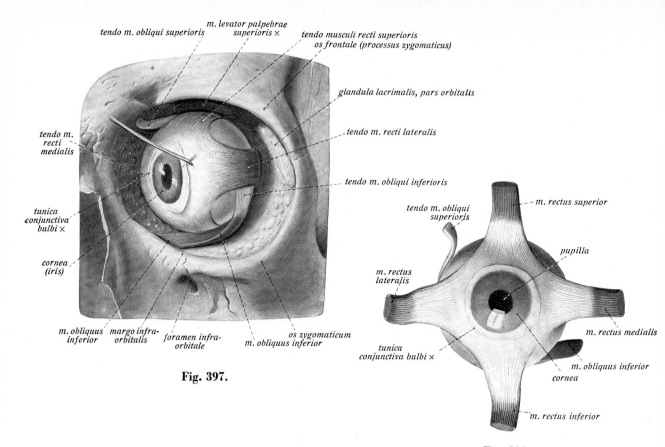

tendo m. obliqui superioris
m. levator palpebrae superioris ×
tendo musculi recti superioris
os frontale (processus zygomaticus)
glandula lacrimalis, pars orbitalis
tendo m. recti medialis
tendo m. recti lateralis
tendo m. obliqui inferioris
tunica conjunctiva bulbi ×
cornea (iris)
m. obliquus inferior
margo infra-orbitalis
foramen infra-orbitale
os zygomaticum
m. obliquus inferior

**Fig. 397.**

m. rectus superior
tendo m. obliqui superioris
pupilla
m. rectus lateralis
m. rectus medialis
tunica conjunctiva bulbi ×
m. obliquus inferior
cornea
m. rectus inferior

**Fig. 398.**

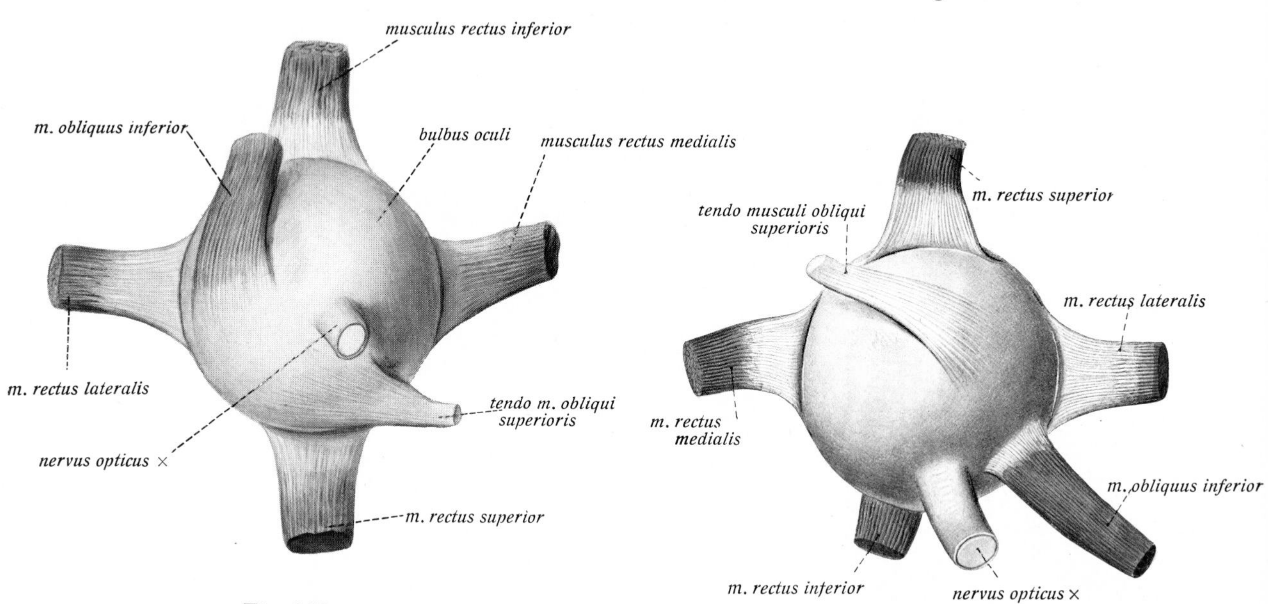
musculus rectus inferior
m. obliquus inferior
bulbus oculi
musculus rectus medialis
m. rectus lateralis
tendo m. obliqui superioris
nervus opticus ×
m. rectus superior
m. rectus superior
tendo musculi obliqui superioris
m. rectus lateralis
m. rectus medialis
m. obliquus inferior
m. rectus inferior
nervus opticus ×

**Fig. 399.**

**Fig. 400.**

## 397. Muscles of Left Eye. (ventrolateral view) (4/3)

Skin, lids, and fascia removed. Eyeball with muscles, orbital part of lacrimal gland, and some orbital fat left in place.

1 **Tendon of Superior Rectus Muscle**
*tendo musculi recti superioris*
**Frontal Bone, (Zygomatic Process)**
*os frontale (processus zygomaticus)*

2 **Lacrimal Gland, Orbital Part**
*glandula lacrimalis, pars orbitalis*
**Tendon of Lateral Rectus Muscle**
*tendo m. recti lateralis*

3 **Tendon of Inferior Oblique Muscle**
*tendo m. obliqui inferioris*

5 **Zygomatic Bone**
*os zygomaticum*
**Inferior Oblique Muscle**
*m. obliquus inferior*

6 **Infraorbital Foramen**
*foramen infraorbitale*

7 **Infraorbital Margin**
*margo infraorbitalis*
**Inferior Oblique Muscle**
*m. obliquus inferior*

8 **Cornea (Iris)**
*cornea (iris)*

9 **Ocular Conjunctiva**
*tunica conjunctiva bulbi*

10 **Tendon of Medial Rectus Muscle**
*tendo m. recti medialis*

11 **Tendon of Superior Oblique Muscle**
*tendo m. obliqui superioris*

12 **Levator Palpebrae Superioris Muscle**
*m. levator palpebrae superioris*

## 398. Right Bulbus Oculi and Insertions of Eye Muscles. (front view) (4/3)

1 **Superior Rectus Muscle**
*m. rectus superior*

2 **Pupil**
*pupilla*

3 **Medial Rectus Muscle**
*m. rectus medialis*

4 **Inferior Oblique Muscle**
*m. obliquus inferior*

5 **Cornea**
*cornea*

**Inferior Rectus Muscle**
*m. rectus inferior*

8 **Ocular Conjunctiva**
*tunica conjunctiva bulbi*

9 **Lateral Rectus Muscle**
*m. rectus lateralis*

11 **Tendon of Superior Oblique Muscle**
*tendo m. obliqui superioris*

## 399. Right Bulbus Oculi and Insertions of Eye Muscles. (from behind and below) (4/3)

1 **Inferior Rectus Muscle**
*musculus rectus inferior*
**Bulbus Oculi**
*bulbus oculi*

2 **Medial Rectus Muscle**
*musculus rectus medialis*

4 **Tendon of Superior Oblique Muscle**
*tendo m. obliqui superioris*

5 **Superior Rectus Muscle**
*m. rectus superior*

8 **Optic Nerve**
*nervus opticus*
**Lateral Rectus Muscle**
*m. rectus lateralis*

10 **Inferior Oblique Muscle**
*m. obliquus inferior*

## 400. Right Bulbus Oculi and Insertions of Eye Muscles. (from behind and above) (4/3)

2 **Lateral Rectus Muscle**
*m. rectus lateralis*

4 **Inferior Oblique Muscle**
*m. obliquus inferior*

6 **Optic Nerve**
*nervus opticus*

7 **Inferior Rectus Muscle**
*m. rectus inferior*

9 **Medial Rectus Muscle**
*m. rectus medialis*

10 **Tendon of Superior Oblique Muscle**
*tendo musculi obliqui superioris*

12 **Superior Rectus Muscle**
*m. rectus superior*

## 401. The Muscles of the Orbital Cavity. (seen from above) (1/1)

On the **left** side: Only the roof of the orbital cavity and the periorbita were removed. The nerves were also resected.

On the **right** side: The deeper muscles were displayed by reflecting the levator palpebrae superioris muscle-1 and by removing the fat and other structures in the orbit.

1 **Trochlea (The Superior Oblique Muscle)**
*trochlea m. obliqui superioris*
**Superior Oblique Muscle, Tendon**
*tendo m. obliqui superioris*
**Bulbus Oculi**
*bulbus oculi*

2 **Levator Palpebrae Superioris Muscle**
*m. levator palpebrae superioris*
**Medial Rectus Muscle**
*m. rectus medialis*

4 **Sphenoid Bone, Greater Wing**
*ala major ossis sphenoidalis*
**Lateral Rectus Muscle**
*m. rectus-lateralis*

5 **Superior Rectus Muscle**
*m. rectus superior*
**Levator Palpebrae Superioris Muscle**
*m. levator palpebrae superioris*

6 **Superior Oblique Muscle**
*m. obliquus superior*
**Optic Nerve**
*nervus opticus*
**Optic Chiasma**
*chiasma opticum*

8 **Anterior Cranial Fossa, Dura Mater**
*dura mater fossae cranii anterioris*
**Common Tendinous Ring**
*anulus tendineus communis*
**Superior Rectus Muscle**
*m. rectus superior*
**Lateral Rectus Muscle**
*m. rectus lateralis*

10 **Lacrimal Gland, Orbital Part**
*glandula lacrimalis, pars orbitalis*
**Levator Palpebrae Superioris Muscle, Tendon**
*tendo m. levatoris palpebrae superioris*
**Levator Palpebrae Superioris Muscle**
*m. levator palpebrae superioris*
**Tendon of Superior Oblique Muscle**
*tendo musculi obliqui superioris*

12 **Adipose Body of Orbit**
*corpus adiposum orbitae*
**Superior Oblique Muscle**
*m. obliquus superior*
**Crista Galli**
*crista galli*

## 402. Horizontal Section Through Both Orbits. (2/3)

1 **Medial Rectus Muscle**
*m. rectus medialis*
**Optic Nerve**
*nervus opticus*

2 **Lateral Rectus Muscle**
*m. rectus lateralis*
**Cerebral Hemisphere**
*hemispherium telencephali*
**External Sheath of Optic Nerve**
*vagina externa nervi optici*
**Fat Body of Orbit**
*corpus adiposum orbitae*
**Temporal Muscle**
*musc. temporalis*

3 **Vagina Bulbi**
*vagina bulbi*
**Muscular Fascia**
*fascia muscularis*
**Greater Wing of Sphenoid Bone**
*ala major ossis sphenoidalis*
**Tendon of Lateral Rectus Muscle**
*tendo m. recti lateralis*

4 **Optic Part of Retina**
*pars optica retinae*
**Ciliary Part of Retina**
*pars ciliaris retinae*
**Ciliary Processes**
*processus ciliares*
**Lens**
*lens*

5 **Cornea**
*cornea*
**Intervaginal Space**
*spatium intervaginale*
**Eyelid**
*palpebra*
**Tendon of Medial Rectus Muscle**
*tendo m. tecti medialis*

6 **Nasal Septum**
*septum nasi*

7 **Nasal Cavity**
*cavum nasi*
**Ethmoidal Cells**
*cellulae ethmoidales*
**Ora Serrata**
*ora serrata*

8 **Retina**
*retina*
**Sclera**
*sclera*
**Lateral Rectus Muscle**
*m. rectus lateralis*

10 **Optic Canal**
*canalis opticus*

11 **Internal Carotid Artery**
*arteria carotis interna*

12 **Sphenoidal Sinus**
*sinus sphenoidalis*

**Note:** 1. The orbital cavities are separated from the slit-like narrow nasal cavities-7 by the ethmoidal sinuses-7 or air cells.

### Etymology:

*crista* = L. a crest. Crista galli = cock's comb.
*trochlea* = L. pulley (superior oblique muscle once called the trochlear muscle, the nerve retained the name.)

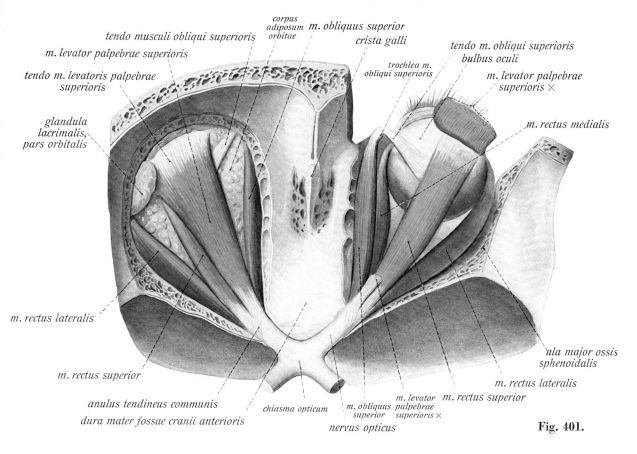

corpus adiposum orbitae
m. obliquus superior
tendo musculi obliqui superioris
crista galli
m. levator palpebrae superioris
tendo m. obliqui superioris
bulbus oculi
trochlea m. obliqui superioris
tendo m. levatoris palpebrae superioris
m. levator palpebrae superioris ×
glandula lacrimalis, pars orbitalis
m. rectus medialis
m. rectus lateralis
ala major ossis sphenoidalis
m. rectus superior
m. rectus lateralis
m. levator palpebrae superioris ×
m. rectus superior
anulus tendineus communis
chiasma opticum
m. obliquus superior
dura mater fossae cranii anterioris
nervus opticus

**Fig. 401.**

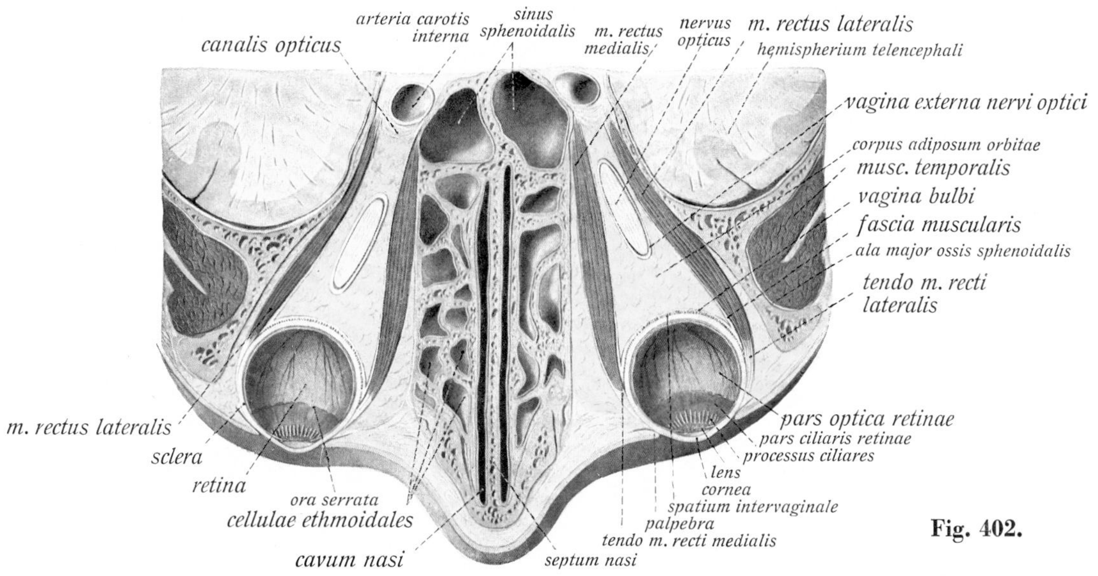

arteria carotis interna
sinus sphenoidalis
m. rectus medialis
nervus opticus
m. rectus lateralis
canalis opticus
hemispherium telencephali
vagina externa nervi optici
corpus adiposum orbitae
musc. temporalis
vagina bulbi
fascia muscularis
ala major ossis sphenoidalis
tendo m. recti lateralis
pars optica retinae
m. rectus lateralis
pars ciliaris retinae
processus ciliares
sclera
lens
cornea
retina
ora serrata
spatium intervaginale
cellulae ethmoidales
palpebra
tendo m. recti medialis
cavum nasi
septum nasi


**Fig. 402.**

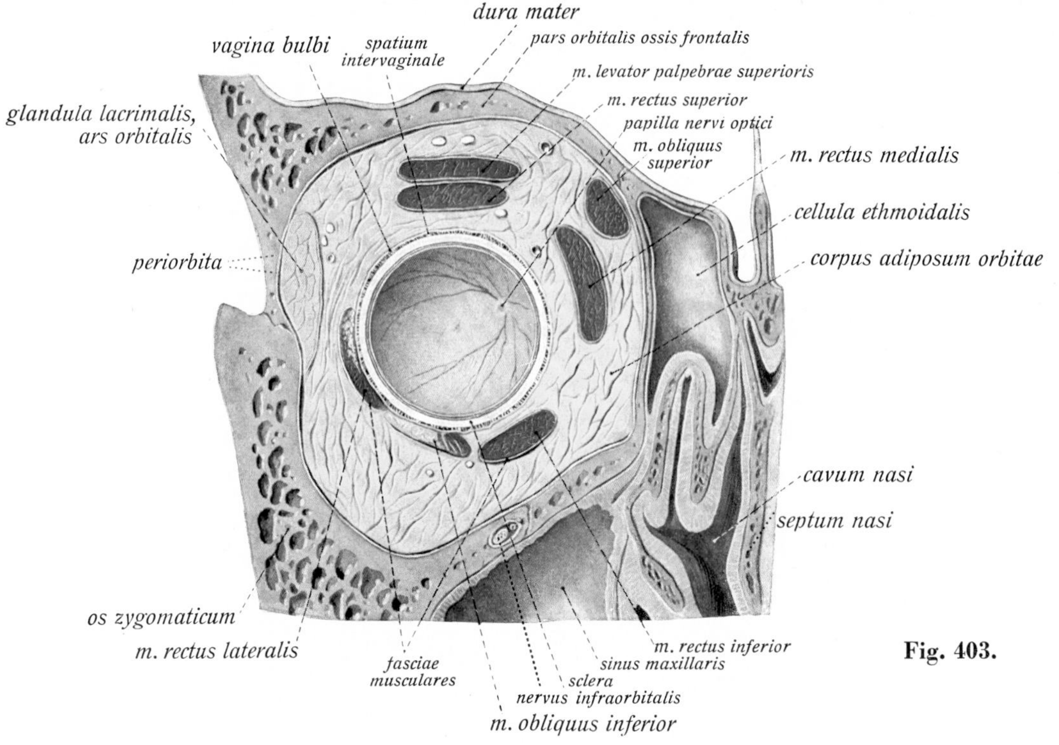
dura mater
vagina bulbi
spatium intervaginale
pars orbitalis ossis frontalis
m. levator palpebrae superioris
glandula lacrimalis, ars orbitalis
m. rectus superior
papilla nervi optici
m. obliquus superior
m. rectus medialis
cellula ethmoidalis
periorbita
corpus adiposum orbitae
cavum nasi
septum nasi
os zygomaticum
m. rectus lateralis
m. rectus inferior
fasciae musculares
sinus maxillaris
sclera
nervus infraorbitalis
m. obliquus inferior

Fig. 403.

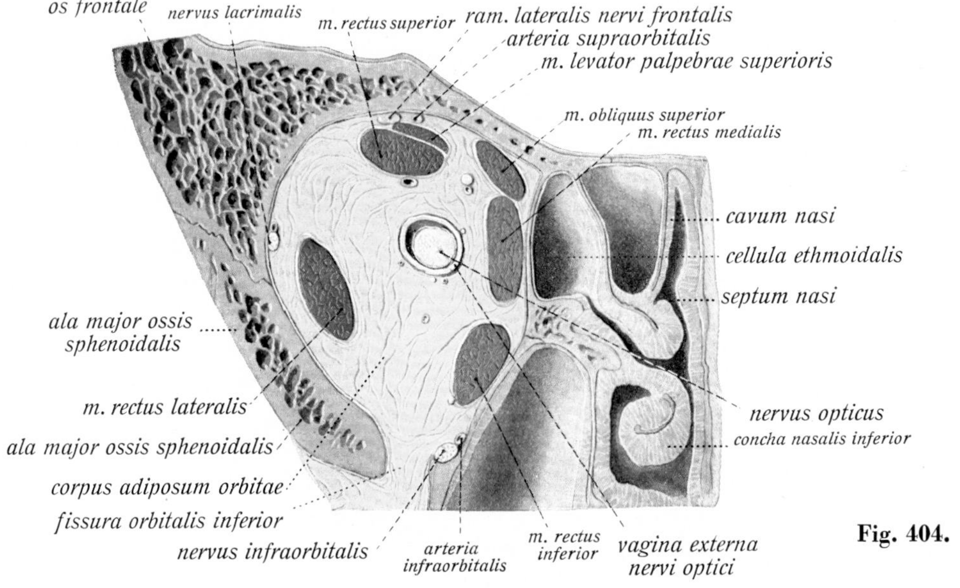
os frontale
nervus lacrimalis
m. rectus superior
ram. lateralis nervi frontalis
arteria supraorbitalis
m. levator palpebrae superioris
m. obliquus superior
m. rectus medialis
cavum nasi
cellula ethmoidalis
septum nasi
ala major ossis sphenoidalis
m. rectus lateralis
nervus opticus
concha nasalis inferior
ala major ossis sphenoidalis
corpus adiposum orbitae
fissura orbitalis inferior
nervus infraorbitalis
arteria infraorbitalis
m. rectus inferior
vagina externa nervi optici

Fig. 404.

## 403. Frontal Section of Right Orbit Through the Dorsal Third of the Bulbus Oculi. (from in front) (about 4/3)

1 **Levator Palpebrae Superioris M.**
*m. levator palpebrae superioris*
**Superior Rectus Muscle**
*m. rectus superior*
**Optic Disc**
*papilla nervi optici [discus n. optici]*
**Superior Oblique Muscle**
*m. obliquus superior*

2 **Medial Rectus Muscle**
*m. rectus medialis*
**Ethmoidal Cells**
*cellula ethmoidalis*
**Orbital Fat Body**
*corpus adiposum orbitae*

4 **Nasal Cavity**
*cavum nasi*
**Nasal Septum**
*septum nasi*

5 **Inferior Rectus Muscle**
*m. rectus inferior*
**Maxillary Sinus**
*sinus maxillaris*
**Sclera**
*sclera*

6 **Infraorbital Nerve**
*nervus infraorbitalis*
**Inferior Oblique Muscle**
*m. obliquus inferior*
**Muscular Fasciae**
*fasciae musculares*

7 **Lateral Rectus Muscle**
*m. rectus lateralis*

8 **Zygomatic Bone**
*os zygomaticum*

9 **Periorbita**
*periorbita*

10 **Orbital Part of Lacrimal Gland**
*glandula lacrimalis, pars orbitalis*

11 **Vagina Bulbi**
*vagina bulbi*
**Intervaginal Space**
*spatium intervaginale*

12 **Dura Mater**
*dura mater*
**Orbital Part of Frontal Bone**
*pars orbitalis ossis frontalis*

**Note:** 1. The eyeball is cushioned with fat in the orbital cavity. Fat completely fills all the spaces not occupied by accessory ocular structures.

2. The **infraorbital nerve**-6, branch of maxillary division of trigeminal.

## 404. Frontal Section of the Right Orbital Cavity, Dorsal to the Bulbus Oculi. (from in front) (about 4/3)

1 **Supraorbital Artery**
*arteria supraorbitalis*
**Levator Palpebrae Superioris Muscle**
*m. levator palpebrae superioris*
**Superior Oblique Muscle**
*m. obliquus superior*

2 **Medial Rectus Muscle**
*m. rectus medialis*

3 **Nasal Cavity**
*cavum nasi*
**Ethmoidal Cell**
*cellula ethmoidalis*
**Nasal Septum**
*septum nasi*

4 **Optic Nerve**
*nervus opticus*
**Inferior Nasal Concha**
*concha nasalis inferior*

5 **External Sheath, Optic Nerve**
*vagina externa nervi optici*
**Inferior Rectus Muscle**
*m. rectus inferior*

6 **Infraorbital Artery**
*arteria infraorbitalis*

7 **Infraorbital Nerve**
*nervus infraorbitalis*

8 **Inferior Orbital Fissure**
*fissura orbitalis inferior*
**Orbital Adipose Body**
*corpus adiposum orbitae*
**Sphenoid Bone, Greater Wing**
*ala major ossis sphenoidalis*
**Lateral Rectus Muscle**
*m. rectus lateralis*

9 **Sphenoid Bone, Greater Wing**
*ala major ossis sphenoidalis*

10 **Frontal Bone**
*os frontale*

11 **Lacrimal Nerve**
*nervus lacrimalis*
**Superior Rectus Muscle**
*m. rectus superior*

12 **Frontal Nerve, Lateral Branch**
*ram. lateralis nervi frontalis*

**Note:** 1. The position of the four recti muscles and the superior oblique-1 and levator palpebrae superioris-1.

2. The positions of the main nerves, passing through the orbital cavity: The **lacrimal nerve**-11, the **frontal nerve**-12, and the **infraorbital nerve**-7. The infraorbital nerve is near the infraorbital fissure, just before it enters the infraorbital canal. The infraorbital artery-6 accompanies it.

3. Relation of the orbital cavity to the ethmoidal air cells-3, the nasal cavity-3, and inferior concha.

## 405. Origins of Muscles from Apex of Left Orbital Cavity near Opening of Optic Canal. (4/3)

A frontal section through orbit viewed from in front. Most orbital structures were removed. Stumps of muscles were left attached. Optic nerve-9 was cut off close to optic canal. Stump of inferior branch of oculomotor nerve was retained.

1 **Orbital M., Sup. Orbital Fissure**
*musculus orbitalis*
*(fissurae orbitalis superioris)*
**Frontal Bone**
*os frontale*

2 **Superior Orbital Fissure**
*fissura orbitalis superior*

3 **Lacertus Lateral Rectus Muscle**
*lacertus m. recti lateralis*
**Sphenoid Bone, Greater Wing**
*ala major ossis sphenoidalis*

4 **Lateral Rectus Muscle**
*m. rectus lateralis*

5 **Oculomotor Nerve, Inf. Br.**
*nervus oculomotorius (ramus inferior)*

6 **Infraorbital Nerve**
*nervus infraorbitalis*

8 **Inferior Rectus Muscle**
*m. rectus inferior*
**Periorbita**
*periorbita*
**External Sheath of Optic Nerve and Common Tendinous Ring**
*vagina externa nervi optici + anulus tendineus communis*

9 **Medial Rectus Muscle**
*m. rectus medialis*
**Ethmoidal Cell**
*cellula ethmoidalis*
**Optic Nerve**
*nervus opticus*

10 **Superior Oblique Muscle**
*m. obliquus superior*

11 **Superior Rectus Muscle**
*m. rectus superior*

12 **Levator Palpebrae Sup. M.**
*m. levator palpebrae superioris*

**Note:** 1. All **ocular muscles** except the inferior oblique muscle originate from apex of orbital cavity. Their very short tendons attach to the **common tendinous ring**-8 **of the orbital muscles**. (Fig. 395–2). This surrounds the optic nerve where it enters the orbital cavity through the optic canal.

2. Orbital muscle-1 (smooth) stretches across superior orbital fissure.

## 406. Sagittal Section of the Orbital Cavity and Eyeball. (4/3)

(after Virchow)

1 **Levator Palpebrae Sup. M.**
*m. levator palpebrae superioris*
**Bulbar Fascia**
*vagina bulbi*
**Muscular Fascia**
*fascia muscularis*

2 **Superior Rectus Muscle**
*m. rectus superior*
**External Sheath of Optic Nerve**
*vagina externa nervi optici*
**Optic Nerve**
*nervus opticus*

4 **Inferior Rectus Muscle**
*m. rectus inferior*

5 **Orbital Fat Body**
*corpus adiposum orbitae*
**Intervaginal Space**
*spatium intervaginale*

6 **Fascia of Inf. Oblique M.**
*fascia m. obliqui inferioris*
**Fascial Muscle Sleeve from Vagina Bulbi**
*conjunctio vaginae bulbi et musculi*

7 **Inferior Oblique Muscle**
*m. obliquus inferior*

8 **Tendon of Inf. Rectus M.**
*tendo m. recti inferioris*
**Inferior Fornix of Conjunctiva**
*fornix conjunctivae inferior*
**Inferior Tarsus**
*tarsus inferior*

9 **Superior Tarsus**
*tarsus superior*

10 **Tendon (1) of Levator Palpebrae Superioris Muscle**
*tendo m. levatoris palpebrae superioris (1)*
**Superior Fornix of Conjunctiva**
*fornix conjunctivae superior*
**Tendon (2) of Levator Palpebrae Superioris Muscle**
*tendo m. levatoris palpebrae superioris (2)*

11 **Orbital Septum**
*septum orbitale*

12 **Bulbar Fascia**
*vagina bulbi*

**Note:** 1. **Orbital septum**-11, a connective tissue sheet resembling a fascia, is fastened along circumference of the margin of the orbital cavity. It covers the dorsal surface of the eyelids, and fuses with dorsal fascia of orbicularis oculi muscle.

2. **Bulbar fascia**-1 is a membrane which loosely surrounds the dorsal 75 percent of the bulbus oculi and separates it from fat-5, muscles, and other tissues. It forms a hammock-like suspensory structure that facilitates movements of eyeball in any direction. The fascia bulbi is actually separated from the sclera by intervaginal space-5 which contains loose connective tissue that make the movements possible. Muscles pierce fascia bulbi, but a sleeve of the fascial sheath extends along them. These sleeve-like openings form the so-called check ligaments. (See Fig. 407.)

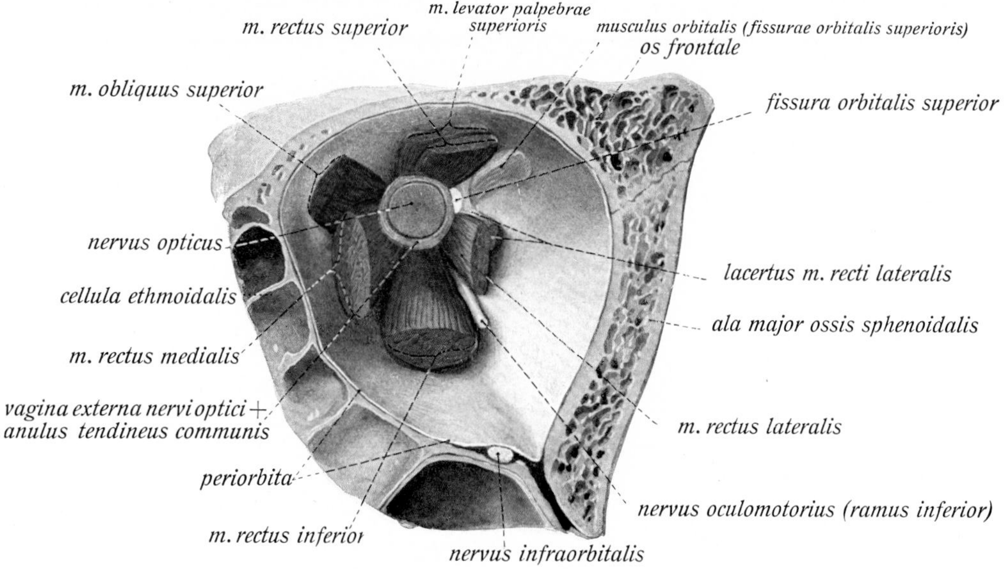
m. rectus superior
m. levator palpebrae superioris
musculus orbitalis (fissurae orbitalis superioris)
os frontale
m. obliquus superior
fissura orbitalis superior
nervus opticus
cellula ethmoidalis
lacertus m. recti lateralis
ala major ossis sphenoidalis
m. rectus medialis
vagina externa nervi optici +
anulus tendineus communis
m. rectus lateralis
periorbita
nervus oculomotorius (ramus inferior)
m. rectus inferior
nervus infraorbitalis

**Fig. 405.**

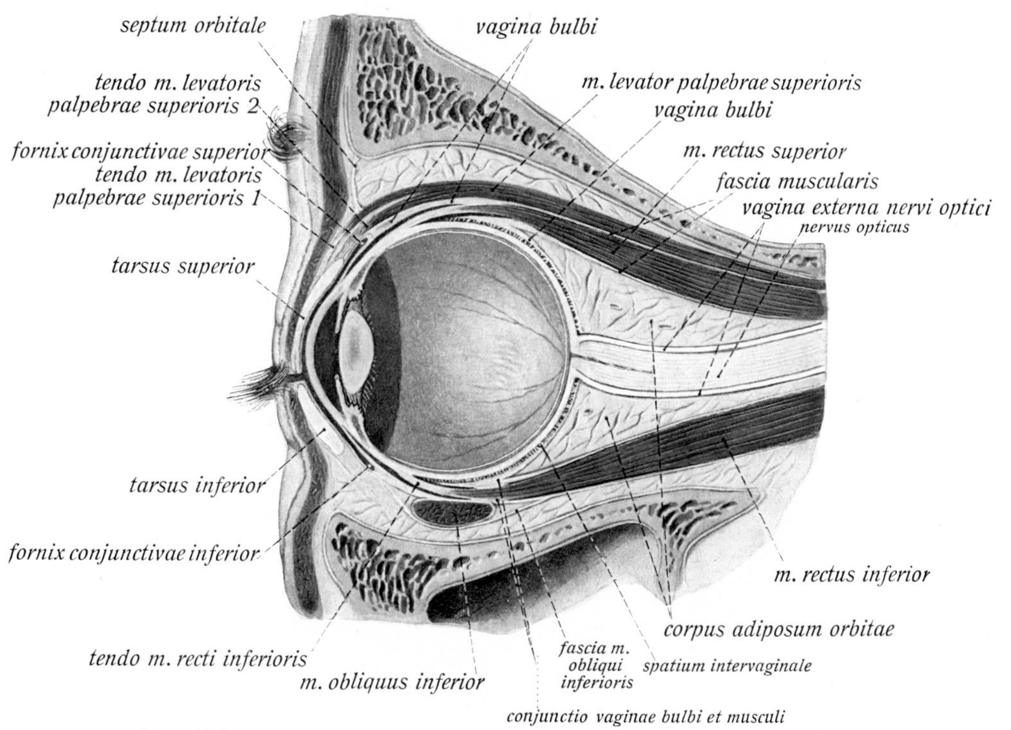
septum orbitale
vagina bulbi
tendo m. levatoris
palpebrae superioris 2
m. levator palpebrae superioris
vagina bulbi
fornix conjunctivae superior
tendo m. levatoris
palpebrae superioris 1
m. rectus superior
fascia muscularis
vagina externa nervi optici
nervus opticus
tarsus superior
tarsus inferior
fornix conjunctivae inferior
m. rectus inferior
corpus adiposum orbitae
tendo m. recti inferioris
fascia m.
obliqui
inferioris
spatium intervaginale
m. obliquus inferior
conjunctio vaginae bulbi et musculi

**Fig. 406.**

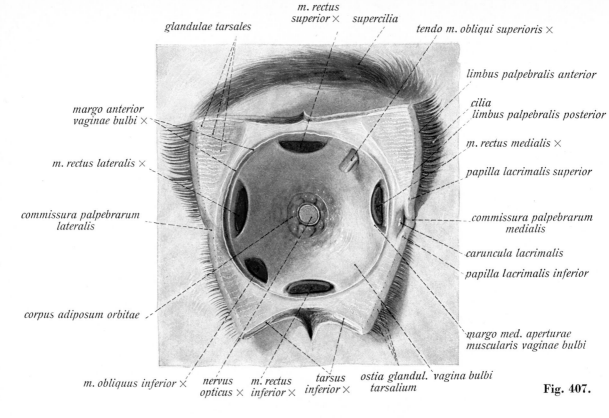

m. rectus superior ×
supercilia
glandulae tarsales
tendo m. obliqui superioris ×
limbus palpebralis anterior
cilia
limbus palpebralis posterior
margo anterior vaginae bulbi ×
m. rectus medialis ×
m. rectus lateralis ×
papilla lacrimalis superior
commissura palpebrarum lateralis
commissura palpebrarum medialis
caruncula lacrimalis
papilla lacrimalis inferior
corpus adiposum orbitae
margo med. aperturae muscularis vaginae bulbi
m. obliquus inferior ×
nervus opticus ×
m. rectus inferior ×
tarsus inferior ×
ostia glandul. tarsalium
vagina bulbi

**Fig. 407.**

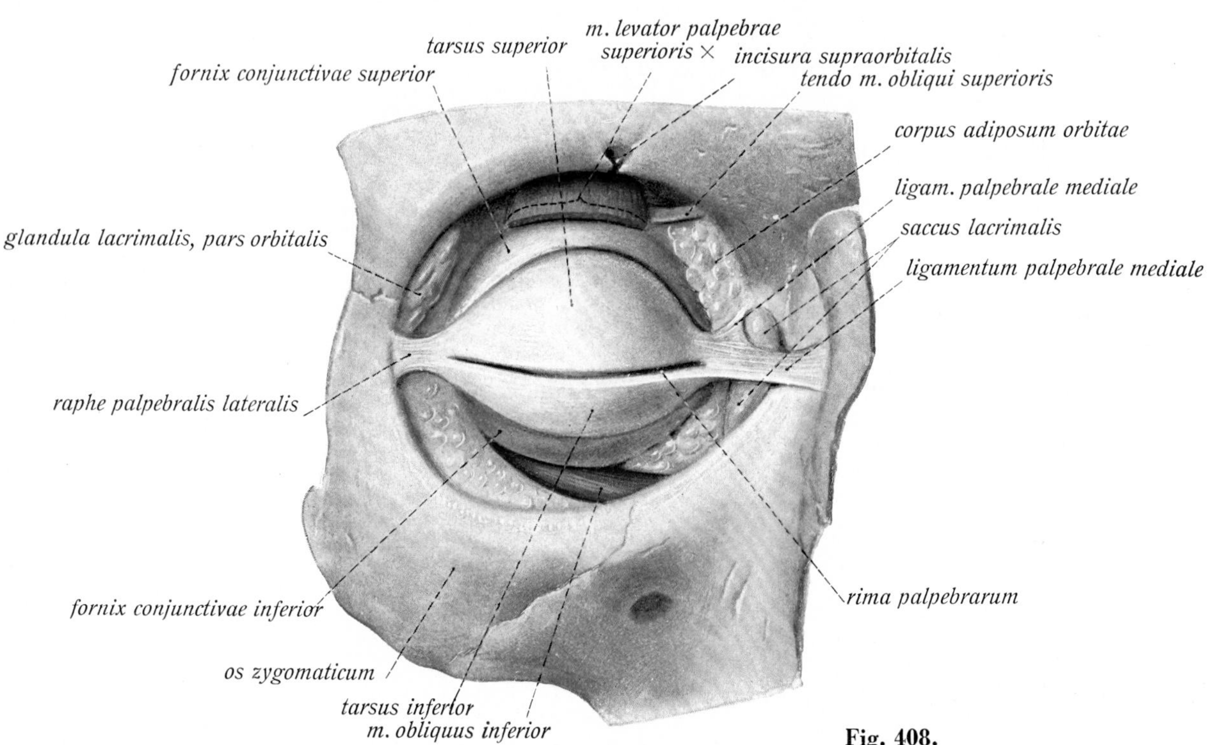
m. levator palpebrae superioris ×
tarsus superior
incisura supraorbitalis
fornix conjunctivae superior
tendo m. obliqui superioris
corpus adiposum orbitae
ligam. palpebrale mediale
glandula lacrimalis, pars orbitalis
saccus lacrimalis
ligamentum palpebrale mediale
raphe palpebralis lateralis
fornix conjunctivae inferior
rima palpebrarum
os zygomaticum
tarsus inferior
m. obliquus inferior

**Fig. 408.**

## 407. Bulbar Fascia. (Tenon's capsule, vagina bulbi of right eye) (from in front; slightly enlarged.)

Eyeball has been removed and both eyelids divided and reflected to fully expose bulbar fascia.

1 **Eyebrow**
*supercilia*
**Tendon of Sup. Oblique M.**
*tendo m. obliqui superioris*

2 **Border of Eyelid**
*limbus palpebralis anterior*
**Eyelashes**
*cilia*
**Posterior Palpebral Border**
*limbus palpebralis posterior*
**Medial Rectus Muscle**
*m. rectus medialis*

3 **Superior Lacrimal Papilla**
*papilla lacrimalis superior*
**Middle Palpebral Commissure**
*commissura palpebrarum medialis*

**Lacrimal Caruncle**
*caruncula lacrimalis*

4 **Inferior Lacrimal Papilla**
*papilla lacrimalis inferior*
**Inner Lip of Fascial Sleeve for Muscle**
*margo med. aperturae muscularis vaginae bulbi*

5 **Vagina Bulbi**
*vagina bulbi*
**Openings of Tarsal Glands**
*ostia glandul. tarsalium*

6 **Inferior Tarsus**
*tarsus inferior*

7 **Inferior Rectus Muscle**
*m. rectus inferior*

**Optic Nerve**
*nervus opticus*

8 **Inferior Oblique Muscle**
*m. obliquus inferior*
**Adipose Body of Orbit**
*corpus adiposum orbitae*

9 **Lateral Palpebral Commissure**
*commissura palpebrarum lateralis*
**Lateral Rectus Muscle**
*m. rectus lateralis*

10 **Anterior Margin of Bulbar Fascia**
*margo anterior vaginae bulbi*

11 **Tarsal Glands**
*glandulae tarsales*

12 **Superior Rectus Muscle**
*m. rectus superior*

**Note:** 1. **Bulbar fascia** forms a hammock-like structure in which the eyeball is able to move.

2. Muscles pierce this bulbar fascia through sleeve-like extensions of the fascia.

## 408. The Tarsofascial Layer of Eyelids and Palpebral Ligaments. (1/1)

Skin and musculature of eyelids have been removed and insertion of levator palpebrae superioris-12 cut off. (see Fig. 406).

1 **Supraorbital Notch**
*incisura supraorbitalis*
**Superior Oblique Muscle Tendon**
*tendo m. obliqui superioris*

2 **Adipose Body of Orbit**
*corpus adiposum orbitae*
**Medial Palpebral Ligament**
*ligam. palpebrae mediale*
**Lacrimal Sac**
*saccus lacrimalis*
**Medial Palpebral Ligament**
*ligamentum palpebrale mediale*

4 **Rima Palpebrarum**
*rima palpebrarum*

7 **Inferior Oblique Muscle**
*m. obliquus inferior*
**Inferior Tarsus**
*tarsus inferior*
**Zygomatic Bone**
*os zygomaticum*

8 **Inferior Conjunctical Fornix**
*fornix conjunctivae inferior*

9 **Lateral Palpebral Raphe**
*raphe palpebralis lateralis*

**Lacrimal Gland (Orbital Portion)**
*glandula lacrimalis pars orbitalis*

11 **Superior Conjunctival Fornix**
*fornix conjunctivae superior*
**Superior Tarsus**
*tarsus superior*

12 **Levator Palpebrae Superioris Muscle**
*m. levator palpebrae superioris*

**Note:** 1. **Tarsal plates** are composed of very dense connective tissue containing tarsal glands. They provide a very firm, but flexible support for the eyelids and permit eversion of the lids for removal of foreign particles. (see Fig. 388).

2. **Medial palpebral ligament**-2 is ventral to lacrimal sac-2 and attaches to frontal process of maxilla. **Lateral palpebral ligament** (raphe)-9 attaches to zygomatic bone-7 at margin of orbit. Both are attached to tarsal plates of eyelids-7, -11.

3. **Inferior oblique muscle**-7 is the only eye muscle that does not originate near apex of orbit. It takes origin from maxilla near fossa for lacrimal sac-2.

# THE EAR and VESTIBULAR APPARATUS

## 409. Diagram of the Membranous Labyrinth.

**Note:** 1. Sounds are associated with vibratory or oscillatory movements of the air, which cause the tympanum to vibrate. These movements are transmitted across the middle ear by the chain of auditory ossicles. The **stapes**-6 vibrates in the **fenestra vestibuli**-6 at the same frequency as the sounding body and the tympanic membrane. This sets the perilymph in the vestibule-7 in motion to produce vibratory surges of the perilymph in the **scala vestibuli**-4.

2. These vibratory movements of the perilymph are possible because the bony labyrinth is incomplete at the **fenestra cochlea** (round window)-6. This non-rigid part of the labyrinth vibrates in unison (but out of phase) with the stapes in the vestibular window.

3. The oscillatory movements in the scala vestibuli may be transmitted to the scala tympani:

a.) by passing up through the perilymph of the scala vestibuli-4 through the **cupula cochleae**-2 **(helicotrema)** and down the scala tympani-5 to the fenestra cochleae-6 (round window); and/or

b.) they may, depending on their frequency, set into motion the endolymph and membranes of various parts of the **cochlear duct**-4 (see Fig. 410) (membranous labyrinth or **scala media** and the **endolymph** which forms a part of the partition between the scala vestibuli and scala tympani.

4. The sensory cells that detect oscillatory movements of the perilymph and endolymph are probably the hair cells in the spiral organ (Corti) of the cochlear duct (see Fig. 410). The fibers of the cochlear nerve terminate on these hair cells.

## 409. Diagram of the Membranous Labyrinth.

Endolymphatic spaces indicated in black; bone, cross-hatched; perilymphatic spaces, white.

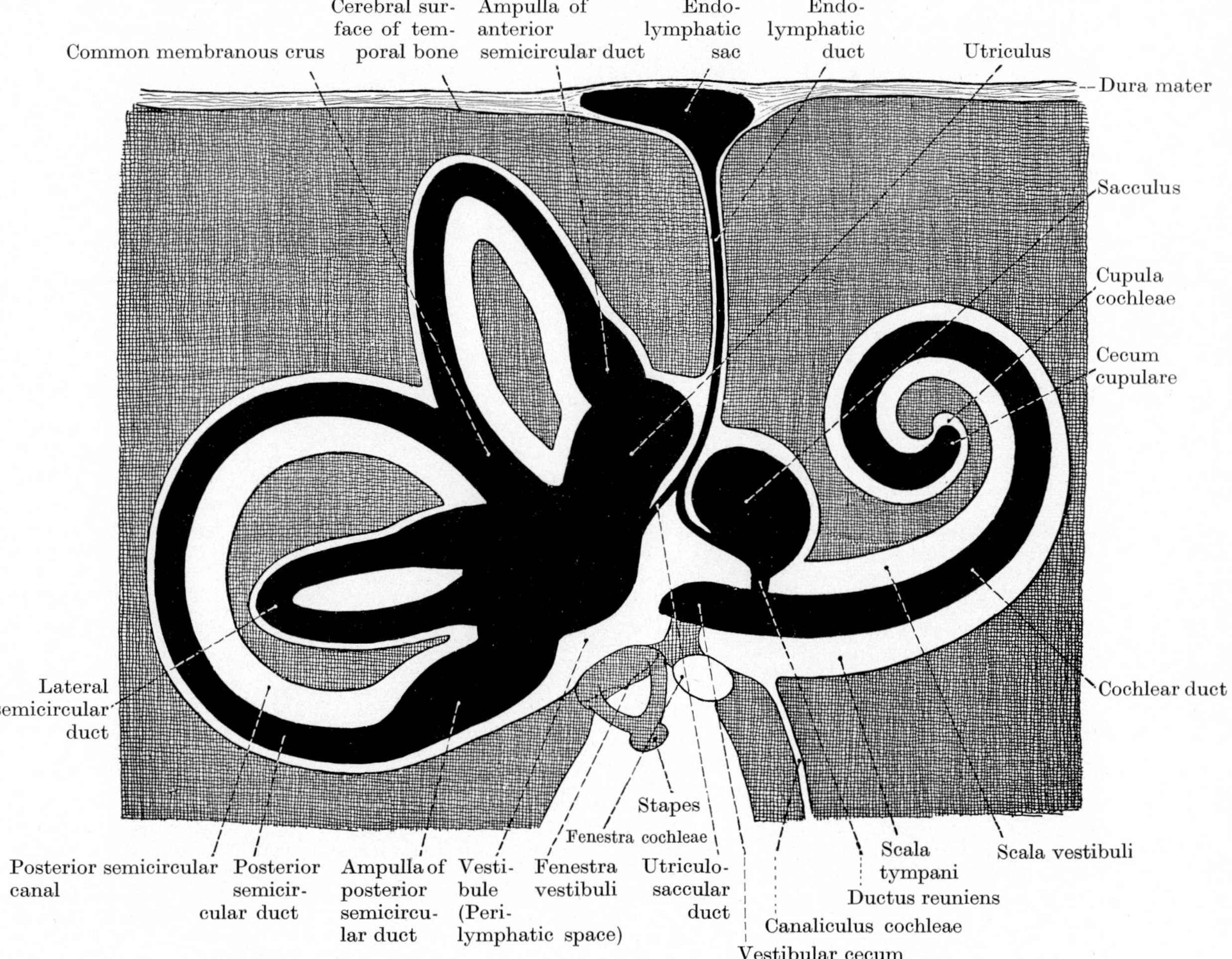

Common membranous crus
Cerebral surface of temporal bone
Ampulla of anterior semicircular duct
Endolymphatic sac
Endolymphatic duct
Utriculus
Dura mater
Sacculus
Cupula cochleae
Cecum cupulare
Cochlear duct
Lateral semicircular duct
Posterior semicircular canal
Posterior semicircular duct
Ampulla of posterior semicircular duct
Vestibule (Perilymphatic space)
Fenestra vestibuli
Fenestra cochleae
Stapes
Utriculosaccular duct
Vestibular cecum
Canaliculus cochleae
Ductus reuniens
Scala tympani
Scala vestibuli

# 410. Diagram of Cross Section of a Cochlear Coil, Endolymphatic Space – Linear Dots.

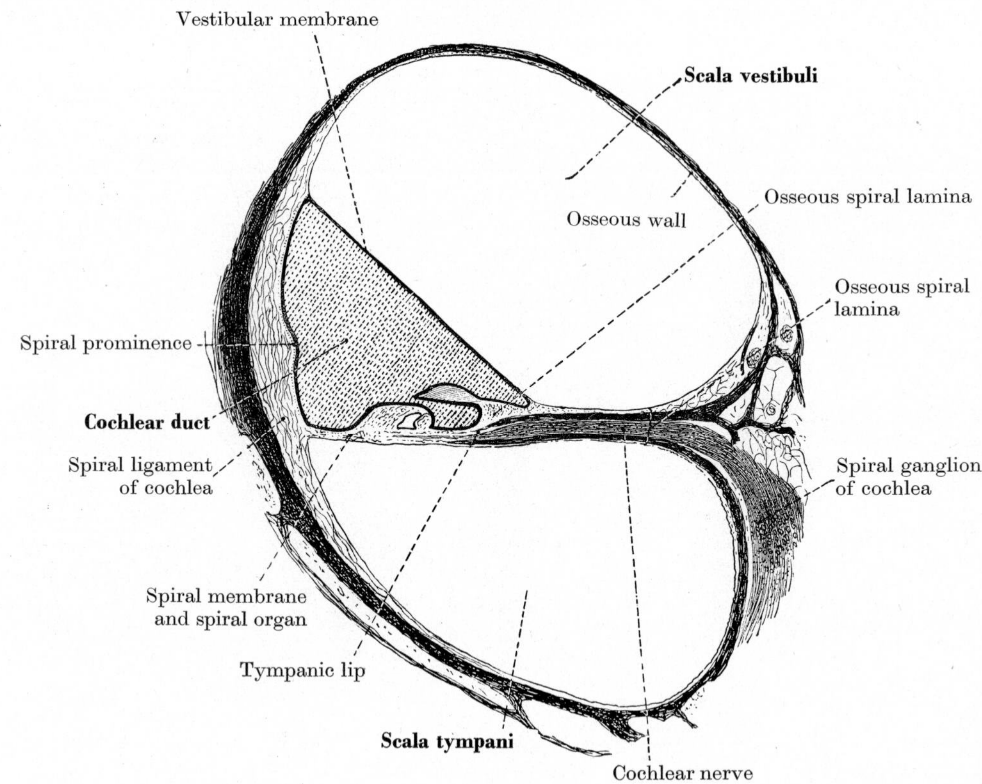
Vestibular membrane
Scala vestibuli
Osseous wall
Osseous spiral lamina
Osseous spiral lamina
Spiral prominence
Cochlear duct
Spiral ligament of cochlea
Spiral ganglion of cochlea
Spiral membrane and spiral organ
Tympanic lip
Scala tympani
Cochlear nerve

**Note:** 1. The **cochlear duct**-9 with its non-rigid and variable width **spiral membrane**-8 and spiral organ (of Corti) separate the **scala vestibuli**-1 from the **scala tympani**-6.

**Etymology:**

tympanum = Gr. *tympanon,* drum (cavity of middle ear)

vestibulum = L. *vestibule,* entrance or courtyard

cochlea = L. *cochlea,* snail or shell
= Gr. *kochlias,* snail with spiral shell

# 411. Phantom View of Osseous Labyrinths in Natural Positions.

(projected on inner cranial base with nerve supply on left)

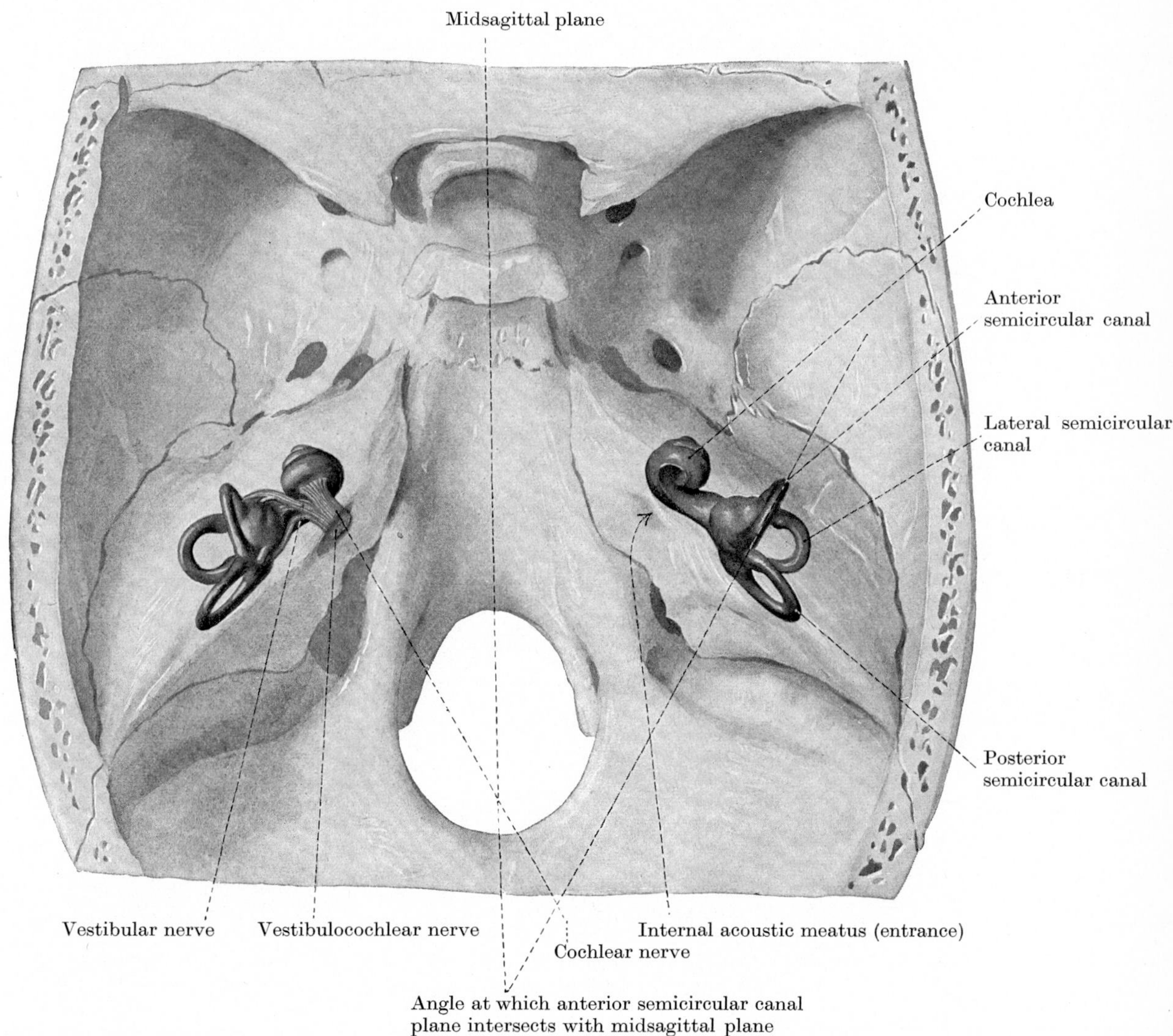
Midsagittal plane
Cochlea
Anterior
semicircular canal
Lateral semicircular
canal
Posterior
semicircular canal
Vestibular nerve
Vestibulocochlear nerve
Internal acoustic meatus (entrance)
Cochlear nerve
Angle at which anterior semicircular canal
plane intersects with midsagittal plane

**Note:** 1. **On the left**: nerves which go to vestibulocochlear apparatus were included in the diagram.

2. The oblique orientation of the cochlear axis. The cochlea points in the lateral anterior caudal direction.

## 412. Right Membranous Labyrinth and Branches of Vestibulocochlear Nerve. (Isolated and depicted as a stereodiagram) (7/1)

1 **Anterior Semicircular Duct**
*ductus semicircularia anterior*

2 **Ampulla of Lateral Semicircular Duct**
*ampulla membranacea lateralis*

3 **Posterior Semicircular Duct**
*ductus semicircularis posterior*

4 **Lateral Semicircular Duct**
*ductus semicircularis lateralis*

**Crus Membranaceum Simplex**
*crus membranaceum simplex*

5 **Crus Membranaceum Commune**
*crus membranaceum commune*

**Ampulla of Posterior Semicircular Duct**
*ampulla membranacea posterior*

6 **Endolymphatic Duct**
*ductus endolymphaticus*

**Sacculus**
*sacculus*

7 **Saccular Nerve**
*nervus saccularis*

**Cochlear Duct**
*ductus cochlearis*

**Nerve to Posterior Ampulla**
*nervus ampullaris posterior*

8 **Utriculoampullary Nerve**
*nervus utriculoampullaris*

**Vestibular Part of Vestibulocochlear Nerve**
*pars vestibularis (n. statoacustici) [n. vestibulocochlearis]*

9 **Cochlear Part of Vestibulocochlear Nerve**
*pars cochlearis (n. statoacustici) [n. vestibulocochlearis]*

**Cochlear Duct**
*ductus cochlearis*

11 **Utricular Nerve**
*(nervus utriculi)*

**Nerves to Lateral and Anterior Ampullae**
*nervi ampullares later. et ant.*

**Utriculus**
*utriculus*

12 **Ampulla of Anterior Semicircular Duct**
*ampulla membranacea anterior*

## 413. Right Membranous Labyrinth Partly Exposed, by Chiseling Away Wall of Bony Labyrinth. (somewhat diagrammatic) (7/1)

1 **Vestibular Cecum**
*cecum vestibulare*
**Ductus Reuniens**
*ductus reuniens*
**Tympanic Cavity**
*cavum tympani*

2 **Anterior and Lateral Ampullar Nerves**
*nervi ampullares anterior et lateralis*
**Ampulla of Lateral Semicircular Duct**
*ampulla membranacea lateralis*
**Lateral Semicircular Duct**
*ductus semicircularis lateralis*
**Lateral Semicircular Canal**
*canalis semicircularis lateralis*

4 **Utricular Nerve**
*(nervus utriculi)*

5 **Anterior Semicircular Canal**
*canalis semicircularis anterior*

7 **Anterior Semicircular Duct**
*ductus semicircularis anterior*
**Ampulla of Anterior Semicircular Duct**
*ampulla membranacea anterior*
**Utriculus**
*utriculus*
**Sacculus**
*sacculus*

8 **Posterior Ampullar Nerve**
*nervus ampullaris posterior*
**Saccular Nerve**
*nervus saccularis*
**Vestibulocochlear Nerve, Cochlear and Vestibular Parts**
*n. statoacustici, [n. vestibulocochlearis] pars cochlearis, pars vestibularis*

9 **Cochlear Duct**
*ductus cochlearis*
**Scala Tympani**
*scala tympani*

10 **Cochlear Duct**
*ductus cochlearis*
**Scala Vestibuli**
*scala vestibuli*

11 **Cupula Cochlae**
*cupula cochleae*

12 ***Basal Coil of Cochlea (beginning portion)**
*

**Osseous Spiral Lamina**
*lamina spiralis ossea*

**Note: Membranous labyrinth**, blue*-12. **Basal coil of cochlea**-*12, containing vestibular cecum-1, connects with sacculus-7 through the ductus reuniens-1.

### Etymology:

cupula = L. *cupa*, a cask. The diminutive suffix *-ula*, therefore, any cup-shaped structure, such as apex of cochlea.

utriculus = L. diminutive of *uter*, tube – the elongated, tube-shaped part of the labyrinth of the ear.

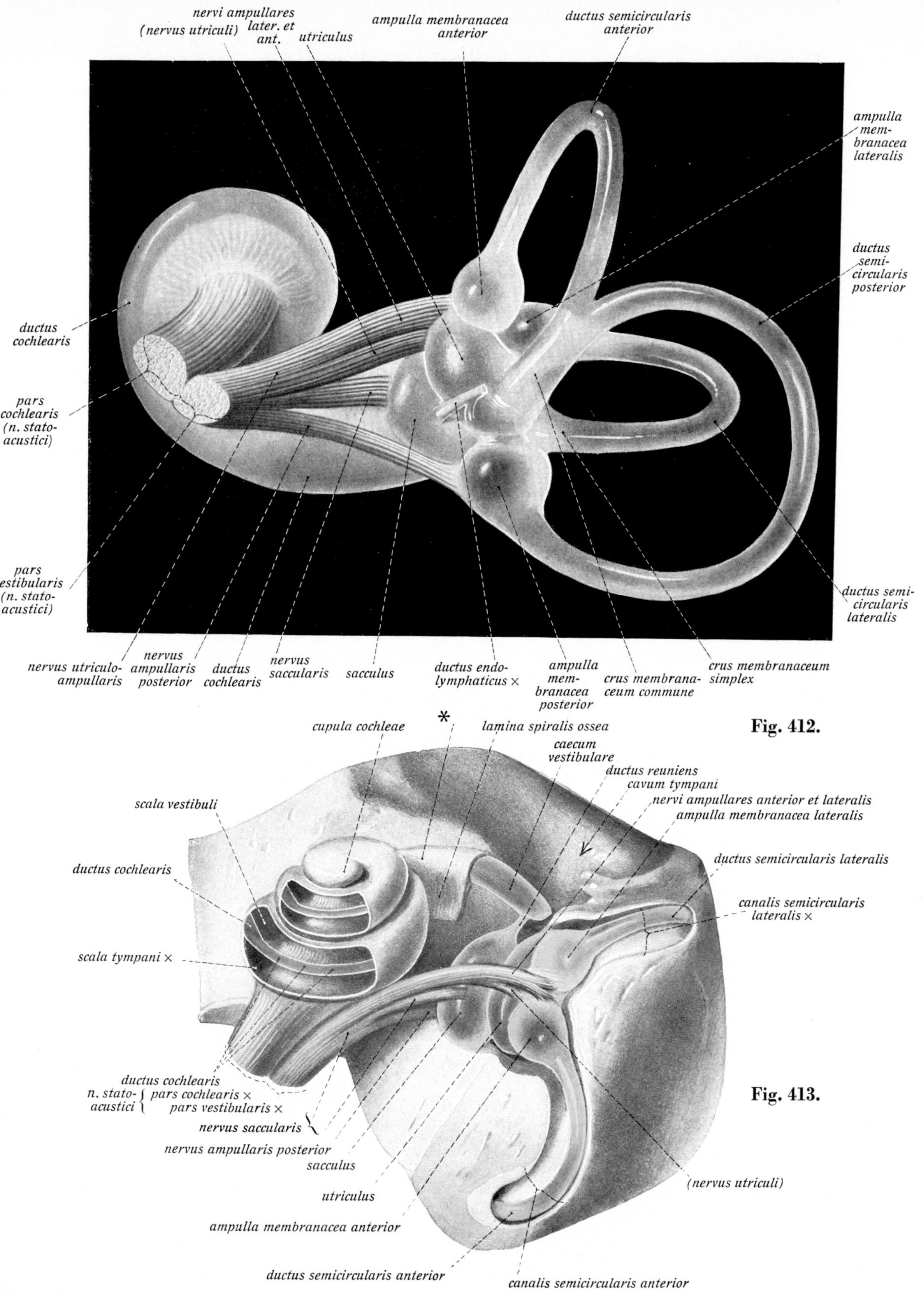
nervi ampullares
(nervus utriculi)
later. et
ant.
utriculus
ampulla membranacea
anterior
ductus semicircularis
anterior
ampulla
mem-
branacea
lateralis
ductus
semi-
circularis
posterior
ductus
cochlearis
pars
cochlearis
(n. stato-
acustici)
pars
vestibularis
(n. stato-
acustici)
ductus semi-
circularis
lateralis
nervus utriculo-
ampullaris
nervus
ampullaris
posterior
ductus
cochlearis
nervus
saccularis
sacculus
ductus endo-
lymphaticus ×
ampulla
mem-
branacea
posterior
crus membrana-
ceum commune
crus membranaceum
simplex

**Fig. 412.**

cupula cochleae
*
lamina spiralis ossea
caecum
vestibulare
ductus reuniens
cavum tympani
nervi ampullares anterior et lateralis
ampulla membranacea lateralis
scala vestibuli
ductus cochlearis
ductus semicircularis lateralis
canalis semicircularis
lateralis ×
scala tympani ×
ductus cochlearis
n. stato- { pars cochlearis ×
acustici { pars vestibularis ×
nervus saccularis
nervus ampullaris posterior
sacculus
utriculus
(nervus utriculi)
ampulla membranacea anterior
ductus semicircularis anterior
canalis semicircularis anterior

**Fig. 413.**

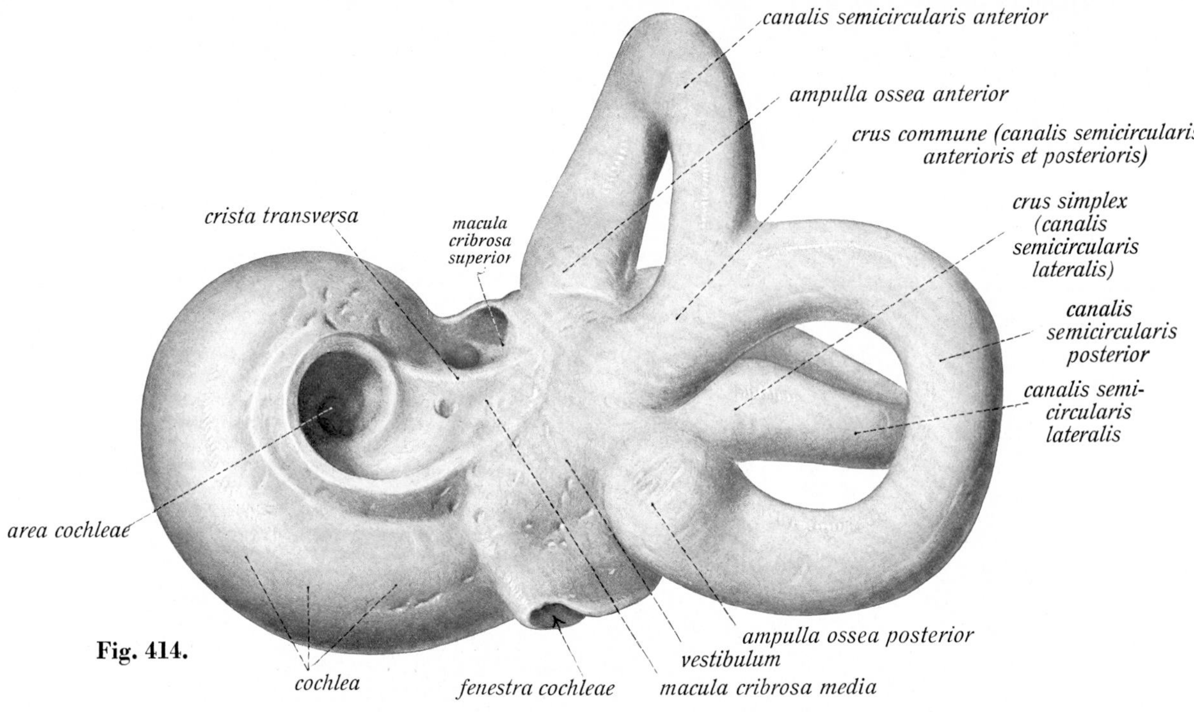
canalis semicircularis anterior
ampulla ossea anterior
crus commune (canalis semicircularis anterioris et posterioris)
crus simplex (canalis semicircularis lateralis)
canalis semicircularis posterior
canalis semi-circularis lateralis
crista transversa
macula cribrosa superior
area cochleae
cochlea
fenestra cochleae
macula cribrosa media
vestibulum
ampulla ossea posterior

**Fig. 414.**

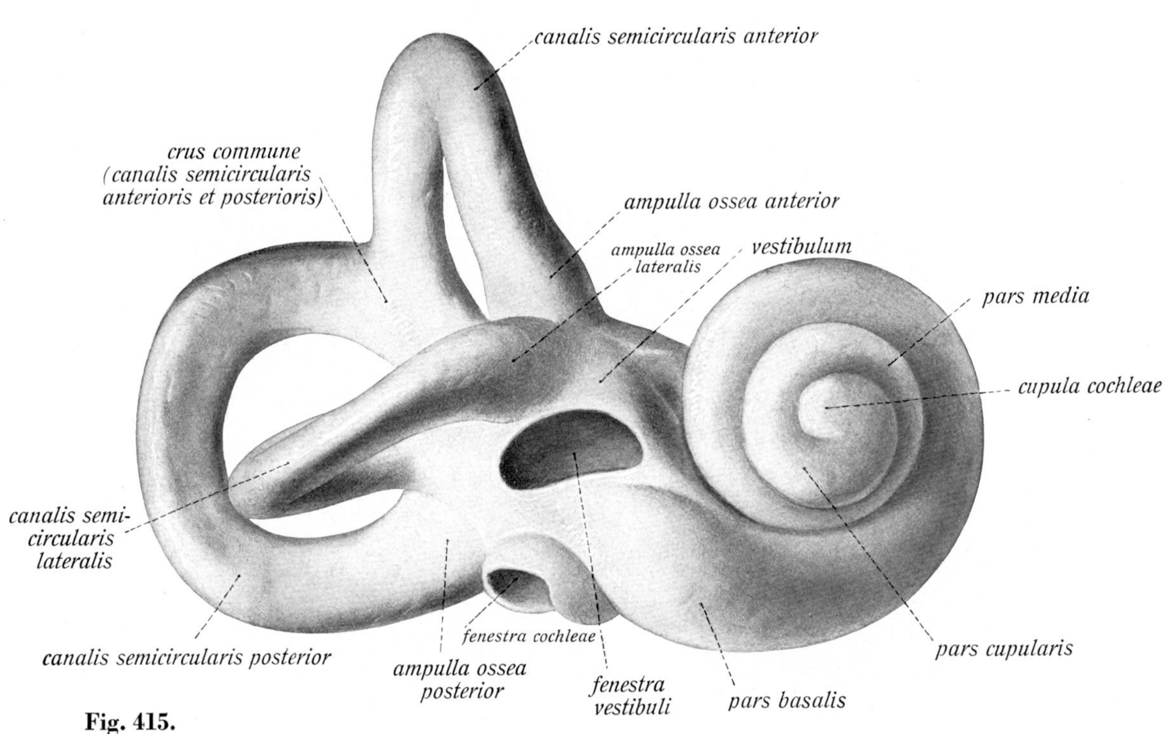
canalis semicircularis anterior
crus commune (canalis semicircularis anterioris et posterioris)
ampulla ossea anterior
ampulla ossea lateralis
vestibulum
pars media
cupula cochleae
canalis semi-circularis lateralis
canalis semicircularis posterior
fenestra cochleae
ampulla ossea posterior
fenestra vestibuli
pars basalis
pars cupularis

**Fig. 415.**

## 414. Right Bony Labyrinth. (Seen from the medial side) (6/1)

1 **Anterior Semicircular Canal**
*canalis semicircularis anterior*

**Ampulla of Anterior Semicircular Canal**
*ampulla ossea anterior*

2 **Common [Bony] Crus (of Anterior and Posterior Semicircular Canals)**
*crus [osseum] commune (canalis semicircularis anterioris et posterioris)*

**Crus [Bony] Simplex (of Lateral Semicircular Canal)**
*crus [osseum] simplex (canalis semicircularis lateralis)*

3 **Posterior Semicircular Canal**
*canalis semicircularis posterior*

**Lateral Semicircular Canal**
*canalis semicircularis lateralis*

5 **Ampulla of Posterior Semicircular Canal**
*ampulla ossea posterior*

**Vestibule**
*vestibulum*

**Macula Cribrosa Media**
*macula cribrosa media*

7 **Fenestra Cochleae**
*fenestra cochleae*

**Cochlea**
*cochlea*

8 **Cochlear Area**
*area cochleae*

10 **Crista Transversa**
*crista transversa*

11 **Macula Cribrosa Superior**
*macula cribrosa superior*

## 415. Right Bony Labyrinth. (lateral aspect) (6/1)

1 **Ampulla of Anterior Semicircular Canals**
*ampulla ossea anterior*

**Ampulla of Lateral Semicircular Canals**
*ampulla ossea lateralis*

2 **Vestibule**
*vestibulum*

3 **Middle Coil of Cochlea**
*pars media*

**Cupula Cochleae**
*cupula cochleae*

4 **Top Coil of Cochlea**
*pars cupularis*

5 **Basal Coil of Cochlea**
*pars basalis*

6 **Fenestra Vestibuli**
*fenestra vestibuli*

7 **Fenestra Cochleae**
*fenestra cochleae*

**Ampulla of Posterior Semicircular Canals**
*ampulla ossea posterior*

8 **Posterior Semicircular Canal**
*canalis semicircularis posterior*

9 **Lateral Semicircular Canal**
*canalis semicircularis lateralis*

10 **Common Bony Crus, Anterior and Posterior Semicircular Canals**
*crus [osseum] commune (canalis semicircularis anterioris et posterioris)*

12 **Anterior Semicircular Canal**
*canalis semicircularis anterior*

## 416. Left Bony Labyrinth. (Seen from in front) (7/1)

The walls of the **semicircular canals** and the **cochlear spiral canal** were ground off to expose the spaces in the bony labyrinth.

1 **Anterior Semicircular Canal**
*canalis semicircularis anterior*

**Ampulla of Anterior Semicircular Canal**
*ampulla ossea anterior*

2 **Crus [Osseum] Commune**
*crus [osseum] commune*

**Ampulla of Lateral Semicircular Canal**
*ampulla ossea lateralis*

3 **Lateral Semicircular Canal**
*canalis semicircularis lateralis*

**Posterior Semicircular Canal**
*canalis semicircularis posterior*

5 **Ampulla of Posterior Semicircular Canal**
*ampulla ossea posterior*
**Fenestra Cochleae**
*fenestra cochleae*

6 **Vestibular Crest**
*crista vestibuli*
**Commencement of Osseous Spiral Lamina**
+

7 **Aperture of Vestibular Cochlear Canal**
++
**Osseous Spiral Lamina**
*lamina spiralis ossea*

8 **Scala Vestibuli**
*scala vestibuli*

**Scala Tympani**
*scala tympani*
**Spiral Cochlear Canal 1**
*canalis spiralis cochleae 1*
**Osseous Spiral Lamina**
*lamina spiralis ossea*
**Spiral Cochlear Canal 3**
*canalis spiralis cochleae 3*

9 **Spiral Cochlear Canal**
*canalis spiralis cochleae*

10 **Spiral Cochlear Canal 2**
*canalis spiralis cochleae 2*
**Cochlear Cupula**
*cupula cochleae*

11 **Fenestra Vestibuli**
*fenestra vestibuli*

**Note:** 1. The beginning of the **spiral bony lamina**+-6.
2. The **aperture of the vestibular cochlear canal** ++-7.

## 417. Right Bony Labyrinth. (7/1)

Same preparation as shown in Figure 416 but, in addition, the **vestibule** was opened up and **the cochlea** was ground open all the way to the **cupula**.

1 **Aqueduct of Vestibule, Internal Aperture**
*apertura interna aqueductus vestibuli*
**Elliptical Recess**
*recessus ellipticus*
Margin of **Fenestra Vestibuli**
**

**Vestibular Crest**
*crista vestibuli*

**Cochlear Canal, Internal Aperture**
*apertura interna can. cochleae*

2 **Osseous Spiral Lamina**
*lamina spiralis ossea*

**Scala Vestibuli**
*scala vestibuli*

**Scala Tympani**
*scala tympani*

3 **Lamina Modioli**
*lamina modioli*

4 **Hamulus of Spiral Lamina**
*hamulus laminae spiralis*
**Osseous Spiral Lamina**
*lamina spiralis ossea*

5 **Secondary Spiral Lamina**
*lamina spiralis secundaria*
**Spherical Recess**
*recessus sphericus*

6 **Cochlear Recess**
*recessus cochlearis*
**Crest of Fenestra Cochleae**
*crista fenestrae cochleae*

7 **Fossula of Fenestra Cochleae**
*fossula fenestrae cochleae*
**Ampulla of Posterior Semicircular Canal**
*ampulla ossea posterior*

8 **Macula Cribrosa Media**
*macula cribrosa media*
**Posterior Semicircular Canal**
*canalis semicircularis posterior*

10 **Lateral Semicircular Canal**
*canalis semicircularis lateralis*

12 **Anterior Semicircular Canal**
*canalis semicircularis anterior*

**Aperture of Crus [Osseum] Commune into Vestibule**
*

**Note:** 1. The aperture of the common crus into the vestibule*-12.
2. Margin of the vestibular window**-1.
3. The vestibulocochlear apparatus or internal ear is composed of a **bony labyrinth** containing a **membranous labyrinth**. (See Figs. 412 and 413.)
4. The bony labyrinth is filled with an aqueous medium called the **perilymph**, which completely surrounds the membranous labyrinth. The membranous labyrinth contains a clear viscous fluid called the **endolymph**.

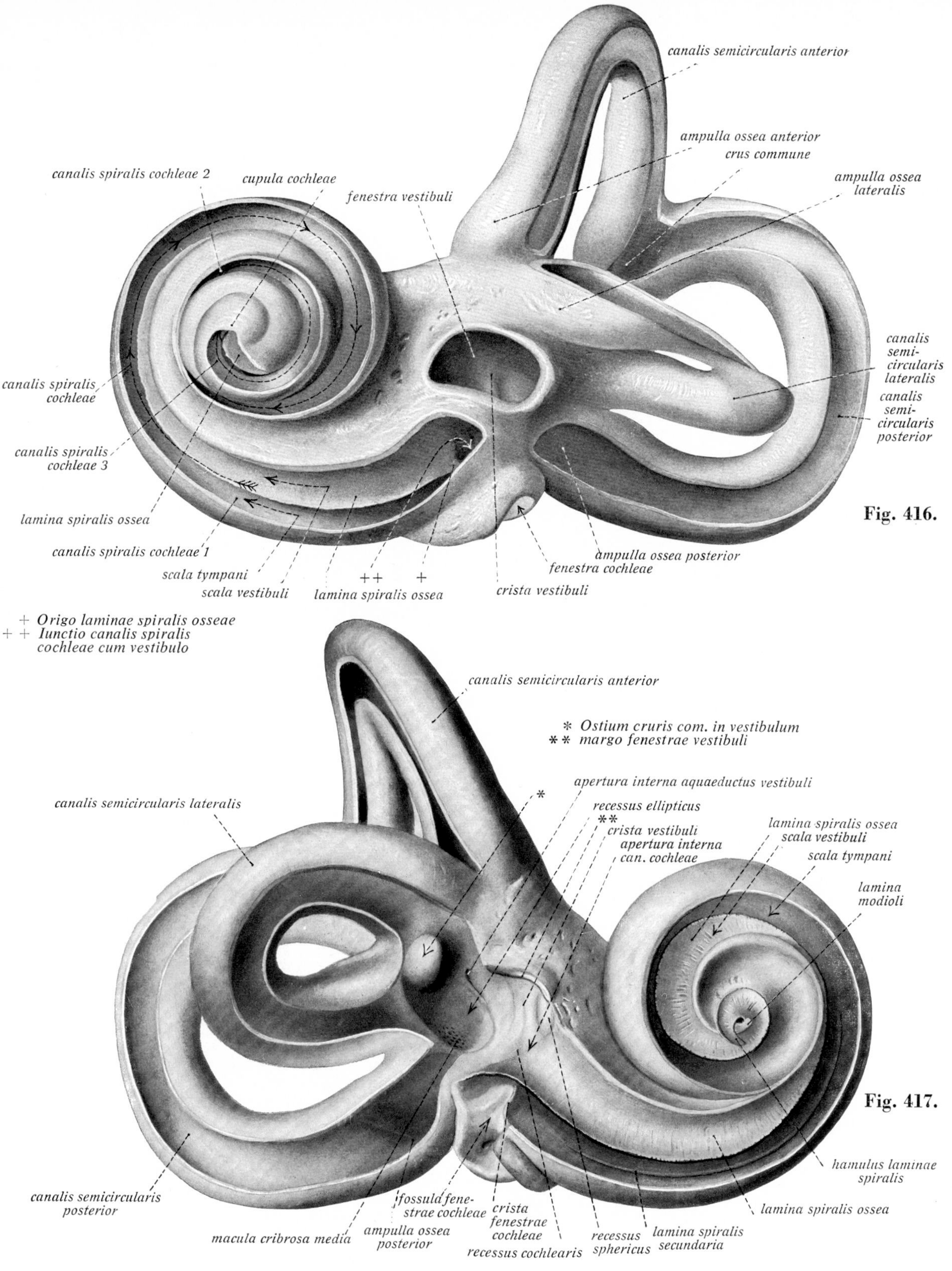
canalis semicircularis anterior
ampulla ossea anterior
crus commune
ampulla ossea lateralis
canalis spiralis cochleae 2
cupula cochleae
fenestra vestibuli
canalis semicircularis lateralis
canalis semicircularis posterior
canalis spiralis cochleae
canalis spiralis cochleae 3
lamina spiralis ossea
canalis spiralis cochleae 1
scala tympani
scala vestibuli
++ +
lamina spiralis ossea
crista vestibuli
fenestra cochleae
ampulla ossea posterior
+ Origo laminae spiralis osseae
+ + Iunctio canalis spiralis cochleae cum vestibulo
canalis semicircularis anterior
* Ostium cruris com. in vestibulum
** margo fenestrae vestibuli
apertura interna aquaeductus vestibuli
canalis semicircularis lateralis
*
recessus ellipticus
**
crista vestibuli
apertura interna can. cochleae
lamina spiralis ossea
scala vestibuli
scala tympani
lamina modioli
hamulus laminae spiralis
lamina spiralis ossea
canalis semicircularis posterior
macula cribrosa media
fossula fenestrae cochleae
ampulla ossea posterior
crista fenestrae cochleae
recessus cochlearis
recessus sphericus
lamina spiralis secundaria

Fig. 416.

Fig. 417.

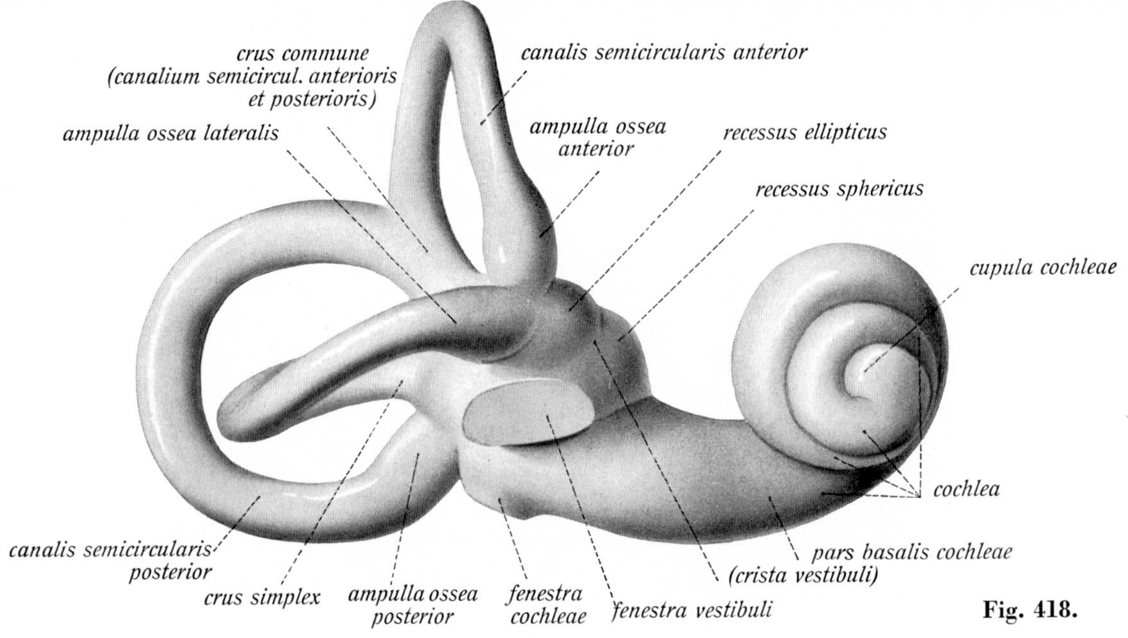
crus commune
(canalium semicircul. anterioris
et posterioris)
canalis semicircularis anterior
ampulla ossea lateralis
ampulla ossea
anterior
recessus ellipticus
recessus sphericus
cupula cochleae
cochlea
canalis semicircularis
posterior
crus simplex
ampulla ossea
posterior
fenestra
cochleae
fenestra vestibuli
(crista vestibuli)
pars basalis cochleae

Fig. 418.

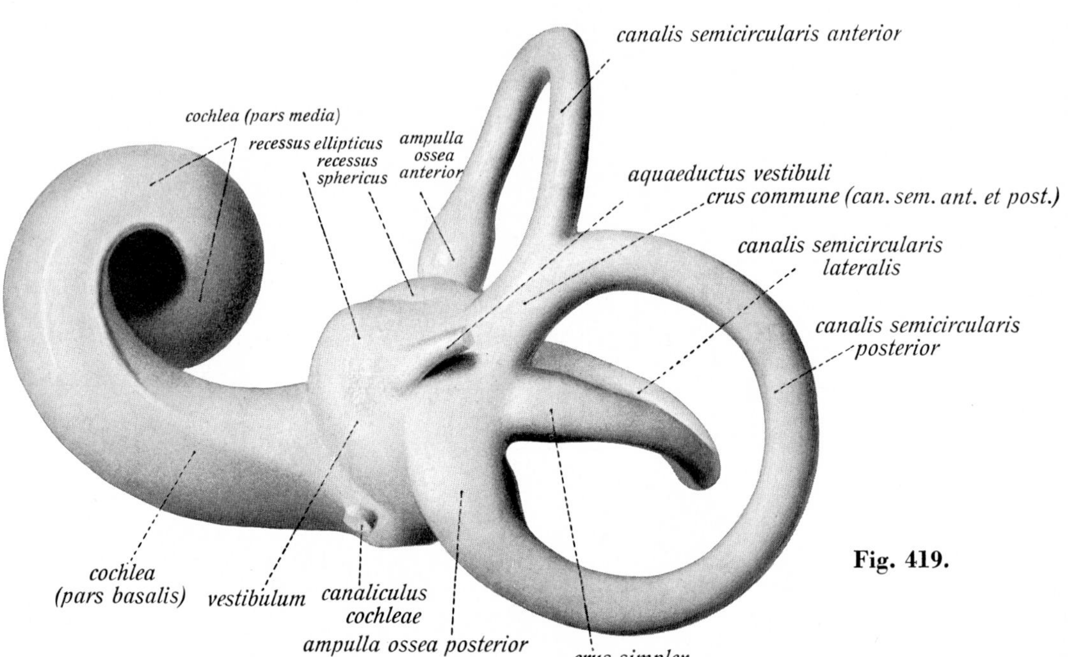
canalis semicircularis anterior
cochlea (pars media)
recessus ellipticus
recessus
sphericus
ampulla
ossea
anterior
aquaeductus vestibuli
crus commune (can. sem. ant. et post.)
canalis semicircularis
lateralis
canalis semicircularis
posterior
cochlea
(pars basalis)
vestibulum
canaliculus
cochleae
ampulla ossea posterior
crus simplex

Fig. 419.

## 418. Cast of Spaces in the Right Bony Labyrinth. (Lateral and ventral view) (7/1)

1 **Recessus Ellipticus**
*recessus ellipticus*

2 **Recessus Sphericus**
*recessus sphericus*

3 **Cupula of Cochlea**
*cupula cochleae*

**Cochlea**
*cochlea*

4 **Basal Coil of Cochlea**
*pars basalis cochleae*

**Crista Vestibuli**
*(crista vestibuli)*

5 **Fenestra Vestibuli**
*fenestra vestibuli*

6 **Fenestra Cochleae**
*fenestra cochleae*

7 **Ampulla of Posterior Semicircular Canal**
*ampulla ossea posterior*

8 **Crus [Osseum] Simplex**
*crus [osseum] simplex*

**Posterior Semicircular Canal**
*canalis semicircularis posterior*

10 **Ampulla of Lateral Semicircular Canal**
*ampulla ossea lateralis*

11 **Common Osseum Crus Anterior and Posterior Semicircular Canals**
*crus [osseum] commune (canalium semicircul. anterioris et posterioris)*

12 **Anterior Semicircular Canal**
*canalis semicircularis anterior*
**Ampulla of Anterior Semicircular Canals**
*ampulla ossea anterior*

**Note:** 1. This is a **cast** of the canals and cavities in the right bony labyrinth. Compare with Figure 415, which is a dissection of the walls of the bony labyrinth. The casts of the canals in Figure 418 are, therefore, much smaller than the bony walls in Figure 415.

## 419. Cast of the Spaces in the Right Bony Labyrinth. (Medial and dorsal aspect) (7/1)

1 **Anterior Semicircular Canal**
*canalis semicircularis anterior*

**Vestibular Aqueduct**
*aqueductus vestibuli*

2 **Crus Osseum Commune (Anterior and Posterior Semicircular Canals)**
*crus [osseum] commune (can. sem. ant. + post.)*

**Lateral Semicircular Canal**
*canalis semicircularis lateralis*

3 **Posterior Semicircular Canal**
*canalis semicircularis posterior*

5 **Crus Osseum Simplex**
*crus [osseum] simplex*

6 **Ampulla of Posterior Semicircular Canal**
*ampulla ossea posterior*

7 **Canaliculus Cochleae**
*canaliculus cochleae*

**Vestibule**
*vestibulum*

8 **Cochlea (Basal Coil)**
*cochlea (pars basalis)*

11 **Cochlea (Middle Coil)**
*cochlea (pars media)*

**Elliptical Recess**
*recessus ellipticus*

**Spherical Recess**
*recessus sphericus*

12 **Ampulla of Anterior Semicircular Canal**
*ampulla ossea anterior*

**Note:** 1. See Figure 414, for the dissection of the bony labyrinth.

## 420. Cast of Spaces in Right Bony Labyrinth. (Caudal aspect) (7/1)

1 **Cupula Cochleae**
*cupula cochleae*

2 **Cochlea**
*cochlea*

4 **Basal Coil of Cochlea**
*pars basalis*

5 **Fenestra Cochleae**
*fenestra cochleae*

6 **Vestibule**
*vestibulum*

7 **Ampulla of Posterior Semicircular Canal**
*ampulla ossea posterior*

8 **Crus Osseum Simplex**
*crus [osseum] simplex*
**Posterior Semicircular Canal**
*canalis semicircularis posterior*

10 **Lateral Semicircular Canal**
*canalis semicircularis lateralis*

11 **Anterior Semicircular Canal**
*canalis semicircularis anterior*

12 **Ampulla of Lateral Semicircular Canal**
*ampulla ossea lateralis*

**Fenestra Vestibuli**
*fenestra vestibuli*

## 421. Right Internal Auditory Meatus. (Seen from medial side) Part of dorsomedial wall has been removed. (about 5/1)

1 **Area of Facial Nerve**
*area nervi facialis*

2 **Superior Vestibular Area**
*area vestibularis superior*

**Transverse Crest**
*crista transversa*

3 **Wall of Internal Acoustic Meatus** (Partially chiseled away)
*paries meatus acustici int. partim ablatus*
**Inferior Vestibular Area**
*area vestibularis inferior*

4 **Foramen Singulare**
*foramen singulare*

5 **Cochlear Area**
*area cochleae*

6 **Fundus Internal Acoustic Meatus**
*fundus meatus acustici interni*

8 **Tractus Spiralis Foraminosus**
*tractus spiralis foraminosus*
**Internal Acoustic Meatus**
*meatus acusticus internus*

## 422. Internal Auditory Meatus. (medial aspect)

Same preparation as Figure 421, but more of the dorsomedial wall has been chiseled away.

1 **Area of Facial Nerve**
*area nervi facialis*

3 **Transverse Crest**
*crista transversa*

**Inferior Vestibular Area**
*area vestibularis inferior*

6 **Foramen Singulare**
*foramen singulare*

**Fundus, Internal Acoustic Meatus**
*fundus meatus acustici interni*

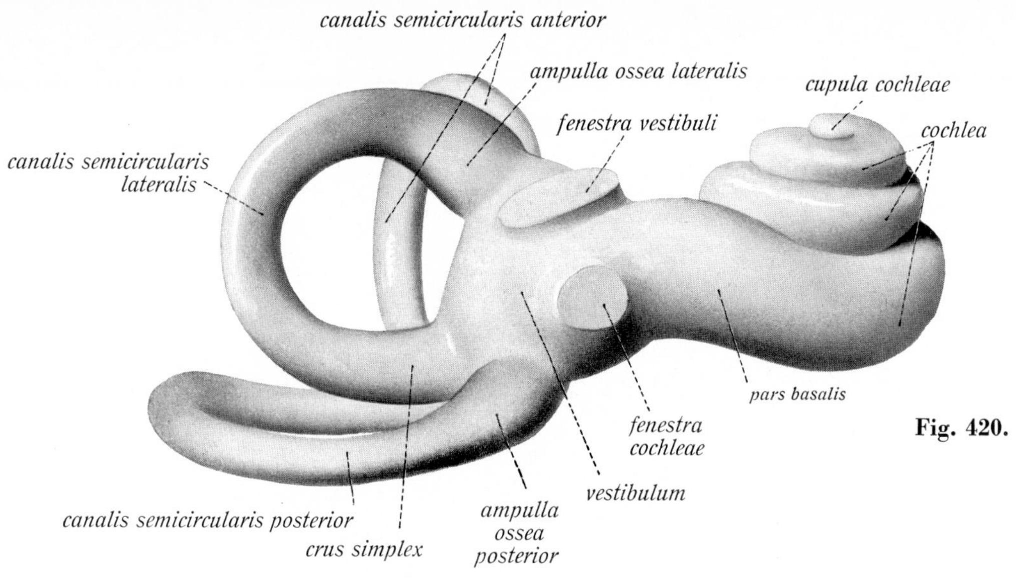
canalis semicircularis anterior
ampulla ossea lateralis
cupula cochleae
fenestra vestibuli
cochlea
canalis semicircularis lateralis
pars basalis
fenestra cochleae
vestibulum
canalis semicircularis posterior
crus simplex
ampulla ossea posterior

**Fig. 420.**

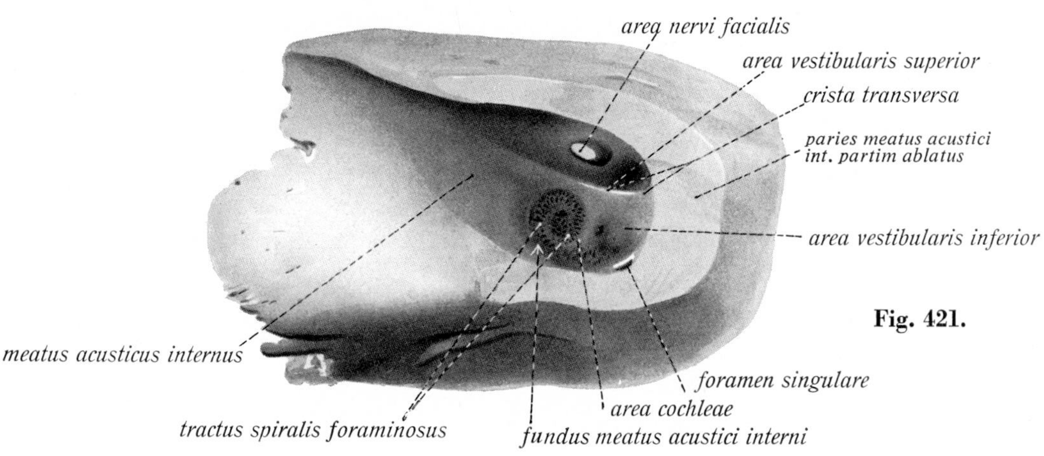
area nervi facialis
area vestibularis superior
crista transversa
paries meatus acustici int. partim ablatus
area vestibularis inferior
meatus acusticus internus
foramen singulare
area cochleae
tractus spiralis foraminosus
fundus meatus acustici interni

**Fig. 421.**

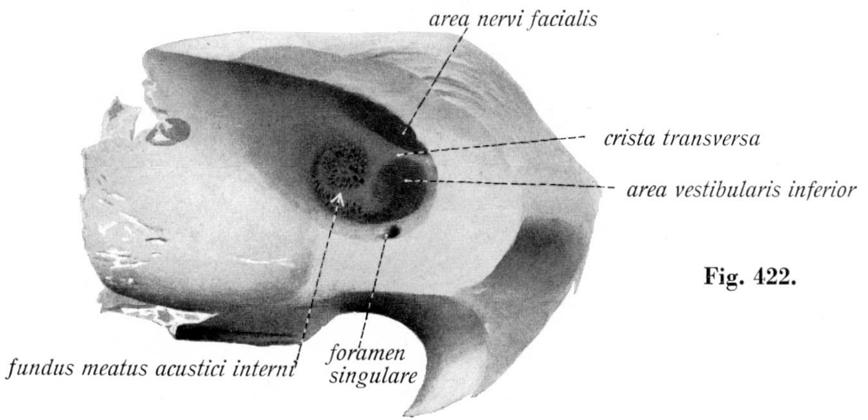
area nervi facialis
crista transversa
area vestibularis inferior
fundus meatus acustici interni
foramen singulare

**Fig. 422.**

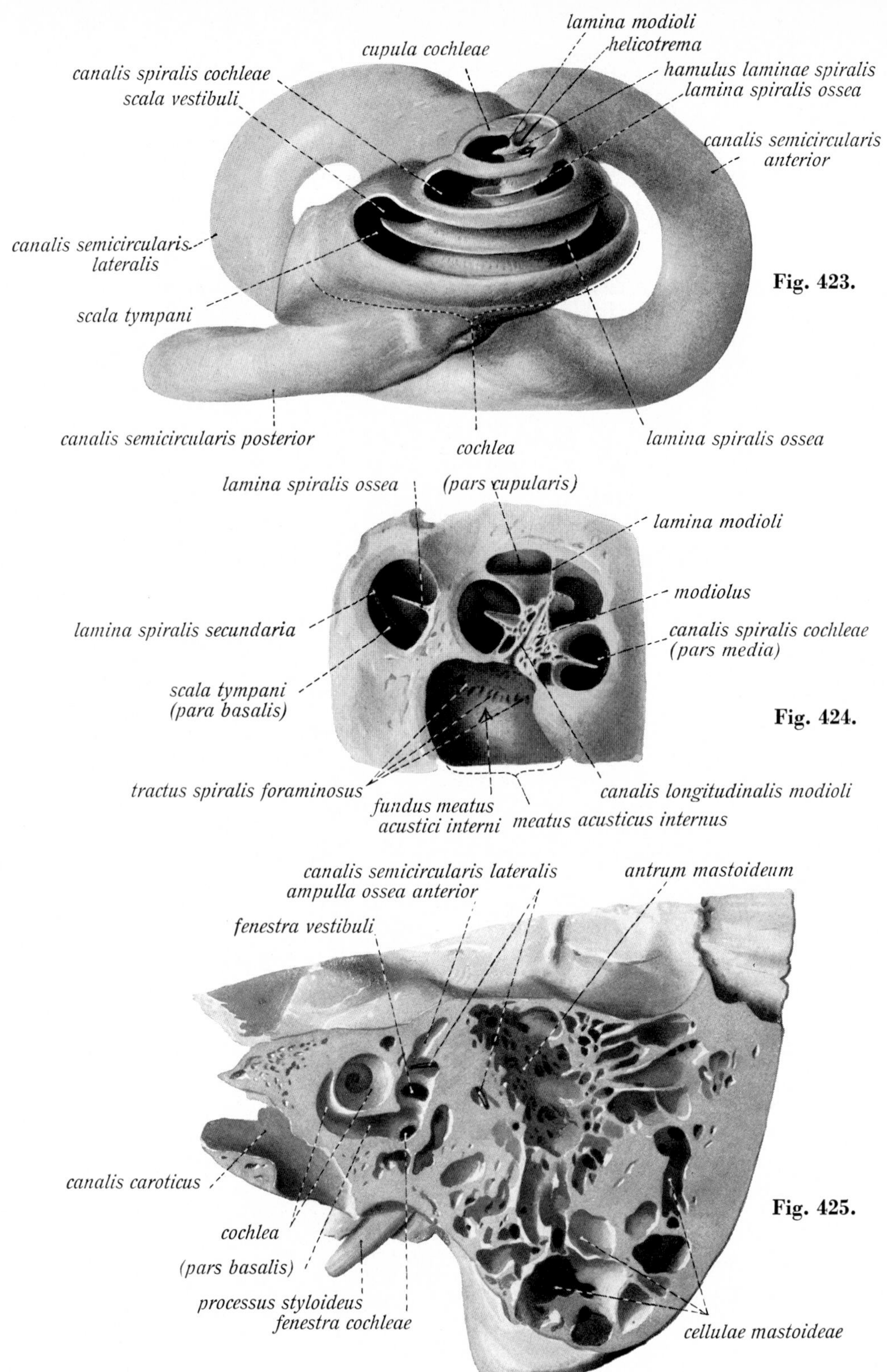
lamina modioli
helicotrema
cupula cochleae
hamulus laminae spiralis
lamina spiralis ossea
canalis spiralis cochleae
scala vestibuli
canalis semicircularis
anterior
canalis semicircularis
lateralis
scala tympani
canalis semicircularis posterior
cochlea
lamina spiralis ossea
lamina spiralis ossea
(pars cupularis)
lamina modioli
modiolus
lamina spiralis secundaria
canalis spiralis cochleae
(pars media)
scala tympani
(para basalis)
tractus spiralis foraminosus
fundus meatus
acustici interni
meatus acusticus internus
canalis longitudinalis modioli
canalis semicircularis lateralis
ampulla ossea anterior
antrum mastoideum
fenestra vestibuli
canalis caroticus
cochlea
(pars basalis)
processus styloideus
fenestra cochleae
cellulae mastoideae

Fig. 423.

Fig. 424.

Fig. 425.

## 423. Right Bony Labyrinth. (Viewed from in front and medial) (about 7/1)

The cochlear bony labyrinth was ground open on one side.

1 **Lamina Modioli**
*lamina modioli*

**Helicotrema**
*helicotrema*

**Hamulus of Spiral Lamina**
*hamulus laminae spiralis*

2 **Bony Spiral Lamina**
*lamina spiralis ossea*

**Anterior Semicircular Canal**
*canalis semicircularis anterior*

4 **Bony Spiral Lamina**
*lamina spiralis ossea*

6 **Cochlea**
*cochlea*

8 **Posterior Semicircular Canal**
*canalis semicircularis posterior*

9 **Scala Tympani**
*scala tympani*
**Lateral Semicircular Canal**
*canalis semicircularis lateralis*

10 **Scala Vestibuli**
*scala vestibuli*
**Cochlear Spiral Canal**
*canalis spiralis cochleae*

11 **Cupula Cochleae**
*cupula cochleae*

## 424. Section of Petrous Portion of Temporal Bone, Passing Through the Left Cochlea. (about 6/1)

1 **Lamina Modioli**
*lamina modioli*

2 **Modiolus**
*modiolus*

3 **Cochlear Spiral Canal (Middle Coil)**
*canalis spiralis cochleae (pars media)*

5 **Longitudinal Canal of Modiolus**
*canalis longitudinalis modioli*

6 **Internal Acoustic Meatus**
*meatus acusticus internus*

7 **Fundus of Internal Acoustic Meatus**
*fundus meatus acustici interni*

8 **Tractus Spiralis Foraminosus**
*tractus spiralis foraminosus*

9 **Scala Tympani (Basal Coil)**
*scala tympani (pars basalis)*

**Secondary Spiral Lamina**
*lamina spiralis secundaria*

10 **Bony Spiral Lamina**
*lamina spiralis ossea*

12 **Cupular Portion (of Cochlea)**
*(pars cupularis)*

**Note:** 1. The basal coil-9; the middle coil-3; apex of coil-12.

## 425. Lateral Wall of Vestibule of Inner Ear. (Seen from medial side) (2/1)

The temporal bone was sectioned through the long axis of the petrous portion.

1 **Mastoid Antrum**
*antrum mastoideum*

4 **Mastoid Cells**
*cellulae mastoideae*

7 **Fenestra Cochleae**
*fenestra cochleae*

8 **Styloid Process**
*processus styloideus*
**Basal Coil**
*(pars basalis)*
**Cochlea**
*cochlea*

9 **Carotid Canal**
*canalis caroticus*

10 **Fenestra Vestibuli**
*fenestra vestibuli*

11 **Ampulla of Anterior Semicircular Canal**
*ampulla ossea anterior*
**Lateral Semicircular Canal**
*canalis semicircularis lateralis*

**Note:** 1. This section displays a portion of the **carotid canal**-9.

2. Basal coil of the cochlea and its vestibular and cochlear apertures or opening.

3. **Mastoid antrum**-1, **mastoid air cells**-4, and the lateral and anterior semicircular canals.

## 426. Medial Walls of Vestibule of Inner Ear. (3/1)

A section of the right temporal bone displaying the vertical portion of the facial canal-7, the carotid canal-3, and the vestibule-8, and other parts of the bony labyrinth.

1 **Macula Cribrosa Superior**
*macula cribrosa superior*
**Facial Canal**
*canalis facialis*
**Crista Vestibuli**
*crista vestibuli*
**Sulcus for Greater Petrosal Nerve**
*sulcus n. petrosi majoris*
**Spherical Recess**
*recessus sphericus*

2 **Macula Cribrosa Media**
*macula cribrosa media*
**Scala Vestibuli**
*scala vestibuli*
**Osseus Spiral Lamina**
*lamina spiralis ossea*

3 **Carotid Canal**
*canalis caroticus*

5 **Spiral Canal of Cochlea**
*canalis spiralis cochleae*
**Cochlear Recess**
*recessus cochlearis*

6 **Crest of Fenestra Cochlea**
*crista fenestrae cochleae*

7 **Tympanic Cavity (Fossula Fenestra Cochlea)**
*cavum tympani (fossula fenestrae cochleae)*
**Facial Canal**
*canalis facialis*

8 **Vestibule**
*vestibulum*
**Elliptic Recess**
*recessus ellipticus*

9 **Ampulla of Lateral Semicircular Canal**
*ampulla ossea lateralis*
**Lateral Semicircular Canal**
*canalis semicircularis lateralis*

10 **Anterior Semicircular Canal**
*canalis semicircularis anterior*

11 **Ampulla of Anterior Semicircular Canal**
*ampulla ossea anterior*

12 **Internal Orifice of Aqueduct of Vestibule**
*apertura int. aqueductus vestibuli*
**Pyramid of Vestibule**
*pyramis vestibuli*

**Note:** 1. Lateral semicircular canal-9, anterior semicircular canal-10 and their ampullae were opened up by removing the lateral part of the bony labyrinth.

2. The horizontal portion of the **facial canal** cut in cross section-1 and the **sulcus for the greater petrosal nerve**-1 extends ventrally from the canal.

## 427. Section of Right Temporal Bone Through Tympanic Cavity and Mastoid Antrum, Parallel to Long Axis of Petrous Portion of Temporal Bone. (Viewed from lateral side) (2/1)

1 **Arcuate Eminence**
*eminentia arcuata*

2 **Tegmen Tympani**
*tegmen tympani*
**Cochleariform Process**
*processus cochleariformis*
**Fenestra Vestibuli**
*fenestra vestibuli*

3 **Septum Canalis Musculotubarii**
*septum canalis musculotubarii*
**Semicanal of Tensor Tympani Muscle**
*semicanalis m. tensoris tympani*
**Trigeminal Impression**
*impressio trigemini*
**Apex of Petrous Portion**
*apex partis petrosae*
**Carotid Canal**
*canalis caroticus*

4 **Semicanal of Auditory Tube**
*semicanalis tubae auditivae*

5 **Carotid Canal**
*canalis caroticus*
**Tympanic Air Cells**
*cellulae tympanicae.*
**Fossula of Fenestra Cochlea**
*fossula fenestra cochleae*
**Promontory Sulcus**
*sulcus promontorii*

6 **Tympanic Cavity, Labyrinthine Wall**
*cavum tympani paries labyrinthicus*

7 **Foramen for Stapedius Tendon**
*foramen tendinis musc. stapedii*
**Tympanic Sinus**
*sinus tympani*

8 **Pyramidal Eminence**
*eminentia pyramidalis*

9 **Mastoid Process**
*processus mastoideus*
**Mastoid Air Cells**
*cellulae mastoideae*

11 **Mastoid Antrum**
*antrum mastoideum*
**Tegmen of Mastoid Antrum**
*(tegmen antri mastoidei)*

12 **Posterior Sinus**
*sinus posterior*
**Prominence of Facial Canal**
*prominentia canalis facialis*

**Note:** 1. **Carotid canal**-3 near **apex of petrous portion**-3 of the temporal bone.
2. Septum of **canalis musculotubarii**-3.
3. **Sulci on promontory**-5 for **nerves** which form **tympanic plexus**.
4. Position of the **cochlear window**-5 (round) and **vestibular window**-2 (oval).
5. Leader to fossula fenestrae cochleae has been misplaced so it joins leaders for cellulae tympanica-5.

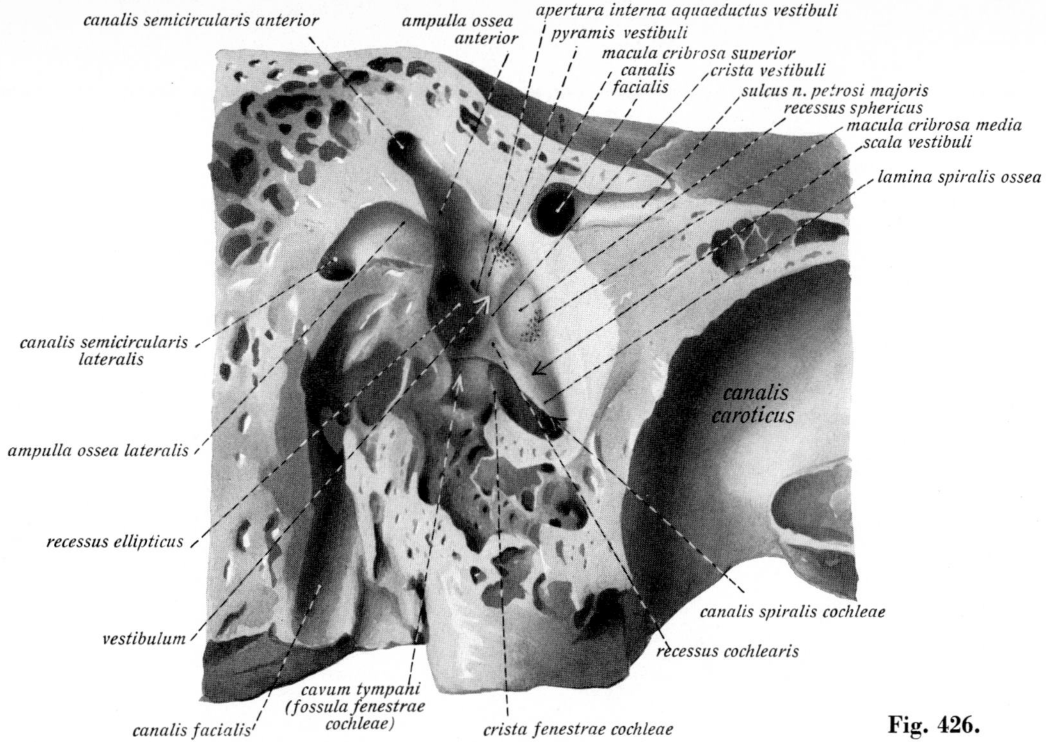
canalis semicircularis anterior
ampulla ossea anterior
apertura interna aquaeductus vestibuli
pyramis vestibuli
macula cribrosa superior
canalis facialis
crista vestibuli
sulcus n. petrosi majoris
recessus sphericus
macula cribrosa media
scala vestibuli
lamina spiralis ossea
canalis semicircularis lateralis
canalis caroticus
ampulla ossea lateralis
recessus ellipticus
canalis spiralis cochleae
vestibulum
recessus cochlearis
cavum tympani (fossula fenestrae cochleae)
canalis facialis
crista fenestrae cochleae

Fig. 426.

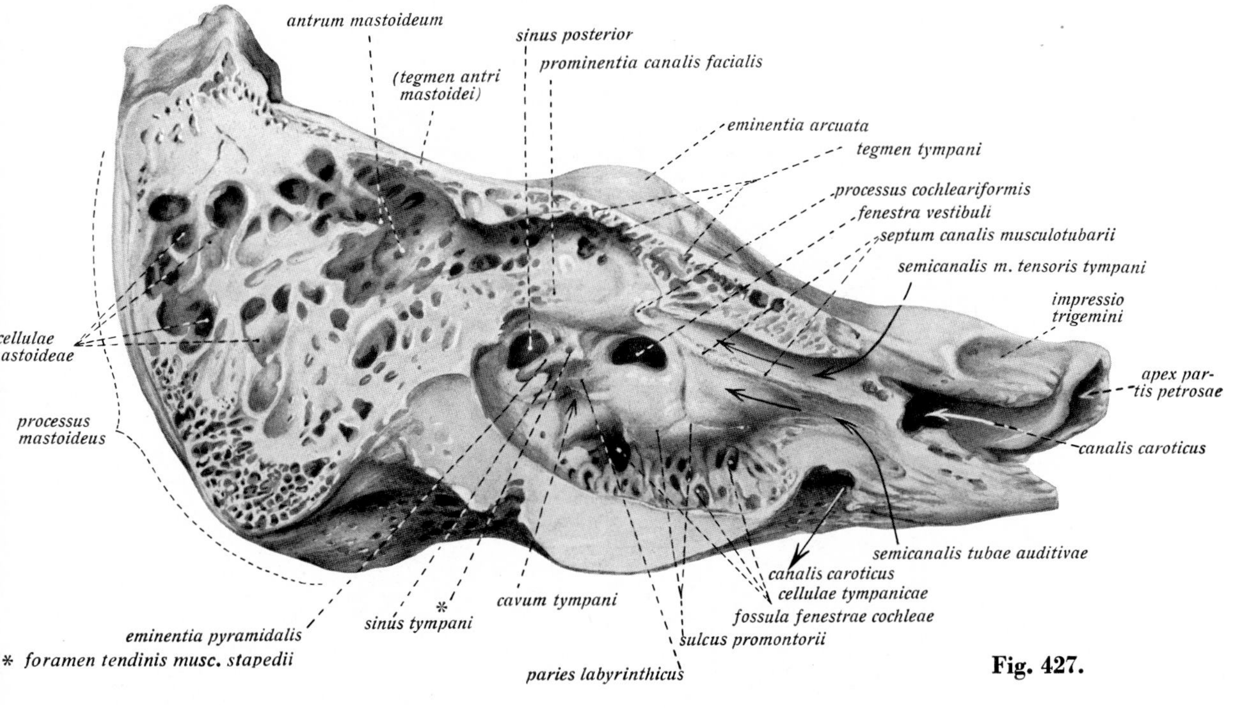
antrum mastoideum
sinus posterior
prominentia canalis facialis
(tegmen antri mastoidei)
eminentia arcuata
tegmen tympani
processus cochleariformis
fenestra vestibuli
septum canalis musculotubarii
semicanalis m. tensoris tympani
impressio trigemini
cellulae mastoideae
apex partis petrosae
processus mastoideus
canalis caroticus
semicanalis tubae auditivae
canalis caroticus
cellulae tympanicae
*
cavum tympani
fossula fenestrae cochleae
sinus tympani
eminentia pyramidalis
sulcus promontorii
* foramen tendinis musc. stapedii
paries labyrinthicus

Fig. 427.

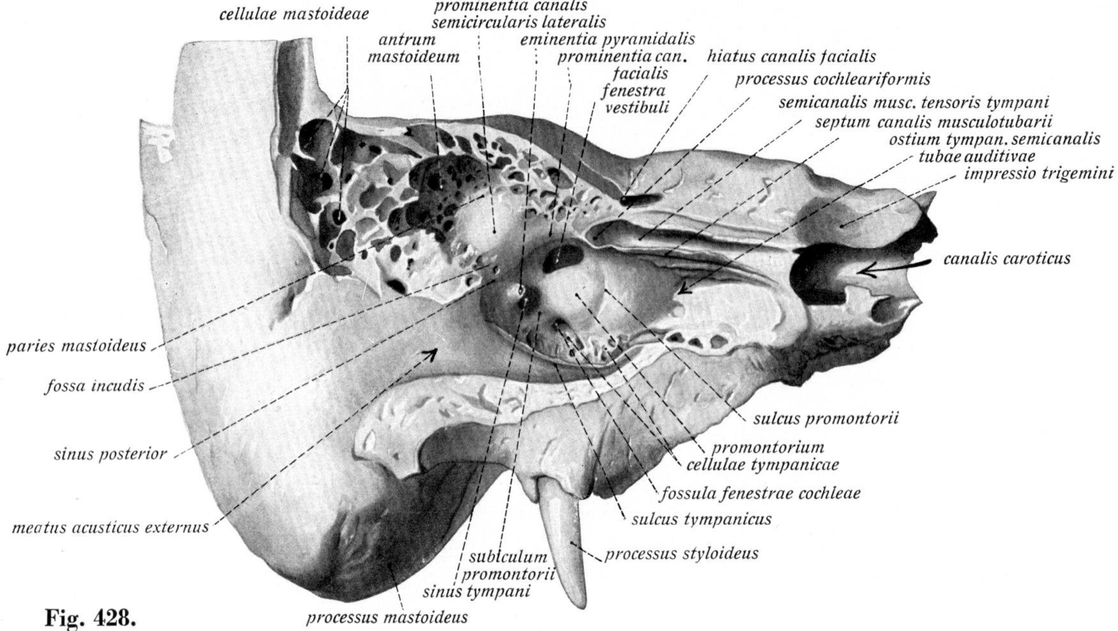
cellulae mastoideae
prominentia canalis
semicircularis lateralis
antrum
mastoideum
eminentia pyramidalis
prominentia can.
facialis
fenestra
vestibuli
hiatus canalis facialis
processus cochleariformis
semicanalis musc. tensoris tympani
septum canalis musculotubarii
ostium tympan. semicanalis
tubae auditivae
impressio trigemini
canalis caroticus
paries mastoideus
fossa incudis
sinus posterior
meatus acusticus externus
sulcus promontorii
promontorium
cellulae tympanicae
fossula fenestrae cochleae
sulcus tympanicus
processus styloideus
subiculum
promontorii
sinus tympani
processus mastoideus

**Fig. 428.**

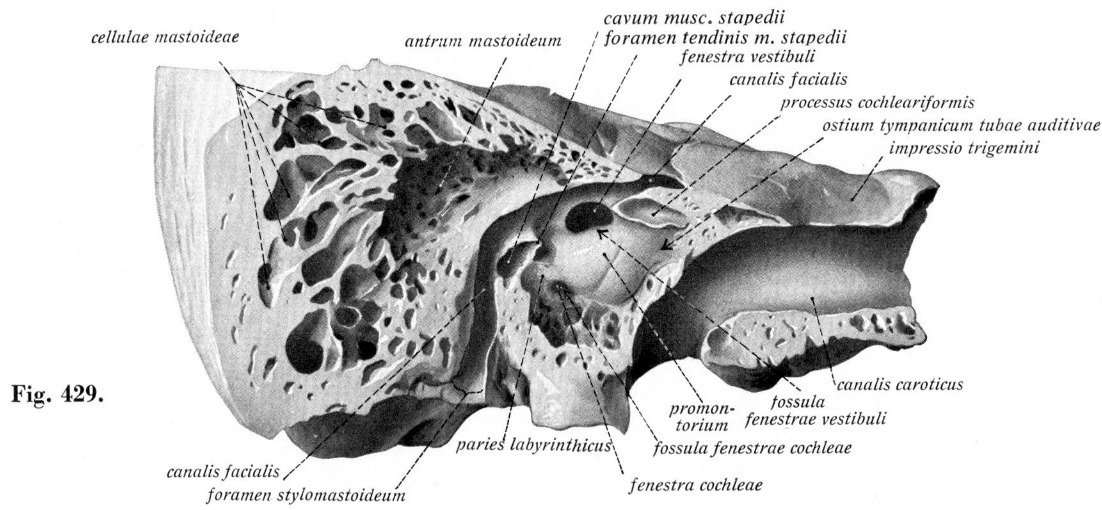
cellulae mastoideae
antrum mastoideum
cavum musc. stapedii
foramen tendinis m. stapedii
fenestra vestibuli
canalis facialis
processus cochleariformis
ostium tympanicum tubae auditivae
impressio trigemini
canalis caroticus
fossula
fenestrae vestibuli
promon-
torium
fossula fenestrae cochleae
fenestra cochleae
paries labyrinthicus
canalis facialis
foramen stylomastoideum

**Fig. 429.**

## 428. A Dissection of Right Temporal Bone. (from lateral side) (5/3)

The right tympanic cavity has been opened by removal of some of the lateral parts of the bone and parts of its ventral and cranial walls.

1 **Fenestra Vestibuli**
*fenestra vestibuli*
**Hiatus of Facial Canal**
*hiatus canalis facialis*

2 **Cochleariform Process**
*processus cochleariformis*
**Semicanal of Tensor Tympani**
*semicanalis musc. tensoris tympani*
**Septum Canalis Musculotubarii**
*septum canalis musculotubarii*
**Tympanic Opening of Auditory Tube**
*ostium tympan. tubae auditivae*
**Trigeminal Recess**
*impressio trigemini*

3 **Carotid Canal**
*canalis caroticus*

4 **Promontory Sulcus**
*sulcus promontorii*
**Promontory**
*promontorium*
**Tympanic Air Cells**
*cellulae tympanicae*

5 **Fossula Fenestra Cochlea**
*fossula fenestrae cochleae*
**Tympanic Sulcus**
*sulcus tympanicus*
**Styloid Process**
*processus styloideus*

6 **Subiculum Promontorii**
*subiculum promontorii*

7 **Tympanic Sinus**
*sinus tympani*
**Mastoid Process**
*processus mastoideus*

8 **External Auditory Meatus**
*meatus acusticus externus*
**Posterior Sinus**
*sinus posterior*

9 **Fossa Incudis**
*fossa incudis*
**Mastoid Wall**
*paries mastoideus*

11 **Mastoid Air Cells**
*cellulae mastoideae*
**Mastoid Antrum**
*antrum mastoideum*
**Prominence of Lateral Semicircular Canal**
*prominentia canalis semicircularis lateralis*

12 **Pyramidal Eminence**
*eminentia pyramidalis*
**Prominence of Facial Canal**
*prominentia can. facialis*

**Note:** 1. Good view of **pyramidal eminence**-12, **promontory**-4, and other structures on medial wall of middle ear.

## 429. Section of Right Temporal Bone Along Longitudinal Axis of Petrous Portion of Temporal Bone. (More medial than in Fig. 428) (5/3)

1 **Cavity for Stapedius Muscle**
*cavum musc. stapedii*
**Foramen for Stapedius Tendon**
*foramen tendinis m. stapedii*
**Fenestra Vestibuli**
*fenestra vestibuli*

2 **Facial Canal**
*canalis facialis*
**Cochleariformis Process**
*processus cochleariformis*
**Tympanic Opening of Auditory Tube**
*ostium tympanicum tubae auditivae*

3 **Trigeminal Impression**
*impressio trigemini*

4 **Carotid Canal**
*canalis caroticus*
**Fossula of Fenestra Vestibuli**
*fossula fenestrae vestibuli*

5 **Promontory**
*promontorium*
**Fossula of Fenestra Cochlea**
*fossula fenestrae cochleae*
**Fenestra Cochleae**
*fenestra cochleae*

7 **Labyrinthine (Medial) Wall**
*paries labyrinthicus*

8 **Stylomastoid Foramen**
*foramen stylomastoideum*
**Facial Canal**
*canalis facialis*

10 **Mastoid Cells**
*cellulae mastoideae*

11 **Mastoid Antrum**
*antrum mastoideum*

**Note:** 1. **Carotid canal**-4 and facial canal-2, -8 have been opened.

2. **Cavity of the pyramidal eminence**-1 was displayed. In life, this contains the stapedius muscle.

3. **Stapedius muscle** is supplied by a small branch from the **facial nerve**. The tendon of the stapedius muscle attaches to the stapes by passing through an opening in the pyramidal eminence, the foramen for the stapedius tendon-1.

4. Both the stapedius muscle and the stapes are derivatives of the mesoderm of the hyoid or second branchial arch.

**Auditory Ossicles:** Malleus (hammer); Incus (anvil); Stapes (stirrup).

## 430. Right Malleus. (Seen from lateral side) (7/1)

1 **Head of Malleus**
*caput mallei*

2 **Neck of Malleus**
*collum mallei*

**Anterior Process**
*processus anterior*

6 **Manubrium of Malleus**
*manubrium mallei*

8 **Lateral Process**
*processus lateralis*

10 **Articular Surface**
*facies articularis*

## 431. Right Malleus. (Seen from front) (7/1)

6 **Manubrium of Malleus**
*manubrium mallei*

8 **Anterior Process**
*processus anterior*

**Lateral Process**
*processus lateralis*

9 **Neck of Malleus**
*collum mallei*

10 **Head of Malleus**
*caput mallei*

## 432. Right Malleus. (Seen from dorsal side) (7/1)

1 **Articular Surface (for Incus)**
*facies articularis*

5 **Lateral Process**
*processus lateralis*

6 **Insertion of Tensor Tympani Muscle**
*insertio m. tens. tymp.*

7 **Manubrium of Malleus**
*manubrium mallei*

9 **Neck of Malleus**
*collum mallei*

**Spur of Malleus (cog-tooth)**
*dens*

12 **Head of Malleus**
*caput mallei*

## 433. Right Incus. (Seen from lateral side) (7/1)

2 **Spur of Malleus (Cog Tooth)**
*dens*

7 **Long Crus**
*crus longum*

8 **Articular Surface**
*facies articularis*

9 **Body of Incus**
*corpus incudis*

**Short Crus**
*crus breve*

## 434. Right Incus. (Seen from medial side) (7/1)

1 **Articular Surface**
*facies articularis*

2 **Body of Incus**
*corpus incudis*

3 **Short Crus**
*Crus breve*

6 **Lenticular Process**
*processus lenticularis*

8 **Spur of Malleus (cog-tooth)**
*dens*

## 435. Right Stapes. (Seen from above) (7/1)

1 **Head of Stapes**
*caput stapedis*

2 Insertion of **Stapedius Muscle**
*insertio m. stapedii*

3 **Posterior Crus**
*crus posterius*

7 **Base of Stapes**
*basis stapedis*

9 **Anterior Crus**
*crus anterius*

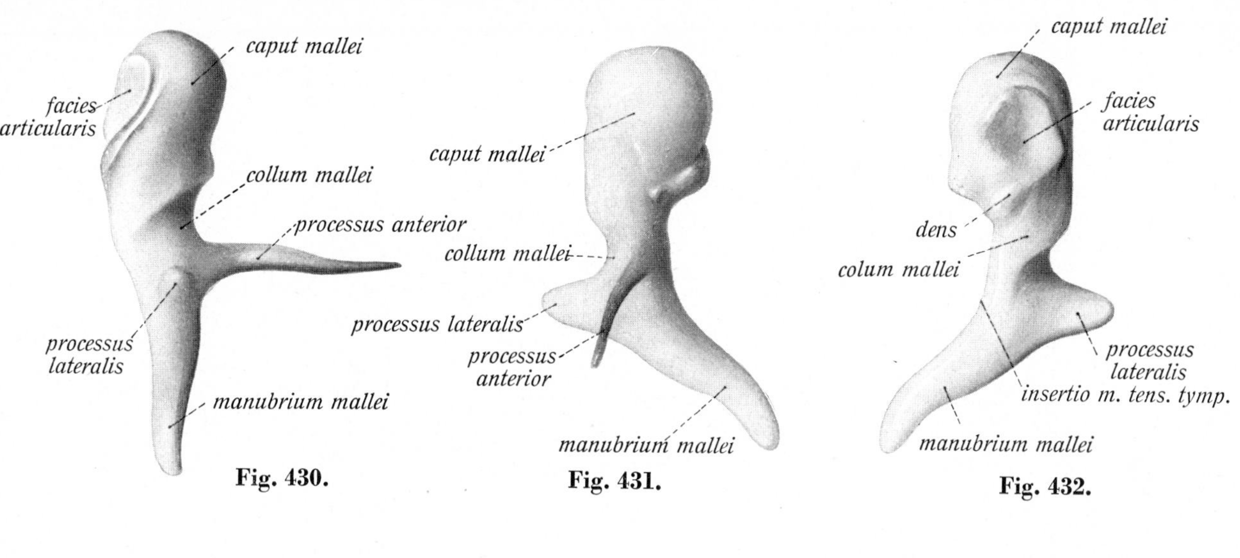
caput mallei
facies articularis
collum mallei
processus anterior
processus lateralis
manubrium mallei
caput mallei
collum mallei
processus lateralis
processus anterior
manubrium mallei
caput mallei
facies articularis
dens
colum mallei
processus lateralis
insertio m. tens. tymp.
manubrium mallei

**Fig. 430.** **Fig. 431.** **Fig. 432.**

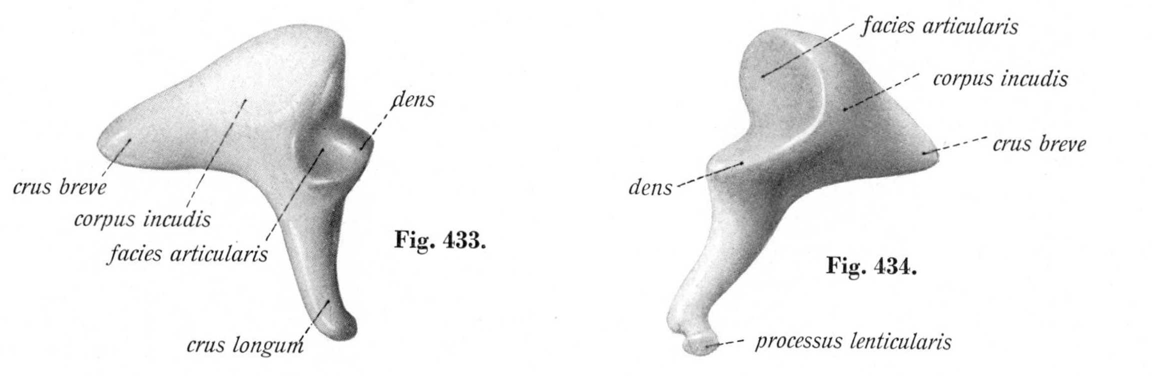
dens
crus breve
corpus incudis
facies articularis
crus longum
facies articularis
corpus incudis
crus breve
dens
processus lenticularis

**Fig. 433.** **Fig. 434.**

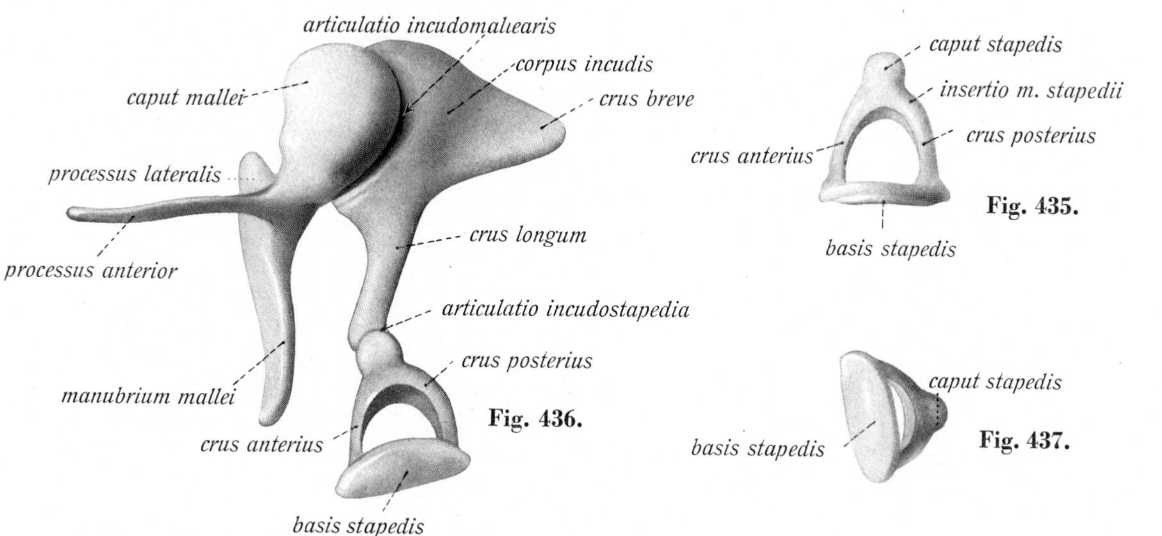
articulatio incudomallearis
corpus incudis
caput mallei
crus breve
processus lateralis
processus anterior
crus longum
articulatio incudostapedia
crus posterius
manubrium mallei
crus anterius
basis stapedis
caput stapedis
insertio m. stapedii
crus posterius
crus anterius
basis stapedis
caput stapedis
basis stapedis

**Fig. 436.** **Fig. 435.** **Fig. 437.**

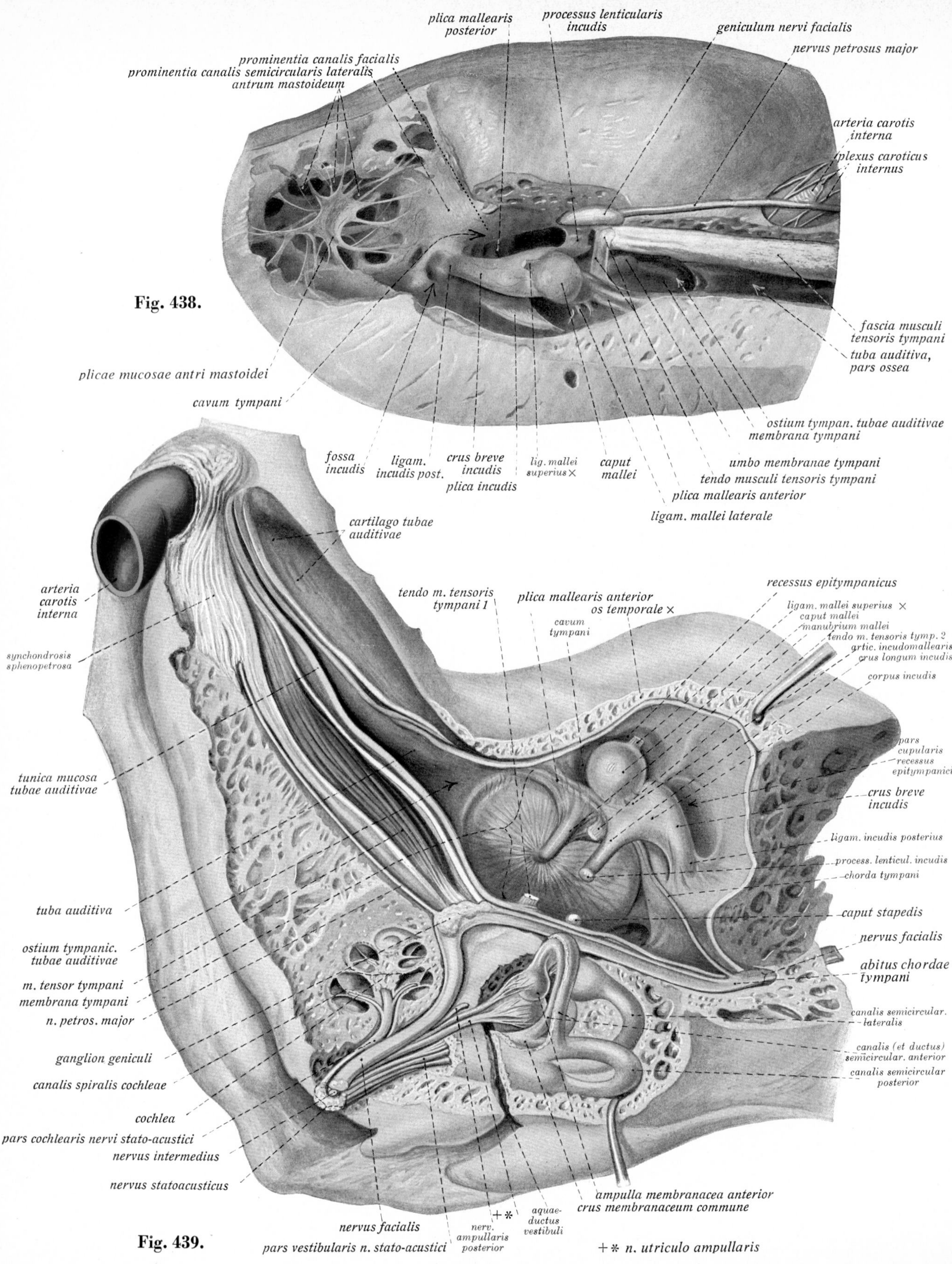
plica mallearis posterior
processus lenticularis incudis
geniculum nervi facialis
nervus petrosus major
prominentia canalis facialis
prominentia canalis semicircularis lateralis
antrum mastoideum
arteria carotis interna
plexus caroticus internus
fascia musculi tensoris tympani
tuba auditiva, pars ossea
plicae mucosae antri mastoidei
cavum tympani
ostium tympan. tubae auditivae
membrana tympani
umbo membranae tympani
tendo musculi tensoris tympani
plica mallearis anterior
ligam. mallei laterale
fossa incudis
ligam. incudis post.
crus breve incudis
plica incudis
lig. mallei superius ×
caput mallei
cartilago tubae auditivae
arteria carotis interna
synchondrosis sphenopetrosa
tendo m. tensoris tympani 1
plica mallearis anterior
os temporale ×
cavum tympani
recessus epitympanicus
ligam. mallei superius ×
caput mallei
manubrium mallei
tendo m. tensoris tymp. 2
artic. incudomallearis
crus longum incudis
corpus incudis
pars cupularis recessus epitympanici
crus breve incudis
ligam. incudis posterius
process. lenticul. incudis
chorda tympani
caput stapedis
nervus facialis
abitus chordae tympani
canalis semicircular. lateralis
canalis (et ductus) semicircular. anterior
canalis semicircular posterior
tunica mucosa tubae auditivae
tuba auditiva
ostium tympanic. tubae auditivae
m. tensor tympani
membrana tympani
n. petros. major
ganglion geniculi
canalis spiralis cochleae
cochlea
pars cochlearis nervi stato-acustici
nervus intermedius
nervus statoacusticus
ampulla membranacea anterior
crus membranaceum commune
nervus facialis
pars vestibularis n. stato-acustici
+ *
nerv. ampullaris posterior
aquae-ductus vestibuli
+ * n. utriculo ampullaris

Fig. 438.

Fig. 439.

## 436. Right Auditory Ossicles of a Child. (relationships when articulated) (7/1)

1 **Body of Incus**
*corpus incudis*

2 **Short Crus**
*crus breve*

3 **Long Crus**
*crus longum*

4 **Incudostapedial articulation**
*articulatio incudostapedia*

**Posterior Crus**
*crus posterius*

6 **Base of Stapes**
*basis stapedis*

7 **Anterior Crus**
*crus anterius*

8 **Manubrium (Handle) of Malleus**
*manubrium mallei*

9 **Anterior Process**
*processus anterior*
**Lateral Process**
*processus lateralis*

10 **Head of Malleus**
*caput mallei*

12 **Incudomallear Articulation**
*articulatio incudomallearis*

## 437. Right Stapes. (Seen from medial and below) (7/1)

**Note:** 1. The **incus, malleus** and **tensor tympani muscle**, which is attached to it, are derived from the **first branchial arch**. This is sometimes referred to as the **mandibular arch,** because parts of the mandible are also derived from it. Muscles of this arch are supplied by the **motor portion of the trigeminal** nerve.

2. The stapes and stapedius muscle are derived from the **second branchial arch** or the **hyoid arch**. Motor nerve for muscles of the hyoid arch is the **facial nerve VII.**

## 438. Right Tympanic Cavity. (Opened from above) (4/1)

Tegmen tympani, cranial wall of musculotubal canal, and roof of mastoid antrum were removed. Facial nerve in facial canal was exposed at geniculate ganglion.

1 **Genu of the Facial Nerve**
*geniculum nervi facialis*

2 **Greater Petrosal Nerve**
*nervus petrosus major*

3 **Internal Carotid Artery**
*arteria carotis interna*
**Internal Carotid Plexus**
*plexus caroticus internus*

4 **Fascia of Tensor Tympani Muscle**
*fascia musculi tensoris tympani*
**Auditory Tube, Bony Portion**
*tuba auditiva, pars ossea*
**Tympanic Opening of Auditory Tube**
*ostium tympan. tubae auditivae*
**Tympanic Membrane**
*membrana tympani*
**Umbo of Tympanic Membrane**
*umbo membranae tympani*

5 **Tendon of Tensor Tympani M.**
*tendo musculi tensoris tympani*
**Anterior Malleolar Fold**
*plica mallearis anterior*
**Lateral Malleolar Ligament**
*ligam. mallei laterale*
**Head of Malleus**
*caput mallei*

6 **Superior Malleolar Ligament**
*lig. mallei superius*

7 **Fold of Incus**
*plica incudis*
**Short Crus of Incus**
*crus breve incudis*
**Posterior Ligament of Incus**
*ligam. incudis post.*

8 **Fossa of Incus**
*fossa incudis*
**Tympanic Cavity**
*cavum tympani*
**Small Fold of Mucosa of Mastoid Antrum**
*plicae mucosae antri mastoidei*

10 **Mastoid Antrum**
*antrum mastoideum*
**Prominence of Lateral Semicircular Canal**
*prominentia canalis semicircularis lateralis*
**Prominence of Facial Canal**
*prominentia canalis facialis*

11 **Posterior Malleolar Fold**
*plica mallearis posterior*

12 **Lenticular Process of Incus**
*processus lenticularis incudis*

**Note:** 1. **Greater petrosal nerve**-2, originating from facial nerve-1, enters cranial fossa. At foramen lacerum it joins deep petrosal nerve to form nerve of pterygoid canal. (See Fig. 439-7)

## 439. A Dissection of a Decalcified Temporal Bone. (5/1)

Temporal bone was decalcified and cranial part of petrous portion was removed. Facial and vestibulocochlear nerves were dissected to show their relation to the labyrinth and tympanic cavity. Walls of tympanic cavity were separated to expose structures in middle ear.

1 **Tympanic Cavity**
*cavum tympani*
**Temporal Bone**
*os temporale*

2 **Epitympanic Recess**
*recessus epitympanicus*
**Superior Ligament of Malleus**
*ligam. mallei superius*
**Head of Malleus**
*caput mallei*
**Handle of Malleus**
*manubrium mallei*
**Tensor Tympani Tendon**
*tendo m. tensoris tymp.*
**Incudomallear Articulation**
*artic. incudomallearis*
**Long Crus of Incus**
*crus longum incudis*
**Body of Incus**
*corpus incudis*
**Epitympanic Recess** (Cupula Portion)
*pars cupularis recessus epitympanici*

3 **Short Crus of Incus**
*crus breve incudis*
**Posterior Ligament of Incus**
*ligam. incudis posterius*
**Lenticular Process of Incus**
*process. lenticul. incudis*
**Chorda Tympani**
*chorda tympani*
**Head of Stapes**
*caput stapedis*
**Facial Nerve**
*nervus facialis*
**Origin of Chorda Tympani**
*chorda tympani*

4 **Lateral Semicircular Canal**
*canalis semicircular lateralis*
**Anterior Semicircular Canal and Duct**
*canalis (+ ductus) semicircular anterior*
**Posterior Semicircular Canal**
*canalis semicircular posterior*

6 **Ampulla of Anterior Semicircular Duct**
*ampulla membranacea anterior*
**Crus Membranaceum Commune**
*crus membranaceum commune*
**Vestibular Aqueduct**
*aqueductus vestibuli*
**Utriculoampullary Nerve**
+*
**Nerve to Posterior Ampulla**
*nerv. ampullaris posterior*

7 **Vestibulocochlear Nerve, Vestibular Part**
*pars vestibularis n. statoacustici [vestibulocochlearis]*
**Facial Nerve**
*nervus facialis*

8 **Vestibulocochlear Nerve**
*nervus statoacusticus [vestibulocochlearis]*
**Intermedius Nerve**
*nervus intermedius*
**Vestibulocochlear Nerve, Cochlear Part**
*pars cochlearis nervi statoacustici [vestibulocochlearis]*
**Cochlea**
*cochlea*
**Spiral Canal of Cochlea**
*canalis spiralis cochleae*
**Geniculate Ganglion**
*ganglion geniculi*

9 **Greater Petrosal Nerve**
*n. petros. major*
**Tympanic Membrane**
*membrana tympani*
**Tensor Tympani Muscle**
*m. tensor tympani*
**Tympanic Opening of Auditory Tube**
*ostium tympanic tubae auditivae*
**Auditory Tube**
*tuba auditiva*
**Auditory Tube, Mucous Membrane**
*tunica mucosa tubae auditivae*

10 **Sphenopetrosal Synchondrosis**
*synchondrosis sphenopetrosa*
**Internal Carotid Artery**
*arteria carotis interna*

11 **Auditory Tube Cartilage**
*cartilago tubae auditivae*
**Tendon of Tensor Tympani Muscle**
*tendo m. tensoris tympani*

12 **Anterior Malleolar Fold**
*plica mallearis anterior*

**Note:** 1. The **chorda tympani**-3 originates from facial nerve-3 near stylomastoid foramen and passes through middle ear.

2. Opening of auditory tube-9, in middle ear and its cartilaginous portion-11.

3. **Intermedius nerve**-8 between facial and vestibulocochlear nerves-8.

**438.** See preceding page.

## 440. Lateral Wall of Right Tympanic Cavity. (Seen from medial side) (5/1)

A saw cut was made approximately parallel to the tympanic membrane. Tendon of tensor tympani was cut and its insertion into the malleus was removed.

1 **Incudomallear Joint**
*articulatio incudomallearis*
**Body of Incus**
*corpus incudis*

2 **Short Crus of Incus**
*crus breve incudis*
**Posterior Ligament of Incus**
*ligament. incudis posterius*

5 **Posterior Malleolar Fold**
*plica mallearis posterior*
**Long Crus of Incus**
*crus longum incudis*

6 **Lenticular Process of Incus**
*processus lenticularis incudis*

7 **Posterior Recess of Tympanic Membrane**
*recessus membranae tympani posterior*
**Tympanic Membrane**
*membrana tympani*

8 **Umbo of Tympanic Membrane**
*umbo membranae tympani*
**Manubrium of Malleus**
*manubrium mallei*

9 **Anterior Recess of Tympanic Membrane**
*recessus membranae tympani anterior*
**Auditory Tube, Bony Portion**
*tuba auditiva (pars ossea)*

11 **Anterior Malleolar Fold**
*plica mallearis anterior*
**Head of Malleus**
*caput mallei*

12 **Epitympanic Recess**
*recessus epitympanicus*
**Chorda Tympani**
*chorda tympani*

**Note:** 1. Relations of **malleus**-11, **incus**-1, **tympanic membrane**-7 and auditory tube-9.

## 441. Lateral Wall of Tympanic Cavity of the Right Middle Ear.

(Seen from medial side) (5/1)

Dissection is similar to that illustrated in Figure 440, but the bone was sectioned so that the chorda tympani and aperture of tympanic canaliculus of chorda tympani-4 and a part of the facial nerve-5 were exposed. The carotid canal-8 was also opened. The tensor tympani tendon was divided, but its insertion on the malleus-10 retained. In both these illustrations, the mucosa or lining of the tympanic cavity is shown in pink.

1 **Head of Malleus**
*caput mallei*
**Superior Malleolar Ligament**
*ligamentum mallei superius*
**Superior Ligament of Incus**
*ligamentum incudis superius*
**Body of Incus**
*corpus incudis*

2 **Mucous Membrane of Tympanic Cavity**
*tunica mucosa tympani*
**Fold of Incus**
*plica incudis*
**Short Crus of Incus**
*crus breve incudis*

3 **Fossa of Incus**
*fossa incudis*
**Posterior Ligament of Incus**
*ligamentum incudis posterius*

4 **Long Crus of Incus**
*crus longum incudis*
**Posterior Malleolar Fold**
*plica mallearis posterior*
**Tympanic Aperture of Canaliculus of Chorda Tympani**
*apertura tympanica canaliculi chordae tympani*
**Posterior Recess of Tympanic Membrane**
*recessus membranae tympani post.*

5 **Lenticular Process of Incus**
*processus lenticularis incudis*
**Facial Nerve**
*nervus facialis*

6 **Handle of Malleus**
*manubrium mallei*
**Tympanic Membrane**
*membrana tympani*

7 **Fibrocartilaginous Ring**
*anulus fibrocartilagineus*

8 **Carotid Canal**
*canalis caroticus*

10 **Auditory Tube**
*tuba auditiva*
**Auditory Tube, Tympanic Opening**
*ostium tympanicum tubae auditivae*
**Anterior Recess of the Tympanic Membrane**
*recessus membranae tympani anterior*
**Tendon of the Tensor Tympani Muscle**
*tendo m. tensoris tympani*

11 **Chorda Tympani**
*chorda tympani*
**Anterior Malleolar Fold**
*plica mallearis anterior*

12 **Epitympanic Recess**
*recessus epitympanicus*

**Note:** 1. **Chorda tympani**-11 originating from **facial nerve**-5 in facial canal. It passes cranially through **canaliculus for the chorda tympani**-4, lateral to long process of incus-4 and medial to handle or manubrium of the malleus-6. (See also Figure 440-12)

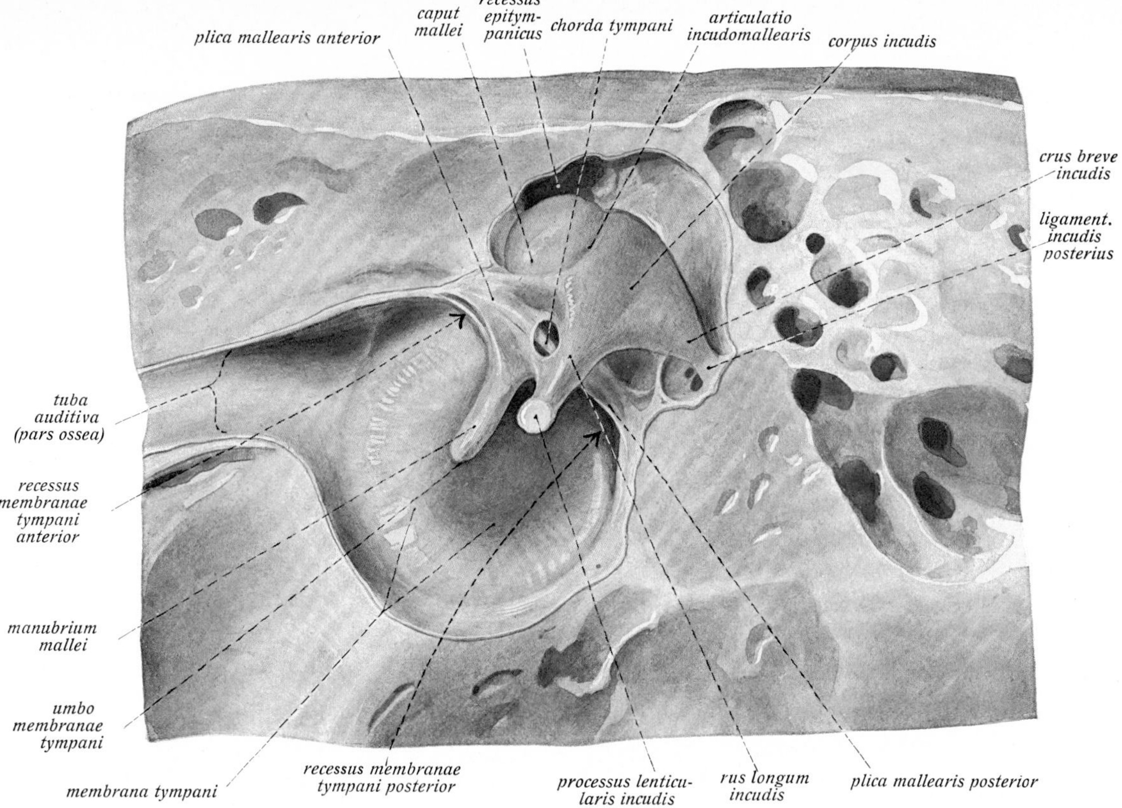

caput mallei
recessus epitym-panicus
chorda tympani
articulatio incudomallearis
plica mallearis anterior
corpus incudis
crus breve incudis
ligament. incudis posterius
tuba auditiva (pars ossea)
recessus membranae tympani anterior
manubrium mallei
umbo membranae tympani
membrana tympani
recessus membranae tympani posterior
processus lenticu-laris incudis
rus longum incudis
plica mallearis posterior


**Fig. 440.**

recessus epitym-panicus
caput mallei
ligamentum mallei superius
ligamentum incudis superius
corpus incudis
tunica mucosa tympani
plica incudis
plica mallearis anterior
chorda tympani
tendo m. tensoris tympani ×
recessus membranae tympani anterior
ostium tympanicum tubae auditivae
tuba auditiva
crus breve incudis
fossa incudis
ligamentum incudis posterius
crus longum incudis
plica mallearis posterior
apertura tympanica canaliculi chordae tympani
recessus membranae tympani post.
processus lenticularis incudis
nervus facialis ×
canalis caroticus
manubrium mallei
membrana tympani
anulus fibrocartilagineus

**Fig. 441.**

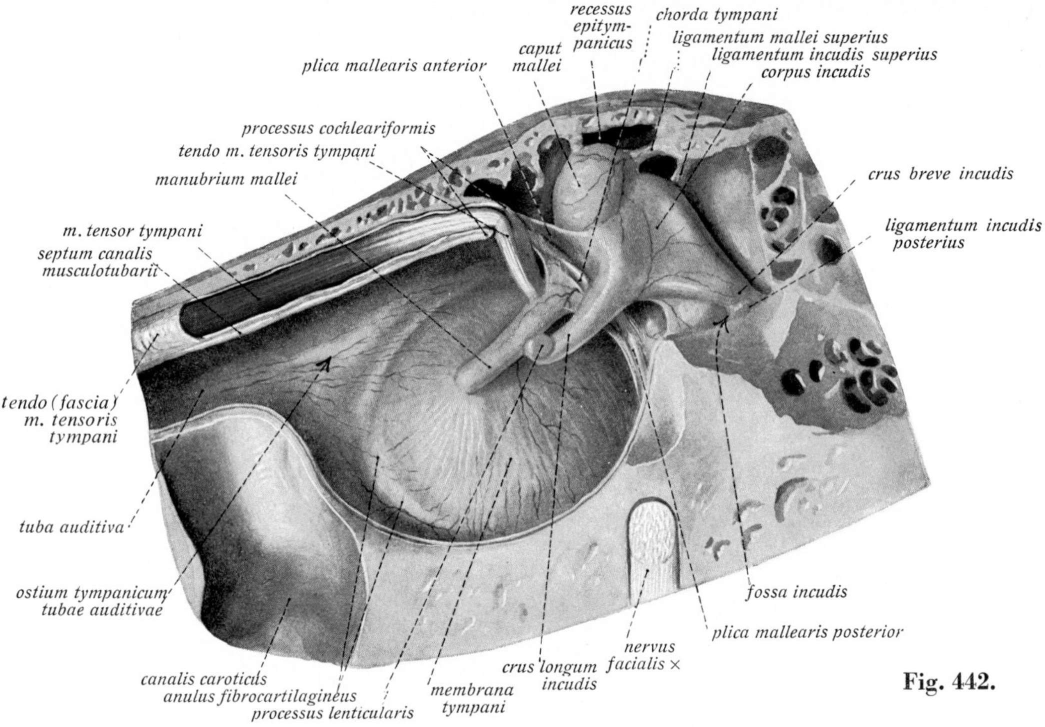
recessus epitympanicus
chorda tympani
caput mallei
ligamentum mallei superius
ligamentum incudis superius
plica mallearis anterior
corpus incudis
processus cochleariformis
tendo m. tensoris tympani
manubrium mallei
crus breve incudis
m. tensor tympani
ligamentum incudis posterius
septum canalis musculotubarii
tendo (fascia) m. tensoris tympani
tuba auditiva
ostium tympanicum tubae auditivae
fossa incudis
plica mallearis posterior
nervus facialis ×
crus longum incudis
canalis caroticus
anulus fibrocartilagineus
membrana tympani
processus lenticularis

**Fig. 442.**

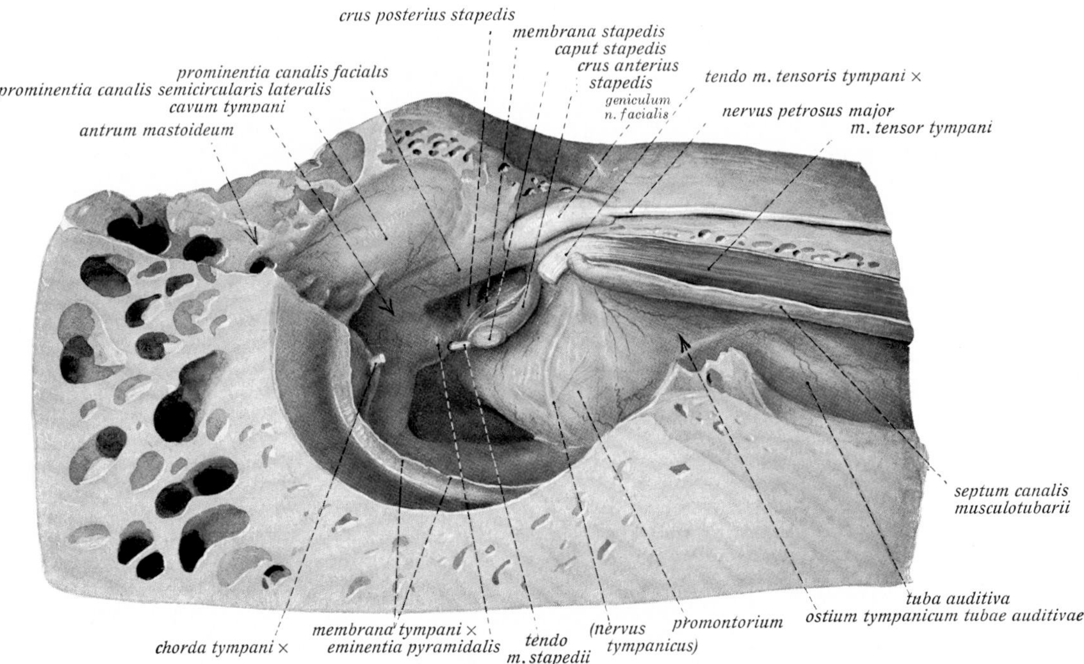
crus posterius stapedis
membrana stapedis
caput stapedis
crus anterius stapedis
prominentia canalis facialis
prominentia canalis semicircularis lateralis
tendo m. tensoris tympani ×
cavum tympani
geniculum n. facialis
nervus petrosus major
antrum mastoideum
m. tensor tympani
septum canalis musculotubarii
tuba auditiva
ostium tympanicum tubae auditivae
membrana tympani ×
(nervus tympanicus)
promontorium
chorda tympani ×
eminentia pyramidalis
tendo m. stapedii

**Fig. 443.**

## 442. Lateral Wall of Tympanic Cavity of Right Ear. (Seen from medial aspect) (5/1)

Dissection similar to Figures 440 and 441. More of roof of tympanic cavity was retained, so that tensor tympani muscle and its tendon-10, attaching to handle of the malleus-10, could be displayed.

1 **Chorda Tympani**
*chorda tympani*
**Superior Malleolar Ligament**
*ligamentum mallei superius*
**Superior Ligament of Incus**
*ligamentum incudis superius*
**Body of Incus**
*corpus incudis*

2 **Short Crus of Incus**
*crus breve incudis*
**Posterior Ligament of Incus**
*ligamentum incudis posterius*

4 **Fossa Incudis**
*fossa incudis*

5 **Posterior Malleolar Fold**
*plica mallearis posterior*
**Facial Nerve**
*nervus facialis*

6 **Long Crus of Incus**
*crus longum incudis*
**Tympanic Membrane**
*membrana tympani*

7 **Lenticular Process**
*processus lenticularis*

8 **Fibrocartilaginous Ring**
*anulus fibrocartilagineus*
**Carotid Canal**
*canalis caroticus*
**Tymp. Opening, Auditory Tube**
*ostium tympanicum tubae auditivae*
**Auditory Tube**
*tuba auditiva*

9 **Aponeurotic Sheath of Tensor Tympani Muscle**
*tendo (fascia) m. tensoria tympani*

10 **Septum Canalis Musculotubarii**
*septum canalis musculotubarii*
**Tensor Tympani Muscle**
*m. tensor tympani*
**Handle of Malleus**
*manubrium mallei*
**Tendon, Tensor Tympani M.**
*tendo m. tensoris tympani*
**Cochleariform Process**
*processus cochleariformis*

11 **Anterior Malleolar Fold**
*plica mallearis anterior*

12 **Head of Malleus**
*caput mallei*
**Epitympanic Recess**
*recessus epitympanicus*

## 443. Medial Wall of Tympanic Cavity of Right Ear. (Seen from lateral aspect) (5/1)

Lateral wall and roof of tympanic cavity and most of the external auditory meatus were removed. A narrow rim of tympanic membrane-7 was retained. Malleus and incus were removed. **Chorda tympani**-8 was divided where it enters tympanic cavity through the tympanic orifice of its caniliculus. Most of the lateral wall of the canalis musculotubarii was removed to expose the **tensor tympani muscle**-2, and its tendon was cut. **Facial nerve**-1 was exposed for a short distance near the geniculate ganglion and the **greater petrosal nerve**-2 was dissected, where it emerges from the hiatus of the facial canal and enters the middle cranial fossa.

1 **Head of Stapes**
*caput stapedis*
**Anterior Crus of Stapes**
*crus anterius stapedis*
**Genu of Facial Nerve**
*geniculum n facialis*
**Tendon, Tensor Tympani M.**
*tendo m. tensoris tympani*

2 **Greater Petrosal Nerve**
*nervus petrosus major*
**Tensor Tympani Muscle**
*m. tensor tympani*

4 **Septum Canalis Musculotubarii**
*septum canalis musculotubarii*
**Auditory Tube**
*tuba auditiva*
**Tymp. Opening, Auditory Tube**
*ostium tympanicum tubae auditivae*

5 **Promontory**
*promontorium*
**Tympanic Nerve**
*(nervus tympanicus)*

6 **Tendon of Stapedius M.**
*tendo m. stapedii*

7 **Pyramidal Eminence**
*eminentia pyramidalis*
**Tympanic Membrane**
*membrana tympani*

8 **Chorda Tympani**
*chorda tympani*

10 **Mastoid Antrum**
*antrum mastoideum*
**Tympanic Cavity**
*cavum tympani*
**Prominence of Lateral Semicircular Canal**
*promin. can. semicircularis lat.*

11 **Prominence of Facial Canal**
*prominentia canalis facialis*

12 **Posterior Crus of Stapes**
*crus posterius stapedis*
**Membrane of Stapes**
*membrana stapedis*

**Note:** 1. **Tympanic nerve**-5 (glossopharyngeal) may be seen through mucous membrane of middle ear as it passes through **tympanic plexus on the promontory**-5.

2. **Tendon of stapedius muscle**-6 emerging from orifice in **pyramidal eminence**-7 to attach to **posterior crus of the stapes**-12 near neck.

## 444. Medial Wall of Tympanic Cavity of Right Ear. (Seen from lateral side) (5/1)

Dissection similar to Figure 443, but part of dorsal wall of tympanic cavity was removed and the lateral wall of pyramidal eminence was chiseled away to display the **stapedius muscle**-9. Facial canal, lateral semicircular canal, and carotid canal were partially opened.

1 **Cochleariform Process**
*processus cochleariformis*
**Greater Petrosal Nerve**
*nervus petrosus major*
**Tensor Tympani Muscle**
*musc. tensor tympani*
**Septum Canalis Musculotubarii**
*septum canalis musculotubarii*
**Auditory Tube, Tympanic Opening**
*ostium tympanicum tubae auditivae*
**Auditory Tube**
*tuba auditiva*

5 **Carotid Canal**
*canalis caroticus*
**Promontory**
*promontorium*

6 **Tympanic Nerve**
*nervus tympanicus*

7 **Fossula of Cochlear Window**
*fossula fenestrae cochleae*

8 **Tympanic Cavity**
*cavum tympani*

9 **Stapedius Muscle**
*musc. stapedius*
**Facial Nerve**
*nervus facialis*

11 **Lateral Semicircular Canal**
*canalis semicircularis lateralis*

12 **Head of Stapes**
*caput stapedis*
**Prominence of Facial Canal**
*prominentia canalis facialis*
**Facial Nerve**
*nervus facialis*

**Note:** 1. **Fossula**-7 of **cochlear window** and **stapes**-12 in fenestra vestibuli.

2. **Tympanic nerve**-6, a branch of glossopharyngeal, entering floor of tympanic cavity near medial wall. It ascends in a groove on **promontory**-5 to unite with other nerve twigs from facial nerve to form tympanic plexus. Most fibers from tympanic nerve continue on through tympanic plexus and emerge in middle cranial fossa as lesser petrosal nerve which passes to otic ganglion through either foramen ovali or canaliculus innominatus.

## 445. Medial Wall of Tympanic Cavity of Right Ear. (Seen from lateral side) (5/1)

This depicts position of **stapes**-8, **facial nerve**-8, and **auditory tube,** and their relationship to each other and the middle ear. Tympanic cavity was divided almost parallel to the long axis of the petrous temporal bone. Lateral half of middle ear removed. Septum of musculotubal canal-3 was removed, but cochleariform process-3 was left intact. The **facial canal**-7 was opened from the hiatus canalis facialis (geniculum) to stylomastoid foramen, and lateral semicircular canal-12 was opened where it bulges into middle ear (prominence of lateral semicircular canal). **Lateral semicircular duct**-11 is visible in canal.

1 **Stapedial Crura**
*crura stapedis*
**Greater Petrosal Nerve**
*nervus petrosus major*

2 **Tensor Tympani Muscle**
*m. tensor tympani*

3 **Semicanal of Tensor Tympani Muscle**
*semicanalis m. tensoris tympani*
**Septum Canalis Musculotubarii**
*septum canalis musculotubarii*
**Auditory Tube, Semicanal**
*semicanalis tubae auditivae*
**Cochleariform Process**
*processus cochleariformis*

4 **Promontory**
*promontorium*
**Tympanic Nerve**
*nervus tympanicus*
**Tympanic Cavity**
*cavum tympani*

6 **Tympanic Sinus**
*sinus tympani*

7 **Facial Canal (Stylomastoid Foramen)**
*canalis facialis (foramen stylomastoideum)*

8 **Facial Nerve**
*nervus facialis*
**Head of Stapes**
*caput stapedis*

9 **Pyramidal Eminence**
*eminentia pyramidalis*

10 **Tendon of Stapedius Muscle**
*tendo musculi stapedii*

11 **Stapedial Membrane**
*membrana stapedis*
**Lateral Semicircular Duct**
*ductus semicircularis lateralis*

12 **Lateral Semicircular Canal**
*canalis semicircularis lateralis*
**Genu of Facial Nerve**
**geniculum n. facialis*
**Tendon of Tensor Tympani Muscle**
*tendo m. tensoris tympani*

**Note:** 1. **Tendon of stapedius muscle**-10, where it emerges from opening in **pyramidal eminence**-9, attaches to posterior crus (or neck) of stapes-1.

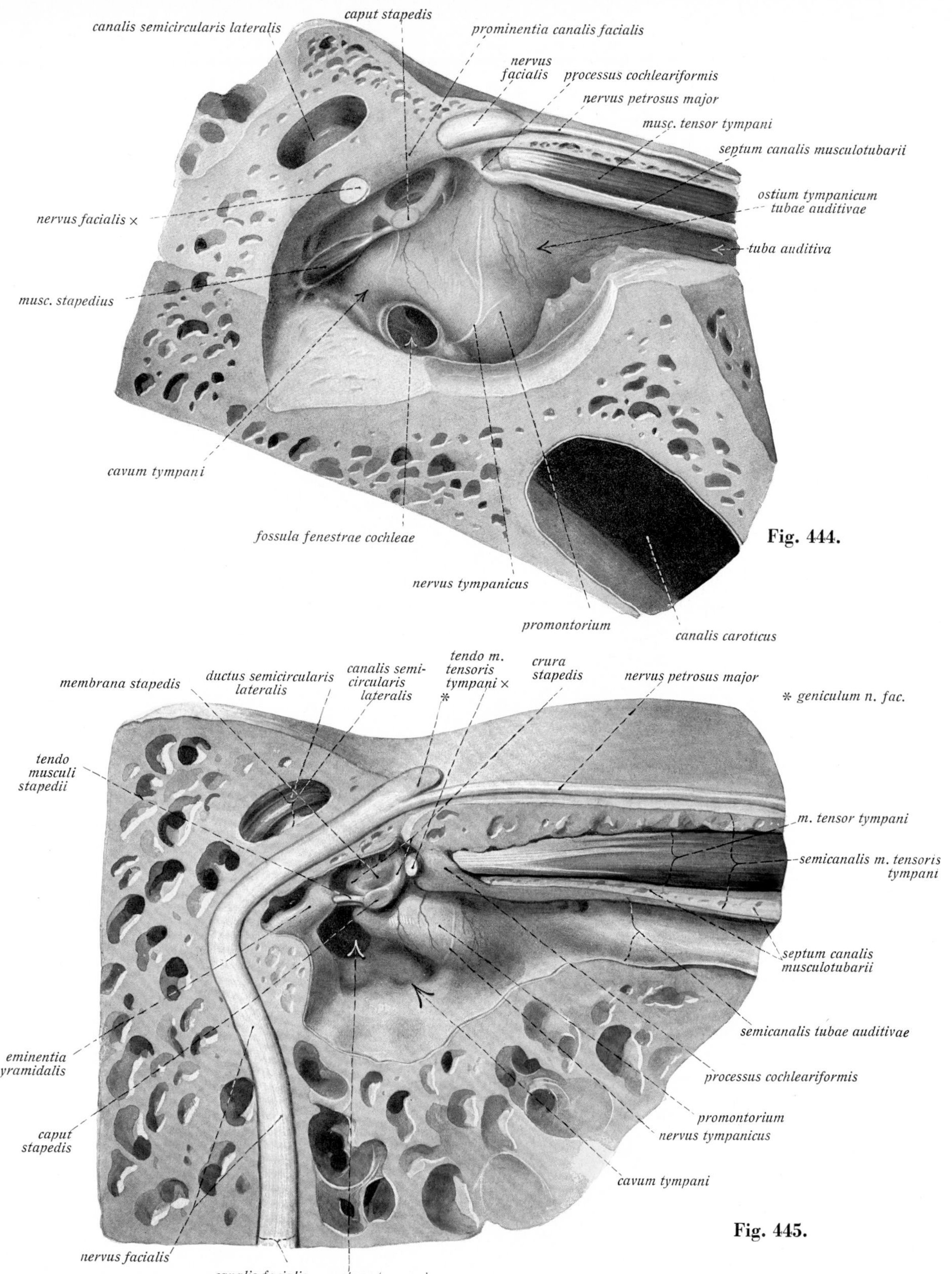
canalis semicircularis lateralis
caput stapedis
prominentia canalis facialis
nervus facialis
processus cochleariformis
nervus petrosus major
musc. tensor tympani
septum canalis musculotubarii
ostium tympanicum tubae auditivae
tuba auditiva
nervus facialis ×
musc. stapedius
cavum tympani
fossula fenestrae cochleae
nervus tympanicus
promontorium
canalis caroticus

Fig. 444.

membrana stapedis
ductus semicircularis lateralis
canalis semicircularis lateralis
tendo m. tensoris tympani ×
*
crura stapedis
nervus petrosus major
* geniculum n. fac.
tendo musculi stapedii
m. tensor tympani
semicanalis m. tensoris tympani
septum canalis musculotubarii
semicanalis tubae auditivae
eminentia pyramidalis
processus cochleariformis
caput stapedis
promontorium
nervus tympanicus
cavum tympani
nervus facialis
canalis facialis (foramen stylomastoideum)
sinus tympani

Fig. 445.

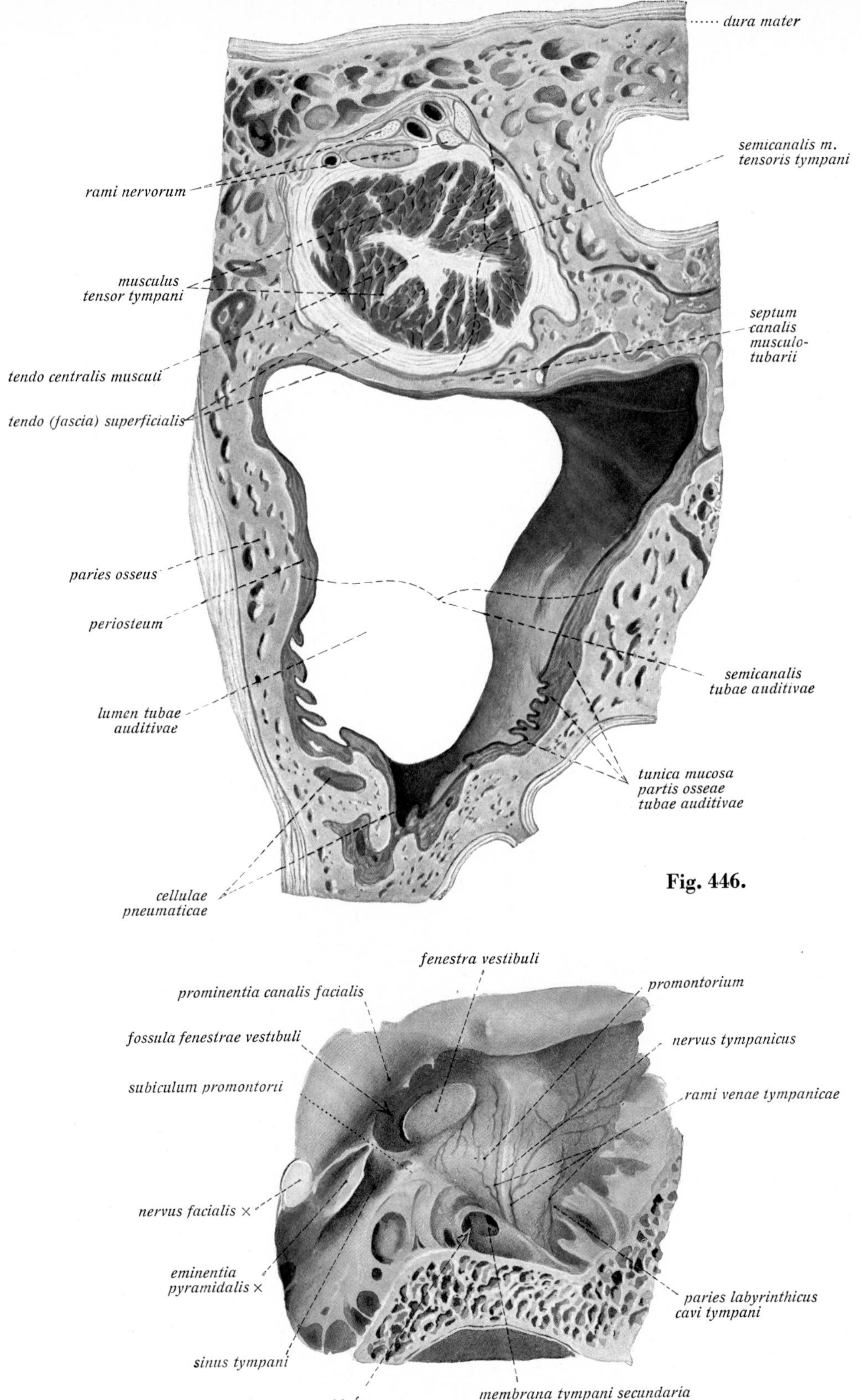
dura mater
semicanalis m. tensoris tympani
rami nervorum
musculus tensor tympani
septum canalis musculo-tubarii
tendo centralis musculi
tendo (fascia) superficialis
paries osseus
periosteum
semicanalis tubae auditivae
lumen tubae auditivae
tunica mucosa partis osseae tubae auditivae
cellulae pneumaticae
fenestra vestibuli
prominentia canalis facialis
promontorium
fossula fenestrae vestibuli
nervus tympanicus
subiculum promontorii
rami venae tympanicae
nervus facialis ×
eminentia pyramidalis ×
paries labyrinthicus cavi tympani
sinus tympani
membrana tympani secundaria
fossula fenestrae cochleae

**Fig. 446.**

**Fig. 447.**

## 446. Cross Section of Canalis Musculotubarius. (Showing tensor tympani muscle and bony portion of auditory tube.) (20/1)

1 **Dura Mater**
*dura mater*

**Semicanal of Tensor Tympani Muscle**
*semicanalis m. tensoris tympani*

2 **Septum Canalis Musculotubarii**
*septum canalis musculotubarii*

4 **Semicanal of Auditory Tube**
*semicanalis tubae auditivae*

5 **Mucosal Layer of Bony Part of Auditory Tube**
*tunica mucosa partis osseae tubae auditivae*

7 **Air Cells**
*cellulae pneumaticae*

8 **Lumen of Auditory Tube**
*lumen tubae auditivae*
**Periosteum**
*periosteum*

**Bony Wall**
*paries osseus*

9 **Periosteal Aponeurotic Sheath**
(See Figs. 438, 442)
*tendo (fascia) superficialis*
**Central Muscular Tendon**
*tendo centralis musculi*

10 **Tensor Tympani Muscle**
*musculus tensor tympani*
**Nerve Branches**
*rami nervorum*

**Note:** 1. Tendo (fascia) superficialis-9 is a thick periosteal aponeurotic sheath which lines semicanal for tensor tympani muscle. (See Figs. 438, 442)

## 447. Fenestra Vestibuli and Fenestra Cochleae of Right Tympanic Cavity. (Seen from lateral side) (6/1)

**Pyramidal eminence**-8 was opened. Stapes and stapedius muscle were removed to expose **fenestra vestibuli**-12. Enough bone was chiseled off to expose fenestra cochleae-7 and **secondary tympanic membrane**-6 as well as adjacent folds of the mucosa. Blood vessels and the tympanic nerves-2 are seen through the mucous membrane on the promontory-1.

1 **Promontory**
*promontorium*

2 **Tympanic Nerve**
*nervus tympanicus*

**Branches of Tympanic Vein**
*rami venae tympanicae*

4 **Labyrinthine Wall of Tympanic Cavity**
*paries labyrinthicus cavi tympani*

6 **Secondary Tympanic Membrane**
*membrana tympani secundaria*

7 **Fossula of Fenestra Cochleae**
*fossula fenestrae cochleae*

8 **Tympanic Sinus**
*sinus tympani*
**Pyramidal Eminence**
*eminentia pyramidalis*

9 **Facial Nerve**
*nervus facialis*

**Subiculum Promontorii**
*subiculum promontorii*

10 **Fossula of Fenestra Vestibuli**
*fossula fenestrae vestibuli*

**Prominence of Facial Canal**
*prominentia canalis facialis*

12 **Fenestra Vestibuli**
*fenestra vestibuli*

## 448. Frontal Section of External Auditory Meatus, Tympanic Cavity, and Cochlea. (2/1)

1 **Temporal Bone**
*os temporale*
**External Acoustic Meatus**
*meatus acusticus externus*
**External Acoustic Aperture (osseous)**
*porus acusticus externus*

2 **Auricular Cartilage**
*cartilago auriculae*
**Cartilaginous Portion of External Acoustic Meatus**
*meatus acusticus externus cartilagineus*

3 **Oblique Section through Wall of External Acoustic Meatus**
*sectio obliqua parietis meati acust. ext.*
**Tragi**
*tragi*
**External Acoustic Meatus**
*meatus acusticus externus*
**Auricular Cartilage**
*cartilago auriculae*

5 **Mastoid Cells**
*cellulae mastoideae*

7 **Hypotympanic Recess**
*recessus hypotympanicus*
**Atlas**
*atlas*
**Atlantooccipital Articulation**
*articulatio atlantooccipitalis*

8 **Superior Bulb of Internal Jugular Vein**
*bulbus venae jugularis superior*
**Occipital Bone**
*os occipitale*

9 **Cochlea**
*cochlea*
**Cochlear Portion of Vestibulocochlear Nerve**
*pars cochlearis n. statoacustici [n. vestibulicochlearis]*

10 **Petrous Portion of Temporal Bone**
*pars petrosa ossis temporalis*

11 **Tensor Tympani Muscle**
*musculus tensor tympani*

12 **Epitympanic Recess**
*recessus epitympanicus*
**Tendon of Tensor Tympani Muscle**
*tendo m. tensoris tympani*
**Superior Malleolar Ligament**
*ligam. mallei superius*
**Head of Malleus**
*caput mallei*
**Epitympanic Recess (Apical Part)**
+
**Chorda Tympani**
*chorda tympani*
**Tympanic Membrane**
*membrana tympani*

**Note:** 1. **Tympanic membrane**-12 occupies a plane which is oblique to the axis of the external auditory meatus-3.

2. **Cochlea**-9 is responsible for a slight protrusion of the osseus wall into the middle ear. This forms the promontory.

3. **Proximity of bulb of jugular vein**-8 to the **cavity of middle ear.**

## 449. Frontal Section Through Right External Auditory Meatus, Tympanic Membrane and Tympanic Cavity. (4/1)

The **tensor tympani muscle**-2 was cut transversely near the point where it becomes tendinous.

1 **Manubrium of Malleus**
*manubrium mallei*
**Tendon of Tensor Tympani Muscle**
*tendo m. tensoris tympani*

2 **Tensor Tympani Muscle**
*m. tensor tympani*
**Processus Cochleariformis**
*processus cochleariformis*
**Promontory**
*promontorium*

3 **Tympanic Cavity (Middle Ear)**
*cavum tympani*
**Hypotympanic Recess**
*recessus hypotympanicus*
**Carotid Canal**
*canalis caroticus*

5 **Carotid Canal**
*canalis caroticus*

6 **Fibrocartilaginous Ring**
*anulus fibrocartilagineus*

7 **Tympanic Sulcus**
*sulcus tympanicus*
**Tympanic Membrane**
*membrana tympani*

8 **Umbo of Tympanic Membrane**
*umbo membranae tympani*
**Stapes**
*stapes*
**Chorda Tympani**
*chorda tympani*

9 **External Acoustic Meatus**
*meatus acusticus externus*
**Sup. Tympanic Membrane Rec.**
*recessus membranae tympani sup.*
**Lateral Ligament of Malleus**
*lig. mallei laterale*
**Tympanic Cavity (Middle Ear)**
*cavum tympani*
**Body of Incus**
*corpus incudis*

10 **Epitympanic Recess, Cupula Part**
*pars cupularis rec. epitympanici*

12 **Superior Ligament of Malleus**
*ligamentum mallei superius*
**Epitympanic Recess**
*recessus epitympanicus*
**Head of Malleus**
*caput mallei*
**Chorda Tympani + Anterior Malleolar Fold**
*chorda tympani + plica mallearis anterior*

**Note:** 1. **Relationship of auditory ossicles** to: a) **tympanic membrane**-7; b) **tensor tympani muscle**-2; c) and **promontory**-2 caused by the bulge of the cochlear apparatus into the middle ear.

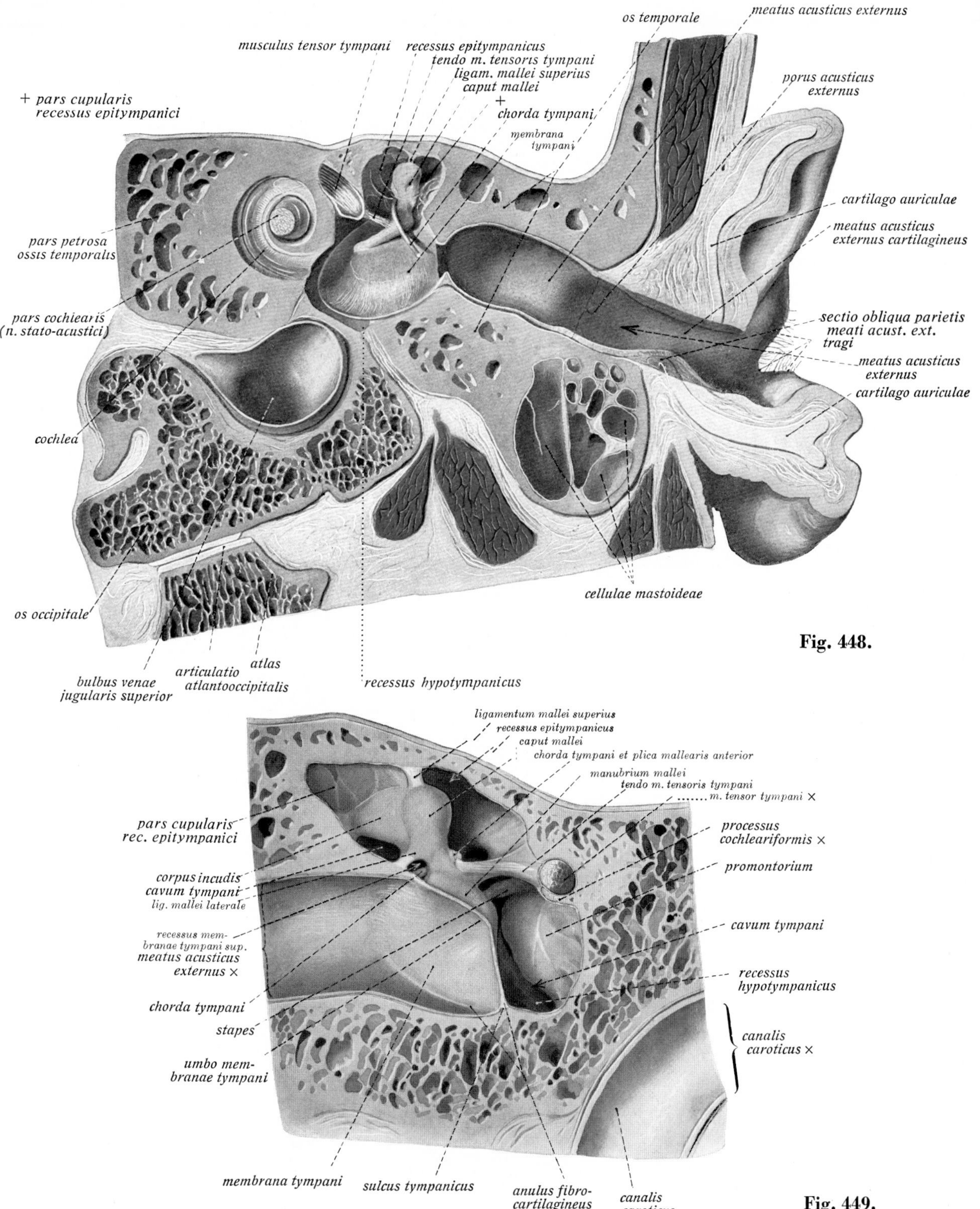
os temporale
meatus acusticus externus
musculus tensor tympani
recessus epitympanicus
tendo m. tensoris tympani
ligam. mallei superius
caput mallei
+ pars cupularis recessus epitympanici
+ chorda tympani
membrana tympani
porus acusticus externus
cartilago auriculae
pars petrosa ossis temporalis
meatus acusticus externus cartilagineus
pars cochlearis (n. stato-acustici)
sectio obliqua parietis meati acust. ext. tragi
meatus acusticus externus
cartilago auriculae
cochlea
cellulae mastoideae
os occipitale
atlas
articulatio atlantooccipitalis
bulbus venae jugularis superior
recessus hypotympanicus

**Fig. 448.**

ligamentum mallei superius
recessus epitympanicus
caput mallei
chorda tympani et plica mallearis anterior
manubrium mallei
tendo m. tensoris tympani
m. tensor tympani ×
pars cupularis rec. epitympanici
processus cochleariformis ×
promontorium
corpus incudis
cavum tympani
lig. mallei laterale
recessus membranae tympani sup.
meatus acusticus externus ×
cavum tympani
recessus hypotympanicus
chorda tympani
stapes
canalis caroticus ×
umbo membranae tympani
membrana tympani
sulcus tympanicus
anulus fibrocartilagineus
canalis caroticus

**Fig. 449.**

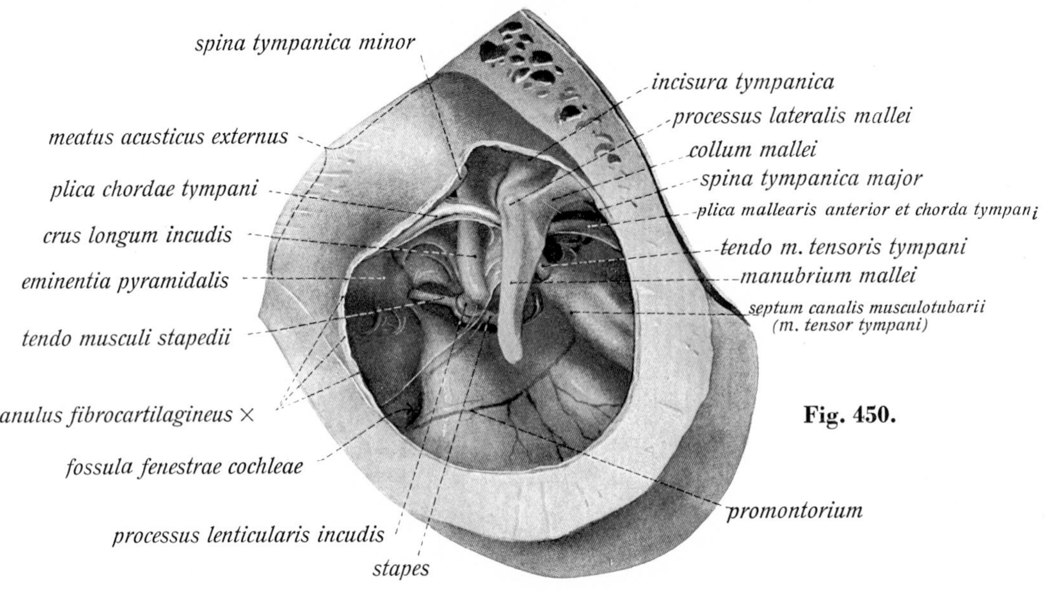
spina tympanica minor
meatus acusticus externus
plica chordae tympani
crus longum incudis
eminentia pyramidalis
tendo musculi stapedii
anulus fibrocartilagineus ×
fossula fenestrae cochleae
processus lenticularis incudis
stapes
incisura tympanica
processus lateralis mallei
collum mallei
spina tympanica major
plica mallearis anterior et chorda tympani
tendo m. tensoris tympani
manubrium mallei
septum canalis musculotubarii
(m. tensor tympani)
promontorium

**Fig. 450.**

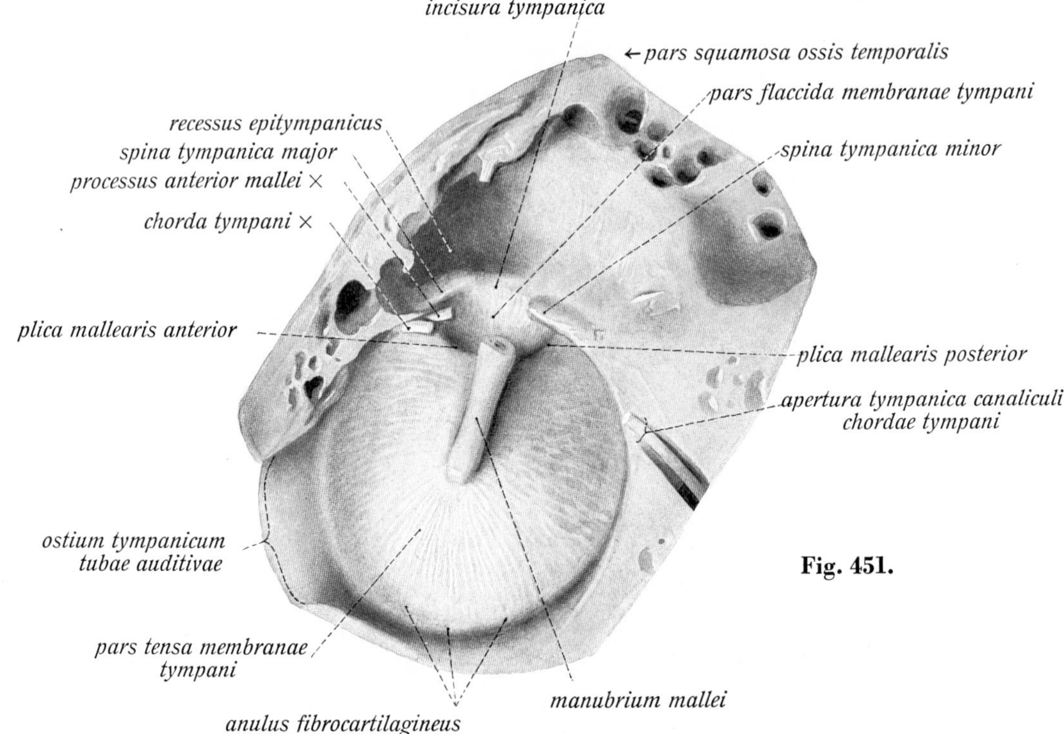
incisura tympanica
← pars squamosa ossis temporalis
pars flaccida membranae tympani
recessus epitympanicus
spina tympanica major
processus anterior mallei ×
chorda tympani ×
spina tympanica minor
plica mallearis anterior
plica mallearis posterior
apertura tympanica canaliculi
chordae tympani
ostium tympanicum
tubae auditivae
pars tensa membranae
tympani
anulus fibrocartilagineus
manubrium mallei

**Fig. 451.**

## 450. Right Tympanic Cavity Viewed Through External Auditory Meatus after Removal of Tympanic Membrane. (5/1)

Most of external auditory meatus was chiseled away and the tympanic membrane was removed, leaving only a very small margin.

1 **Tympanic Notch**
*incisura tympanica*

2 **Lateral Process of Malleus**
*processus lateralis mallei*

**Neck of Malleus**
*collum mallei*

**Greater Tympanic Spine**
*spina tympanica major*

**Anterior Malleolar Fold + Chorda Tympani**
*plica mallearis anterior + chorda tympani*

3 **Tendon of Tensor Tympani Muscle**
*tendo m. tensoris tympani*

**Manubrium of Malleus**
*manubrium mallei*

**Septum Canalis Musculotubarii (Tensor Tympanic Muscle)**
*septum canalis musculotubarii (m. tensor tympani)*

5 **Promontory**
*promontorium*

7 **Stapes**
*stapes*

**Lenticular Process of Incus**
*processus lenticularis incudis*

8 **Fossula of Fenestra Cochleae**
*fossula fenestrae cochleae*

9 **Fibrocartilaginous Ring**
*anulus fibrocartilagineus*

**Tendon of Stapedius Muscle**
*tendo musculi stapedii*

**Pyramidal Eminence**
*eminentia pyramidalis*

**Long Crus of Incus**
*crus longum incudis*

10 **Fold of Chorda Tympani**
*plica chordae tympani*

**External Acoustic Meatus**
*meatus acusticus externus*

11 **Lesser Tympanic Spine**
*spina tympanica minor*

**Note:** 1. The **chain of auditory ossicles.**
2. **Tendons of stapedius**-9 **and tensor tympani muscles**-3.
3. Course of **chorda tympani**-2, -10.

## 451. Lateral Wall of Right Tympanic Cavity (Membranous Wall) and Tympanic Surface of Tympanic Membrane. (Viewed from medial side, the tympanic cavity side) (5/1)

The temporal bone was cut parallel to the tympanic membrane. This cut the bone almost parallel to long axis of petrous portion of temporal bone. **Handle of malleus**-6 was cut off and left attached to **tympanic membrane**-8.

1 **Squamous Portion of Temporal Bone**
*pars squamosa ossis temporalis*
**Tympanic Membrane, Pars Flaccida**
*pars flaccida membranae tympani*

2 **Lesser Tympanic Spine**
*spina tympanica minor*

3 **Posterior Malleolar Fold**
*plica mallearis posterior*
**Tympanic Aperture of Canaliculus for Chorda Tympani**
*apertura tympanica canaliculi chordae tympani*

6 **Handle of Malleus**
*manubrium mallei*

7 **Fibrocartilaginous Ring**
*anulus fibrocartilagineus*

8 **Tympanic Membrane, Pars Tensa**
*pars tensa membranae tympani*

**Tympanic Opening of Auditory Tube**
*ostium tympanicum tubae auditivae*

9 **Anterior Malleolar Fold**
*plica mallearis anterior*

10 **Chorda Tympani**
*chorda tympani*

**Anterior Malleolar Process**
*processus anterior mallei*

**Greater Tympanic Spine**
*spina tympanica major*

11 **Epitympanic Recess**
*recessus epitympanicus*

12 **Tympanic Notch**
*incisura tympanica*

**Note:** 1. Major part of **tympanic membrane**, held taut by pull of tensor tympani muscle on the malleus, is called the **pars tensa**-8. Small upper portion near tympanic notch-12 is not tense, but loose and is, therefore, called the **flaccid portion**-1.

## 452. Right Tympanic Membrane in Living Person as seen through Otoscope. (illustration by Lepier) (about 6/1)

## 453. Natural Size of Eardrum in mm.

**Note:** 1. The normal eardrum is not circular, but oval in shape. The narrow diameter is 8 to 9 mm, and the long diameter is 10 to 11 mm.

## 454. Labeled Line Diagram of Figure 452.

1 **Anterior Malleolar Fold**
*plica mallearis ant.*

**Malleolar Prominence (Lateral Malleolar Process)**
*prominentia mallearis (proc. lateralis mallei)*

2 **Manubrium of Malleus**
*stria mallearis (manubrium mallei)*

3 **Anterior Wall of External Acoustic Meatus**
*paries ant. meatus acustici externi*

**Umbo of Tympanic Membrane**
*umbo membranae tympani*

4 **Tympanic Membrane, Pars Tensa**
*pars tensa membranae tympani*

5 ****Cone of Light**
**

6 **Fibrocartilaginous Ring**
*anulus fibrocartilagineus*

7 **Tympanic Ring**
*anulus tympanicus*

8 **Fossula Fenestrae Cochleae**
*fossula fenestrae cochleae*

**Promontory**
*promontorium*

9 **Posterior Wall of External Acoustic Meatus**
*paries post. meatus acust. ext.*

**Posterior Crus of Stapes**
(+ seen through Tympanic Membrane)
*crus posterius stapedis* +

**Long Crus of Incus**
+ (seen through Tympanic Membrane)
*crus longum incudis* +

10 **Posterior Malleolar Fold**
*plica mallearis post.*

11 **Tympanic Membrane, Pars Flaccida**
*pars flaccida membranae tympani*

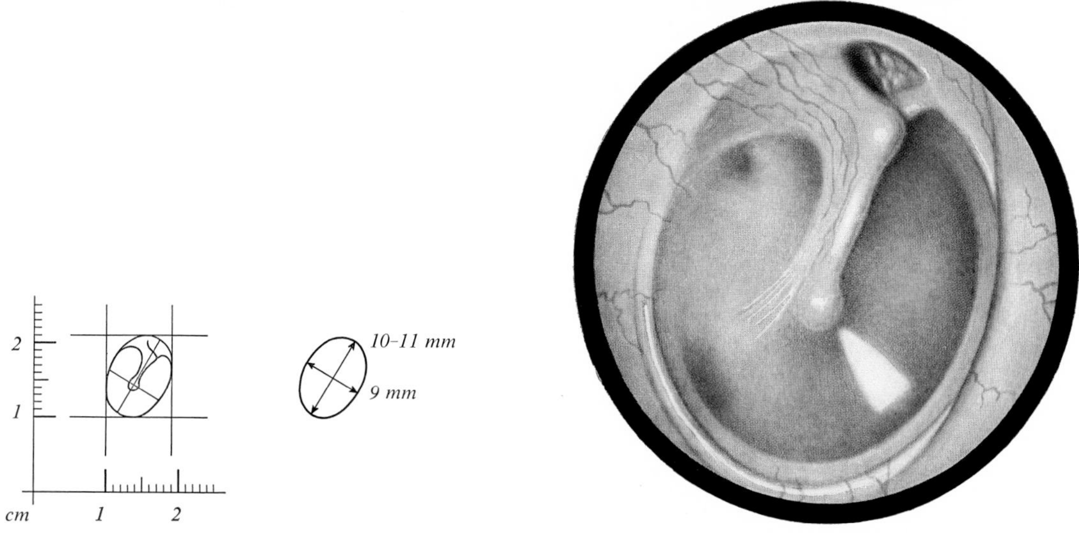

2
1
cm
1
2
10–11 mm
9 mm


**Fig. 453.**

**Fig. 452.**

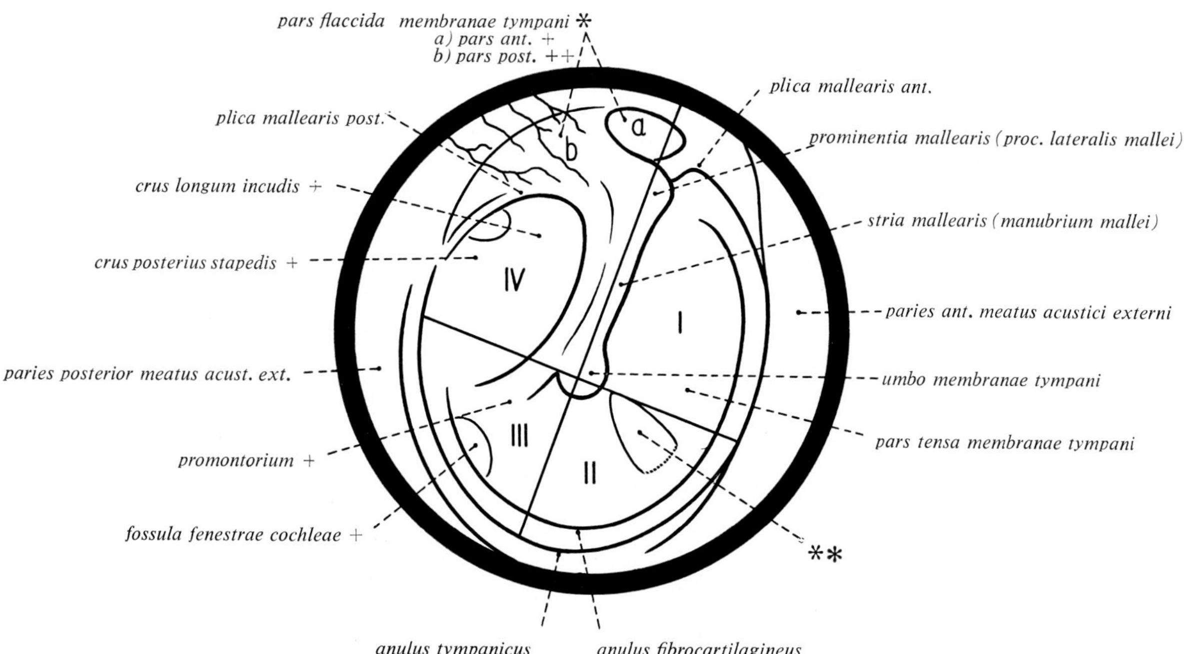

pars flaccida membranae tympani *
a) pars ant. +
b) pars post. ++
plica mallearis ant.
plica mallearis post.
prominentia mallearis (proc. lateralis mallei)
crus longum incudis +
stria mallearis (manubrium mallei)
crus posterius stapedis +
paries ant. meatus acustici externi
paries posterior meatus acust. ext.
umbo membranae tympani
pars tensa membranae tympani
promontorium +
fossula fenestrae cochleae +
**
anulus tympanicus
anulus fibrocartilagineus
a
b
I
II
III
IV


**Fig. 454.**

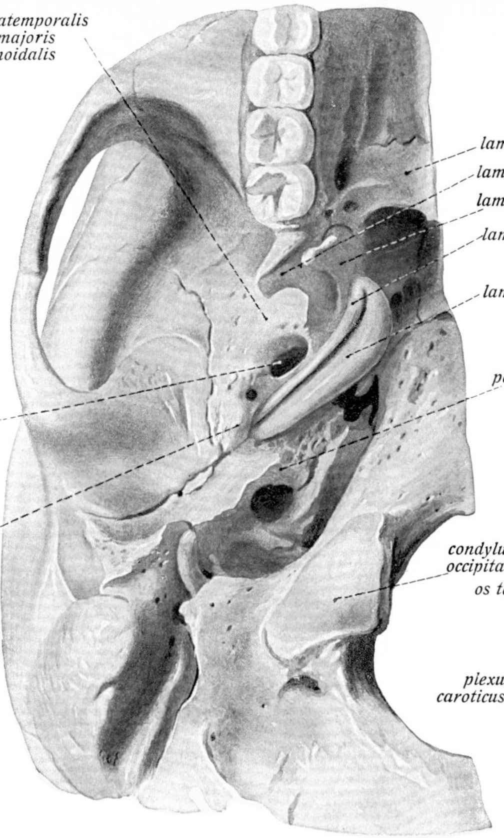

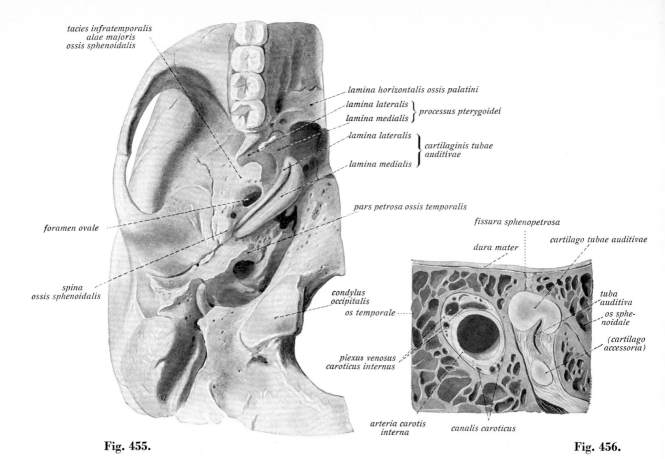

tacies infratemporalis alae majoris ossis sphenoidalis

lamina horizontalis ossis palatini

lamina lateralis } processus pterygoidei
lamina medialis }

lamina lateralis } cartilaginis tubae auditivae
lamina medialis }

foramen ovale

pars petrosa ossis temporalis

spina ossis sphenoidalis

condylus occipitalis

**Fig. 455.**

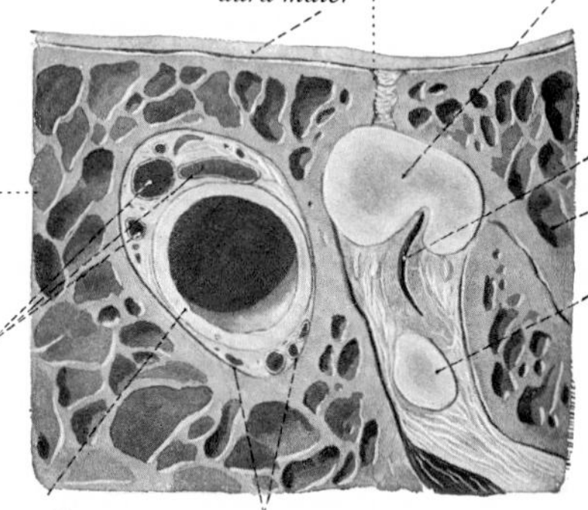

fissura sphenopetrosa

dura mater

cartilago tubae auditivae

tuba auditiva

os temporale

os sphenoidale

(cartilago accessoria)

plexus venosus caroticus internus

arteria carotis interna

canalis caroticus

**Fig. 456.**

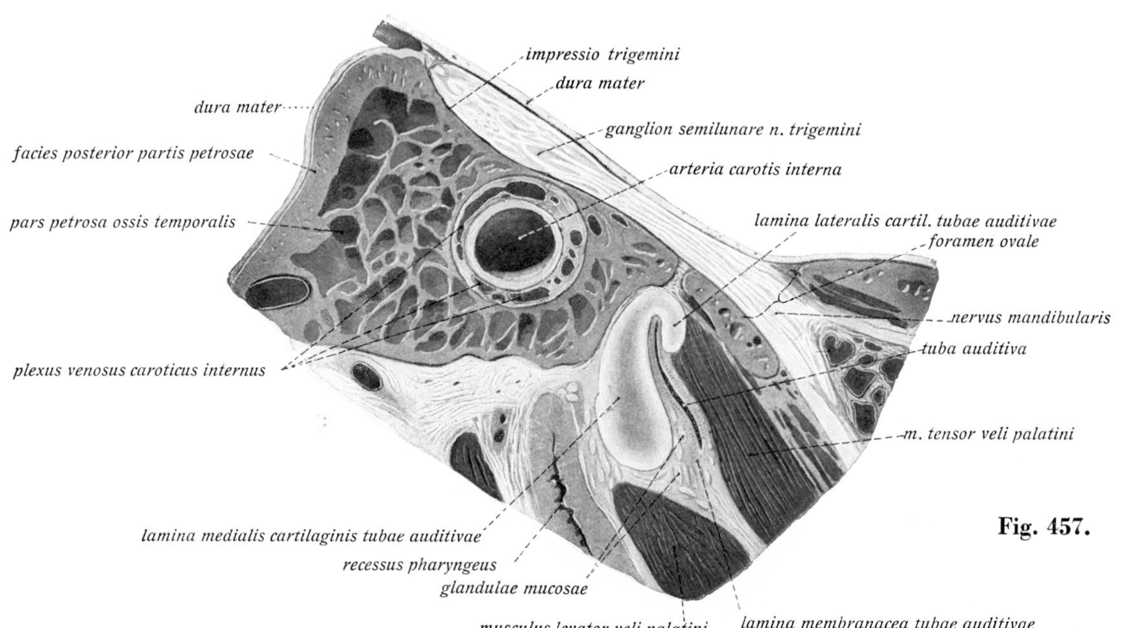
impressio trigemini
dura mater
dura mater
ganglion semilunare n. trigemini
facies posterior partis petrosae
arteria carotis interna
pars petrosa ossis temporalis
lamina lateralis cartil. tubae auditivae
foramen ovale
nervus mandibularis
plexus venosus caroticus internus
tuba auditiva
m. tensor veli palatini
lamina medialis cartilaginis tubae auditivae
recessus pharyngeus
glandulae mucosae
musculus levator veli palatini
lamina membranacea tubae auditivae

**Fig. 457.**

## 455. Cartilage of Right Auditory Tube in Normal Position at Base of Cranium. (1/1)

2 **Palatine Bone, Horizontal Lamina**
*lamina horizontalis ossis palatini*

**Lateral Lamina | Pterygoid**
**Medial Lamina | Process**

*lamina lateralis | processus*
*lamina medialis | pterygoidei*

**Lateral Lamina | Cartilaginous**
**Medial Lamina | Auditory Tube**

*lamina lateralis | cartilaginis*
*lamina medialis | tubae auditivae*

3 **Temporal Bone, Petrous Portion**
*pars petrosa ossis temporalis*

4 **Occipital Condyle**
*condylus occipitalis*

8 **Spine of Sphenoid Bone**
*spina ossis sphenoidalis*

9 **Foramen Ovale**
*foramen ovale*

11 **Sphenoid Bone, Infratemporal Surface of Greater Wing**
*facies infratemporalis alae majoris ossis sphenoidalis*

## 456. Cross Section of Left Auditory Tube Near Junction of Osseous and Cartilaginous Portions. (2/1)

1 **Cartilage of Auditory Tube**
*cartilago tubae auditivae*

2 **Auditory Tube**
*tuba auditiva*

3 **Sphenoid Bone**
*os sphenoidale*
**Accessory Cartilage**
*(cartilago accessoria)*

7 **Carotid Canal**
*canalis caroticus*

8 **Internal Carotid Artery**
*arteria carotis interna*

9 **Internal Carotid Venous Plexus**
*plexus venosus caroticus internus*

**Temporal Bone**
*os temporale*

11 **Dura Mater**
*dura mater*

12 **Sphenopetrosal Fissure**
*fissura sphenopetrosa*

**Note:** 1. At this plane, the lumen of auditory tube is slit-like in contrast to open space in the osseous portion. (See Fig. 446-4)

## 457. Cross Section of Cartilaginous Part of Left Auditory Tube Near Pharyngeal Opening or Ostium. (2/1)

1 **Internal Carotid Artery**
*arteria carotis interna*

2 **Auditory Tube, Lateral Cartilaginous Lamina**
*lamina lateralis cartil. tubae auditivae*

**Foramen Ovale**
*foramen ovale*

**Mandibular Nerve**
*nervus mandibularis*

**Auditory Tube**
*tuba auditiva*

4 **Tensor Veli Palatini Muscle**
*m. tensor veli palatini*

5 **Auditory Tube, Membranous Lamina**
*lamina membranacae tubae auditivae*

6 **Levator Veli Palatini Muscle**
*musculus levator veli palatini*
**Mucus Glands**
*glandulae mucosae*

7 **Pharyngeal Recess**
*recessus pharyngeus*

8 **Medial Cartilaginous Lamina of Auditory Tube**
*lamina medialis cartilaginis tubae auditivae*

9 **Internal Carotid Venous Plexus**
*plexus venosus caroticus int.*

**Petrous Portion of Temporal Bone**
*pars petrosa ossis temporalis*

10 **Post. Surface of Petrous Portion**
*facies posterior partis petrosae*
**Dura Mater**
*dura mater*

12 **Trigeminal Impression**
*impressio trigemini*
**Dura Mater**
*dura mater*
**[Trigeminal Ganglion]**
**Semilunar Ganglion of the Trigeminal Nerve**
*[ganglion trigeminale]*
*ganglion semilunare n. trigemini*

**Note:** 1. Lumen of **auditory tube**-3 is definitely slit-like and is only partially surrounded by cartilage of the auditory tube-2, -8.

2. **Tensor veli palatini** muscle-4 is attached to **lateral lamina**-2 of **cartilage of the auditory tube.**

3. When this muscle contracts during act of swallowing or yawning, it is said to pull on the lateral lamina which tends to open the slit-like auditory tube, thus making possible the equalization of pressures between the middle ear and pharyngeal or external pressures. Knowledge of these anatomical facts may be of value when barometric pressure changes occur with changes in altitude, such as experienced in airplanes and in elevators of tall buildings.

## 458. Cartilage of Right External Ear. (Seen from in front) (1/1)

1 **Spina Helicis**
*spina helicis*

2 **Temp. Bone, Squamous Portion**
*pars squamosa ossis temporalis*

3 **Notches of Cartilaginous Acoustic Meatus**
*incisurae cartilaginis meatus acustici*
**Temporal Bone, Tympanic Portion**
*pars tympanica ossis temporalis*

5 **Styloid Process**
*processus styloideus*

6 **Mastoid Process**
*processus mastoideus*

7 **Cartilage of Acoustic Meatus**
*cartilago meatus acustici*
**Intertragic Notch**
*incisura intertragica*
**Cauda Helicis**
*cauda helicis*

**Fissura Antitragohelicina**
*fissura antitragohelicina*

9 **Lamina Tragi**
*lamina tragi*

10 **Anthelix**
*anthelix*
**Scapha**
*scapha*

11 **Helix**
*helix*

**Note:** 1. This illustration shows natural relation of cartilage-7 to temporal bone. Ventral part of squamous portion-2 of temporal bone was cut off.

## 459. Right External Ear. (Seen from lateral side) (1/1)

1 **Triangular Fossa**
*fossa triangularis*
**Crura of Anthelix**
*crura anthelicis*

2 **Crus of Helix**
*crus helicis*
**Anterior Notch (of Ear)**
*incisura anterior (auris)*

3 **Tuberculum Supratragicum**
*tuberculum supratragicum*
**Tragus**
*tragus*

4 **External Acoustic Meatus**
*meatus acusticus externus*
**Intertragic Notch**
*incisura intertragica*

5 **Antitragus**
*antitragus*
**Lobule of Ear**
*lobulus auriculae*

6 **Antitragohelicine Fissure**
*fiss. antitragohelicina*

7 **Anthelix**
*anthelix*

8 **Helix**
*helix*
**Cavum Conchae**
*cavum conchae*
**Concha of Ear**
*concha auriculae*
**Scapha**
*scapha*

10 **Cymba Conchae**
*cymba conchae*
**Auricular Tubercle (Darwin's)**
*tuberculum auriculae*

12 **Helix**
*helix*

## 460. Cartilage of Right External Ear. (Seen from lateral side) (1/1)

1 **Triangular Fossa**
*fossa triangularis*

3 **Spina Helicis**
*spina helicis*

4 **Lamina Tragi**
*lamina tragi*

5 **Incisura Terminalis Auris**
*incisura terminalis auris*

6 **Intertragic Notch**
*incisura intertragica*
**Antitragus**
*antitragus*

7 **Cauda Helicis**
*cauda helicis*

8 **Fissura Antitragohelicina**
*fissura antitragohelicina*

**Concha (of Ear)**
*concha auriculae*

9 **Crus of Helix**
*crus helicis*

10 **Anthelix**
*anthelix*
**Scapha**
*scapha*
**Helix**
*helix*

## 461. Cartilage of Right External Ear. (Seen from medial side) (1/1)

1 **Eminentia Scaphae**
*eminentia scaphae*
**Sulcus Anthelicis Transversus**
*sulcus anthelicis transversus*
**Eminentia Conchae**
*eminentia conchae*

2 **Sulcus Cruris Helicis**
*sulcus cruris helicis*

4 **Isthmus of Ear Cartilage**
*isthmus cartilaginis auris*

5 **Cauda Helicis**
*cauda helicis*

6 **Fissura Antitragohelicina**
*fissura antitragohelicina*
**Incisura Terminalis Auris**
*incisura terminalis auris*
**Cartilage of Acoustic Meatus**
*cartilago meatus acustici*

8 **Lamina Tragi**
*lamina tragi*

9 **Spina Helicis**
*spina helicis*

11 **Eminentia Fossae Triangularis**
*eminentia fossae triangularis*

12 **Fossa Anthelicis**
*fossa anthelicis*

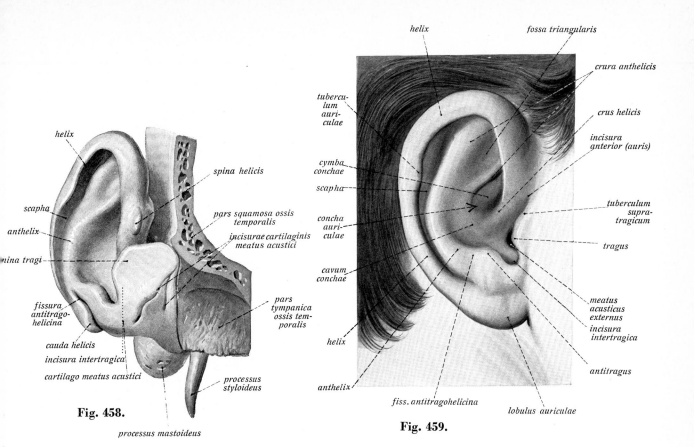

helix
spina helicis
scapha
pars squamosa ossis temporalis
anthelix
incisurae cartilaginis meatus acustici
[la]mina tragi
fissura antitrago-helicina
pars tympanica ossis temporalis
cauda helicis
incisura intertragica
cartilago meatus acustici
processus styloideus
processus mastoideus

**Fig. 458.**

helix
fossa triangularis
crura anthelicis
tuberculum auriculae
crus helicis
incisura anterior (auris)
cymba conchae
scapha
tuberculum supratragicum
concha auriculae
tragus
cavum conchae
meatus acusticus externus
incisura intertragica
helix
antitragus
anthelix
fiss. antitragohelicina
lobulus auriculae

**Fig. 459.**

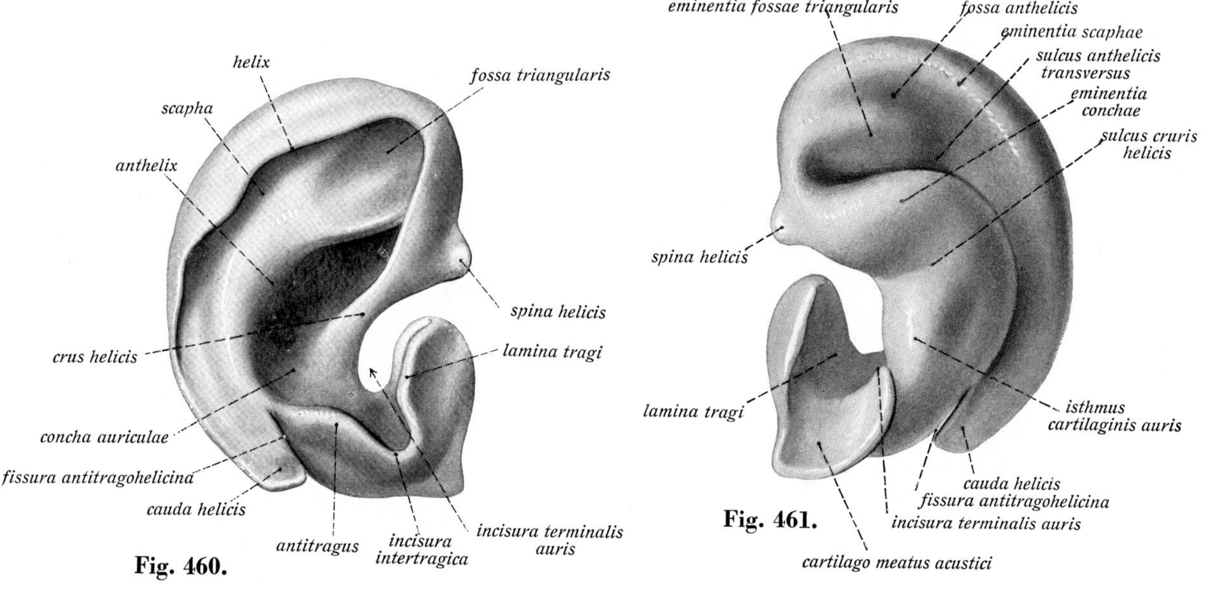
helix
scapha
fossa triangularis
anthelix
spina helicis
crus helicis
lamina tragi
concha auriculae
fissura antitragohelicina
cauda helicis
antitragus
incisura intertragica
incisura terminalis auris
eminentia fossae triangularis
fossa anthelicis
eminentia scaphae
sulcus anthelicis transversus
eminentia conchae
sulcus cruris helicis
spina helicis
lamina tragi
isthmus cartilaginis auris
cauda helicis
fissura antitragohelicina
incisura terminalis auris
cartilago meatus acustici

**Fig. 460.**

**Fig. 461.**

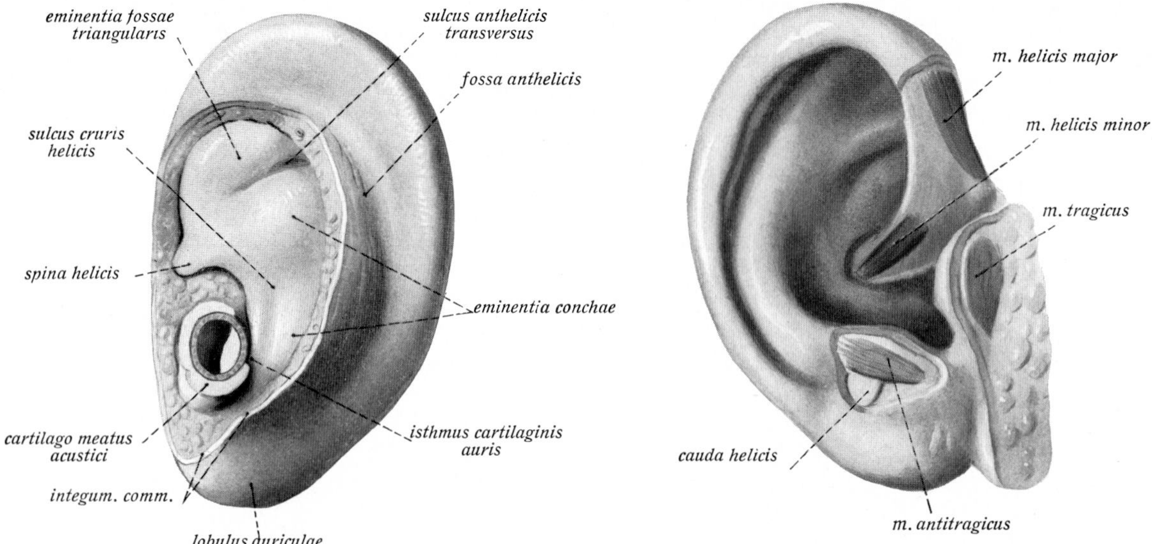
eminentia fossae
triangularis
sulcus anthelicis
transversus
fossa anthelicis
sulcus cruris
helicis
spina helicis
eminentia conchae
cartilago meatus
acustici
isthmus cartilaginis
auris
integum. comm.
lobulus auriculae
m. helicis major
m. helicis minor
m. tragicus
cauda helicis
m. antitragicus

Fig. 462.

Fig. 463.

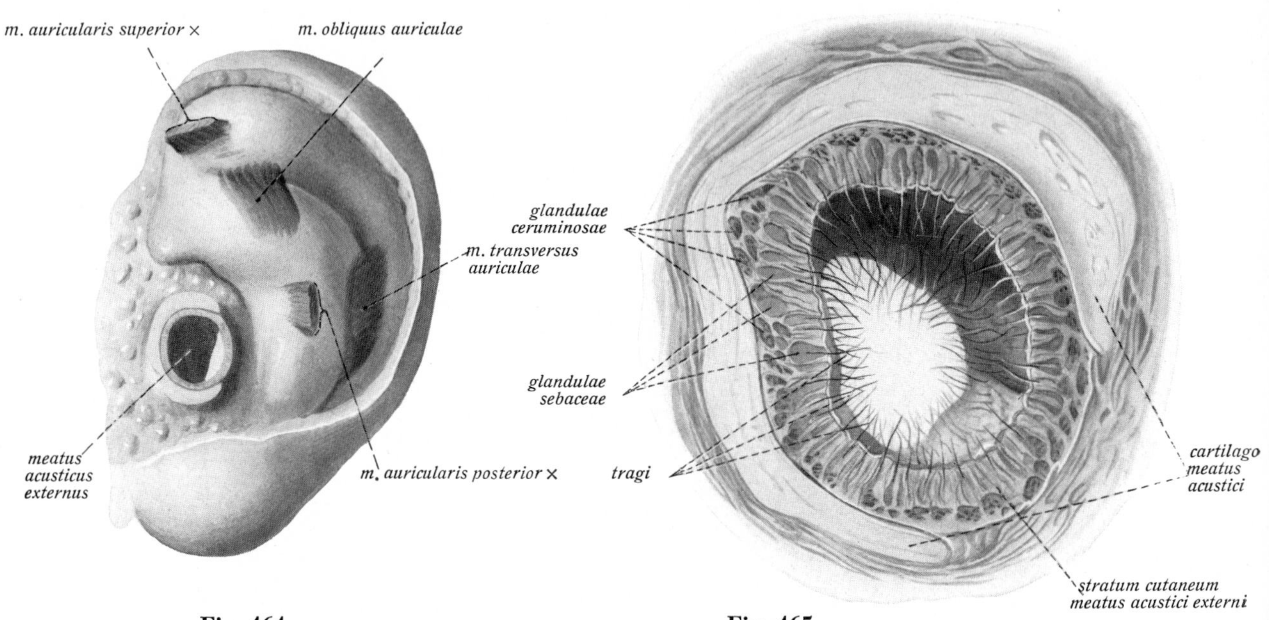
m. auricularis superior ×
m. obliquus auriculae
m. transversus
auriculae
meatus
acusticus
externus
m. auricularis posterior ×
glandulae
ceruminosae
glandulae
sebaceae
tragi
cartilago
meatus
acustici
stratum cutaneum
meatus acustici externi

Fig. 464.

Fig. 465.

## 462. Right External Ear, Removed from Head. (Seen from medial surface) (1/1)

1 **Sulcus Anthelicis Transversus**
*sulcus anthelicis transversus*
**Fossa Anthelicis**
*fossa anthelicis*
3 **Eminentia Conchae**
*eminentia conchae*
4 **Isthmus of Ear Cartilage**
*isthmus cartilaginis auris*

6 **Lobule of Ear**
*lobulus auriculae*

**Cut Margin of Skin**
*integum. comm.*

7 **Cartilage of Acoustic Meatus**
*cartilago meatus acustici*

9 **Spina Helicis**
*spina helicis*

10 **Sulcus Cruris Helicis**
*sulcus cruris helicis*

11 **Eminence of Fossa Triangularis**
*eminentia fossae triangularis*

## 463. Intrinsic Muscles of Lateral Surface of Ear. (1/1)

1 **Helicis Major Muscle**
*m. helicis major*

2 **Helicis Minor Muscle**
*m. helicis minor*

3 **Tragicus Muscle**
*m. tragicus*

6 **Antitragicus Muscle**
*m. antitragicus*

7 **Cauda Helicis**
*cauda helicis*

## 464. Intrinsic Muscles of Medial Surface of Ear. (1/1)

3 **Transverse Auricular Muscle**
*m. transversus auriculae*

5 **Posterior Auricular Muscle**
*m. auricularis posterior*

7 **External Acoustic Meatus**
*meatus acusticus externus*

11 **Superior Auricular Muscle**
*m. auricularis superior*

12 **Oblique Auricular Muscle**
*m. obliquus auriculae*

## 465. Cross Section of External Auditory Meatus at its Cartilaginous Portion. (8/1)

4 **Cartilage of Acoustic Meatus**
*cartilago meatus acustici*

5 **External Acoustic Meatus, Cutaneous Layer**
*stratum cutaneum meatus acustici externi*
8 **Tragi**
*tragi*

**Sebaceous Glands**
*glandulae sebaceae*

9 **Ceruminous Glands**
*glandulae ceruminosae*

# THE SKIN AND ITS DERIVATIVES

## Hair, Mammary and Sebaceous Glands, Nails and Digital Epidermal Ridges

# 466 and 467. Diagrams of the Direction of Hair Streams (flumina pilorum) on Ventral and Dorsal Surface of Body. (after Ludwig)

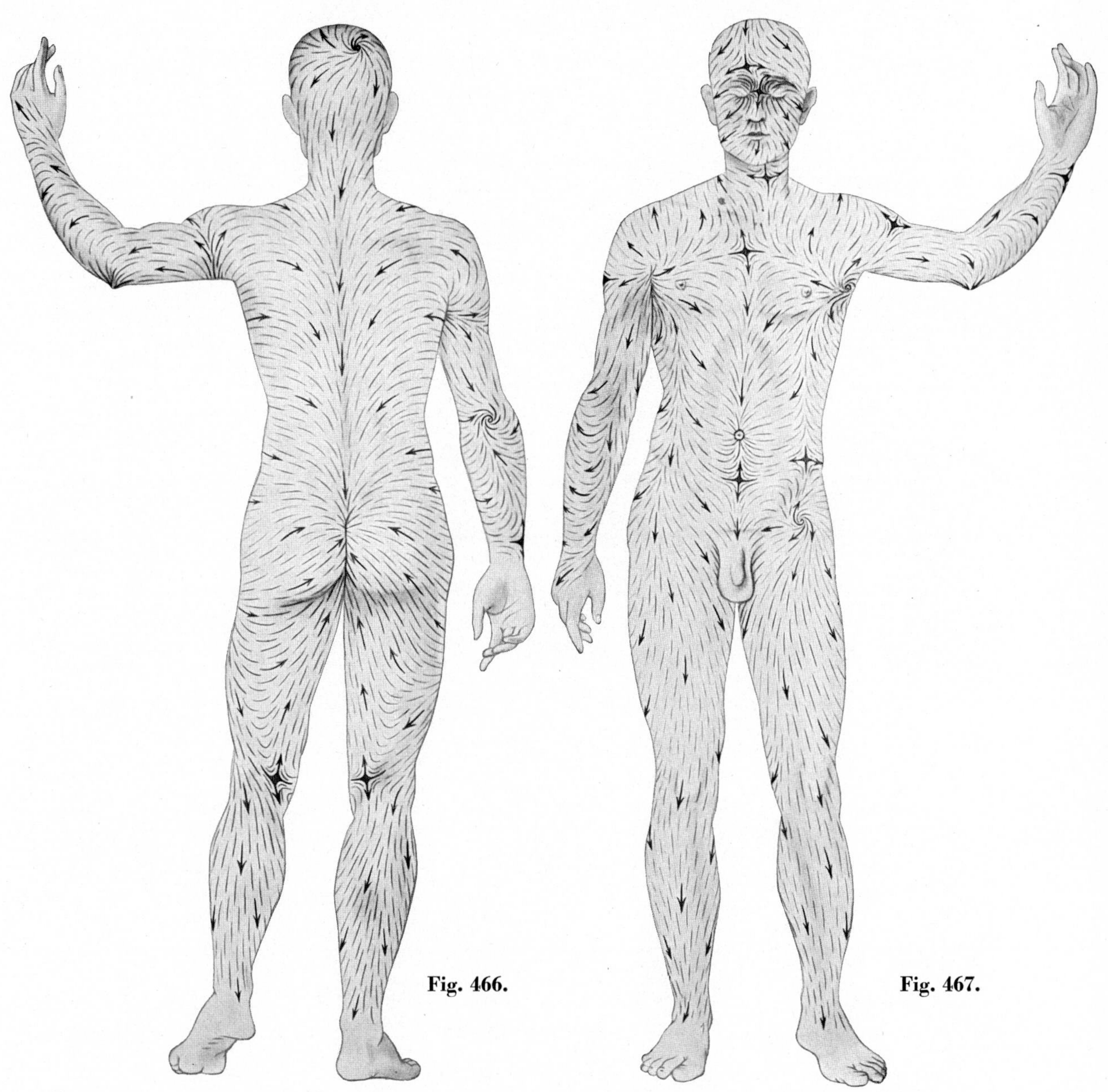

Fig. 466.

Fig. 467.

## 468. Section of a Portion of Scalp, Showing Club-Shaped Hair and Hair Follicles. (12/1)

**1 Club-shaped Hair**
**

**2 Shaft of Hair**
*scapuls pili*
**Epidermis**
*epidermis*

**3 Hair Follicle**
*folliculus pili*

**5 Retinacula Cutis**
*retinacula cutis*

**6 Galea Aponeurotica [Epicranial Aponeurosis]**
*galea aponeurotica [aponeurosis epicranialis]*

**7 Hair Papilla**
*papilla pili*

**Hair Bulb**
*bulbus pili*

**9 Sudoriferous Gland**
*glandula glomiformis (sudorifera)*
**Arrector Pili Muscle**
*musculus arrector pili*
**Sebaceous Glands**
*glandulae sebaceae*

**Note:** 1. Position of sebaceous glands supplying oil to hair and outer epidermal layers.

2. Position of arrector pili muscles-9. These are smooth muscles, under control of autonomic nervous system.

## 469. Sweat Glands of the Axilla. (1/1)

**3 Axillary Fascia**
*fascia axillaris*

**6 Sudoriferous Glands (axillary)**
*glandulae sudoriferae (axillaers)*

**Hairs (of the axilla)**
*hirci*

**Note:** 1. These axillary **sweat glands** are relatively large **apocrine glands** in contrast to sweat glands in most other parts of the body.

## 470. Lanugo Hairs of Human Skin. (5/1)

**2 Cutaneous Area**
*

**3 Lanugo**
*lanugo*

**9 Boundaries of Areas**
+

### Etymology:

arrector = L. *arrigo* + pp-*rectus*, raise up. Erectors of hair which causes skin at base to form papillae commonly referred to as "gooseflesh" or *cutis anserina.*

horripilation = L. *horreo,* to bristle, + *pilus,* hair. The standing up of small hairs over the body. Gooseflesh, *cutis anserina.*

hirci = L. pl. of *hircus,* he-goat. Hairs of axilla. Hircismus refers to offensive odor of axilla.

lanugo = L. *lana,* wool, down. Fine, downy hair covering body except palms and soles of hands and feet, and where hair grows long.

**
scapus pili
epidermis
glandulae sebaceae
musculus arrector pili
folliculus pili
glandula glomiformis (sudorifera)
bulbus pili
papilla pili
galea aponeurotica
retinacula cutis

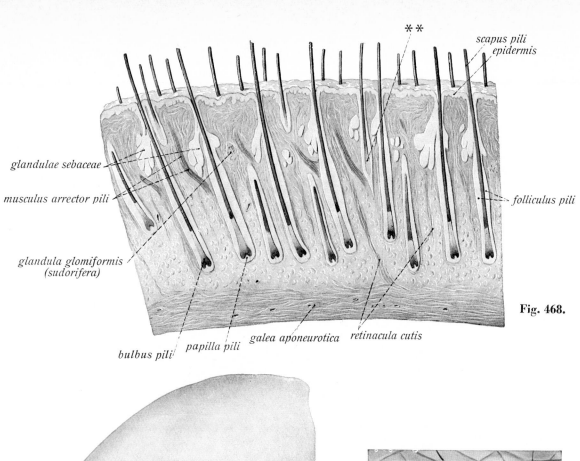

Fig. 468.

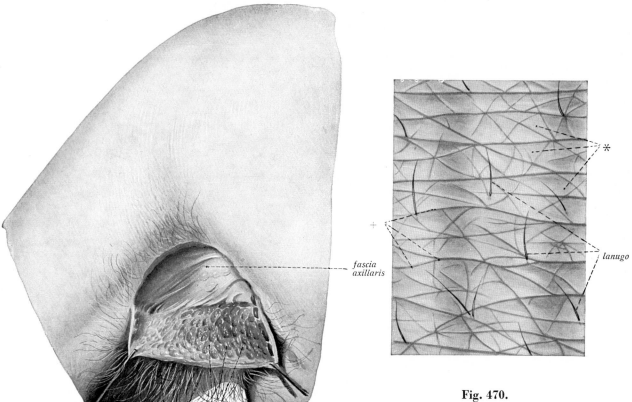

fascia axillaris
glandulae sudoriferae (axillares)
hirci

Fig. 469.

*
+
lanugo

Fig. 470.

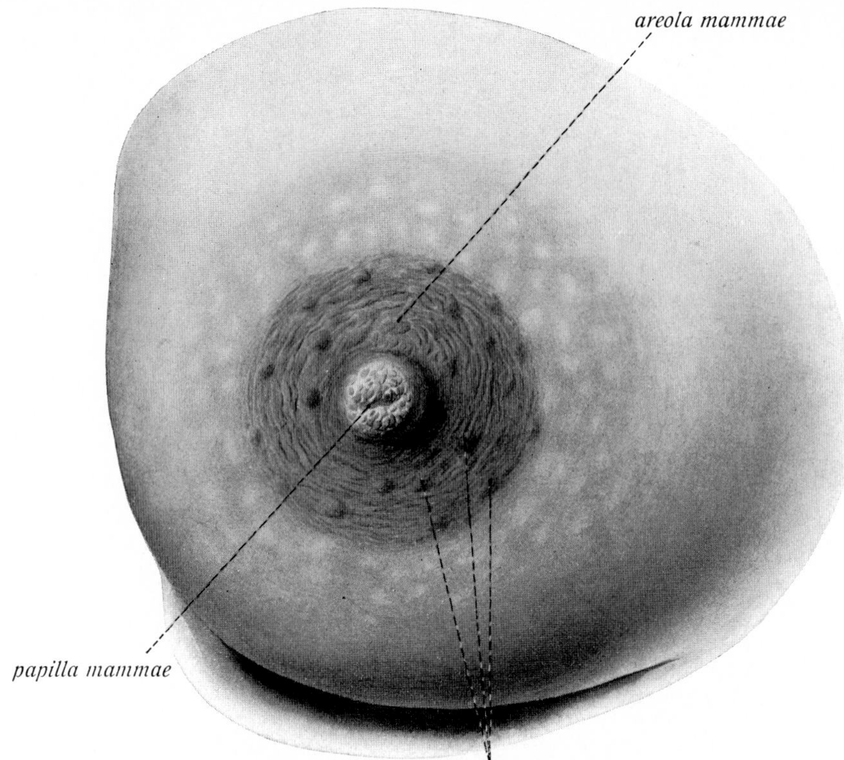
areola mammae
papilla mammae
glandulae areolares
**Fig. 471.**

papilla mammae
lobi glandulae mammariae
**Fig. 472.**

## 471. Right Breast of Gravid Human Subject.

**1 Areola**
*areola mammae*

**6 Areolar Glands**
*glandulae areolares*

**8 Nipple of Breast**
*papilla mammae*

**Note:** 1. Nipple occupies center of a circular pigmented field of skin, the **areola.** The areola is devoid of subcutaneous fat and contains, in its periphery, large coiled glands-6. The areolar glands are responsible for small surface elevations on the areola.

2. The nipple-8 in the human subject is cone-shaped and is variable in length and diameter. It is covered by a delicate, greatly wrinkled skin, rich in smooth muscle fibers. These smooth muscle fibers are responsible for a type of erection of the nipple following stimulation or under the influence of cold.

3. The breasts may vary in size, not only in different individuals, but also in different races, and even in the same individual. They enlarge at puberty and with pregnancy and lactation, and atrophy in old age. Even in older individuals, however, the breast has a rounded contour that is maintained because of its fat content. The breasts also enlarge slightly before, and regress after, each menstrual period. The mammary gland is at the level of the third to the sixth rib. **The nipple is most often found at the level of the fourth intercostal space.**

4. In some individuals, supernumerary nipples and mammary glands are present. They are always somewhere along the embryonic "milkline". (See textbooks of embryology).

5. The functional phases of the mammary glands are regulated by the hormones of pregnancy, which involve not only the ovarian and anterior hypophyseal hormones, but also the hypothalamic neurosecretory substances that are released through the posterior lobe of the hypophysis "milk let-down factor" of so-called posterior pituitary hormones.

## 472. Right Mammary Gland from Gravid Human Subject. (1/2)

The skin was dissected off, except on the nipple.

## 473. Sagittal Section through Right Mammary Gland. (From gravid human subject) (1/2)

**1 Lactiferous Ducts**
*ductus lactiferi*

**Lactiferous Sinus**
*sinus lactiferus*

**6 Pectoral Fascia**
*fascia pectoralis*

**9 Mammary Gland Lobules**
*lobuli glandulae mammariae*

**10 Mammary Gland Lobes**
*lobi glandulae mammariae*

**Mammary Nipple**
*papilla mammae*

**Note:** 1. The **glandular** part of the mammary tissue is made up of fifteen to twenty radially arranged lobes-10 which divide into smaller **lobules**-9. They are reddish in color and imbedded in fat of the subcutaneous tissue. Because the breast is a cutaneous glandular structure, it is mobile with respect to the pectoral muscle and its fascia.

2. Each of the lobes-10 has its own **lactiferous duct**-1, which opens by a very small orifice upon the nipple. The number of ducts corresponds to the number of individual gland lobes. A short distance before its opening each duct shows a spindle-shaped enlargement, the **lactiferous sinus**-1. (Fig. 474-6)

## 474. Right Mammary Gland of a Gravid Human Subject. (1/2)

A ring-shaped piece of skin was cut out around the nipple. Skin around nipple was rolled up to display the lactiferous ducts-6.

**6 Lactiferous Duct**
*ductus lactiferi*

**8 Mammary Nipple**
*papilla mammae*

**Cut Margins of Areolar Skin**
*margines incisi*

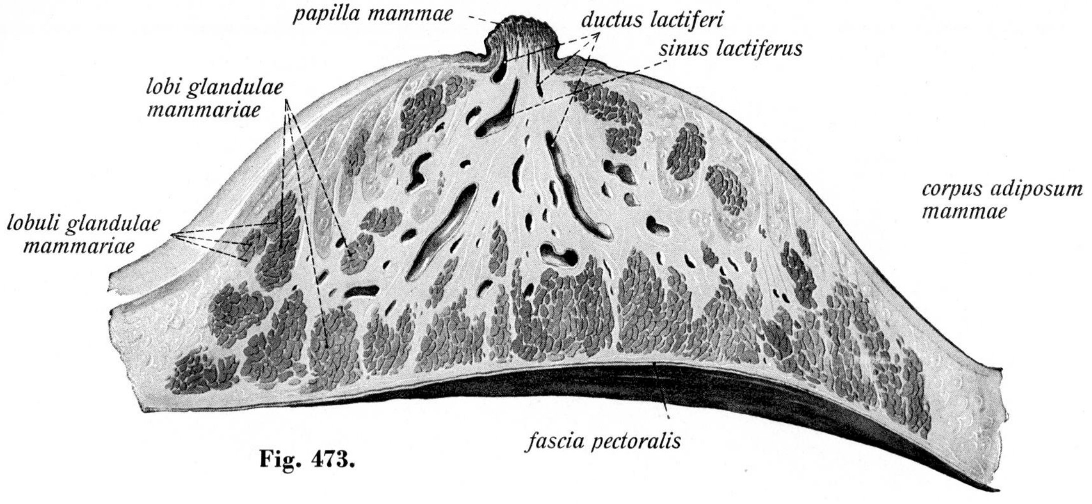
papilla mammae
ductus lactiferi
sinus lactiferus
lobi glandulae
mammariae
lobuli glandulae
mammariae
corpus adiposum
mammae
fascia pectoralis

**Fig. 473.**

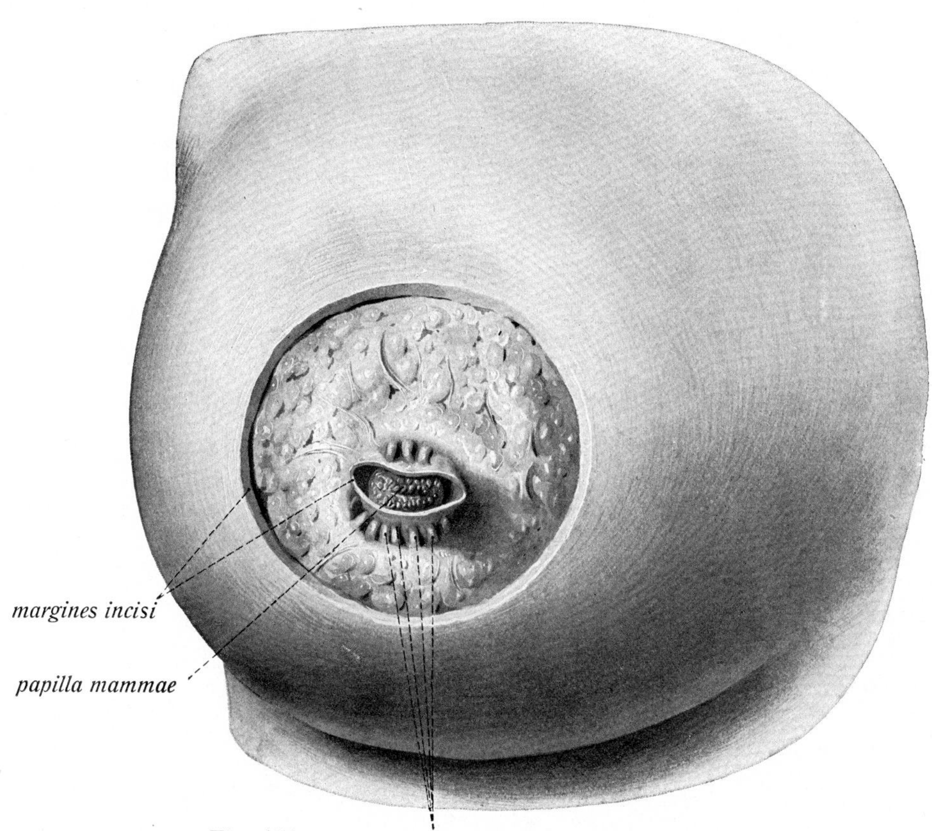
margines incisi
papilla mammae
ductus lactiferi

**Fig. 474.**

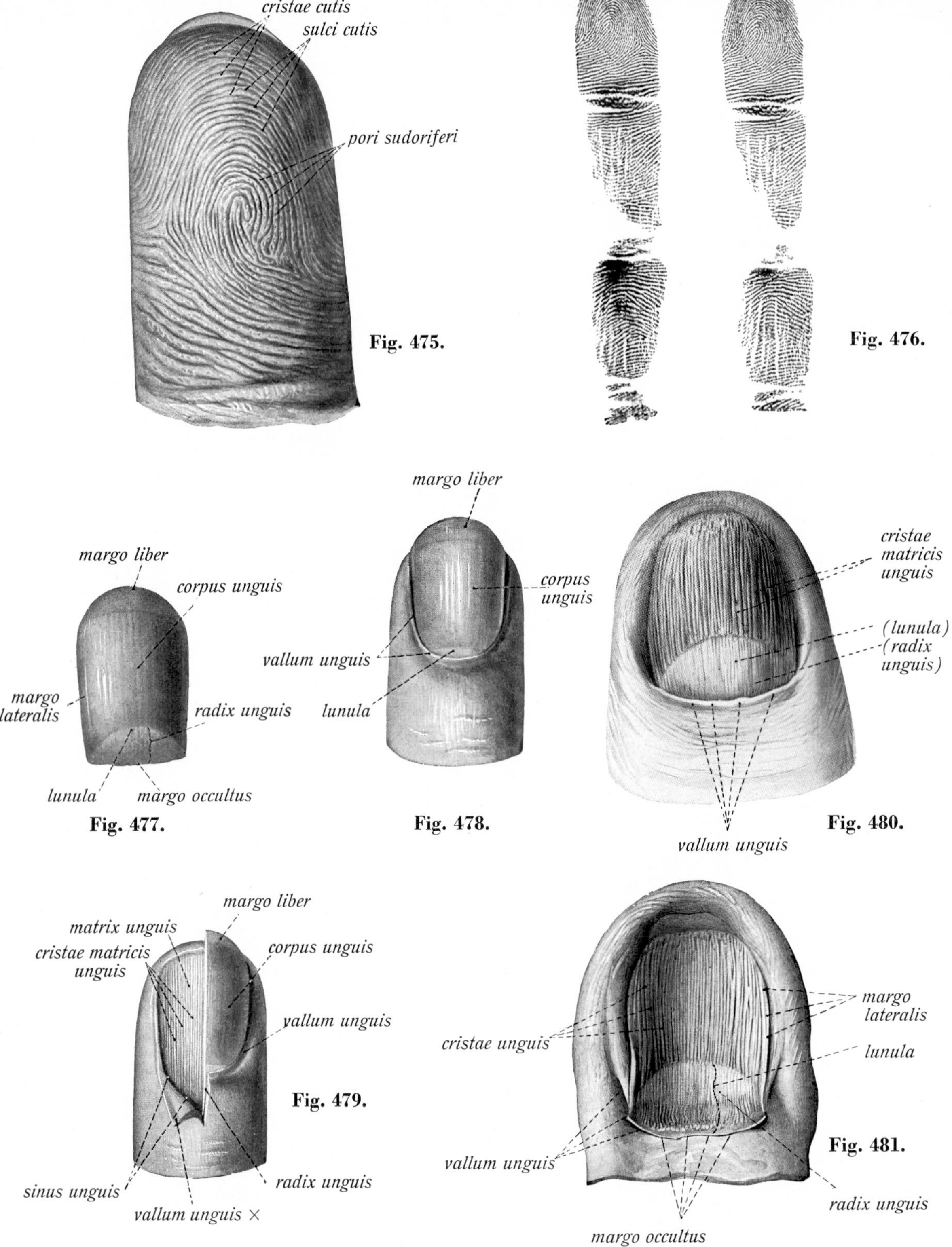
cristae cutis
sulci cutis
pori sudoriferi
margo liber
corpus unguis
margo lateralis
radix unguis
lunula
margo occultus
margo liber
corpus unguis
vallum unguis
lunula
cristae matricis unguis
(lunula)
(radix unguis)
vallum unguis
margo liber
matrix unguis
cristae matricis unguis
corpus unguis
vallum unguis
sinus unguis
vallum unguis ×
radix unguis
margo lateralis
cristae unguis
lunula
vallum unguis
radix unguis
margo occultus

Fig. 475.

Fig. 476.

Fig. 477.

Fig. 478.

Fig. 480.

Fig. 479.

Fig. 481.

## 475. Skin Grooves and Ridges of Palmar Surface of Finger Tip. (2/1)

1 **Cristae Cutis (Ridges)**
*cristae cutis*

**Sulci Cutis (Grooves)**
*sulci cutis*

2 **Sudoriferous Pores**
*pori sudoriferi*

**Note:** 1. **Pattern of grooves and ridges**-1 in the epidermis of finger tips. These whorls are characteristic for each individual, and can be **used for identification.** (Dermatoglyphics)

## 476. Finger Print of Grooves and Ridges of Two Fingers. (1/1)

## 477. Surface of a Finger Nail. (Removed from nail bed) (outer dorsal) (1/1)

1 **Body of Nail**
*corpus unguis*

4 **Root of Nail**
*radix unguis*

6 **Hidden Margin**
*margo occultus*

7 **Lunula (Half-Moon)**
*lunula*

9 **Lateral Margin**
*margo lateralis*

12 **Free Margin**
*margo liber*

## 478. Finger Nail in its Normal Position. (Seen from dorsal aspect) (1/1)

2 **Body of Nail**
*corpus unguis*

8 **Lunula (half Moon)**
*lunula*

9 **Eponychium (Cuticle)**
*vallum unguis*

12 **Free Margin**
*margo liber*

## 479. Finger Nail Bed Seen from Dorsal Aspect. (Left half of finger nail removed to expose nail bed) (1/1)

1 **Body of Nail**
*corpus unguis*

2 **Eponychium (Cuticle)**
*vallum unguis*

5 **Root of Nail**
*radix unguis*

6 **Eponychium (Cuticle)**
*vallum unguis*

7 **Nail Sinus**
*sinus unguis*

10 **Ridges of Nail Matrix**
*cristae matricis unguis*

11 **Nail Matrix**
*matrix unguis*

12 **Free Margin**
*margo liber*

## 480. Nail Bed of Hallux after Removal of Nail. (2/1)

2 **Ridges of Nail Matrix**
*cristae matricis unguis*

3 **Lunula (Half-Moon)**
*(lunula)*

**Root of Nail**
*(radix unguis)*

6 **Eponychium (Cuticle)**
*vallum unguis*

## 481. Nail Bed of Hallux, after Removal of Nail and Reflection of Vallum Unguis. (2/1)

3 **Lateral Margin**
*margo lateralis*

**Lunula (Half-Moon)**
*lunula*

5 **Root of Nail**
*radix unguis*

6 **Hidden Margin**
*margo occultus*

8 **Eponychium (Cuticle)**
*vallum unguis*

9 **Nail Ridges**
*cristae unguis*

# Memorandum on New and Obsolete Anatomical Terminology

It has been over 60 years since the International Anatomical Association standardized terminology throughout the World, but a few of the old eponyms and meaningless terms have survived. These so-called "obsolete terms" are used so extensively that it is untrue to say they are obsolete. Under ideal circumstances, however, they should become obsolete. The medical student is faced with the problem of either not understanding some of the clinical discussions or learning a limited number of the old terms. There is, however, the danger that the students will become so well-versed in the old terminology that, when confronted with the new terms in the National Board Examinations and elsewhere, they would not remember the accepted new terms.

In the following list, the old terms are arranged alphabetically with the English and Latin equivalent of the accepted anatomical terms. This is presented with the hope of helping the student overcome a difficult situation. Those who have an opportunity to teach medical students should make every effort to use the proper terms and thus accelerate the transition to the accepted standard anatomical terminology.

| Old Term | *International Standard Anatomical Terminology N. A.* | |
|---|---|---|
| Achilles' Tendon | **Tendo Calcaneus**<br>*tendo calcaneus (Achilles)* | **English**<br>*Latin* |
| Acoustic Nerve | **Vestibulocochlear Nerve**<br>*nervus vestibulocochlearis* | |
| Adam's Apple | **Laryngeal Prominence**<br>*prominentia laryngea* | |
| Alcock's Canal | **Pudendal Canal**<br>*canalis obturatoris* | |
| Ampulla of Vater | **Greater Papilla**<br>*papilla duodeni major* | |
| Angle of Louis | **Sternal Angle**<br>*angulus sterni* | |
| Ansa Hypoglossi | **Ansa Cervicalis**<br>*ansa cervicalis* | |
| Aqueduct of Sylvius | **Cerebral Aqueduct**<br>*aqueductus cerebri* | |
| Arnold, Nerve of | **Auricular Branch**<br>*ramus auricularis* (of vagus nerve) | |
| Arteria Hemorrhoidalis Inferior | **Inferior Rectal Artery**<br>*arteria rectalis inferior* | |
| Arteria Hypogastrica | **Internal Iliac Artery**<br>*arteria iliaca interna* | |
| Arteria Spermatica Externa | **Cremaster Artery**<br>*arteria cremasterica* | |
| Astragalus | **Talus**<br>*talus* | |
| Auerbach's Plexus | **Myenteric Plexus**<br>*plexus myentericus* | |
| Bartholin, Duct of | **Larger Sublingual Duct**<br>*ductus sublingualis major* | |
| Bartholin's Glands | **Greater Vestibular Glands**<br>*glandula vestibularis major* | |
| Basal Cistern | **Interpeduncular Cistern**<br>*cisterna interpeduncularis* | |
| Bertin's Ligament | **Ischiofemoral Ligament**<br>*ligamentum ischiofemorale* | |
| Bigelow, Ligament of | **Iliofemoral Ligament**<br>*ligamentum iliofemorale* | |

| Old Term | *Nomina Anatomica* |
|---|---|
| Brachium Conjunctivum (cerebelli) | **Superior Cerebellar Peduncle**<br>*pedunculus cerebellaris superior* |
| Brachium Pontis | **Middle Cerebellar Peduncle**<br>*pedunculus cerebellaris medius* |
| Brunner's Glands | **Duodenal Glands**<br>*glandulae duodenales* |
| Buccinator Nerve | **Buccal Nerve V**<br>*nervus buccalis* |
| Buck's Fascia | **Deep Penile Fascia**<br>*fascia penis profunda* |
| Bulbocavernosus Muscle | **Bulbospongiosus Muscle**<br>*musculus bulbospongiosus* |
| Bundle of His | **Atrioventricular Bundle**<br>*fasciculus atrioventricularis* |
| Camper's Fascia | **Superficial Layer of Superficial Fascia of Abdomen**<br>*panniculus adiposus* |
| Caninus Muscle | **Levator Anguli Oris Muscle**<br>*musculus levator anguli oris* |
| Capsule of Zenon | **Bulbar Fascia**<br>*vaginae bulbi* |
| Circle of Willis | **Circulus Arteriosus**<br>*circulus arteriosus cerebri* |
| Cisterna Magna | **Cerebellomedullary Cistern**<br>*cisterna cerebellomedullaris* |
| Clarke's Column | **Dorsal Nucleus**<br>*nucleus dorsalis* |
| Colle's Fascia | **Deep Layer of Superficial Fascia of Perineum**<br>*fascia superficialis perinei* |
| Conjoined Tendon<br>Tendon Conjunctivus | **Inguinal Falx**<br>*falx inguinalis* |
| Cooper's Ligament | **Pectineal Ligament**<br>*ligamentum pectineale* |
| Cooper's Ligaments | **Suspensory Ligament**<br>(Superficial Fascia-Mammary Gland)<br>*ligamenta suspensoria*<br>*(tela subcutanea-glandula mammaria)* |
| Coracocleidopectoralis<br>Coracoclavicular Fascia | **Clavipectoral Fascia**<br>*fascia clavipectoralis* |

| Old Term | *Nomina Anatomica* |
|---|---|
| Cowper's Gland | **Bulbourethral Gland**<br>*glandula bulbourethralis* |
| Cruciate Crural Ligament | **Inferior Extensor Retinaculum**<br>*retinaculum mm. extensorum inferius* |
| Cul-de-sac of Gruber | **Fascial Sling of Omohyoid Muscle** |
| Cutaneous Cervical Nerve | **Transverse Cervical Nerve**<br>*nervus transversus colli* |
| Digastric Triangle | **Submandibular Triangle**<br>*trigonum submandibulare* |
| Diverticulum of Meckel<br>(remnant of yolk stalk or<br>omphalomesenteric duct) | **Blind Appendage of Ileum**<br>(anomalous) |
| Dorsal Carpal Ligament | **Extensor Retinaculum**<br>*retinaculum extensorum* |
| Edinger-Westphal Nucleus | **Accessory Oculomotor Nucleus**<br>*nucleus accessorius (autonomicus)* |
| Ejaculator Urinae<br>Accelerator Urinae | **Bulbospongiosus Muscle**<br>*musculus bulbospongiosus* |
| Eustachian Tube | **Auditory Tube**<br>*tuba auditiva* |
| Eustachian Valve | **Valve of Inferior Vena Cava**<br>*valvula venae cavae inferioris* |
| External Maxillary Artery | **Facial Artery**<br>*arteria facialis* |
| External Respiratory Nerve of Bell<br>Nerve to Serratus Anterior (BNA) | **Long Thoracic Nerve**<br>*nervus thoracicus longus* |
| Fallopian Tube | **Uterine Tube**<br>*tuba uterina* |
| Fifth Ventricle | **Cavity of Septum Pellucidum**<br>*cavum septi pellucidi* |
| Foramen of Magendi | **Median Aperture of the 4th Ventricle**<br>*apertura mediana ventriculi quarti* |
| Foramen of Monro | **Interventricular Foramen**<br>*foramen interventriculare* |
| Foramen of Winslow | **Epiploic Foramen**<br>*foramen epiploicum* |
| Ganglion Jugulare (n. X) | **Superior Ganglion**<br>*ganglion superius* |

| Old Term | *Nomina Anatomica* |
|---|---|
| Ganglion Nodosum (n. X) | **Inferior Ganglion**<br>*ganglion inferius* |
| Ganglion Sphenopalatinum | **Pterygopalatine Ganglion**<br>*ganglion pterygopalatinum* |
| Gasserian Ganglion | **Trigeminal Ganglion**<br>*ganglion trigeminale (semilunar)* |
| Gastrocolic Omentum | **Greater Omentum**<br>*omentum majus* |
| Gastrohepatic Omentum | **Lesser Omentum**<br>*omentum minus* |
| Gimbernat's Ligament | **Lacunar Ligament**<br>*ligamentum lacunare* |
| Glenoid Fossa | **Mandibular Fossa**<br>*fossa mandibularis* |
| Graafian Follicle | **Vesicular Ovarian Follicle**<br>*folliculi ovarici vesiculosi* |
| Greater Multangular Bone | **Trapezium**<br>*os trapezium* |
| Hering, Nerve of | **Carotid Sinus Nerve**<br>*ramus sinus carotici (n. glossopharyngei)* |
| Hesselbach's Ligament | **Interfoveolar Ligament**<br>*ligamentum interfoveolare* |
| Hesselbach's Triangle | **Inguinal Triangle** |
| Highmore's Antrum | **Maxillary Sinus**<br>*sinus maxillaris* |
| Hunter's Canal | **Adductor Canal**<br>*canalis adductorius* |
| Inferior Dental Nerve | **Inferior Alveolar Nerve**<br>*nervus alveolaris inferior* |
| Inferior Maxillary Bone | **Mandible**<br>*mandibula* |
| Inferior Turbinate Bone | **Inferior Nasal Concha**<br>*concha nasalis inferior* |
| Innominate Artery | **Brachiocephalic Trunk**<br>*truncus brachiocephalicus* |
| Innominate Bone | **Hip Bone**<br>*os coxae* |

| Old Term | *Nomina Anatomica* |
|---|---|
| Innominate Vein | **Brachiocephalic Vein**<br>*vena brachiocephalica* |
| Internal Mammary Artery | **Internal Thoracic Artery**<br>*arteria thoracica interna* |
| Internal Spermatic Artery | **Testicular Artery**<br>*arteria testicularis* |
| Island of Reil | **Insula**<br>*insula* |
| Jacobson, Nerve of | **Tympanic Nerve**<br>*nervus tympanicus* |
| Lateral Sinus | **Transverse Sinus**<br>*sinus transversus* |
| Leptomeninx | **Pia-Arachnoid**<br>*pia mater* and *arachnoidea* |
| Lesser Multangular Bone | **Trapezoid**<br>*os trapezoideum* |
| Lesser Peritoneal Sac | **Omental Bursa**<br>bursa omentalis |
| Ligamentum teres femoris | **Ligament of Head of Femor**<br>*ligamentum capitis femoris* |
| Line of Spigelius | **Semilunar Line**<br>*linea semilunaris* |
| Littre's Glands | **Urethral Glands**<br>*glandulae urethrales* |
| Luschka's Foramen | **Lateral Aperture of 4th Ventricle**<br>*apertura lateralis ventriculi quarti* |
| Macewen's Triangle | **Suprameatal Triangle** |
| Malar Bone | **Zygomatic Bone**<br>*os zygomaticum* |
| Malar Process | **Zygomatic Process**<br>*processus zygomaticus* |
| Marshall's Vein | **Oblique Vein of Left Atrium**<br>*vena obliqua atrii sinistri* |
| Meibomian Glands | **Tarsal Glands**<br>*glandulae tarsales* |
| Meissner's Plexus | **Submucosal Plexus**<br>*plexus submucosus* |
| Mitral or Bicuspid Valve | **Left Atrioventricular Valve**<br>*valva atrioventricularis sinsitra* |

| Old Term | *Nomina Anatomica* |
|---|---|
| Müllerian Duct | **Paramesonephric Duct**<br>*ductus paramesonephricus* |
| Musculospiral Nerve | **Radial Nerve**<br>*nervus radialis* |
| Organ of Corti | **Spiral Organ**<br>*organum spirale* |
| Os Naviculare Manus | **Scaphoid Bone**<br>*os scaphoideum* |
| Os Naviculare Pedis | **Navicular Bone**<br>*os naviculare* |
| Pacchionian Bodies | **Arachnoid Granulations**<br>*granulationes arachnoideales* |
| Pachymeninx | **Dura Mater**<br>*dura mater* |
| Peroneal Bone | **Fibula**<br>*fibula* |
| Petrosal Ganglion (n. IX) | **Inferior Ganglion**<br>*ganglion inferius* |
| Peyer's Patches | **Aggregated Lymph Nodes**<br>*folliculi lymphatici aggregati* |
| Pneumogastric Nerve | **Vagus Nerve**<br>*nervus vagus* |
| Poupart's Ligament | **Inguinal Ligament**<br>*ligamentum inguinale* |
| Pouch or Cul-de-sac of Douglas | **Rectouterine Pouch**<br>*excavatio rectouterina* |
| Reissner's Membrane | **Vestibular Wall of Cochlear Duct**<br>*paries vestibularis ductus cochlearis* |
| Restiform Body | **Inferior Cerebellar Peduncle**<br>*pedunculus cerebellaris inferior* |
| Rivinus, Ducts of | **Smaller Sublingual Ducts**<br>*ductus sublinguales minores* |
| Rolando, Fissure of | **Central Fissure (Sulcus)**<br>*sulcus centralis* |
| Rosenmueller, Fossa of | **Pharyngeal Recess**<br>*recessus pharyngeus* |
| Santorini's Cartilage | **Corniculate Cartilage**<br>*cartilago corniculata* |
| Santorini, Duct of | **Accessory Pancreatic Duct**<br>*ductus pancreaticus accessorius* |

| Old Term | *Nomina Anatomica* |
|---|---|
| Scarpa's Fascia | **Deep Layer of Superficial Fascia of Abdomen**<br>*panniculus adiposus* (membranous portion) |
| Scarpa's Triangle | **Femoral Triangle**<br>*trigonum femorale* |
| Schlemm's Canal | **Venous Sinus of the Sclera**<br>*sinus venosus sclerae* |
| Semilunar Bone | **Lunate Bone**<br>*os lunatum* |
| Semicircular Line of Douglas | **Arcuate Line**<br>*linea arcuata* |
| Sinuses of Valsalva | **Aortic Sinuses**<br>*sinus aortae* |
| Spaces of Fontana | **Spaces at Iridocorneal Angle**<br>*spatia anguli iridocornealis* |
| Space of Retzius | **Retropubic Space**<br>*spatium retropubicum* |
| Stensen's Duct | **Parotid Duct**<br>*ductus parotideus* |
| Submaxillary Gland | **Submandibular Gland**<br>*glandula submandibularis* |
| Sylvian Fissure | **Lateral Cerebral Fissure**<br>*sulcus lateralis* |
| Tentorial Sinus | **Straight Sinus**<br>*sinus rectus* |
| Torcular of Herophilus | **Confluence of the Sinuses**<br>*confluens sinuum* |
| Tract of Goll | **Fasciculus Gracilis**<br>*fasciculus gracilis* |
| Transverse Carpal Ligament | **Flexor Retinaculum**<br>*retinaculum flexorum* |
| Treitz' Ligament | **Suspensory Duodenal Muscle**<br>*musculus suspensorius duodeni* |
| Triangular Fascia | **Reflex Inguinal Ligament**<br>*ligamentum inguinale reflexum* |
| Triangularis Muscle | **Depressor Anguli Oris Muscle**<br>*musculus depressor anguli oris* |
| Turbinate Bone | **Ethmoid Bone**<br>*os ethmoidale* |

| Old Term | *Nomina Anatomica* |
|---|---|
| Unciform Bone | **Hamate**<br>*os hamatum* |
| Valve of Heister | **Spital Valve**<br>*plica spiralis* |
| Valve of Thebesius | **Valve of Coronary Sinus**<br>*valvula sinus coronarii* |
| Vas Deferens<br>Seminal Duct | **Ductus Deferens**<br>*ductus deferens* |
| Vein of Galen | **Great Cerebral Vein**<br>*vena cerebri magna* |
| Veins of Thebesius | **Venae Cordis Minimae**<br>*venae cordis minimae* |
| Ventricle of Morgagni | **Laryngeal Ventricle**<br>*ventriculus laryngis* |
| Vidian Canal | **Pterygoid Canal**<br>*canalis pterygoidei* |
| Vidian Nerve | **Nerve of Pterygoid Canal**<br>*nervus canalis pterygoidei* |
| Submaxillary Duct (Wharton's) | **Submandibular Duct**<br>*ductus submandibularis* |
| Wirsung, Duct of | **Pancreatic Duct**<br>*ductus pancreaticus* |
| Wrisberg Cartilages | **Cuneiform Cartilage**<br>*cartilago cuneiformis* |
| Wrisberg, Nerve of | **Intermediate Nerve**<br>*nervus intermedius* |
| Wolffian Duct | **Mesonephric Duct**<br>*ductus mesonephricus* |
| Wormian Bones | **Sutural Bones**<br>*ossa suturarum* |

# INDEX

## English and Latin

(with clock position)

The English and Latin names of structures are listed alphabetically. Latin terms that are commonly used in English are not usually italicized. The number after each item refers to the illustration number. The clock number, following the hyphen, gives the approximate position of the label on the illustration. This will permit finding the illustration of any given structure in the minimum time. References that are most pertinent are given in bold type.


### A

**ABDOMEN** 120–126
**Abdominal** aorta 4-3; 7-11; 55-6; 120-2; 123-2; **126**-2; 127-10; 129-12; **170**-2; 171-12; 354-6.
– muscles, layers of 50-2, 3; 53-5, 8
**Abducens** nerve **103**-4, 7; **104**-4, 6; **105**-4, 6; **106**-5, 6; 114-3; 232-5; 236-8; 238-10; 239-2; 241-9; **247**-5; 272-2; 318; 333-5; 350-12
– –, root filaments 330-1
– nucleus 229-9; 230-3; 318; **330**-1; 333-8
**Abductor** digiti minimi muscle
(foot) 159-1; 160-1
(hand) 88-4
– hallucis muscle 159-11; 160-12
– pollicis brevis muscle 87-7; 88-9; 89-8
– – longus muscle 80-7; 81-7; 86-11; 89-8
**Accessory** nerve 39-4; 40-4; 41-4; **42**-3; 43-1; 44-2; **51**-10; **52**-4, 8; 114-4; 115-2, 10, 11; 116-1, 11; 183-1; 232-5, 7; 239-3; 241-7; **247**-7; 272-5; 350-3; 351-3
**Accessory** nerve rootlets 290-7; 332-3, 9; 339-9; 341-9
– –, spinal nucleus of 230-7
– oculomotor nucleus (Ed. Westphal) 299-11; 230-1; 326-2
– phrenic nerve 58-9; 169-10
– saphenous vein 174-1
**Acetabulum** 355-5
**Acoustic meatus,** cartilage of 448-3; 458-7; 461-6; 462-7; 465-4
– –, external 100-10; 101-10; 102-11; 428-8, 9; **448**-1, 2, 3; 449-9; 450-10; 454-3, 9; 459-4; 464-7
– –, internal 411-5; 421-6, 8; 422-8; 424-6
– – nerve, external 100-9; 101-9; 102-9
**Adductor brevis muscle** 144-1
– canal 143-7
– longus muscle 142-2
– magnus muscle 144-3; 147-3, 4; 148-6
– pollicis muscle 86-8; 87-10; 88-9, 12; 89–9
– tendon, hiatus of 144-4
*Adhesio interthalamica* 218-11; 223-1; 225-3; 248-1; 261-2; 271-10; **274**-12; 281-1; **283**-3; 288-2

*Aditus laryngis* 117-2
**Air** cells, mastoid 112-9; **425**-4; 427-9; 428-11; 429-10; 448-5
– –, tympanic 427-5; 428-4
– sinus, ethmoidal cells 384-5; 402-7; 403-2; 404-3; 405-9
**Ala cinerea** 332-11
– of ilium 180-5
– *lobuli centralis* 293-1
– *major ossis sphenoidalis* 264-3
– *minor ossis sphenoidalis* 264-9
– *ossis ilii* 180-5
**Alveolar** artery, inferior 94-7; 99-5; 100-6, 8; 101-5, 8; 102-8; 109-8; 110-6, 7
– –, superior posterior 94-9; 101-4; 350-9
– nerve, inferior 92-6, 7; 99-5; **100**-6, 7; **101**-5, 8; 102-8; 109-8; 110-7; **111**-9; 350-8; 351-8, 9
– –, superior 92-3; 101-2; 102-2; **111**-12; 112-4, 5, 6; 350-8, 9; 351-9
**Ambiguus** nucleus (IX, X, XI) 229-7; 230-5; **331**-1; **332**-4; 336-2, 9, 10; **337**-3; 339-3; 340-9
*Ampulla membranacea* 409-7, 12; 412-2, 5, 12; 413-2, 7; 439-6
– *ossea*, (semicircular canals) 414-1, 5; 415-1, 7; 416-1, 2, 5; 417-7; 418-7, 10, 12; 419-6, 12; 420-7, 12; 425-11; 426-9, 12
**Amygdaloid** body 221a; 224-4; 286-8; 323-8
**Anastomoses** of arteries at ankle joint 152-6; 153-7; 157-1, 10; 159-12
– – – at elbow 73-6; 74-5; 80-1
– – – at hip joint 147-2; 148-4
– – – at knee joint 138-7; 142-7; 144-7; 153-1
– – – at shoulder 53-1; 62-2, 10; 69-12
– – – at wrist 80-6; 85-12; 86-10; 88-5; 89-4
"**Anatomical** snuffbox" 89-7
**Anconeus** muscle 73-6; 74-6; 80-10; 81-1
**Angle,** iridocorneal 356-1; 368-1; 369-1; 383-3
**Angular** artery **94**-9; 95–2; 98-3; 99-3; 100-2; 101-2; 102-2
– gyrus 207; 249-3; 253-8
– vein 95-2
*Angulus iridocornealis* **356**-1; 368-1; 369-1; 383-3
– *oculi* 386-4, 8; 387-5, 8; 388-3; 389-3, 9; 390-3, 8
– *venosus* 46-7
**Anococcygeal** ligament 134-12
– nerves 119-6; 133-12; 134-12
**Ansa** cervicalis **37**-10; 41-8; **42**-4, 8, 9; **43**-8; 44-10; 45-3; 46-3; 102-7; 350-3, 4; 351-3, 5
– –, thyrohyoid branch 42-9
– hypoglossi - - - - see Ansa cervicalis
– *lenticularis* 317
– peduncularis 288-3
– subclavia 58-8; 116-8; 348-10; 352-10; 354-11
**Antebrachial** cutaneous nerve, lateral 67-4; **68**-1, 4; 71-5; 72-5; 73-7; 74-7; 82-7
– – –, medial 37-7; 61-6; 67-7; **68**-11; 71-11
– – –, posterior 67-5; **69**-7; 70-5, 12; 73-7; 74-7; 83-11; 89-5
– flexor muscles 72-7; 77-10; 78-4
– vein, median 67-5; 68-10
**Anteriolateral** sulcus 183-1; 188-10; 191-5; 290-7
**Anterior** cardiac veins 34-8
– cerebral artery 200-2; 241-11, 12; **242**-8, 10; 243
– chorioidal artery 200-3; **241**-9; 259-8; 260-1; **262**-10; **265**-9; 280-8
– ciliary artery 358-1, 10; 359-2; 369-2
– circumflex humeral artery 61-4; 71-1
– commissure 218-10; 223-10; 224-9; 226-11; 248-3; 251-8; 257-2; 263-10; 274-11; 276-1, 2; **277**-2, 10; 286-5, 7; 287-4, 8; 321; **323**-8, 9
– –, olfactory portion 323
– communicating artery 200-2; 241-11; 242-8

**Anterior** ethmoidal artery 103-10; 105-10; 106-9; 107-1, 12; 232-1
– femoral cutaneous nerve 50-7; 138-3
– funiculus 199-6
– inferior cerebellar artery 200-3; 241-5; 242-7
– intercostal vessels 54-1
– interosseus artery 77-8; 80-6; 81-5; 86-1, 11; 90-7
– jugular vein **40**-9; 42-6; **45**-3, 12; 46-8; 169-9
– limiting membrane (cornea) 356-12
– lobe (hypophysis) 226-7; 248-6; 274-8; 275-8
– longitudinal ligament 56-3; 58-12; 184-3
– median fissure (medulla oblongata) 186-5; 331-6; 338-6; 340-7
– – – (spinal cord) 183-1; 186-5; 187-12; 188-11; 189-6; 190-1; 191-6; 192-7; 193-7; 194-7
– meningeal artery 103-10; 105-11; **106**-11; 107-12; 232-12
– palatine nerve – – – – see Greater palatine nerve
– perforated substance 305; 323-9
– spinal artery 184-1, 4; 186-5; 200-4; 241-7; 242-6
– – vein 184-1
– thalamic nucleus 383-2
– tibial artery 7-7
– white commissure 191-8; 192-7
**Anthelix** (ear) 458-10; 459-7; 460-10
–, fossa of 461-12; 462-1
**Antitragicus** muscle 463-6
**Antitragus** (ear) 459-5; 460-6
*Antrum mastoideum* 425-1; 427-11; 428-11; 429-11; 438-10; 443-10
*Anulus femoralis* 127-8; 171-3
– *fibrocartilagineus (membranae tympani)* 441-7; 442-7; 449-6; 450-8; 451-6; 454-6
– *fibrosus* 20-3, 9
– – *disci intervertebralis* 186-3
– *inguinalis, profundus* 127-8
– –, *superficialis* 130-1
*Anulus iridis* 370-7, 8; 371-1, 2
– *tendineus communis* (eye muscles) 367; 369-8; 395-2; 401-7; 405-9
– *tympanicus* 454-7
– *umbilicalis* 3-7
**Aorta** 5-4; 21-1; 22-12; 24-11; 25-1; 26-1; 35-1; 128-12
–, arch of **17**-1; 18-12; 19-1; 34-12; 36-1; 46-6; **55**-12; 58-6; 116-6; 167-10
– *abdominalis* 4-3; 7-11; 55-6; 120-2; 123-2; **126**-2; 127-10; **129**-12; **170**-2; 171-12; 354-6
– *ascendens* 18-2; 19-10; 33-12; 46-6; 55-11; 354-10
– *descendens thoracica* 18-11; 46-5; **55**-3; 184-4; 353-6; **354**-3
– *thoracica* 7-1; 184-4
**Aortic** bifurcation 123-9; 132-11
– bulb 23-11
– hiatus 125-12; 348-4
– pericardial recess 17-10
– plexus (of nerves) **125**; 184-4; 348-3, 9; 353-6; 354-1; 355-2
– semilunar valves 20-1; 33 C
– sinus 23-2
*Apertura interna aqueductus vestibuli* 417-1; 426-12
– *lateralis (vent. quartus)* 199-8; 247-7; 276-5
– *mediana (vent. quartus)* 197-5; 199-8; 218-5; 276-6
**Aperture** of larynx, superior 117-2
*Apex cordis* 11; 17-5; 18-7; 19-5; 25-5; 26-6; 34-6; 35-7
– *cornus posterioris* 191-2; 192-2
– *partis petrosae* 427-3
– *pulmonis* 34-1
*Aponeurosis epicranialis* 237-9; 468-6
– *musculus bicipitis brachii* 71-6; 75-1, 11; 78-2; 158-1
– *palmaris* 82-7
– *plantaris* 158-1
**Appendices** epiploicae 125-5
**Appendicular** vein 124-8
*Appendix vermiformis* 122-6
– *vesiculosa* 131-9

*Aqueductus cerebri* (Sylvii) **218**-3; 223-2; **248**-7; 255-7; 263-4; **273**-12; **274**-2; 324-1; 325-1; 326-1; 327-12
– *mesencephalis* (Sylvii) – – – – see *Aqueductus cerebri*
– *vestibuli* 417-1; 419-1; 426-12; 439-6
– – *apertura interna* 417-1; 426-12
**ARACHNOID,** cranial 197; 199; **235**; 237; **239**; 240; 284
–, spinal 184; 185; 187; 198
**Arachnoidal** granulation 195-11; 197-2; 199-11, 12; 234-2; **240**-5
*Arachnoidea encephali* 197; 199; 235; 237; 239; 240; 284
– *spinalis* 184; 185; 187; 198
**Arch** of aorta 3-1; 7-1; **17**-1; 18-12; 19-1; 34-12; 36-1; 46-6; **55**-12; 58-6; 116-6; 167-10
– of atlas 52-3; 181-1
–, palmar, deep 7-9; 88-8; **90**-8
–, –, superficial 7-9; 87-8; **90**-4
–, plantar 160-3
–, venous (of foot) 155-7
–, – (of hand) 83-7
–, vertebral 181-2, 4, 5; 354-4
**Arcuate** artery 7-5; 157-9
– eminence 427-1
– fibers 331-8; 332-6; 337-3, 8
– line 50-4; 127-6
– nucleus, medulla oblongata 331-7; 332-5; 338-7
*Arcus aortae* 3-1; 7-1; **17**-1; 18-12; 19-1; 34-12; 36-1; 46-6; **55**-12; 58-6; 116-6; 167-10
– *atlantis* 52-3; 181-7
– *costalis* 50-2
– *palatopharyngeus* 116-10
– *palmaris profundus* 7-9; **88**-8; **90**-8
– – *superficialis* 7-9; **87**-8; **90**-4
– *palpebralis* 95-2, 3
– *plantaris* 160-3
– *venosus juguli* 40-8; 45-6
– *vertebrae* 181-2, 4, 5; 184-10; 354-4
– *zygomaticus* 101-11; 102-12
**Areola** of mamma 471-1
**Areolar** glands 471-6
**Arrector** pili muscle 468-9

**Arteria or Arteriae, Artery or Arteries**

*Arteria alveolaris, inferior* **94**-7; 99-5; 100-6, 8; **101**-5, 8; 102-8; 109-8; 110-6, 7
– –, *superior posterior* **94**-9; **101**-4; 350-9
– *angularis* **94**-9; 95-2; 98-3; 99-3; 100-2; 101-2; 102-2
– *arcuata* 7-5; 157-9
– *auricularis posterior* 39-2; 42-1; 51-1; **94**-4, 5; 95-7; 98-9; 99-8; 100-8; 101-9; **102**-9
– – *profunda* 101-8; 102-9; 110-9
– *axillaris* 7-11; 38-7; 43-6; **44**-3; 53-2; **60**-1, 3; 61-2; 71-12; 72-12; 166-2
– *basilaris* 197-8; 200-3; 239-9; **241**-8; 242-7; 367
– *brachialis* 7-11; 61-6; **71**-10; **72**-5; **73**-3; **74**-1; **75**-12; **76**-12; **77**-12; **78**-1; **79**-10
– *buccalis* 94-8; 99-5; 100-4; **101**-5; 102-4
– *bulbi penis* 133-5
– *canalis pterygoidei* 109-9
– *carotis, communis* 3-12; 7-1; 17-12; 18-12; 34-12; 35-12; 36-1; **38**-3, 4; 41-9; 42-7; **43**-9; 44-8; 45-9; 46-5; 56-12; 57-1; 58-5; 60-11; 94-6; 102-7; **115**-5; 116-7; 118-4; 165-8; 167-1, 11; 348-2; 352-12; 354-12
– –, *externa* 7-12; 41-9; 42-9; 43-9; 44-12; **94**-6; 99-6, 7; 100-7, 8; **101**-8; **109**-8; 115-9; 118-3, 8; 350-7
– –, *interna* 7-12; 43-9; 44-12; 93-3, 4; 94-6; 99-7; 100-7; 103-7; 104-6; 105-7; 106-7; **109**-10, 11; 110-8, 10, 12; 112-7; 114-2; 115-2, 12; **116**-1; 164-12; 200-3; 232-1; **233** C; **236**-5, 6, 10; 238-3, 12; 239-1; **241**-1; **243**; 350-2, 12; 367; 384-11; 402-11; 438-3; 439-1; 456-7; 457-1
– *cerebelli inferior anterior* 200-3; **241**-5; 242-7
– – – *posterior* 200-4; **241**-6; 242-6

*Arteria cerebelli superior* 200-3; 241-2, 8; **242**-7; 278-5
– *cerebri anterior* 200-2; 241-11, 12; **242**-8, 10
– – *media* 200-2; **204**; 234-8; **241**-10
– – *posterior* 200-2; **241**-2, 8; 242-3, 7; 284-8
– *cervicalis ascendens* 38-3; 42-9; 43-8; **44**-10
– – *profunda* 14-10; 38-10; **52**-3, 9; 55-11; 58-9
– – *superficialis* **38**-3; 41-8; 42-8; 43-3; **44**-2; 50-8, 11; 169-10
– *cervicothoracicum (stellatum)* 348-2
– *chorioidea anterior* 200-3; **241**-9; 259-8; 260-1; **262**-10; **265**-9; 280-8
– *ciliaris* 105-4
– – *anterior* 358-1, 10; 359-2; 369-2
– – *posterior* 358-6; 359-3, 6; 369-7, 9
– *circumflexa femoris lateralis* 7-3; 143-10, 11; 144-10
– – – *medialis* 7-3; 143-1; **144**-12; **148**-6
– – *humeri anterior* 7-11; 61-4; 71-1
– – – *posterior* 7-11; 53-2; 59-1; 61-3; 62-6; 69-2; 74-1, 11; 169-3
– – *ilium profunda* 125-8; 126-5; 128-10; **142**-11
– – – *superficialis* 50-4, 8; 138-10
– – *scapulae* 53-3; 59-4; 61-7; 62-5
– *colica dextra* 122-3
– – *media* 122-12; 123-3
– – *sinistra* 122-1; 123–4
– *collateralis media* 74-4
– – *radialis* 80-12; **81**-12
– – *ulnaris inferior* 71-8; 72-7; 73-5; 74-4; 75-11; 77-11; 78-12; 81-1
– – – *superior* **71**-8; 72-8; 75-12; 77-12; 78-11
– *communicans anterior* 241-11; 242-8
– – *posterior* 200-2; 241-2; 242-8
– *cordis anterior* 19-9
– *coronaria dextra* **17**-8; **18**-5; **19**-9; 20-2, 6; 23-10; 27-10; 31-6; 34-8
– – *sinistra* **17**-3; **18**-9; **19**-2, 3; 20-10; 27-2; 31-11; 34-4
– *cremasterica* 130-3; 132-9
*Arteria cystica* 120-12
– *digitalis dorsalis* (foot) 156-10; 157-16
– – – (hand) 84-2; 85-7, 10
– – – *pollicis* 89-9; 90-1, 3, 9
– – *palmaris communis* (hand) 82-2; 84-4; 87-3; 90-4
– – – *propria* (hand) 82-2; 84-6; 85-1, 2, 7; 87-1, 11; 88-12
– – *plantaris propria* 156-6; 158-5, 6; 159-6
– *dorsalis nasi* 98-2; 99-2; 100-2; 105-10
– – *pedis* 153-5, 6, 7
– – *penis* 128-8; 130-11
– *ductus deferentis* 127-4; 128-11
– *epigastrica inferior* 7-2; 50-5; 54-5, 6; 122-7; 123-7; 125-8; 126-5; 127-7; 128-10; 132-7; 171-9
– – *superficialis* 50-8; 138-11
– – *superior* 50-2; **54**-9; 138-11
– *epiploica* 120-4
– *episcleralia* 359-6
– *esophageae* 184-4
– *ethmoidalis anterior* 103-10; 105-10; 106-9; 107-12; 232-1
– – – *ram. nasalis* 107-1; 108-1; 109-2
– – *posterior* 105:8; 106-9; 107-12; 108-12
– *facialis* 7-12; 43-10; 44-11; 45-1; 46-1; **94**-6, 7; **95**-5; 98-5; 99-4, 5, 7; 100-2, 6, 7; 101-5, 6; 102-7, 8; 115-3, 9; 350-7
– *femoralis* 7-3; 127-8; 137-1; 138-12; 142-10; **143**-12; 144-4, 12; 170-7
– *fibularis* (see Peroneal artery) 7-6
– *gastrica brevis* 121-1
– – *dextra* 120-12
– – *sinistra* 4-1; 7-1; 120-1; 121-12; 122-12; 125-1; 170-12
– *gastroduodenalis* 120-9; 121-9
– *gastroepiploica* 4-9; **120**-9; **121**-9
– *genu descendens* 7-4; 137-11; 138-5; 142-7; **143**-7; 144-7; 154-10
– – *inferior* 144-6; 150-11; 152-11; 153-12; **154**-4, 7
– – *media* 137-3; 154-9
– – *superior* 137-3; 144-5; 145-5; 149-3; 151-11; **153**-1, 12; 154-2, 9

*Arteria gluteal inferior* 7-2; 132-2; 147-12; **148**-11
– – *superior* 7-2; 127-3; 132-1; 147-12; **148**-11
– *hemorrhoidalis* – – – – see *Arteria rectalis*
– *hepatica communis* 3-6; 7-1; 120-2; 121-12; 170-2
– – *propria* 4-11; 120-12
– *ileocolica* 122-6
– *iliaca communis* 7-2; 126-3; 127-9; **128**-12; **129**-11; 132-10; 170-3
– – *externa* 7-2; 54-5; 126-5; **127**-8; **128**-10; **129**-9, 10; 132-10; 142-12; 171-9
– – *interna* 7-2; 126-5; 127-3; **128**-1; **129**-12; **132**-10; 142-12
– *iliolumbalis* 126-3, 5; 132-10; 171-2
– *infraorbitalis* 94-8; 98-3; 101-2; 102-2; 106-5; 350-9; 404-6
– *intercostalis* 7-11; 18-11; 38-6, 7; 50-2; 54-1; **55**-2; 56-1; 184-2; 9; 353-7
– – *suprema* 38-7; 55-11
– *interossea anterior* 77-8; 80-6; 81-5; 86-1, 11; 90-7
– – *communis* 76-3; 77-9
– – *posterior* 77-4; 80-7; 8; 81-4
– – *recurrens* 74-6; 79-5; 80-2; 81-3
– *jejunales* 122-2; 123-9
– *labialis inferior* 94-7; 98-5
– – *superior* 94-8
– *labyrinthi* 200-3; 232-3; 241-2
– *lacrimalis* 103-3; **104**-1; 105-4; **113**-1; 350-12; 390-9
– *laryngea inferior* 117-7
– – *superior* 41-9; 42-9; 43-9; 116-2; 117-10; 118-3
– *linealis* 4-2; 7-1; 120-2; 121-2; 170-2
– *lingualis* 7-12; 42-9; 94-6; 99-7; 102-8; 107-7; 115-3, 9; **118**-9
– –, *ramus suprahyoideus* 41-10; 118-8
– *lumbalis* 7-2; 126-2; 127-1
– *malleolaris lateralis* 152-6; 153-7; 157-10
– – *medialis* 152-7; 157-2, 12
– *mammary interna* – – see *Arteria thoracica interna*
*Arteria maxillaris* 7-12; 94-5; 100-8; 101-8; 102-5; 109-9; 110-8; 243; 350-9
– *mediana* 77-9
– *meningea anterior* 103-10; 105-11; **106**-11; 107-12; 232-12
– – *media* 7-12; **94**-5; 101-8; 102-8; **103**-5; 110-8; 119-2; **232**-1, 2, 3; **233**-11
– – *posterior* 115-1; 116-12
– *mentalis* 94-7; 98-5; 99-5; 100-5; 101-5
– *mesenterica inferior* 1-5; 4-3; 7-2; **123**-3; 126-2; 127-3; 128-11; 132-11
– – *superior* 1-4; 4-3; 7-1; 55-5; 121-3; **122**-1; 123-1; 126-12; 170-2; 355-2
– *metacarpea dorsalis* 85-7; 86-6; 89-2
– – *palmaris* 88-3; 90-3, 8
– *metatarsea dorsalis* 7-5; 153-6; 157-6
– – *plantaris* 158-6; 159-6; 160-5
– *musculophrenica* 54-2, 10
– *nasal septi posterior* 107-11; 109-3
– *obturatoria* 7-2; 127-8; **128**-11; 132-7, 9; 143-1; **144**-1; 171-9
– *occipitalis* 39-3; 40-3; 41-3; 43-2, 3; **44**-12; **51**-1, 10, 11; 52-2, 9, 10; 53-12; **94**-3, 5; 95-9; 99-7, 9; 100-8; 101-8; 102-9; 116-1
– – *ramus auricularis* 39-2
– – – *mastoideus* 43-3; 44-1; 51-10; 52-10
– – *r. meningeus* 232-5
– – *r. occipitalis* 51-10; 52-9; 94-3; 98-10; 232-5
– *ophthalmica* 103-8, 9; 104-5, 6, 12; **105**-7; 106-7, 8; 200-2; 232-10; **236**-1; 243
– *ovarica* 125-3, 9; 129-7, 11; 131-3, 9; 171-11
– *palatina ascendens* 94-5; 102-8; 109-8; 115-3
– – – *ram. tonsillaris* 108-7; 117-1, 11
– – *descendens* 94-8; 109-2
– – *major* 108-5; 109-6
– – *minor* 108-11; 109-8
– *palpebralis medialis* 98-2
– *pancreaticoduodenalis, inferior* 121-2; 123-12

*Arteria pancreaticoduodenalis, superior* 4-9; 121-9
– *perforans* 7-3, 4; 144-2, 9; 145-8, 10; 147-3, 4, 5; 154-1
– *pericardiacophrenica* 36-2; 54-11; **57**-3, 9; 166-2; 184-7
– *perinealis* 133-8
– *peronea (fibularis)* 137-5; 151-2; 152-1; 153-7; 154-6; 157-11
– *pharyngea ascendens* 94-5; 115-2, 3
– *phrenica inferior* 120-2; 121-1; 125-1, 10, 12; 126-11; 170-10
– *plantaris lateralis* 159-1; 160-1
– – *medialis* 7-5; 159-11; 160-9
– *poplitea* 7-7; 137-2, 4; **145**-5; 146-7; 147-7; **149**-2; 151-11; 12; 152-12; **154**-3; 174-8
– *princeps pollicis* 86-7; 88-10; 90-4
– *profunda brachii* 7-11; 53-2; 71-9; **72**-10; 73-3; **74**-2
– – *femoris* 7-3; 142-11; 143-10; 144-9, 11
– – *linguae* 107-6; 118-1, 9
– *pudenda externa* 50-7; 130-2; 138-2
– – *interna* 128-5; 129-5; 132-5; 133-1, 5; 134-1, 5; 147-11; 148-7; 171-3
– – – *rami labiales* 134-8
– – – *r. scrotales posteriores* 128-6
– *pulmonalis* 3-11; 17-1, 10; 18-2, 10; 19-1, 10; 25-1, 12; 34-2, 3, 9, 10; 35-2, 3, 9, 10; 36-2; 166-2, 9; 167-3, 9
– *radialis* 7-10; **75**-1, 5; 76-1, 5; 77-5; 78-5; 79-8; **85**-10; 11; **86**-9, 10; **87**-6; **88**-7; **89**-4, 6, 7; **90**-5
– – *ram. palmaris superficialis* 75-6; 76-6; 77-5; 87-7; 88-7; 98-7; 90-5
– *rectalis inferior* 128-5; 129-5; 133-11; 134-10
– – *media* 128-4; 129-2, 4, 5; 132-5; 171-3, 4
– – *superior* 123-6; 128-2; 129-1; 171-2
– *recurrens radialis* 75-2; 76-1; 77-1; 79-7
– – *tibialis* 137-5; 152-1; 153-10; 154-4
– – *ulnaris* 74-5; 76-9; 77-10; 78-7; 80-1
*Arteria renalis* 4-2; 7-1; 125-2; 126-11; 170-2; 355-10
– *sacralis lateralis* 132-12
– – *media* 7-2; 123-9; 126-6; 128-12; 129-12; **132**-10; 171-2
– *scapularis descendens* 38-9; 42-4; 44-2; 60-1
– *sigmoidea* 123-4; 124; 127-3
– *sphenopalatina* 94-10; 102-2; 108-11; 109-9
– *spinalis anterior* 184-1; 186-3, 4; 200-4; 241-7; 242-6
– – *posterior* 186-3, 10; 200-4; 242-6
– *sternocleidomastoidea* 42-12; 94-5; 102-5
– *stylomastoidea* 94-4; 100-8; 101-9
– *subclavia* 3-11; 7-12; 17-12; 18-12; 34-12; 35-12; 36-1; **38**-4; 41-6; 42-4; 43-8; **44**-9; 46-3, 7; **55**-1, 11; 58-4, 7; **60**-12; 116-4, 8; 167-1, 10; 354-1, 11
– *subcostalis* 7-11; 55-7; 56-7
– *sublingualis* 102-6; 107-6; 118-1, 9, 11
– *submentalis* 42-11; 43-10; 44-11; 94-7; 100-5; 101-6; 102-6
– *subscapularis* 7-11; 61-6
– *supraorbitalis* 95-2; 98-2; 99-2; 103-1; 104-12; 105;12; 404-1
– *suprarenalis* 125-10; 126-1
– *suprascapularis* 38-4; 41-6; 43-4; 44-3; 60-12; 61-1; 62-11
– *supratrochlearis* 95-2; 98-2; 99-2; 101-2; 105-12
– *surales* 137-4; 149-3; 150-11; 154-3
– *tarsea* 157-3, 9
– *temporalis media* 94-2; 99-10; 100-10; 101-11; 102-12
– – *profunda* 94-10; 101-11, 12; 102-1, 12
– – *superficialis* 95-11; 98-10; 99-8; 100-9; 102-10
– – – *ramus frontalis* 94-11; 95-1; 96; 97; 98-1; 99-1; 100-1
– – – *r. parietalis* 94-1; 98-11; 99-11; 100-11; 101-11; 102-11
– *testicularis* 7-2; 126-7, 11; 127-8, 9; 128-1; 130-8

*Arteria thoracica interna* 3-1; 7-11; **38**-5; 40-8; 43-7; 44-9; 45-6; 50-2; **54**-1, 11; 55-1; 57-2; 58-8; 60-10; 166-11
– – – *rami intercostales* 54-10
– – – *r. perforans* 40-8; 44-8; 45-7; 54-11; 60-10
– – *lateralis* 7-11; 40-7; 44-6; 45-6; 50-11; 59-12; 60-4; 169-5
– – *suprema* 7-1; 169-7
– *thoracoacromialis* 7-1; 42-6; **43**-6; 44-3; 46-7; 60-1; 69-12
– – *ramus deltoideus* 41-5
– – *r. pectorales* 60-1
– *thoracodorsalis* 50-10; 59-4; 60-4; 61-8
– *thyreoidea inferior* 38-4; 43-8; 44-9; **115**-5, 7; **116**-8; **117**-5; 118-5
– – – *ramus pharyngeus* 115-6
– – – *r. trachealis* 117-7
– – *superior* 41-9; 42-9; 43-9; **44**-10; 46-9; 94-6; 102-7; 115-4, 9; 118-3, 9
– – – *ramus infrahyoideus* 41-9
– – – *r. pharyngeus* 115-4
– – – *r. sternocleidomastoideus* 41-8
– *tibialis anterior* 7-7; 137-5; 150-7; 152-12; 153-1, 8, 10; 154-6; 157-11; 175-7, 9
– – *posterior* 7-7; 137-5; 150-7; 151-7, 10; **152**-6, 7, 11; 154-5, 6; **158**-11; 159-11; 160-12
– *transversa colli* 41-8; 52-8; 60-12
– – – *ram. ascend.* 60-12
– – – *r. descendens* 42-4; 43-4
– – – *r. profundus* 41-4; 51-9; 52-8
– – – *r. superficialis* **41**-4; 42-4; 43-3; **44**-2; 46-9; **52**-8
– – *faciei* 94-5; 95-5; 98-9; 101-10
– *tympanica* 101-8; 102-9; 110-9; 115-12; 232-2
– *ulnaris* 7-10; **75**-7; **76**-1, 7; **77**-7; **78**-6; 82-5; 87-6; 88-5; **90**-7, 8
– – *ramus carpeus dorsalis* 86-2; 87-5; 88-3, 5
– – – *palmaris profundus* 87-5; 88-3, 5
*Arteria ulnaris recurrens* 74-5; 76-9; 77-10; 78-7; 80-1
– *umbilicalis* 3-6; 5-1, 11; **127**-6; **128**-11; **129**-11; 132-10
– *uterina* 129-1, 4, 8; 131-3, 9, 10; 171-3
– *vaginalis* 129-4; 131-4; 171-3
– *vertebralis* 7-1; **38**-2; 43-8; 44-9; 52-1, 10; 53-11; 58-1, 9; 60-12; 199-5, 7; 200-4; 232-7; 239-7; **241**-7; 242-6; 367
– – *ramus meningeus* 232-6
– *vesicalis* 127-3, 8; **128**-1, 4, 9, 11; 129-6; 131-4, 8; 132-6; 171-8
– *zygomaticoorbitalis* 94-10; 95-1; 98-2; 99-8; 101-10

## ARTERIOGRAMS 243–244

*Arteriola retinae* 360-1, 2, 4, 6
**Artery,** brachiocephalic trunk 17-11; 18-1; 34-12; 35-1; 36-1; **38**-5; 46-7; **55**-12; 56-12; 57-11; 116-5; 167-1; 352-2
–, celiac trunk 4-2; 7-1; 55-5; **120**-1; **121**-12; 125-2; 126-12; 170-2; 355-2
–, cerebral distribution 201–204
–, costocervical trunk 38-9; 55-11
–, thyrocervical trunk 38-4; 43-8; 44-9; 60-12; 116-8
**Articular capsule,** shoulder joint 62-6; 74-12
*Articulatio atlantooccipitalis* 448-17
– *incudomallearis* (ear) 436-12; 439-2; 440-1
**Aryepiglottic** fold 116-10
**Arytenoid** muscle, oblique 116-2, 3; 117-3
**Ascending** aorta 18-2; 19-10; 33-12; **46**-6; **55**-11; 354-10
– cervical artery 38-3; 42-9; 43-8; **44**-10
– colon 122-7
– palatine artery 94-5; 102-8; 108-7; 109-8; 115-3
– – –, tonsillar branch 108-7; 117-1, 4
– pharyngeal artery 94-5; **115**-2, 10
**Atlantooccipital** articulation 448-7
**Atlas** 448
–, arch of 52-3; 181-1

**Atrioventricular** bundle (of His) 12; 20-7; 32-1; 33-1
– node 12; 32-1
– opening, right 24-1; 25-7; 26-1; 28-2, 9
– valve, left 23-2; 33-3
*Atrium dextrum cordis* 3-2; 5-3; 17-8; 18-4; 19-9; 21-10; 22-2; 25-1; 35-6
– *sinistrum cordis* 3-10; 5-8; 18-3; 19-2; 22-9; 23-1; 27-1; 33-2; 35-7
**Auditory** ossicles, articulation of incudomallear 436-12; 439-2; 440-1
– pathways 304
– tracts 304
– tube 110-9; 112-6; 350-2; **439**-9; 441-10; 442-8; 443-4; 444-2; **456**-2; **457**-3
– –, bony portion 438-4; 440-9
– –, cartilage 109-9; 439-11; 456-1
– –, lateral cartilaginous lamina 455-2; 457-2
– –, lumen of 446-8
– –, membranous portion 457-5
– –, mucous membrane 439-9; 446-5
– –, pharyngeal orifice 107-9; 116-12
– –, semicanal of 427-4; 445-3; 446-4
– –, tympanic opening of 428-2; 429-2; 438-4; 439-9; 441-10; 442-8; 443-4; 444-2; 451-8
*Auricula atrii sinistra* 3-10
– *cordis dextra* 17-9; 19-9; 26-1; 27-10; 28-9; 34-9
– – *sinistra* 17-3; 18-9; 19-2; 24-10; 25-2; 34-7
**Auricular** cartilage 448-2, 3
– muscles of ear 463; 464
– –, posterior 95-8, 11; 99-9
– –, superior 464-5, 11
– nerve, great 37-11; **39**-3, 10, 11; **40**-4; 51-1; 53-11, 12; 95-7; 98-8
– tubercle (Darwin's) 459-10
– vein, posterior 52-1
**Auriculotemporal** nerve 92-8; **95**-12; 96; 97; 98-9; 99-8; 100-10, 11; 101-9; 102-9, 11; 110-9

**AUTONOMIC NERVOUS SYSTEM** 345–355
**AXILLA 58–62**
**Axillary** artery 7-11; 38-7; 43-6; **44**-3; **60**-1, 3; 61-2; 71-12; 72-12; 166-2
– fascia 67-11; 469-3
– lymph nodes 168-2; 169-2
– nerve 37-8; 53; 59-3; 61-7; **62**-6; 69-11; 72-11; **74**-12
– vein 43-7; 44-3; 45-5; 59-1; 60-1, 4; 166-2; 168-12
*Axis* 264-6
– *lentis* 379-8
– *oculi* 356-7 C
– *opticus* 356-5 C
–, spinous process of 52-3
**Azygos** vein 3-1; 18-2; 35-1; **55**-2, 7, 11; **56**-2, 9, 11; 124-12; 167-2; 184-6; 353-12

## B

**BASAL GANGLIA of CEREBRUM** **221; 278–282; 285–288**
**Basal** vein 205
**Base** of brain 247; 272
**Basilar** artery 197-8; 200-3; 239-9; 241-8; 242-7; 367
– plexus, venous plexus 235-8
– portion of pons 329-4; 330-4
– sulcus of pons 272-8; 330-5
**Basilic** vein **65**-2; 67–6, 7; 68-10, 11; 70-5; 71-9; 83-1; 168-5
*Basis stapedis* 435-7; 436-6; 437-9
**Basivertebral** veins 186-8
**Biceps** brachii muscle **71**-5; 72-2; 73-8; 74-8; 75-1, 12; 76-12; 77-2, 12; 78-1; 79-11
– femoris muscle 145-9; 146-5, 6; **147**-5, 8; 149-1, 5; 150-12; 154-2, 12
– muscle, long head 169-4
**Bicipital** aponeurosis 71-6; 75-1, 11; 78-2; 158-1
*Bifurcatio aortae* 123-9; 132-11
– *tracheae* 35-1; 167-1

**Bifurcation** of common carotid artery 350-6
**Biventral** lobule 292-2; 294-3
**Bladder**, gall 120-11
–, urinary 125-7; 126-6; 128-11; 129-9; 171-7
–, –, venous plexus 128-8

**BLOOD SUPPLY OF BRAIN 195**; **196**; **200–205**; **232–238**; **241**; **242**

**Body**, amygdaloid 221a; 286-8; 323-8
–, carotid 350-6
–, ciliary 356-10C; 368-10; 377-8; 383-5
–, – vessels of 359-1 C
–, lateral geniculate 222-4; 229-2; 273-10; 276-3; 290-10; 321; 322
–, – –, nucleus of 278-8; 281-5; 284-9
–, medial geniculate 273-11; 276-3; 290-10; 321; 322; 326-2
–, pineal 242-2; 248-12; **261**-5; 271-5; 274-2; **276**-10; 281-7
–, of sphenoid bone 238-6; 275-7
–, trapezoid 330-3; 333-8
**Bone,** frontal 113-12; 395-11; 396-12; 404-10; 405-1
–, –, orbital portion of 280-1; 403-12
–, –, zygomatic process of 397-1
–, hyoid 102-6; 118-7
–, –, greater cornu 107-7; 117-10
–, occipital 115-12; 180-11; 236-2; 448-8
–, palatine, horizontal lamina 455-2
–, parietal 237-10
–, pisiform 87-5
–, pubic 128-10; 129-8
–, sphenoid 107-11; 395-3; 396-3; 456-3
–, –, greater wing 113-2; 384-2, 8; 385-2, 9; 401-4; 402-3; 404-8, 9; 405-3; 455-11
–, –, lesser wing 236-9; 384-10
–, –, spine of 455-8
–, temporal 110-10; 115-1; 439-1; 448-1; 456-9
–, zygomatic 100-1; 101-1; 102-2; 397-5; 403-8; 408-7

**BONY LABYRINTH 411**; **414–424**

**Brachial** artery 7-11; 61-6; **71**-10; **72**-5; **73**-3; **74**-1; **75**-12; **76**-12; **77**-12; **78**-1; **79**-10
– –, deep 53-2; 71-9; 72-10; 73-3; 74-2
– cutaneous nerve, lateral (see superior) 53-2; 62-6; 69-1; 73-10
– – –, medial 37-6; 61-6; 67-10; 68-11; 69-3; 70-12; 71-11; 169-4
– – –, posterior 53-2; **69**-9; 70-12; 73-9; 74-1
– – –, superior 62-6; 69-1; 73-10
– plexus (of nerves) 37-4; 41-4, 6; 42-4; 43-5; 44-2, 5; 46-3; 58-2; 59-2; 60-1, 12; 165-6; 166-1; 348-10; 352-11
– –, lateral cord 61-3; 71-12
– –, medial cord 61-2; 71-12
– –, posterior cord 61-7; 71-11
– vein 53-2; 59-2; 61-4; 71-11
**Brachialis** muscle 72-5; 73-7; 74-7; 75-11; 76-11; 77-11; 78-2
**Brachiocephalic** trunk, artery 3-12; 7-11; 17-11; 18-1; 34-12; 35-1; 36-1; **38**-5; 46-7; **55**-12; 56-12; 57-11; 58-6; 116-7; 167-1; 352-2
– vein 18-1, 12; 34-10; 36-11, 12; **42**-7; **43**-7; **44**-8; **46**-6, 7; 56-11, 12; 57-9, 11; 58-7; 60-11; 116-5, 7; 162-12
**Brachioradialis** muscle 72-5; 75-1, 5; 76-2, 5; 78-3, 4, 5; 79-7; 80-7, 11; 81-11
*Brachium conjunctivum* - - - - see *Pedunculus cerebellaris superior* or Cerebellar peduncle, superior
– *pontis* - - - see *Pedunculus cerebellaris medius* or Cerebellar peduncle, middle
**Bronchoesophageal** muscle 35-1
**Bronchomediastinal** trunk 169-8
**Bronchopulmonary** lymph nodes 34-3; 35-9; 166-3, 9

**BRAIN, Blood Supply 234**; **241–246**
**–, Cranial Nerves 239**; **241**; **247**; **272**

**BRAIN SECTIONS, Frontal 279; 285–288**
– –, **Horizontal 278; 280–282**
– –, **Sagittal 242; 248; 251; 252; 274**
**BRAIN STEM, Dorsal view 276; 289**
– –, **Nuclei 229–231**
– –, **Sagittal section 274**
– –, **Side view 290**
–, ventricles 218-220
**Broca,** diagonal band of 305
**Bronchus,** inferior lobe 34-3
–, main 35-2, 10; 55-1, 10; 166-10; 167-2; 352-4; 354-2, 9
–, superior lobe 34-2; 35-11
**Buccal** artery 94-8; 99-5; 100-4; **101**-5; 102-4
– lymph node 165-9
– nerve **97**; 98-5; 99-5; 100-3, 4; **101**-4; 103-3
**Buccinator** lymph nodes 163-1
– muscle 98-4; 99-5; 100-4; 101-5; 102-4; 350-8
**Bulb** of penis, artery to 133-5
– of posterior cornu 259-6; 262-7; 266-5
**Bulbar** fascia 402-3; 403-11; 406-1, 12; **407**-5
**Bulbocavernosus** muscle - - - - see bulbospongiosus muscle
**Bulbospongiosus** muscle 133-7; 134-7
*Bulbus aortae* 23-11
– *oculi* 105-1; 106-1; 232-11; 367; 385-2, 10; 395-1; 396-9; 399-1; 401-1
– *olfactorius* 241-1; 247-1; 257-4; 272-12; 305; 323-9; 367
– *pili* 468-7
– *venae jugularis superior* 115-1; 116-8; 448-8
– *vestibuli* 129-6; 134-5
*(Bursa coccygea)* 53-6
*(Bursa subcutanea sacralis)* 53-5

## C

**Calamus** scriptorius 274-6; 289-5
**Calcaneus** tendon 150-6; 151-6; 152-6
**Calcar** avis 259-6; 261-8; 262-4; 265-7; 266-6; 267-7; 323-3
**Calcarine** cortex 303
– sulcus 209-6; 248-9; **251**-3; 252; 255-7; 257-9; 259-6; 260-6; 266-5; 282; 301a; 303; 321; 322; 323-3
*Camera anterior bulbi* 356-11; 368-12; 383-8
– *posterior bulbi* 356-11; 368-10
*Canaliculus cochleae* 409-5; 419-7
– *lacrimalis inferior* 392-2, 3; 393-6; 394-5
– – *superior* 392-1, 12; 393-12; 394-11
*Canalis adductorius* 143-7
– *caroticus* 112-7; 425-9; 426-3; 427-3, 5; 428-3; 429-4; 441-8; 442-8; 444-5; 449-3, 5; 456-7
– *centralis (medulla oblongata)* 218-5; 248-8; 274-6; 339-1; 341-12; 342-10
– – *(medulla spinalis)* 191-8
– *facialis* 114-5; 350-2; 426-1, 7; 429-2, 8
– *incisivus* 108-3
– *opticus* 103-8; 106-7; 402-10
– *sacralis* 128-1
– *semicircularis anterior* **411**-2; 413-5; 414-1; 415-12; 416-1; 417-12; 418-12; 419-2; 420-11; 423-2; 426-10; 439-4
– – *lateralis* 330-4; **411**-3; 413-2; 414-3; 415-9; 416-3; 417-10; 419-2; 420-10; 423-9; 425-11; 426-9; 444-11; 445-12
– – *posterior* **409**-8; **411**-4; 414-3; 415-8; 416-3; 417-8; 418-8; 419-3; 420-8; 423-8; 439-4
– *spiralis cochleae* 416-8, 9, 10; 423-10; 424-3; 426-5; 439-8
*Capsula articularis* 62-6; 74-12
– *externa* 278-10; 279-2; **280**-11; 281-2; 282; 284-12; 285-10; 286-4; 287-3; 288-2
– *extrema* 281-3; 282
– *interna* 222; 224-9; 225-11; **279**-2; **281**-3; 283-3; 284-10; 286-10; 287-10; 288-10; **300**-1; 320

*Capsula interna crus anterius* 278-1; **280**-11; 281-10; 282
– – *crus posterius* 278-2; **280**-8; 281-8; 282
– – *genu* 278-2; **280**-11; 282
– *lentis* 380-7
*Caput fibulae* 137-4
– *mallei* 430-1; 431-10; 432-12; 436-10; 438-5; 439-2; 440-11; 441-1, 12; 448-12; 449-12
– *nuclei caudati* 264-10
– *stapedis* 112-9; 435-1; 437-2; 439-3; 443-1; 444-12; 445-8
**Cardiac** artery 19-9
– ganglion 352-3
– nerve 348-1, 2, 10
– –, cervical 44-8, 10; 57-2; 115-4, 5; 352-1
– –, superior 348-10
– plexus (of nerves) 36-2; 57-9; 354-1
– veins 124-1
– –, anterior 19-9; 34-8
– –, great 17-3; 18-9; 19-3; 20-9; 25-3
– –, middle 18-7; 20-6; 35-6
– –, smallest 19-8; 20-5; 35-6

## CARDIOVASCULAR SYSTEM (General) 1–8

**Caroticotympanic** nerve 93-1; 112-6
**Carotid** artery, common 3-12; 7-1; 17-12; 18-12; 34-1; 35-12; 36-1; **38**-3, 4; 41-9; 42-7; **43**-9; 44-8; 45-9; 46-5; 56-12; 57-1; 58-5; 60-11; 94-6; 102-7; 115-5; 116-7; 118-4; 164-8; 165-8; 167-1, 11; 348-2; 352-12; 354-12
– –, external 7-12; 41-9; 42-9; 43-9; 44-12; **94**-6; 99-6, 7; 100-7, 8; **101**-8; **109**-8; 115-9; 118-3, 8; 350-7
– –, internal 7-12; 43-9; 44-12; 93-3, 4; 94-6; 99-7; 100-7; 103-7; 104-6; 105-7; 106-7; **109**-10; 110-8, 10, 12; 112-7; 114-2; 115-2, 12; **116**-1; 164-12; 200-3; **232**-1; 233-C; **236**-5, 6, 10; 238-3, 12; 239-1; **241**-1; **243**-8; 350-2, 12; 367; 384-11; 402-11; 438-3; 439-10; 456-8; 457-1
**Carotid** body 350-6; 351-6
– canal **112**-7; 425-9; 426-3; 427-3, 5; 428-3; **429**-4; 441-8; 442-8; 444-5; 449-3, 5; 456-7
– plexus, common (of nerves) 115-5; 116-3
– –, internal (of nerves) 93-3, 4; 109-10; **112**-11; 232-2; 438-3
**Cartilage,** thyroid 117-8, 10; 118-4
*Cartilagines tracheales* 352-1
**Cartilaginous** auditory tube 109-9; 116-12; 439-11; 455-2; 456-1
*Cartilago auriculae* 448-2, 3
– *meatus acustici* 458-7; 461-6; 462-7; 465-4
– *thyreoidea* 117-8, 10; 118-4
*Caruncula lacrimalis* 386-3; 388-2; 392-1; 393-2; 394-3; 407-3
**Cauda** equina 127-1; **180**-7; 182-7; **190**-7
– helicis 458-7; 460-7; 461-5; 463-7
**Caudate** lobe, of liver **120**-12
– nucleus 219-10; **222**; 224-2; 225-1; 260-11; 262-10; 265-2; 271-8; 283-2
– –, body of 221; 222-12; 259-8; 288-2
– –, head 222-3; 259-10; 260-1; 261-1; 262-11; 264-10; 265-11; 271-1; 276-11; **278**-1; **279**-10; **280**-1, 11; **281**-1, 11; **282**; 285-2; 286-10; 287-2
– –, tail of 222-9; 276-9; **278**-3; 279-3; 280-3; 281-4
**Cavernous** sinus 232-10; 233-7; 238-5
*Cavum epidurale* 186-3; 198-11
– *nasi* 384-5; 402-7; 403-4; 404-3
– *septi pellucidi* 260-1; 261-1; **262**-1; 265-1; **271**-1; 278-11; 285-1
– *subarachnoideale* 184-2; 185-2; 186-11; 197-2; 198-11; 199-1, 4; 284-2, 3, 9; 362-8
– *subdurale* 184-2; 197-5; 198-11
– *tympani* 112-6, 8; 413-1; 426-6; 427-6; **438**-8; **439**-12; **443**-10; **444**-8; **445**-4; 449-3, 9

*Cavum tympani paries labyrinthicus* 427-6; 429-6; 447-5
**Cecum 122**-7
– cupulare (cochlea) 409-3
– vestibulare 409-5; 413-1
**Celiac** ganglion 125-2; 355-10
– plexus (of nerves) 125-1; 355-10
– trunk, artery 4-2; 7-1; 55-5; **120**-1; **121**-12; 125-1; 126-12; 170-2; 355-2
*Cellulae ethmoidales* 264-9; 384-5; 402-7; 403-2; 404-3; 405-9
– *mastoideae* 112-9; 425-4; 427-9; 428-11; 429-10; 448-5
– *tympanicae* 427-5; 428-4
**Central** canal (medulla oblongata) 218-5; 248-8; 274-6; 339-1; 341-12; 342-10
– – (spinal medulla) 191-8
– caudal nucleus, oculomotor nucleus 229-12; 230-1
– gray matter 273-12; 324-2; 325-1; 329-1

## CENTRAL NERVOUS SYSTEM 179–343

– – –, **Total view 180**

**Central** portion, lateral ventricle 218-12; 219-2; 235-2; 259-10; **260**-2; 262-2; 265-9; 279-11; 283-2
– sulcus 207; 208; 248-12; **249**-1; 250; 251-1; 252; 253-4, 10
– tegmental tract 327-2; 328-12; 333-3; 334-5; 335-5; 336-5
– vessels of retina 106-1; 356-6; 359-7; 362-8; 368-6
**Centrum** semiovale 258-9; 277-1
**Cephalic** vein **41**-6; **42**-6; **43**-6; **44**-3, 7; **45**-5, 7; **46**-5; 50-1, 10; 60-1; 65-11; 67-3; 68-1, 5; 69-8; 70-7, 12; 71-4, 12; 83-7, 11; 168-1, 5
**Cerebellar** artery, anterior inferior 200-3; 241-5; 242-7
– –, posterior inferior 200-4; 241-6; 242-6
**Cerebellar** artery, superior 200-3; 241-2, 8; 242-7; 278-5
– cortex, granular layer 296-10; 333-1; 335-2
– fissures 296-9
– –, horizontal 292-3; 293-3; 294-3
– flocculus **247**-8; **272**-4; **276**-5; **277**-4; 279-5; 292-1; **293**-3; **294**-2, 10; 335-3
– gyri 278-7
– hemisphere 241-5; 248-8; 271-7; 274-4; 277-5; 279-6; 292-11
– peduncle, inferior 209; **289**-8; 290-8; 330-10; 331-10; 332-10; 337-10; 343
– –, middle 276-4; **289**-9; 290-2; 293-2; 327-2; 328-9; 330-8; 333-2; 335-10
– –, superior 276-4; **289**-9, 10; 290-2; 293-2; 294-2; 295-1; **296**-10; 327-2; 328-11; 329-11; 333-1; 334-2; 335-2
– –, –, decussation of 274-8; **296**-11; 325-2, 3
– tonsil 247-5; 292-2; 294-5; 295-7; 334-2
**Cerebellomedullary** cistern (Cisterna magna) 197-5; 199-4; 239-6
**Cerebellorubral** tract 343

## CEREBELLUM 227; 228; 291–296; 343

**Cerebellum** 180-1; 227; 228; 235-8; 237-7; **239**-8; **247**-8; 260-6; 274-3; 278-6; **291-296;** 367
–, emboliform nucleus 296-8; 334-1
–, fastigial nucleus 296-1; 335-12
–, globose nucleus 296-7; 335-1
–, lingula of 228; 276-8; 291-12; 293-1; 295-2; 296-1
–, medullary substance 295-3; 296-8; 343
–, vermis 227; 228
**Cerebral** aqueduct **218**-3; 223-2; **248**-7; 255-7; 263-4; **273**-12; 274-2; 324-1; 325-1; 326-1; 327-12

**Cerebral** artery, anterior 200-2; 241-11, 12; **242**-8, 10; 243-3
– –, distribution 201–204
– –, middle 200-2; **204**; 234-8; 241-10
– –, posterior 200-3; **241**-2, 8; **242**-3, 7; 284-8
– cortex, auditory area 215-5
– –, autonomic region 216-10
– –, motor centers 215–217
– –, motor cortex 217
– –, precentral gyrus 217
– –, taste center 216-6
– –, visual memory center 215-3
– – visual perception center 216-3
– –, visual speech center 215-2
– fissure, longitudinal **247**-12; 253-6, 12; **255**-12; 258-12; 259-4, 12; 260-12; 261-12; 262-11; 265-12; 277-1; 278-11; 279-12; **280**-1
– fossa (fissure), lateral 255-10; 258-2; 272-1
– hemisphere 180-1; 250; 252; 254; 402-2
– –, association tracts 297; 298
– –, basal ganglia 221
– –, cingulum 298-11
– –, decorticated 254
– –, fasciculus, inferior longitudinal 298-5
– –, –, superior longitudinal 297-2
– –, –, uncinate 297–8
– –, frontal pole 206; 247-12; 248-4; 249-9; 251-8; 253-12; 255-12; 367
– –, functional areas 215; 216
– –, gyrus 207–210
– –, medullary substance 250; 252
– –, occipital pole 206; 247-5; 248-9; 249-4; 253-7; 255-6
– –, sulcus 207–210
– –, temporal pole 206; 247-11; 249-8; 251-8; 255-10; 266-12; 367
– peduncle 242-7; 247-10; **272**-8; 273-9; **274**-8; 276-9; 283-8; 290-10; **324**-7; **325**-4; 343; 384-12
– –, tegmentum of 326-3
– vein, great (of Galen) 197-3; **232**-7; **233**-2; 242-2; **246**; **262**-5; **265**-7

**Cerebral** vein, inferior 233-5
– –, internal 242-2; **246**; 265-9
– –, superior **233**-1; **234**-1, 7, 10, 12; 235-10; 237-2; 278-12

**CEREBROSPINAL FLUID, CIRCULATION of 197–199**

**CEREBRUM 249–255**

–, **Diagrams 207–217**
–, **Dissections 206, 256–262, 265–271, 277, 320–323**
–, **Principal association pathways 297–298**
–, frontal lobe 208; 209; 234-1; 256-3; 258-11; 280-1; 285-10; 286-10
–, occipital lobe 251-3; 256-9; 257-8; 258-7
–, parietal lobe 208; 256-12; 258-9; 279-2
–, temporal lobe 209; 241-10; 256-7; 258-3; 279-3; 284-3; 285-3; 286-4; 288-4

**Ceruminous** Glands 465-9

**Cervical** artery, ascending 38-3; 42-9; 43-8; **44**-10
– –, deep 38-10; 52-3, 9; 55-11; 58-9
– –, superficial **38**-3; 41-8; 42-8; 43-3; **44**-2; 50-11; 169-10
– –, transverse 41-8; 52-8; 60-1
– –, – ascending branch 60-12
– –, – deep branch 41-4; 51-9; 52-8
– –, – superficial branch 41-4; 42-4; 43-3; 44-2; 46-9; 52-8
– cardiac nerve 44-8, 10; 57-2; 115-4, 5; 352-1
– enlargement (spinal cord) 180-1; 183-2
– lymph nodes, inferior deep 163; 164-4; 165; 169-7, 8, 10
– – –, superficial 163-4, 9; 165-4; 169-12
– – –, superior deep 163-3; 164-3; 165-7, 8; 169-12; 470-6
– – –, supraclavicular deep 164-7
– nerve 43-3, 4; 181-11; 199-5; 348-1; 350-3, 4; 351-3, 4, 5
– –, dorsal ramus 52-9; 53-1, 12
– –, dorsal root 182-11; 290-6
– –, root filaments 187-10; 188-1; 290-6, 7; 342-4

**Cervical** nerve, ventral ramus 42-2, 4; 350-4; 352-11
– –, ventral root 199-6; 290-7; 342-4
– plexus (of nerves) 37-2; 41-3
– sympathetic ganglion, inferior 58-9; 115-6; **116**-8; 348-10; 351-2, 3; **352**-11; **354**-11
– – –, middle **44**-9; 58-10; **115**-5; **116**-8; 348-1, 10; 352-1, 12; 354-12
– – –, superior **44**–11; 58-10; 109-8; 110-8; **115**-2; 116-1; 301a; 348-11; **350**-2, 3; 351-3
– – trunk 348-10
– vein, superficial branches 45-9; **46**-9; 50-11; 52-4; 58-9; 169-10
– vertebra 38-12; 58-12
**Cervicothoracic** ganglion (stellate) 352-11
*Cervix uteri* 131-3
*Chiasma opticum* 218-9; 226-9; 241-1; **247**-1; 248-5; 255-12; 272-11; **273**-6; **274**-9; 277-2; 286-6; 320–322; 343; 367; 384-12; 385-7; 401-6
**Chiasmatic** cistern 197-8; 239-1
**Choana** 107-9; 116-10
**Chorda tympani** **92**-7; 93-6; 102-8; **109**-9; **110**-9; 112-8; **114**-12; **350**-2; 351-2; 439-3; 440-12; **441**-11; 442-1; 443-8; 448-12; 449-8, 12; **450**-2; 451-10
– –, canaliculus 441-4; 451-3
*Chordae esophageae anteriores (n. vagus)* 184-4
– *tendineae* 9-3; 24-3; 29-8
**Choriocapillary** lamina 359-5
**Chorioid** (of eye) 356-4; **359**-6 C; **368**-10; 370-5; 372-4; 373-9; 376-8
– glomus 259-7; 260-2; 262-7; 265-3
– plexus, fourth ventricle 197-5; 223-8; 235-8; 241-5; **247**-7; **248**-7; 274-6; **276**-5; 279-6; 295-2; 334-1, 8; 336-12
– –, lateral ventricle **219**-10; 220-1; 235-2; 259-8; **260**-1, 8; **262**-3; **265**-3; 272; **283**-9; **284**-1; 288-6, 11
– –, third ventricle 197-1; 219-11; 223-1; 235-9; 274-1; 283-9; 288-10
**Chorioid** vein 265-9
**Chorioidal** artery, anterior 200-3; **241**-9; 259-8; **260**-1; **262**-10; 265-9; 280-8
*Cilia* 363-6; 387-7; 407-2
**Ciliary** artery 105-4
– –, anterior 358-1, 10; 359-2; 369-2
– –, posterior 358-6; 359-3, 6; 369-7, 9
– body 356-10 C; 368-10; 377-8; 383-5
– –, vessels of 359-1 C
– corona 372-7; 376-5
– folds 376-1; 377-10; 382-6
– ganglion 104-4; **105**-4; 350-12; 351-12
– –, oculomotor root 105-5
– glands 363-5
– muscle 356-1; 368-1, 10; 369-2; 370-10
– nerves 369-3, 6; 370-9, 12; 383-9,10
– –, long 105-8
– –, short 105-4
– processes 368-10; 372-10; **376**-2; 377-10; **382**-5, 12; 383-2; 384-8; 402-4
**Cingulate** gyrus 210; 242-10; 248-1; 255-5; 286-1
– sulcus 248-2, 12; 251-1, 9, 11; 252; 253-6; 257-11
**Cingulum** 298-11
**Circle** of Willis - - - - see *Circulus arteriosus cerebri*
**Circular** sulcus of insula 256-2; 258-2
**CIRCULATORY DIAGRAMS 1, 2, 4, 5, 7**
*Circulus arteriosus cerebri* (Circle of Willis) 200
– – *iridis* 358-11; 359-1, 12
**Circumflex** artery, lateral femoral 7-3; 143-10, 11; 144-10
– –, medial femoral 7-3; 143-1; **144**-12; **148**-6
– humeral artery, anterior 7-11; 61-4; 71-1
– – –, posterior 7-11; 53-2; 59-1; 61-3; **62**-6; 69-2; 74-1, 11; 169-3
– – vein 59-1; 69-2; 71-1
– iliac artery, deep 125-8; 126-5; 128-10; **142**-11
– – –, superficial 50-4, 8; 138-10
– – vein, deep 50-4; 125-8; 126-5; 128-10

**Circumflex** iliac vein, superficial 50-8; 138-10
– scapular artery 53-3; 59-4; 61-7; 62-5
– – vein 53-3; 59-4
**Cistern** of lateral cerebral fossa 239-10
**Cisterna** ambiens 197-3; 239-9
– *cerebellomedullaris (magna)* 197-5; 199-4; 239-6
– *chiasmatis* 197-8; 239-1
– chyli **56**-4; 125-2; 162-5; 170-10
– *corporis callosi* 197-10; 240-6
– *interpeduncularis* 197-8; 239-3
– *magna* ---- see Cerebellomedullary cistern
– *pontis* 197-7
**Clavicle** 38-5; 41-4; 44-3; 45-4; 46-4, 8; 57-1; 61-1; 62-10
**Claustrum** 278-2, 10; 279-3; **280**-2; 281-2, 9; 284-12; **285**-9; 286-3; 287-8; 288-3
**Clitoris,** dorsal nerve of 134-4
**Cluneal** nerves 53-7; 119-7; 131-11; 133-11; 134-10; **140**-10, 11, 12; 145-1; 146-1, 11
**Coccygeal** ganglion 348-5
– nerve 132-5; 181-6; 190-6; 348-5; 355-6
– plexus (of nerves) **119**-5; 355-6
**Coccygeus** muscle 128-2; 132-5; 355-7
**Coccyx** 128-4; 181-6
**Cochlea** 334-4; 409-5; **410**; 411-2; 414-7; 418-3; 419-7; 420-2; **423**-6; 425-8; 439-8; 448-9
– basal coil 418-4; 420-4; 424-9; 425-8
–, canaliculus of 409-5; 419-7
–, cupula of 409-2; 413-11; 415-3; 416-10; 418-3; 420-1; 423-11
–, fenestra 409-6; 414-7; 415-7; 416-5; 417-6; 418-6; 420-5; 425-7; 426-6; 429-5
–, fenestra, fossula of 417-7; 426-6; 427-5; 428-5; 429-4, 5; 444-7; 445-8; 447-7, 10; 450-8; 454-8
–, middle coil 424-3
–, modiolus of 424-2, 5
–, spiral canal of 416-8, 9, 10; 423-10; 424-3; 426-5; 439-8
**Cochlea,** spiral ganglion of 410-3
–, – ligament of 410-8
–, – membrane of 410-8
**Cochlear** duct 409-4; 410-9; 412-7, 9; 413-9, 10
– nucleus, dorsal 229-3; 304; 332-2; 334-9
– –, ventral 229-3; 331-9; 334-8; 335-3
– recess 417-6; 426-5
**Cochleariform** process 427-2; 428-2; 429-2; 442-10; 444-1; **445**-3; 449-2
**Colic** artery, left 122-2; 123-4
– –, middle 122-1, 12; 123-2, 11
– –, right 122-9
– flexure **122**-3, 9; **123**-3
– vein 4-3, 8; 122-1, 9, 11; **123**-2, 11; **124**-3, 8, 9
**Collateral** artery, radial 80-12; 81-12
– –, middle 74-4
– sulcus (fissure) 220-6; 251-6; 255-8; 268-6
– trigone 263-3; 265-8; 267-8; 268-10; 363-3
**Collicular** nucleus, inferior 304; 325-12
**Colliculi** tectal 295-1
*Colliculus facialis* 218-7; 289-8; 330-1
–, inferior 271-8; 276-3; 289-11; 290-1
–, –, brachium of 276-9; 289-1; 290-10
–, superior 180-1; 229-1; 255-5; 271-5; 276-10; 278-7; 281-5, 8; 289-1; 290-1; 324-11
–, –, brachium of 276-2, 9; 290-1
–, –, gray matter of 281-5; 324-11; 326-1
*Collum mallei* 430-2; 431-9; 432-9; 450-2
**Colon** 122-1, 7, 12; 123-3, 12
– *sigmoideum* 122-5; 123-4, 5; 125-5; 127-3; 170-4
*Columna anterior (medulla spinalis)* 189-5, 7; **191**-4; **192**-8; 194-8; 232-8; 313-3; 338-8; 339-5; 340-8; 341-8; 342-4
– *fornicis* 224-9; 242-8; 248-2; 251-2; **257**-1, 5; 260-11; 261-10; **262**-11; **265**-6, 9; 271-11; **274**-12; 276-1, 11; 278-8; 279-1; 280-9; 281-1, 11; 286-6; 287-7; 323-10
– *lateralis (medulla spinalis)* 192-2

*Columna posterior (medulla spinalis)* 189-2; **191**-2; **192**-1; 193-2; 194-1; 338-2; 340-10
*Commissura alba anterior (medulla spinalis)* 191-8; 192-7
– *anterior (cerebri)* 218-10; 223-10; 224-9; 226-11; 248-3; 251-8; 257-2; 263-10; 274-11; 276-1; **277**-2, 10; 286-5, 7; 287-4, 8; 321; 322; **323**-8, 9
– *habenularum* 261-2; 276-2
– *hippocampi* 259-3; 265-7
– *palpebrarum lateralis* 386-7; 407-9
– – *medialis* 407-3
– *posterior (cerebri)* 223-2; 248-1; 274-1
**Common** bile duct 120-9
– carotid artery 3-12; 7-1; 17-12; 18-12; 34-1; 35-12; 36-1; **38**-3, 4; 41-9; 42-7; **43**-9; 44-8; 45-9; 46-5; 56-12; 57-1; 58-5; 60-11; 94-6; 102-7; 115-5; 116-7; 118-4; 164-8; 165-8; 167-1, 11; 348-2; 350-6; 352-12; 354-12;
– digital artery (hand) 82-2; 84-4; 87-3
– – plantar nerves 158-6; 159-5
– hepatic artery 7-1; 120-2; 121-12; 170-2
– iliac artery 7-2; 126-2; 127-9; 128-12; 129-11; 132-10
– – vein 126-2; 128-12; 129-11; 132-10; 170-3
– interosseous artery 76-3; 77-9
– peroneal nerve (fibular) 119-8; 145-8; 146-5; **147**-2, 5; **149**-5; 150-1; 151-1; **153**-11
– tendinous ring (eye muscles) 367; 395-2; 401-8; 405-8
**Communicating** artery, anterior 200-2; 241-11; 242-8
– –, posterior 200-2; 241-2; 242-8
*Concha auricula* 459-9; 460-8
– *nasalis* 264-4; 392-3, 4
*Condylus occipitalis* 455-4
*Confluens sinuum* 233-4; 237-3; 246-8 C
**Conjunctiva,** bulbar portion 356-1, 10; 386-5; **388**-8; 392-9; 397-9; 398-8
*Conjunctiva caruncula lacrimalis* 386-3; 388-2; 393-2; 394-3; 407-3
–, fornix of 363-10; **388**-7; 390-12; 392-9, 11; **406**-8, 10; 408-8, 11
– palpebral 363-8; **388**-7; 390-1; 392-8
**Conjunctival** lymph nodes 363-10
– vessels 359-1
**Constrictor** muscles of pharynx, inferior 115-8; 352-1
– – – –, middle 107-7; 115-9
– – – –, superior 115-12
**Conus** arteriosus 17-3; 19-3; 25-1; 34-8
– medullaris 180-7; 183-5; 190-3; 198-2
**Coracobrachialis** muscle 72-2
**Coracoid** process 61-2
**Cord,** spermatic 128-7; 130-2, 11
–, spinal (see Spinal cord) 179-194
**Cornea** 356-11, 12; 359-12; 368-12; 369-1; 395-9; 397-8; 398-5; 402-5
**Corniculate** tubercle 116-9
*Cornu majus ossis hyoidei* 116-10
*Corona ciliaris* 372-7; 376-5
– radiata 222; 320

## CORONARY CIRCULATION
**17–20**

– artery, left 17-3; 18-9; 19-2; 20-10; 27-2; 31-11
– –, – anterior interventricular branch 19-3; 34-4
– –, – circumflex branch 19-3; 20-9
– –, right 17-8; 18-5; 19-9; 20-2, 6; 23-10; 27-10; 31-6; 34-8
– ligament of liver 3-3; 125-10
– sinus of heart 18-8; 20-6, 8; 26-9; 28-9; 35-6
– sulcus 18-5
– vein of stomach - - - - see Gastric vein
**Coronoid** process of mandible 100-12
*Corpus adiposum orbitae* 103-11; 186-3; 391-8; 401-12; 402-2; 403-2; 404-3; 406-5; 407-8; 408-2
– *amygdaloideum* 221a; 224-4; 286-8; 323-8
– callosum 219-1; 223-11; 224-10; 225-11; **242**-8; **248**-4, 11; **251**-2, 8, 11;

257-1, 2, 4; 258-1, 7; **259**-2; 260-1; 261-1; 270-11; **274**-2, 10, 12; 276-12; 278-11; 286-1; 287-2; 320; 323-2, 9

*Corpus* callosum, cistern of 197-10; 240-6

– –, genu of 248-4; 251-8; 257-2; 258-1; **259**-1; 260-12; 262-1; 271-1; 274-10; 281-1; 323-9

– –, radiation 279-11; 285-1; 287-2; 288-1; 321; 322

– –, rostrum of 248-4; 251-8; 257-4; 274-11; 285-8

– –, splenium of **248**-11; **251**-2; 255-6; **257**-11; **258**-7; 259-3; 260-7; 270-11; **274**-2; 280-8; 282; 321; 322; 323-1

– –, sulcus of 248-11; 251-11; 283-11

– –, trunk of 185-12; 199-2; **248**-2; **251**-12; **257**-1; **258**-1; 265-1, 6; **274**-12; 279-1; 283-2

– *cavernosum penis* 128-6

– *ciliare* 356-10 C; 368-10; 377-8; 383-5

– *fornicis* 223-12; 248-2; 257-12; 262-8; 274-12; 283-2; 288-11; 323-10

– *geniculatum laterale* 222; 229-2; **273**-10; 276-3; **290**-10; 321; 322

– – *mediale* **273**-11; **276**-3; **290**-10; 321; 322; 326-2

– *incudis* 433-9; 434-2; 436-1; 439-2; 440-1; 441-1; 442-1; 449-9

– *mamillare* 223-9; 225-8; **226**-3; **247**-10; **248**-6; 255-2; 257-5; 272-11; 273-3; 274-9; 283-7; 323-7; 343

– *medullare (cerebelli)* 248-8; 274-5; 295-3; 296-8

– *ossis sphenoidalis* 238-6; 275-7

– *pineale* 223-2; 242-2; 248-12; **261**-5; 271-5; 274-2; **276**-10; 281-7

– *restiforme* - - - - see *Pedunculus cerebellaris inferior*

– *spongiosum penis* 133-6

– *striatum* 285-2

– *trapezoideum* 330-3; 333-8

– *unguis* 477-1; 478-2; 479-1

– *uteri* 131-2

**Corpuscles,** lamellated (Pacinian) 178

*Cortex lentis* 380-11

– *vermis* 334-12; 335-12

**Cortical** projection tracts 299

**Corticobulbar** tract - - - - see Corticonuclear tract

**Corticonuclear** tract 326-4; 327-5; 328-5; 333-7

**Corticopontine** tracts 326-3, 5; 327-3; 328-7; 333-6

**Corticospinal** tract **299**; **312**; 320; 326-4; 327-5; 328-5; 333-7; 334-6; 335-5; 336-6; 341-5

– –, lateral 340-9

*Costa* 38-6; 46-5; 47-3; 54-1; 55-7; 57-3; 58-4; 180-8; 355-1, 10, 11

**Costal** arch 50-2

– fovea for head of rib 184-9

– pleura 184-4, 8

**Costoaxillary** vein 59-12; 60-5

**Costocervical** trunk, artery 38-9; 55-11

**Costomediastinal** recess 57-5

**CRANIAL CAVITY 232, 233**

– –, **Cavernous sinus 236; 238**

– –, **Cranial nerves 232; 239; 301–306**

– –, – –, **nuclei of 229–231**

– –, **Dura mater 232; 233**

– –, **Venous sinuses 231–233; 235–238**

**Cremasteric** artery 130-2; 132-9

– vein 130-2

**Cribriform** fascia 50-7; 170-4

– plate (ethmoid) 107-11; 385-1

**Cricoarytenoid** muscle, posterior 116-3; 117-4

**Cricothyroid** ligament 118-5

– muscle 118-7; 352-1

*Crista fenestrae cochleae* 417-6; 426-6

– galli 385-12; 401-12

– *iliaca* 53-8; 148-1; 355-9

– terminalis 27-11; 28-9

– vestibuli 416-6; 417-1; 418-4; 426-1

**Cristae** cutis (ridges) 475-1

– *matricis unguis* 479-10; 480-2; 481-9

*Crura stapedius* 435-3, 9; 436-4, 7; 443-1, 12; 445-1

**Crural** cutaneous nerves, medial 139-7, 9; 141-9
– fascia 174-4
**Crus** cerebri 255-2; **273**-2; **279**-5; 284-8; 320; 324-7; 325-8; 326-8
– *fornicis* 224-10; 251-7; **257**-8; 259-2; **260**-3, 8; **262**-6; 265-5; 280-5; 282; 323-1
– membranaceum commune (labyrinth) 409-10; 412-5; 439-6
– osseum commune (labyrinth) 414-2; 415-10; 416-2; 418-11; 419-2
– – simplex 414-2; 418-8; 419-5; 420-7
**Cubital** lymph nodes 168-5
– vein, median 65
**Culmen** 228; 274-3; 291-10; 293-12
**Cuneate** nucleus 336-10; 337-10; 338-11; 339-10; 341-10
**Cuneus** (cerebri) 210; 248-10; 251-3; 255-6; 257-10
*Cupula cochleae* 307-12; 409-2; 413-11; 415-3; 416-10; 418-3; 420-1;423-11
**Cutaneous** nerves of foot 139-7; 141-6; 155-8, 10
– – of forearm, lateral 50-2, 3, 11; 53-2; 67-4; 68-1, 4; 69-3; 71-5; 72-5; 73-7; 74-7; 82-7; 348-5
– – –, medial 37-7; 61-6; 67-7; 68-11; 71-11; 169-4
– – –, posterior 53-2; 67-5; **69**-7; 70-5, 12; 73-7; 74-7; 83-11; 89-5
– – (sural) 139–141
– – (thigh) 138; 140
**Cuticle** eponychium 478-9; 479-2, 6; 480-6; 481-8
**Cymba** conchae 459-10
**Cystic** artery 120-12
– vein 120-10

## D

**Declive** 228; 274-3; 291-9; 293-12
*Decussatio lemniscorum* 337-5; 338-2; 341-8
– *nervorum trochlearium* 327-12
*Decussatio pedunculorum cerebellarium superiorum* 274-8; 296-11; 325-2, 3; 343
– *pyramidum* 183-11; **247**-6; 272-6; **279**-6; 339-5; **340**-5; 342-6
– *tegmenti* 324-3
**Deep** auricular artery 101-9; 102-9; 110-9
– brachial artery **71**-9; **72**-10; **73**-3; **74**-2
– cervical artery 38-10; 52-3, 9; 55-11; 58-9
– – vein 52-4; 58-9
– circumflex iliac artery 125-8; 126-5; 128-10; **142**-11
– – – vein 125-8; 126-5; 128-10
– femoral artery 7-3; 142-11; 143-10; 144-9, 11
– – vein 144-2
– palmar arch 7-9; 88-8; 90-8
– peroneal nerve 153-5, 11; 155-4; 157-11
– petrosal nerve 92-12; 109-10; 112-1
– temporal artery 94-10; 101-11, 12; 102-1, 12
– – nerve 101-12; 102-1, 12
**Deltoid** muscle 41-5; 42-5; 43-4; 44-3; 45-7; 51-9; 53-2; 60-1; 61-2; 62-1, 8; 71-1; 72-1; **73**-11; 74-11
**Deltopectoral** sulcus 50-1
**Dens** of axis 264-6
**Dental** plexus (of nerves), inferior 100-5; 111-6
– –, superior 111-12; 112-4; 350-9; 351-9
**Dentate** gyrus 257-7; 266-2; 268-3; 269-3; 270-1; 284-6; 323-3
– nucleus (of cerebellum) **295**-2, 10; **296**-2; 318; 333-1; 334-2; 335-10; 343
**Denticulate** ligament **184**-11; 185-8; 186-3 **187**-1; 198-1; 199-1
**Depressor** anguli oris muscle 95-4; 98-5
**DERMATOMES**
**Trunk 48; 49**
**Superior extremity 63; 64**
**Head 91**
**Inferior extremity 135; 136**

**Descending** colon 123-3
– genicular artery 7-4; 137-11; 138-5; 142-7; 143-7; 144-7; 154-10
– palatine artery 94-8; 109-2
– thoracic aorta 18-11; 46-5; **55**-3; 184-4; 353-6; **354**-3
**Diaphragm** 3-2; 36-8; 54-3; **55**-7; 57-7; 126-1; 167-7
–, central tendon of 184-8
–, urogenital 128-5; 129-6; 134-8
*Diaphragma sellae* 226-8; 275-12
**Diaphragmatic** pleura 36-8; 57-7; 184-8

**DIENCEPHALON 223–226; 274; 275**

**Digastric** muscle 42-10; 109-4; 114-6; 116-10; 165-8
– –, anterior belly 41-10; 43-11; 45-12; 46-12; 99-6; 100-5; 102-5
– –, posterior belly 99-7; 100-7; 102-8; 115-2, 9
**Digital** artery, common (hand) 82-2; 84-4; 87-3
– –, dorsal (foot) 156-10; 157-6
– –, – (hand) 84-2; 85-7, 10
– –, – (thumb) 85-9; 89-9
– –, proper (foot) 156-6; 158-5, 6; 159-6
– –, – (hand) 82-2; 84-6; 87-1, 11; 88-12
– fibrous sheaths of hand 87-2
– nerves, dorsal (foot) 155-6; 156-12; 157-6
– –, – (hand) 83-7; 84-1; 85-10
– –, – (thumb) 89-9
– –, palmar 82-3; 84-8; 85-7; 87-1, 3, 4, 8, 11; 88-12
– –, plantar 156-6; 158-5, 6, 8; 159-5, 6
– veins, dorsal (foot) 155-6
– –, (hand) 83
*Digitationes hippocampi* 218-8; 261-10; 266-1; 267-10; 268-1; 323-8
**Diploic** veins 53-7; **196**-5, 6, 8; 197-12
*Discus intervertebralis* 58-1; 186-3
– *nervi optici* 356-7 C; 358-6; 360-2; 373-2; 384-3; 403-1
**Dorsal** artery of penis 128-8; 130-11
**Dorsal** cutaneous nerve (foot) 139-7; 141-6; 155-8, 10
– digital artery (foot) 156-10; 157-6
– – – (hand) 84-2; 85-7, 10; 89-1
– – – (thumb) 85-9; 89-9
– – nerve (foot) 155-6; 156-12; 157-6
– – – (hand) 83-7; 84-1; 85-10; 178
– – – (thumb) 89-9
– interosseus muscle 85-7; 86-9; 88-11
– metacarpal artery 85-7; 86-6; 89-2
– metatarsal artery 7-5; 153-6; 157-6
– motor nucleus of vagus nerve 229-8; 230-5
– nasal artery 98-3; 99-2; 100-2; 105-10
– nerve of clitoris 134-4
– – of penis 130-11; 133-4
– portion of pons 329-2; 330-2
– scapular nerve 37-9; 51-10; 52-4, 7
– vein of penis 128-8; 130-7, 12
**Dorsalis** pedis artery 7-6; 153-5
**Dorsomedial** nucleus (hypothalamus) 226-1
*Dorsum linguae* 108-5
*Ductuli excretorii glandulae lacrimalis* 391-9; 392-10
**Ductus** arteriosus 3-11; 5-4
– *choledochus* 120-9
– *cochlearis* 409-4; 410-9; 412-7, 9; 413-9, 10
– deferens 126-5, 7; 128-10
– – artery 127-4, 8; 128-11
– *endolymphaticus* 409-1; 412-6
– *lactiferi* 50-11; 473-1; 474-6
– *nasolacrimalis* 392-4; 393-6; 394-7
– *parotideus* 95-4
– reuniens 409-5; 413-1
– *semicircularis anterior* 412-1; 413-7; 439-4
– – *lateralis* 409-8; 412-4; 413-2; 445-11
– – *posterior* 409-7; 412-3
– *submandibularis* 102-6
– *thoracicus* 55-3; **56**-1; 127-10; 162-1, 3, 12; 184-5; 353-6, 7
– *utriculosaccularis* 409-6
– *venosus* 3-9; 5-2
**Duodenojejunal** flexure 123-12

**Duodenum** 354-7
**Dura mater,** cranial 195-3, 9; 197-5; 199-4, 5, 7; **232**-7; **233**-5; **235**-9; 238-8, 12; 280-2, 4
– –, filum of 181-6; 182-6; 183-6
– –, spinal 181-3; 182-10; 183-3; 184-1, 12; 185-2; 186-2, 8, 10; **187**-1, 7; 190-4, 8; 198-12

## E

**EAR** - - - - (see **Internal, Middle,** and **External**) **409–465**
**Ear,** concha of 459-9; 460-8
–, lobule of 459-5; 462-6
–, middle 112-6, 8; 413-1; **438**-8; **439**-12; **443**-10; **444**-8; **445**-4; 449-3, 9
–, –, promontory **428**-4; **429**-5; **443**-5; **444**-5; 445-4; **447**-1; 449-2; 450-5; 454
–, pyramis vestibuli 426-12
–, tuberculum supratragicum 459-3
**Edinger-Westphal** nucleus - - - - see Accessory oculomotor nucleus
**Elliptical** recess 417-1; 418-1; 419-11; 426-8
Emboliform, nucleus 296-8; 334-1
*Eminentia arcuata* 427-1
– *collateralis* 259-7; 261-8; 262-4; 266-7
– *conchae* (ear) 461-1; 462-3
– *fossae triangularis* (ear) 461-11; 462-11
– *medialis (vent. quartus)* 289-2; 329-1
– *pyramidalis* 427-8; 428-12; 443-7; 445-9; 447-8; 450-9

**ENCEPHALON 239–242, 247, 248, 272, 277, 279**

**Endocardium** 24-8
**Endolymphatic** duct 409-1; 412-6
– sac 409-12
**Endothoracic** fascia 184-4, 8
**Enlargement,** cervical (spinal cord) 180-1; 183-2
–, lumbar (spinal cord) 180-8; 183-4
**Ependyma** of third ventricle 238-3
**Epicardium** 24-6; 26-7
**Epicondyle,** lateral (humerus) 69-7; 73-7; 74-7; 80-11
–, medial (humerus) 72-7; 75-11; 76-11; 77-11; 78-9; 80-1
**Epicranial** aponeurosis 237-9; 468-6

**EPIDERMAL RIDGES 475; 476**

**Epidermis** 468-2
**Epidural** space 186-3; 198-11
**Epigastric** artery, inferior 7-2; 50-5; 54-5, 6; 122-7; 123-7; 125-8; 126-5; **127**-7; 128-10; **132**-7; 171-9
– –, superficial 50-8; 138-11
– –, superior 50-2; **54**-9
– vein, inferior 50-5; 54-5, 6; 122-7; 123-7; 124-4, 8; 125-8; 126-5; **127**-7; 128-10; 171-9
– –, superficial 50-8; 138-11; 173-1
– –, superior 50-2; 54-3; 138-11
**Epiglottic** vallecula 117-2
**Epiglottis** 116-2; 117-10
**Epiploic** vessels 120-4
**Episcleral** vessels 359-6
**Epitympanic** recess **439**-2; 440-12; 441-12; **442**-12; 448-12; 449-10, 12; 451-11
**Eponychium** (cuticle) 478-9; 479-2, 6; 480-6; 481-8
*Equator lentis* 361; 378-3, 12; 379-2
**Erector** spinae muscle 53
**Esophageal** arteries 184-4
– hiatus **125**-12; 126-12; 167-6
vein 124-1; 184-4
**Esophagus** 36-8; 55-2; 56-1; 115-6; **167**-8, 11; 184-4; 352-1, 6, 8; 353-3, 12; 354-9
–, muscle layers 116-3
**Ethmoid,** cribriform plate of 385-1
**Ethmoidal** air sinus (cells) 264-9; 384-5; 402-7; 403-2; 404-3; 405-9
– artery, anterior 103-10; 105-10; 106-9; 107-12; 232-1
– –, –, nasal branch 107-1; 108-1; 109-2

**Ethmoidal** artery, posterior 105-8; 106-9; 107-12; 108-12
– nerve, anterior 92-2; **95**-3; 105-9; 106-9; 107-12
– –, posterior 105-8; 106-9
**Extensor** carpi radialis muscles 73-6; 74–6
– – – –, brevis 80-7, 11; 81-7, 9; 85-12
– – – –, longus 80-7, 11; 81-7, 11; 85-11; 89-7
– – ulnaris muscle 80-5, 10; 81-5; 86-1, 12
– digitorum muscle 80-8; 81-5; 85-1; 89-3; 157-10
– – –, brevis 153-7; 157-7
– – –, longus 153-7, 10, 11; 157-7, 10, 12; 175-7, 10
– hallucis brevis muscle 115-10
– – longus muscle 111-7; 115-5, 6, 12
– pollicis brevis muscle 80-6; 81-7; 85-10; 86-11
– – longus muscle 81–5, 7; 85-10; 86-9
– retinaculum (wrist) 80-6; 81-6; 85-1; 86-10; 89-7
**External** capsule 278-10; 279-2; **280**-11; 281-2; 282; 284-12; 285-10; **286**–4; 287-3; 288-2

## EXTERNAL EAR **448**; **458–465**

– iliac artery 7-2; 54-5; 126-5; 127-8; **128**-10; **129**-10; 132-10; 142-12; 171-9
– – veins 124-7; 126-5; 129-10
– jugular veins 39-9; 40-4; 41-7; 42-10; 43; 44-7; **45**-2, 3, 9, 10; **46**-1, 10; 51-2; 56-1; 95-7; 169-9
– oblique abdoninal muscle 50-2; 53-5, 8; 59-10; 60-7; 148-1

## EXTREMITY, LOWER 135–160
–, **UPPER 61–90**

## EYE 356–408
–, **Horizontal section 356**; **368**
–, **Iris 370**; **371**; **376**; **377**
–, **Lacrimal apparatus 390**; **392–394**
–, **Lens 378–380**
**EYE**, **Muscles** (eye) **103–106**; **364–366**; **395–408**
–, **Retina** eye ground (fundus) **360**; **373–375**
–, –, vessels 358-360; 373-375
**Eye**, anterior chamber 356-11; 368-12; 383-8
–, bulbus oculi 105-1; **106**-1; 232-11; 367; 385-2, 10; **395**-1; **396**-9; **399**-1; 401-1
–, chorioid 356-4; 359-6C; 368-10; 370-5; 372-4; 373-9; 376-8
–, conjunctiva, bulbar portion 356-1, 10; 386-5; **388**-8; **397**-9; **398**-8
–, cornea 356-11, 12; 359-12; 368-12; 369-1; 395-9; 397-8; 398-5; 402-5
–, eyebrow 387-12; 407-1
–, eyelashes 387-7; 363-6; 407-2
–, lacrimal caruncula 386-3; 388-2; 393-2; 394-3; 407-3
–, lateral angle 386-8; 387-8; 389-9; 390-8
–, lower eyelid 113-8; 384-8; 386-7; 387-6; 393-4; 394-4
–, medial angle 386-4; 387-5; 388-3; 389-3; 390-3
– muscles 231
–, palpebral arch 95-2, 3
–, – conjunctiva 363-8; **388**-7; 390-1
–, posterior chamber 356-11; 368-10
–, retina 359-5C; **368**-9; 372-1, 3, 5; **373**-9; 376-8; 402-8
–, –, fovea centralis 356-6; 368-6; 373-8; 374; 375
–, rima palpebrarum 390-4, 8, 408-4
–, tarsus inferior 389-6; 390-6; 391-6; 406-8; 407-6; 408-7
–, tarsus superior 363-10; 389-12; 390-2; 391-1; 406-9; 408-11
–, upper eyelid 113-9; 386-1; 387-10; 390-11; 393-1; 394-1
**Eyeball** 105-1; 106-1; 232-11; 367; 385-2, 10; **395**-1; 396-9; 399-1; 401-1
**Eyelids**, tarsal gland (Meibomian) **363**-9; 388-7; **389**-2, 5; 407-11

## F


**Facial** artery 7-12; 43-10; 44-11; 45-1; 46-1; **94**-6, 7; **95**-5; 98-5; 99-4, 5, 7; 100-2, 6, 7; 101-5, 6; 102-7, 8; 115-3, 9; 350-7
– canal **114**-5; **350**-2; 426-1, 7; 429-2, 8; 445-7
– –, hiatus of 428-1
– –, prominence of 427-12; 428-12; 438-10; 443-11; 444-12; 447-10
– colliculus 218-7; 289-8; 330-1

**FACIAL NERVE**
**in Skull 92; 93; 112; 114**
**in Face 95–98**

**Facial nerve** 91; 92-10; 93-2, 7; **95**-5, 6, 8; **99**-8; 100-9; 101-9; 102-9; 114-3, 6; 232-4; 239-3; 241-5; **247**-9; **272**-4; 279-7; 290-8; 350-2; 351-2; 439-3, 7; 441-5; 442-5; 444-9, 12; **445**-8; 447-9
– – branches, buccal **95**-4, 5; 98-7
– – –, cervical 40-11; 41-11; 95-6; 98-6
– – –, digastric 99-8; 102-9; 114-6
– – – in facial canal 92-8; 93-1
– – –, mandibular 95-5; 98-6
– – –, posterior auricular 39-1; 42-1; 93-8; **95**-8; **99**-9; 100-9; 102-9
– – –, stylohyoid 114-7
– – –, temporal 95-7; 98-9
– – –, zygomatic **95**-7; 98-9
– –, geniculate ganglion 92-11; **112**-10; 114-2; 438-1; **439**-8
– –, geniculum of 438-1; 443-1; 445-12
– –, genu of 330-1; 333-1
– – in internal acoustic aperture 92-10; 93-2
– –, nucleus 229-9; 230-3; 330-10; 335-3, 7
– – –, superior salivatory 229-9; 230-4
– –, parotid plexus 98-8
– –, rootlets 330-10; 335-6
– vein 40-10; 41-9, 11; 42-11; 45-1, 2, 10, 11; 46-1, 2, 10, 11; **95**-4, 5, 6; 98-6; 99-6; 100-5, 6

**Facial** vein, deep 99-4; 100-2
*Facies lentis anterior* 356-1C; 370-1; 379-5; 383-4, 8
– – *posterior* 356-11 C; 372-2; 376-2; 379-10
– *sternocostalis cordis* 25-6
**Falciform** ligament of liver 124-10
**Falx** cerebelli 233-2
– cerebri 197-4; 199-1; 232-6, 12; **233**-2, 4, 10; 235-1; 237-2; 280-1, 6
*Fascia axillaris* 67-11; 469-3
– *cribrosa hiatus sapheni* 50-7; 170-4
– *cruris* 174-4
– *endothoracica* 184-4, 8
– *glutea* 145-1; 146-12
– *iliaca* 125-8
– *infraspinata* 51-4
– *lumbalis (retroperitonealis)* 125-3
– *parotidea* 95-7
– *pectoralis* 473-6
– *penis superficialis* 130-8
– *pharyngobasilaris* 116-12
– *temporalis* 99-12; 100-12
– *transversalis* 56-7
*Fasciculus atrioventricularis* (His) 12
– cuneatus **191**-1; 289-6; 290-5; 340-12; 342-2
– gracilis **191**-1; 276-6; 289-6; 340-12; 342-1
– *lateralis plexus brachialis* 61-3; 71-12
– *longitudinalis inferior* 298
– – *medialis* 274-7; 296-10; **318**; 324-3; **325**-2; 326-10; 327-10; 328-12; 329-1; 330-1; **331**-12
– – *pontis* 274-7; 279-5; 320; 329-8; 330-7
– – *superior (frontooccipitalis)* 297
– *mamillothalamicus* 225-9; 257-7; 279-1
– *medialis plexus brachialis* 61-2; 71-12
– *posterior plexus brachialis* 61-7; 71-11
– proprius 310
– *transversus* 82-11
– *uncinatus* 297
**Fasciola** gyrus 251-6; 270-12
**Fastigial** nucleus, cerebellum 296-1; 335-12

**Fastigium** 218-5
**Femoral** artery 7-3; 127-8; 137-1; 138-12; **142**-10, 11; 143-1, 2, 10; 144-4, 9, 11, 12; 170-7
– –, deep 142-11; 143-10; 144-9, 11
– –, lateral circumflex 7-3; 143-10, 11; 144-10
– –, medial circumflex 7-3; 143-1; 144-12; 148-6
– cutaneous nerve, anterior 50-7; 138-3
– – –, lateral 50-8; 119-10; 125-8; 126-3, 7; 127-9; **138**-11; 140-3; 142-11; 348-5, 8
– – –, posterior 119-7; 133-4; 134-3; **140**-7; **141**-11, 12; 145-2; 146-5; 147-11; 148-7
– fossa (foveola) 127-4
– nerve 119-9; 125-8; 126-5, 7; 127-8; 142-11, 12; **143**-11; **144**-11; 170-7; 348-5, 7
– –, anterior cutaneous branches 138-3
– ring (vascular lacuna) 127-8; 171-8
– vein 127-8; **138**-12; 142-1; **143**-2; 144-2, 3, 12; 170-7; 173-3
**Fenestra** cochlea **409**-6; 414-7; **415**-7; 416-5; 418-6; 420-5; 425-7; **429**-5
– – *fossula* 417-7; 426-7; 427-5; 428-5; 429-4, 5; 444-7; 445-8; 447-7, 10; 450-8; 454
– vestibuli **409**-6; **415**-6; 416-11; 418-5; 420-12; 425-10; 427-2; 428-1; **429**-1; 447-12

## FETAL CIRCULATION 3; 5

**Fibers,** arcuate 331-8; 332-6; 337-3, 8
–, transverse pontine 272-8; 320; 325-5; 328-8; 329-3, 7; 330-8; 333-9
–, zonular 356-11 C; 377-1; 383-4
**Fibrocartilaginous ring**, tympanic membrane 441-7; **442**-7; **449**-6; 450-8; 451-6; 454-6
**Fibrous** sheaths of hand 87-2
**Fibula** 137-4; 175-11
**Fibular** artery 7-6
*Fila radicularia dorsalia* 187-10; 188-1
– – *nervi abducentis* 330-1
*Fila radicularia nervi accessorii* 290-7; 332-3, 9; 339-8; 341-9
– – – *glossopharyngei* 279-7; 290-8; 331-8
– – *hypoglossi* 332-8; 336-7, 8
– – – *oculomotorii* 324-3; 326-6
– – – *vagi* 279-7; 290-8; 332-3, 9; 337-9
– – *radicis ventralis* 184-11; 188-1; 193-5
**Filaments**, dorsal root 187-10; 188-1
–, ventral root 188-1; 193-5
*Filum durae matris spinalis* 181-6; 182-6; 183-6
– terminale 183-5; 190-4, 7; 198-4, 6
*Fimbria hippocampi* 220-2; 257-8; **261**-8; 262-4; **266**-3; 267-4; 268-3, 7; 269-3; 270-8, 10; 284-6; 288-6; 323-5
**Final** common pathway 315
*Fissura antitragohelicina* 458-8; 459-6; 460-8; 461-6
– *calcarinus* - - - - see *Sulcus calcarinus*
– *cerebelli* 296-9
– *cerebrocerebellaris* 248-8
– *horizontalis cerebelli* 292-3; 293-3; 294-3
– *lateralis* 249-5, 8; 253-9; 279-9; 281-2, 9; 285-3; 286-9; 287-9; 288-3, 9
– *longitudinalis cerebelli* 219-1; 240-12; **247**-12; 253-6, 12; **255**-12; 258-12; 259-4, 12; 260-12; 261-12; 262-11; 265-12; 272-12; 277-1; 278-11; 279-12; **280**-1; 286-12; 287-1; 288-12
– *mediana anterior* (medulla oblongata) 186-5; 331-6; 338-6; 340-7
– – – (spinal cord) 183-1; 187-12; 188-11; 189-6; 190-1; **191**-6; 192-7; 193-7; 194-7
– *orbitalis inferior* 113-4; 395-6; 396-4; 397-8
– – *superior* 405-2
– *parietoöccipitalis* – – see *Sulcus parietoöccipitalis*
– *petrooccipitalis* 362-2
– *transversa cerebri* 260-8; 262-5

**Flexor** carpi radialis muscle 75-9; 76-6, 9; 77-6; 87-6; 88-7; 89-7
– – ulnaris muscle 75-8; 76-7; 77-6, 7; 78-8; 87-6; 88-5
– – – –, humeral head 73-5
– digiti minimi brevis muscle (foot) 160-4
– digitorum brevis muscle (foot) 159-1, 5
– – longus muscle (foot) 151-8; 152-9; 159-9
– – profundus muscle 77-6, 8; 78-7
– – superficialis muscle 75-7; **76**-8; 77-3, 6
– hallucis brevis muscle 159-8; 160-8
– – longus muscle 151-5; 152-5, 7; 159-8; 160-7, 9
– pollicis brevis muscle 87-8; 88-8
– – longus muscle 75-4; 76-4; 77-5; 88-8; 90-3, 5
– retinaculum (wrist) 82-5; 87-7; 88-7
– – (ankle) 150-7; 151-7; 158-11; 159-11
*Flexura coli* **122**-3, 9; **123**-3
– *duodenojejunalis* 123-12
**Floccular** peduncle 276-4; 293-2; 294-10
*Flocculus cerebelli* **247**-8; **272**-4; **276**-5; 277-4; 279-5; 292-1; **293**-3; **294**-2, 10; 335-3
**Fold**, aryepiglottic 116-10
–, malleolar, anterior 438-5; 439-12; 440-11; **441**-11; 442-11; 449-12; 450-2; 451-9; 454-1
–, –, posterior 438-11; 440-5; **441**-4; 442-5; 451-3; 454-10
–, rectouterine 129-2; 171-4
–, salpingopharyngea 116-10
– umbilical 127-4, 5; 128-10
*Folliculus pili* 468-3
**Folium** vermis 228; 274-4; 291-7; 292-5
**Foramen** cecum 272-8
– *infraorbitale* 397-6
– *interventriculare* (Monroi) 197-1; 218-10; 223-11; 248-2; 257-2; **259**-1; **260**-10; **261**-1; **262**-1; 263-11; **265**-10; 274-12; 276-10; 278-8; 280-3; 287-2
– *jugulare* 115-1; 232-5
**Foramen** (Magendii) - - - - see **Median aperture** of 4th ventricle
– magnum 233-5
– ovale 5-C; 455-9; 457-3
– *rotundum* 264-8
– *singulare* 421-4; 422-6
– *stylomastoideum* 112-8; 114-7; 429-8
– *venae cavae* (diaphragm) 353-4
– *zygomaticoorbitale* 113-7
*Foramina venarum minimarum* (Thebesii) 26-12; 28-10
*Formatio reticularis* 191-10; **317 a**; 327-1; 328-2; 329-2; 330-2; 333-6; 334-7; 335-7; 336-1; 338-8; 339-9
**Fornix** 219-2; 225-11
–, body of 223-12; **248**-2; **257**-12; 262-8; 274-12; 283-2; 288-11; 323-10
–, column of 224-9; 242-8; 248-2; 251-2; **257**-1; 260-11; 261-10; **262**-11; **265**-6, 9; 271-11; **274**-12; 276-1, 11; 278-8; 279-1; 280-9; 281-1, 11; 286-6; 287-7; 323-10
– *conjunctivae* 363-10; **388**-7; 390-12; 392-9, 11; **406**-8, 10; 408-8, 11
–, crus of 224-10; 251-7; **257**-8; 259-2; **260**-3; 8, **262**-6; 265-5; 280-5; 282; 323-1
– of lacrimal sac 392-2; 393-11
**Fossa** anthelicis 461-12; 462-1
– *(foveola) femoris* 127-4
– incudis 428-9; 438-8; 441-3; 442-4
– *infratemporalis* 395-5
– *inguinalis medialis* 127-4
– *intercondyloidea posterior* 137-3
– *interpeduncularis* 247-4; 272-2; 274-8; 279-5; 324-5; 325-3
– *lateralis cerebri* 207; 255-10; 258-2; 272-1
– *obturatoria* 127-4
– ovalis - - - - see Saphenous hiatus
– ovalis 26-11; 28-10
– *pterygopalatina* 112-6
– *rhomboidea* 181-12; 235-8; 274-7; 276-5; **289**-4; 290-4; 296-1; 330-12; 337-12; 417-12
– *supravesicalis* 127-4

**Fossa** *triangularis* (ear) 459-1; 460-1
*Fossula fenestrae cochleae* 417-7; 426-7; 427-5; 428-5; 429-4, 5; 444-7; 445-8; 447-7, 10; 450-8; 454-8
**Fourth** ventricle **218**-5; **248**-7; 263-4; **274**-2; 295-10; 320; 328-12; 329-1; 330-12; 333-12; 334-1; 336-12
– –, chorioid plexus 197-5; 223-8; 235-8; 241-5; **247**-7; 274-6; **276**-5; **279**-6; 295-2; 334-1, 8; 336-12
– –, lateral aperture (Luschka) 199-8; 276-5
– –, median aperture (Magendi) 197-5; 199-8; 218-5; **276**-6
– –, roof 276-7; 293-11
– –, striae medullares 289-8; 290-4
– –, tela chorioid 197-1; 248-7; 336-12
– –, tenia 289-5, 8; 337-11
*Fovea centralis* (retina) 356-6; 360-8; **368**-6; **373**-8; 374; 375
– *costalis capituli costae* 184-9
– – *transversalis* 184-10
*Foveola radialis* 85-11
**Frontal** bone 113-12; 395-11; 396-12; 397-1; 404-10; 405-1
– –, orbital portion of 280-1; 403-12
– –, zygomatic process of 397-1
– diploic vein 196-5
– gyrus, inferior 207; **249**-8; **285**-2
– –, –, opercular part of 249-11
– –, middle 207; 208; **249**-9; 253-10; 285-1
– –, superior **207**; 208; 210; 248-3; **249**-10; 251-9; 253-11; 262-12; 279-12; 285-12
– lobe (cerebral) 208; 209; 234-1; 256-3; 258-11; 280-1; 285-10; 286-10
– nerve 92-2; 95-2; 103-8; 350-12; 351-12
– –, lateral branch 92-2; **95**-2; 98-1, 2; 99-2; 100-1; 101-1; 102-1; 103-1; 104-12; 350-11, 12; 351-10, 12; 404-12
– –, medial branch 92-2; **95**-2; 98-2; 99-2; 100-1; 101-1; 102-1; 103-11; 104-12; 350-10, 12; 351-1, 11
**Frontal** process of maxilla 391-4; 393-8; 394-8
– sinus 264-9; 280-12
– sulcus 208; 253-1, 11
**Frontalis** muscle 280-12
**Frontoparietal** operculum 249-12
**Fundiform** ligament of penis 130-12

**FUNDUS OCULI 360**; **373–375**

*Fundus uteri* 125-7; 131-12
*Funiculus, anterior* 191-8; 192-5; 199-6; 340-6
–, *lateralis* 191-9; 192-3
–, *posterior* 191-1, 11; 192-12; 289-6; 313; 340-12; 341-1
– *spermaticus* 128-7; 130-2, 11; 170-6
– *umbilicalis* 3-7

## G

**Galea** aponeurotica 237-9; 468-6
**Gall** bladder 3-4; 120-11
**Gamelli** muscles 147-1; 148-5, 7
**Ganglion** or **Ganglia**
*Ganglion cardiacum* 352-3
– *celiacum* 125-2; 355-10
– *cervicale inferius* 58-9; 115-6; **116**-8; 348-10; 351-2, 3; 352-11; 354-11
– – *medium* **44**-9; 58-10; **115**-5; **116**-8; 348-1, 10; 352-1, 12; 354-12
– – *superius* **44**-11; 109-8; 110-8; **115**-2; 116-1; 301-a; 348-11; **350**-2, 3; 351-2, 3
– *cervicothoracicum* 352-11
– *ciliare* 104-4; **105**-4; 350-12; 351-1
– *coccygeum* 348-5
– *geniculi nervus facialis* 92-11; 112-10; 114-2; 439-8; 450-8
– impar 355-6
– *inferius nervi vagi (nodosum)* 110-9; **115**-2, 10; 116-11; 350-3; 351-2, 3
– *lumbale* 125-9; 180-4; 355-8
– *mesentericum inferius* 125-3; 355-3
– – *superius* 125-2; 355-9
– *oticum* 92-2; **110**-9; 350-1; 351-1

*Ganglion pterygopalatinum* 92-2; 109-9; **110**-2; **112**-6; 350-1; 351-10
– *renale* 125-2
– *sacralia truncus sympathici* **132**-2; 348-5; 355-7
– *semilunare* – – see *Ganglion trigeminale*
– *spinale* 47-5; 176-2; 180-1; 181-1, 4; 182-6; 184-1, 2, 10; 185-9; **186**-9; 187-5; 188-2; **189**-3; 190-1; 198-1, 199-5
– – *sacralia* 180-7; 182-5
– *spirale cochleae* 334-5; 410-3
– *splanchnicum* 125-3; 348-9
– *submandibulare* 92-6; **102**-7; 350-7; 351-7
– *superius nervi glossopharyngei* 334-8
– – – *vagi* 110-9; 155-11; 336-4
– *sympathicum* 47-6; 55-8; 56-6; 176 -10 C; 184-9
– *thoracicum* 56-11; 116-8; 348-10; **352**-7, 8, 9, 11; **353**-8, 9, 10, 11; 354-9, 10; 355-10
– *trigeminale nervus trigeminus (ganglion semilunare)* 103-5; 104-6; 110-10; **111**-11; **114**-3; **247**-3; 328-5; 351-1; 457-12
–, vestibular 335-4
**Gastric** artery, left 4-1; 7-1; **120**-1; **121**-12; 125-1; 170-12
– –, right 120-12
– –, short 121-1
– lymph nodes 125-12; 170-1
– plexus (of nerves) 125-1; 354-6
– vein 120-4; 124-2, 10
**Gastrocnemius** muscle 145-5, 7; 146-6; 149-6; 150-1, 9, 11; 154-4, 8; 174-7
**Gastrocolic** ligament 121-8
**Gastroduodenal** artery 120-9; 121-9
**Gastroepiploic** artery 4-9; **120**-3, 9; **121**-1, 9, 11
– vein 4-3; 120-3, 9; 121-1, 9, 11; 124-2, 9
**Genicular** artery, descending 7-4; 137-11; **138**-5; 142-7; 143-7; 144-7; 154-10
**Genicular** artery, inferior **144**-6; 150-11; 152-11; 153-12; 154-4, 7
– –, middle 137-3; 154-9
– –, superior 137-3; 144-5; 145-5; 149-3; 151-11; 153-1, 12; 154-2, 9
– vein 141-12
**Geniculate** body, lateral 222-4; 229-2; **273**-10; 276-3; 290-10; 321; 322
– –, –, nucleus of 229-1; 278-8; 281-5; 284-9
– –, medial **273**-11; **276**-3; 290-10; 321; 322; 326-2
– ganglion of facial nerve 92-11; 112-10; 114-2; 438-1; 439-8
**Geniculum** of facial nerve 438-1; 443-1; 445-12
**Genioglossus** muscle 107-3; 109-4; 110-4; 118-1
**Geniohyoid** muscle 107-6; 109-4; 110-4; 118-8
**Genitofemoral** nerve 50-8; 119-10; 125-8; 126-4, 7; 11, 127-9; 130-10; 132-9; 138-10; 171-10; 348-8
– –, femoral branch 50-7; 119-10; 126-7; 138-10; 348-5
– –, genital branch 119-10; 126-4, 7; 130-10; 132-9; 348-5
*Genu capsula interna* 278-2; 280-11; 282
– *corporis callosi* **248**-4; **251**-8; **257**-2; **258**-1; 259-1; 260-1; 262-1; 271-1; **274**-10; 281-1; 323-9
– of facial nerve 330-1; 333-1
**Gland** or **Glands**, **Glandula** or **Glandulae**
*Glandulae areolares* 471-6
– *ceruminosae* 465-9
– *ciliares* 363-5
– *glomiformis* 468-9; 469-6
– *lacrimalis pars orbitalis* 103-1; 104-1; 105-1; **113**-1; 363-10; 390-9; **391** -10; 397-2; 401-10; 403-10; 408-9
– – – *palpebralis* 391-9
**Gland,** mammary lobes of 472-5; 473-9, 10
–, – lobules 473-9
*Glandula mucosa* 457-6
– *parathyreoidea* 116-4

*Glandula parotis* 39-12; 45-1; 46-1; 95-7, 8
*Glandula pituitaria* - - - - see *Hypophysis*
*Glandula pituitaria, hypophysis* 223; **226**; 232-10; 233-C; 238-2; 239-11; **247**-11; **248**-6; 367
– –, *lobus anterior* 248-5; 274-9; 275-9
– –, – *posterior* 248-6; 274-8; 275-10
– – *pars intermedia hypophyseos* 226-8; 275-9
– *sebacea* 465-8; 468-9
– *sublingualis* **102**-5; 118-1; 350-7
– *submandibularis* 41-10; 42-11; 43-9; 45-11; 101-6; **102**-7; 350-7
– *suprarenalis* 125-2, 10
– *tarsalis* (Meibomi) **363**-9; **389**-2, 3; 5; 407-11
– *thyreoidea* 42-8; 43-8; 44-9; 46-9; 57-1; **115**-7; 116-4; **117**-5; 167-12; 354-12
– –, *isthmus* 45-3; 118-6
**Globose** nucleus, cerebellum 296-7; 335-1
**Globus** pallidus 278-3; 279-8; 280-9; 281-8; 283-8; 286-5; 287-4; 288-8
*Glomus caroticum* 350-6; 351-6
– *chorioideum* 259-7; 260-2; 262-7; 265-3
**Glossopharyngeal** nerve 91; 92-8; **93**-6; 107-8; **108**-7; 114-4; **115**-3, 10, 11; 116-11; **117**-1, 11; 166-11; 181-12; **232**-8; 239-3; 241-3; **247**-7; 272-5; 350-3; 351-3
– –, ganglia of 92-9; 93-5; 112-8; 115-2; 334-8; 350-2
**Gluteal** artery, inferior 7-2; 132-2; 147-12; 148-10, 11
– –, superior 7-2; 127-3; 132-1; 147-12; 148-10, 11
– fascia 145-1; 146-12
– nerve, inferior 119-8, 9; 147-11; 148-10, 11
– –, superior 199-9; 148-11
– vein 148-10, 11
**Gluteus maximus** muscle 53-7; 133-1; 134-1, 10; 145-11; **146**-11; 147-1, 11; 148-4, 10
– medius muscle 147-1; 148-2
**Gluteus** minimus muscle 148-2
**Gracile** nucleus 231-6; 338-11; 339-11; 341-10; 342-11
– –, tubercle of 289-5; 290-5; 338-1
**Gracilis** muscle 142-2; 143-4; 144-3; 145-5; 146-9; 149-11
**Granular** layer, cerebellar cortex 296–10
*Granulatio arachnoidealis* 194-11; 197-2; 199-11; 12; 234-2; 240-5
**Great** auricular nerve 37-11; **39**-3, 10, 11; **40**-4; 51-1; 53-11, 12; 95-7; 98-8
– cerebral vein (of Galen) 197-3; **232**-7; 233-2; 242-2; 246; **262**-5; **265**-7
– saphenous vein 50-7; **138**-2, 5; **139**-1, 6; 140-7; 141-11; 142-1; 144-12; **155**-1, 12; 170-5, 7; **173**-5; 174-7, 11
**Greater** occipital nerve 39-3; 40-3; 41-3; 44-2; 51-1, 11; 52-1; 53-12; 95-9, 11; 98-9; 99-9
– omentum 120-6
– palatine artery 108-5; 109-6
– – nerve 92-3; 108-6; 109-7; **110**-3
– petrosal nerve 92-11; 93-2; 109-9; 110-10; **112**-10; 114-1; **232**-2; 350-1; 351-1; **438**-2; 439-9; 443-2; 444-1; 445-1
– splanchnic nerve **55**-6, 8; 56-8; 126-12; 184-8; 348-4, 8; **352**-7; **353**-7; 354-8; **355**-12
**Gyrus and Gyri 207–210**
*Gyrus angularis* 207; 249-3; 253-8
– *cerebelli* 278-7
– of cerebral hemisphere 207-210
– *cinguli* 210; 242-10; 248-1; 255-5; 286-1
– *dentatus* 257-7; **266**-2; 268-4; 269-3; 270-1; 284-6; 323-3
– *fasciolaris* 251-6; 270-12
– *frontalis, inferior* 207; **249**-8, 11; 285-2
– –, *medius* 207; 208; **249**-9; 253-10; 285-1
– –, *superior* 207; 208; 210; 248-3; **249**-10; 251-9; 253-11; 262-12; 279-12; 285-12

*Gyrus insulae* 256-4, 6; 278-9; 279-10; 280-2; 281-2; 287-9
– *occipitalis* 249-4; 253-7; 255-11; 259-5; 280-5; 285-5
– *occipitotemporalis lateralis* 209; 210; 220-8; 247-9; 251-5; 255-4
– – *medialis* 209; 210; 248-9; 251-5; 255-5
– *olfactorius* 305
– *orbitales lobi frontalis* 207; 209; 247-11; 255-11; 285-5
– *parahippocampalis* 209; 210; 220-4; 247-9; 251-7; 255-4, 6; **261**-9; 266-2; 267-3; 268-4; 269-3; 270-1, 12; **288**-7; 323-5
– *paraterminalis* 210; 223-10; 248-4; 274-10; 286-7
– *postcentralis* 207; 208; 249-1; 253-4
– *precentralis* 207; 208; 249-1; 253-2
– *rectus* 209; 255-1
– *supramarginalis* 207; 249-2; 253-8
– *temporalis inferior* 207; 209; 210; **249**-6; 251-5; 255-4
– – *medius* 207; **249**-7
– – *superior* 206; 207; 235-3; **249**-8
– – *transversus* 206; **258**-3; 269-1
– vermis 274-3

## H

**Habenula** 281-8
**Habenular** commissure 261-2; 276-2
– trigone 261-2; 274-1; 276-11
**HAIR 466–470**
Hair follicle 468-3
**Hamulus** of spiral lamina 417-4; 423-1

**HEAD** and **NECK REGION 91–118**

**HEART 9–36**
**Coronary circulation 17–20**
**Percussion areas 13**
**Roentgen shadows 14**
**Sternocostal projection 13**

**Heart,** apex of **17**-5; **18**-7; 19-5; **25**-5; **26**-6; **34**-6; 35-7
–, left ventricle 3-10; **17**-4; 18-8; 21-5; 22-8; 31-7, 10; 35-5
–, right ventricle **17**-8; 18-6; 21-8; 22-5; **25**-1; 7; 26-7; 31-2, 5; 34-7; 35-7
–, sternocostal surface 25-6
**Helicis** muscle 463-1, 2
**Helicotrema** 423-1
**Helix** 458-11; 459-8, 12; 460-11
**Hemiazygos** vein **55**-2; **56**-2, 4; 124-12; 125-2; 184-3
– –, accessory 56-2
*Hemispherium cerebelli* 241-5; **248**-8; 271-7; 274-4; 277-5; 279-6; **292**-11
– *telencephali* 180-1; 402-2
*Hemorrhoidal* - - - - see **Rectal**
**Hepatic** artery, common 3-6; 7-1; **120**-2; 121-12; 170-2
– –, proper 4-10; 120-12
– veins 3-9; **124**-11; **125**-11; 170-11; 184-6
*Hiatus aorticus* 125-12; 348-4
– *canalis facialis* 428-1
– *esophageus* 126-12; 167-6
– *saphenus* 50-7; 138-1; 173-2
– *tendineus (adductorius)* 144-4; 145-4
*Hilus nuclei dentati* 295-10; 296-2
**Hippocampal** commissure 259-3; 265-7
– digitations 218-8; **261**-10; 266-1; 267-10; 268-1; 323-8
– gyrus, uncus of 305
– sulcus 220-2; 255-8; 266-3; 268-4; 269-4
**Hippocampus** 225-4; 259-7; 261; 262; **266**–270; **284**-4, 5
–, fimbria of 220-2; 257-8; 261-8; 262-4; **266**-3; 267-4; 268-3, 7; 269-3; 270-10; **284**-6; **288**-6; 323-5
–, pes 220-8; 261-8; 266-8; 267-8; **268**-12; **269**-5, 6; 272-9; 276; 278-4; 279-8; 288-8; 323-6
*Hirci* 469-6
**Horizontal** cerebellar fissure 292-3; 293-3; 294-3

**Hyoglossus** muscle 45-1; 46-11; 102-8; 107-8; 118-2, 8, 10
**Hyoid** bone 102-6; 116-10; 118-7
– –, greater cornu 107-7; 116-10; 117-10
**Hypogastric** plexus, superior 125-4; 127-9
**Hypoglossal** nerve 37-12; 42-9; 43-11; **44**-11; 45-1; **46**-12; **102**-6, 7; 107-6; 115-10; 116-1, 11; **118**-2; 181-12; 183-12; 241-8; 247-7; 272-5; 350-2, 3, 7; 351-3, 7
– –, trigone 289-8
– nucleus 229-6; 230-5; 336-10, 11
**Hypophyseal** tracts 226
*Hypophysis* - - - - see *Glandula pituitaria*
**HYPOPHYSIS** *(in situ)* **232; 233; 238; 275**
*Hypophysis pars intermedia* 226-8; 275-9
– pituitary gland 223-9; **232**-10; 233-C; 238-2; 239-11; **247**-11; **248**-6; 275-9; 367
**Hypothalamic** mammillary body, nuclei of 279-8; 283-5; 288-6
– nucleus, lateral 224-3
– –, posterior 223-6; 225-6
– sulcus 226-1; 242-12; 248-5; 263-C; 274-1
– tracts 226
**HYPOTHALAMUS 223–226; 274; 281; 283; 287; 288**
**Hypothalamus** 223; **226**; 283-4
–, interpeduncular nucleus of 324-4
–, subthalamic nucleus of 279-1; 281-4
**Hypotympanic** recess 448-7; 449-3

## I

**Ileocolic** artery 122-6
– vein 124-8
**Ileum** 122-6
**Iliac** artery, common 7-2; **126**-2; 127-9, 11; **128**-12; 132-10; 170-3
– –, external 7-2; 54-5; 126-5; **127**-8; **128**-10; **129**-10; 132-10; 142-12; 171-9
**Iliac** artery, internal 7-2; 126-C; 127-3; **128**-1; **129**-12; **132**-10; 142-12
– crest 53-8; 148-1; 355-9
– fascia 125-8
– lymph nodes 125-8; 171-9
– – –, external 127-8; 170-8
– – –, internal 127-9; 170-4; 171-9, 10
– plexus (of nerves) 355-8
– vein, common **126**-2; **128**-12; **129**-11; 132-10; 170-3
– –, external 124-7; **126**-5; 128-11; 129-10; 142-12; 171-9
– –, internal 124-7; **126**-5; 128-1; **129**-1
**Iliacus** muscle 127-10; 355-8
**Iliocostalis** thoracis muscle 53-10
**Iliohypogastric** nerve 50-8- 53-8; 55; 119-11; 125-9; **126**-11; **127**-11; 138-1; 140-1; 148-1; 348-8
**Ilioinguinal** nerve 50-5, 8; 119-10; 125-9; **126**-3, 10; **127**-12; 130-1; 138-1; 170-6; 348-8
**Iliolumbar** artery **126**-3, 5; 132-10; 171-2
– ligament 125-8; 348-5
**Iliopsoas** muscle 143-11; 144-11
**Ilium**, ala of 180-5
*Impressio trigemini (semilunar)* 427-3; 428-2; 429-3; 457-12
**Incisive** canal 108-3
**Incisura** - - - - see Notch
*Incisura apicis cordis* 19-5; 35-7
– *cerebelli* 292-6, 12; 293-6; 294-6; 296-6
– *interarytenoidea* 116-9; 117-9
– *intertragica* 458-7; 459-4; 460-6
– *supraorbitalis* 408-1
– *terminalis auris* 460-5; 461-6
– *tympanica* 450-1; 451-12
**Incus,** body of **433**-9; **434**-2; 436-1; 439-2; 440-1; 441-1; 442-1; 449-9
–, fossa of 428-9; 438-8; 441-3; 442-4
–, lenticular process **434**-6; 438-12; 439-3; 440-6; 441-5; 442-7; 450-7
–, ligaments of 438-7; **439**-3; 440-2; 441-1, 3; 442-1, 2
–, long crus **433**-7; **436**-3; 439-2; 440-5; 441-4; 442-6; 450-9; 454-9

**Incus**, short crus **433**-9; 434-3; 436-2; 438-7; 439-3; 440-2; 441-2; 442-2

*Indusium griseum corporis callosi* 219-1; **258**-1, 2; **259**-1, 2; 283-1

– – *striae longitudinales mediales* **258**-1, 2; **259**-1, 2; 283-1; 323-11, 12

**Inferior** alveolar artery 94-7; 99-5; 100-6, 8; **101**-5, 8; 102-8; 109-8; 110-6, 7

– – nerve 92-6, 7; **99**-5; **100**-6, 7; **101**-5, 8; 102-8; 109-8; 110-7; **111**-9; 350-8

– cerebral vein 233-5

– cluneal nerve 119-7; 131-2, 11; 133-11; 134-2, 10; **140**-10, 11, 12; 145-1; 146-1, 11

– colliculus 271-5; 276-3; 289-11; 290-1, 2

– collicular nucleus 304; 325-12

– deep cervical lymph nodes 164-4

– epigastric artery 7-3; 50-5; **54**-6; 122-7; 123-7; 125-8; 126-5; **127**-7; 128-10; **132**-7; 171-9

– – vein 50-5; **54**-5; 122-7; 123-7; 124-4, 8; 125-8; 126-5; **127**-7; 128-10; 171-9

– ganglion of vagus nerve (nodosum) 110-9; **115**-2, 10; 116-11; 350-3; 351-2

– genicular artery 144-6; 150-11; 152-11; 153-12; **154**-4, 7

– gluteal artery 7-2; 132-2; **147**-12; **148**-11

– – nerve 119-8, 9; **147**-11; **148**-10, 11

– – vein 148-11

– labial artery 94-7; 98-5

– laryngeal artery 117-7

– – nerve 177-4

– longitudinal fasciculus 298

– mesenteric artery 1-4; 7-2; **123**-3; 124-9; 126-2; 127-2, 3; 128-11; 132-11

– – ganglion 125-3; 355-3

– – plexus (of nerves) 125-6; 355-9

– oblique muscle 106-4; 364; 393-5; 394-5; 395-8; 396-8; **397**-5, 7; 398-4; 399-11; 400-4; 403-6; 406-7; 407-8; 408-7

**Inferior** orbital fissure 113-4; 395-6; 396-4

– phrenic artery 120-2; 121-1; 125-1, 10, 12; 126-11; 170-10

– rectal artery (hemorrhoidal) 124-5; 128-5; **129**-5; **133**-11; **134**-10

– – nerves 119-7; 132-4; 133-1

– rectus muscle 398-5; 399-1; 400-7

– retinaculum of extensor muscles (ankle) 153-5; 155-11; 175-5

– tarsus 391-6

– thyroid artery 38-4; 43-8; 44-9; **115**-5, 7; **116**-8; **117**-5; 118-5

– ulnar collateral artery 71-7; 72-7; 73-5; 74-4; 75-11; 77-11; 78-12; 81-1

– velum of medulla 295-8

– vena cava 3-4; 4-8; 5-3; 18-5; 22-2; 26-9, 11; 35-6; 36-7; 56-6; 120-12; 121-11; **124**-11; **125**-11; **126**-11; **127**-10; 167-5; 170-9; 184-6; 353-4

– – –, orifice of 35-6; 36-8; 124-10, 11; 125-11; 127-10; 170-9, 11; 184-6

– vesical artery 127-3

**Infraclavicular** lymph nodes 169-8

**Infraorbital** artery 94-8; 98-3; 101-2; 102-2; 106-5; 350-9; 404-6

– foramen 397-6

– margin 395-9; 397-7

– nerve 92-3; 98-3; **99**-3, 4; **100**-2; 101-2, 3; 102-1, 2; 106-5; 110-2; 111-2; **112**-2, 3; 113-5; 350-9; 351-9; 392-7; 403-6; 404-7; 405-6

**Infraspinatus** fascia 51-4

– muscle 53-3; 62-2, 5

**Infratemporal** fossa 395-5

**Infratrochlear** nerve 92-2; **95**-2; 98-3; 99-3; 100-2; 101-2; 102-2; **105**-9; 106-12

**Infundibular** nucleus 226-5

– recess 218-8; 226-5; 248-5; 263-9; 274-8

**Infundibulum** 223-9; 226-5; 247-12; 248-5; **272**-11; 273-5; **274**-9; **275**-12; 286-6; 287-6; 343; 350-1
–, *tuba uterina* 129-10; 131-3, 9
**Inguinal** fossa 127-4
– ligament 127-8; 142-11
– lymph nodes, deep 127-8; 170-4, 5, 7; 171-8
– – –, superficial 50-7, 8; 173-2, 8
– ring, deep 127-8
– –, superficial 130-1
**Insula** 206; 241-10; **256**; 258-2; 286-3; 305
–, circular sulcus 256-2; 258-2
**Insular** gyri **256**-4, 6; 278-9; 279-10; 280-2; 281-2; 287-9
**INTEGUMENT** see **SKIN**
*Integumentum commune* 47-1; 237-9; 462-7
**Interarytenoid** notch 116-9; 117-9
**Interatrial** septum 24-12; 26-12; 27-12
**Intercalatus** nucleus 332-12
**Intercapitular** vein 83-3
**Intercavernous** sinus 232-1, 8
**Intercondyloid** fossa, posterior 137-3
**Intercostal** arteries 7-11; 18-11; **38**-6, 7; 50-9; **54**-1; 55-2, 11; 56-1, 2; 184-2, 9; 186-9; 353-7
– muscle 55-9; 56-1; 184-8, 9
– nerve 37-5, 6; 47-4; 50-2, 3, 10; **55**-8; **56**-3; 126-1, 11; 180-3; 184-9; 348-5, 8, 10; **352**-7, 8, 9, 10; 353-7, 8; **354**-2, 7; **355**-1, 2, 12
– –, anterior cutaneous branch 45-7; 60-10; 138-1
– –, lateral cutaneous branches 59-6, 12; 60-5, 6, 9
– vein 50-2; 54-1; **55**-10; **56**-8; 184-9; 186-9; 353-7
**Intercostobrachial** nerve 37-6; **44**-5; 50-11; 53-3; 59-1, 3; 60-4; **67**-10; 169-4, 6
**Interfoveolar** ligament and muscle 127-8
**Intermediate** nerve 112-10; **114**-3; **232**-5; **247**-8; 272-4; 279-7; 439-8
**Intermediate** part of hypophysis 275-9
**Internal** capsule 222; 224-9; 225-11; 279-2; **281**-3; 283-3; 284-10; 286-10; 287-10; 288-10; 299; **300**; 320
– –, anterior limb 278-1; 280-11; 281-10
– –, genu of 278-2; 280-11
– –, posterior limb 278-2; 280-8; **281**-8
– carotid artery 7-12; 43-9; 44-12; 93-3, 4; 94-6; 99-7; 100-7; 103-7; 104-6; 105-7; 106-7; **109**-10; 110-8, 10, 12; 112-7; 114-2; 115-2, 12; **116**-1; 164-12; 200-3; 232-1; 233-C; **236**-5, 6, 10; 238-3, 12; 239-1; **241**-1; 243; 350-2, 12; 367; 384-11; 402-11; 437-3; 439-10; 456-8; 457-1
– – nerve 112-8; 115-1; 116-1; 350-2; 351-8
– cerebral vein 205; 242-2; 246; 265-9

## INTERNAL EAR 409–424

**Bony labyrinth 411; 414–424**
**Cochlea 409; 410; 413-417; 423; 424**
**Membranous labyrinth 409; 410; 412; 413**

**Internal** frontoparietal vein 205
– iliac artery 7-2; 126-C; 127-3; **128**-1; **129**-12; **132**-10; 142-12
– jugular veins 41-3; 43; 44-7, 12; 45-3, 9; 46-3; 56-1; 57-11; 115-4; 162-12; 164-13; 165-7; 350-5
– – –, inferior bulb of 42-7; 46-3; 115-5; 116-4
– – –, superior bulb of 115-2; 116-1; 448-8
– pudendal artery 128-5, 6; 129-4, 5; 132-5, 11; 133-1, 5; 134-1, 4, 8, 11; 147-11; 148-7; 171-3
– – plexus, venous plexus 134-4
– – vein 124-5
– temporal vein 205

**Internal** thoracic artery 18-1; **38**-5; 40-7; 43-7; 44-6, 9; 50-2; **54**-1, 11; 55-1; 57-2; 58-8; 60-10; 166-11
– – –, intercostal branches 54-10
– – –, perforating branch 40-7; 44-8; 45-7; 54-11
– – vein 34-10; 40-7; 45-6; **54**-1; 58-8; 60-10; 166-11
**Interosseous** artery, anterior **77**-8; 80-6; 81-5; 86-1, 11; 90-7
– –, common 76-3; 77-9
– –, posterior 77-4; 80-7, 8; **81**-4
– –, recurrent 74-6; 79-5; 80-2; 81-3
– membrane (forearm) 81-7; 86-12
– muscle, dorsal 85-7; 86-9; 88-11; 89-10
– nerve, anterior 77-8
– –, posterior 81-5; 86-1
**Interpeduncular** cistern 197-8; 239-2
– fossa 247-4; **272**-2; 274-8; 279-5; 324-5; 325-3
– nucleus 301b; 324-4
**Interthalamic** adhesion (massa intermedia) 218-11; 223-1; 225-3; 248-1; 261-2; 271-10; **274**-12; 281-12; **283**-3; 288-2
**Intertragic** notch 458-7; 459-4; 460-6
**Intervaginal** space (optic nerve) 356-6; 362-2; 402-5; 403-11; 406-5
**Interventricular** foramen 197-1; 218-10; 223-11; 248-2; 257-2; **259**-1; **260**-10; **261**-1; **262**-1; **265**-10; 274-12; 278-8; 280-3; 287-2
– septum 23-8; 24-4; 25-4; 26-7; **27**-7; 31-1; 32-1; 33-1, 8
– –, muscular portion 31-2; 33-8
– sulcus anterior 21-7; 25-3
– –, posterior 22-6
**Intervertebral** disc 58-1; 186-3
**Intestinal** trunk, lymphatic 125-2; 162-6; 170-10
**Intestine,** large 122-5, 7, 12; 123-3, 4, 5, 12
–, small 123-7
*Intestinum tenue* 123-7
**Intraparietal** sulcus 207-1; 208-5; 249-3; 253-5, 8
**Intrinsic** muscles of ear 463; 464
*Intumescentia cervicalis (medulla spinalis)* 180-1; 183-2
– *lumbalis (medullae spinalis)* 180-8; 183-4
**Iris** 356-1; 358-1; 368-12; 369-12; **370**; **371**; **376**; **377**; 386-7; 397-7, 8
–, arterial circle 358-11; 359-1, 12
–, pupillary margin 368-1; **370**-2, 8; **371**-1; 377-9
–, ring **370**-7, 8; **371**
–, surface 356-11; 363-3; **370**-4; 377-7; 379-5; 382-2; 383-4, 8
**Ischiocavernosus** muscle 133-8; 134-7
**Isthmus** of thyroid gland 45-3; 118-6

## J

**Jejunal** arteries 122-2; 123-9
– vein 4-4; 122-3; 123-9; 124-4
**Jejunum** 122-3
**Jugular** foramen 115-1; 232-5
– trunk (lymphatic) 162-11; 12; 169-10
– vein, anterior **40**-9; 42-6; **45**-3, 12; 46-8; 169-9
– –, external 39-9; 40-4; 41-7; 42-10; 43; 44-7; **45**-2, 3, 9, 10; 46-10; 51-2; 56-1; **95**-7; 100-9; 169-9
– –, internal 41-3; **43**; **44**-7; 12; **45**-3, 9; **46**-3; 56-1; 57-11; 115-4; 162-12; 164-12; 165-7; 350-2
– –, –, inferior bulb 42-7; 46-3; 115-5
– – –, superior bulb 115-2; 116-1; 448-8
– venous arch 40-8; 45-6
**Jugulodigastric** lymph node 165-2
**Juguloomohyoid** lymph node 165-8

## K

Kidney 103-3; **127**-2; 180-4

## L

**Labial** artery 94-6, 8; 98-5
– nerves, posterior 134-7
**Labium** minus 134-5
**Labyrinth,** bony 411; 414–424
**Labyrinthine** artery 200-3; 232-3; 241-2
*Labyrinthus membranaceus* 409; **412**; **413**; 439

**LACRIMAL APPARATUS** **390; 392–394**

**Lacrimal** artery 103-3; 104-1; 105-4; 113-1; 350-12; 390-9
– canaliculus 392-1, 2, 3; 393-6, 12; 394-5, 11
– caruncula 386-3; 388-2; 392-1; 393-2; 394-3; 407-3
– gland 103-1; 104-1; 105-1; 113-1; **390**-9; **391**-9, 10; 392-10; 397-2; 401-10; 403-10; 408-9
– –, accessory 363-10
– nerve 92-1; **103**-8; 104-2; 105-3; **113**-1; 390-9; 404-11
– papilla 388-2, 8; 392-3, 12; 393-1, 4; 407-3, 4
– punctum, inferior 388-2; 390-4; 392-3, 12; 393-4
– sac 393-9; 394-9; 408-2
– vein 232-11; 350-10
**Lactiferous** ducts 50-11; 473-1; 474-6
– sinus 50-11; 473-1
*Lacuna lateralis (sinus sagittalis superioris)* 234-2, 10
*Lacus lacrimalis* 388-2; 393-3
**Lamellated corpuscles** (Pacinian) 178
**Lamina** affixa 259-10; 260-10; **262**-3; 265-2; 271-2; 276-2; 283-9
– *choriocapillaris* 359-5
– *cribrosa* 107-11; 197-8
– – *ethmoidalis* 385-1
– *elastica* - - - - see *Lamina limitans*
– *horizontalis ossis palatini* 455-2
– *lateralis (cartilaginis tubae auditivae)* 455-2; 457-2
– *limitans (cornea)* 356-12
**Lamina** *medullaris* 278-3
– –, *thalami* 283-9
– *membranace, tubae auditivae* 457-5
– *modioli* 417-3; 423-1; 424-2
– *quadrigemina* - - - - *see Lamina tecti*
– *septi pellucidi* 223-11; **248**-2; 259-1; **260**-11; 261-11; 262-1; 265-1; 271-1; **274**-11; 276-12; **278**-11; 281-1; 285-11; 287-10
– *spiralis humulus* 417-4; 423-1
– – *ossea* **410**-3; 413-12; 416-7, 8; **417**-2, 4; 423-2, 4; 424-10; 426-2
– – *secundaris* 417-5; 424-9
– *suprachorioidea* 369-4
– *tecti (quadrigemina)* 223-2; 248-10; 261-5; 274-2; 276-8; 324-2; 325-11
– terminalis 223-10; 226-11; 248-5; 257-4; 272-12; 274-9, 11
– *tragi* (ear) 458-9; 460-4; 461-8
**Lanugo** 470-3
**Large** intestine 122-5, 7, 12; 123-3, 4, 5, 12
**Laryngeal** artery, inferior 117-7
– –, superior 41-9; 42-9; 43-9; 116-3; 117-10; 118-3
– nerve, inferior 117-4
– –, recurrent 44-9; 46-3, 6; 55-1, 11, 12; 57-1, 2, 11; 116-5, 7; **117**-6, 7; 166-2; **352**-1, 2; **354**-1, 10
– –, superior 43-9; **115**-3, 4, 8, 9, 10; 116-2; 117-9; 118-3; **350**-6, 7; 351-7
– prominence (Adam's apple) 45-2; 46-9
**Larynx**, superior aperture of 117-2
**Lateral** aperture, fourth ventricle (Luschka) 199-8; 276-5
– brachial cutaneous nerve - - - - see **Superior** brachial cutaneous nerve
– – circumflex femoral artery 7-3; 143-10, 11; 144-10
– cord of brachial plexus 61-3; 71-12
– corticospinal tract 340-9
– femoral cutaneous nerve 50-8; 348-5, 8
– fissure (sulcus) **249**-5, 8; 253-9; **279**-9; 281-2, 9; 285-3; 286-9; 287-9; 288-3, 9

**Lateral** geniculate body 222-4; 229-1; **273**-10; 276-3; **290**-10; 321; 322
– – –, nucleus of 278-8; 281-5; 284-9
– lacuna of superior sagittal sinus 234-2, 10
– lemniscus 325-11; 327-2; 328-2, 8; 329-10, 11
– malleolar artery 152-6; 153-7; 157-10
– nasal nerves 108-12; 110-2
– olfactory gyrus 305
– pectoral nerve 44-6
– plantar artery 159-1; 160-1
– – nerve 158-11; 159-2, 11; 160-1, 12
– rectus muscle 318; 398-9; 399-8; 400-2
– sulcus **249**-5, 8; 250; 253-9; **279**-9; 281-2, 9; 285-3; 286-9; 287-9; 288-3, 9
– – of mesencephalon 273-11; 325-10
– thoracic artery 44-6; 59-12; 60-4; 169-5
– – vein 44-6; 59-12; 60-4; 168-12; 169-5
– umbilical fold 128-10
– ventricle **218**; 219; **262–264**; 269
– –, anterior horn **218**-10; 259-11; **260**-1; 261-1; 262-1; **263**; 265-11; 277-11; 278-1; 280-11; 281-11; 285-10; 286-11; 287-10
– –, central portion **218**-12; 219-2; 235-2; 259-10; **260**-2; 262-2; 265-9; 279-11; 283-2
– –, chorioid plexus 219-10; 235-2; 259-8; **260**-1, 8; 262-3; **265**-3; 272-2; 278-4; 280-8; 283-9; 284-1; 288-6, 11
– –, collateral eminence 259-7; 261-8; 262-4; 266-7
– –, inferior horn **218**-4; 220-12; 259-7; 260-3; **261**-2; 262-3; **263**; 265-8; 266-11; 267-12; 269-6; 272-2; 279-8; 284; 287-8; 288-5
– –, posterior horn 259-6; 260-5; **261**-3, 7; 262-7; **263**; 265-9; 266-7; 267-7; 278-4; 280-3; 323-3
**Latissimus** dorsi muscle 51-7; 53-4, 8; 59-4; 60-5; 61-8; 169-4
**Left** ventricle (heart) 3-10; 17-4; 18-8; 21-5; 22-8; 31-7, 10; 34-5
**Lemniscus,** decussation of 337-5; 338-2; 341-8
–, lateral 325-11; 327-2; 328-2, 8; 329-10, 11
–, medial 324-10; **325**-10; 326-9; 327-10; 328-8; **329**-10; 330-3; 331-4; **332**-6; 334-7; 336-7; 341-7
**Lens** 359-11; 361; 368-1; 369-12; 370-1; 372-1; 376-2; **378–381**; 402-4
–, anterior surface 356-1 C; 370-1; 371-8; 379-5; 383-8
–, axis of 379-8
–, capsule 380-7
–, cortex of 380-11
–, equator 361; 378-3, 12; 379-2
–, *facies anterior* 356-1 C; 370-1; 371-8; 379-5; 383-8
–, – *posterior* 356-11 C; 372-2; 376-2; 379-10
–, nucleus 380-1
–, pole of 356-6, 12, 12 C; 370-11; 379-6, 11; 383-2
–, posterior surface 356-11 C; 372-2; 376-2; 379-10
–, radii 378-2; 379-1; 381-12; 383-5
**Lenticular** process, incus 434-6; 438-12; 439-3; 440-6; 441-5; 442-7; 450-7
**Lentiform** nucleus 278-9; 279-2; **280**-10; 281-1; 284-11; 285-2; 286-10; 287-8; **288**-3; 321; 322
**Lesser** occipital nerve 37-11; **39**-3; **40**-3; **41**-2; **42**-1; **44**-1; 51-1, 10; 53-11; 95-8; 98-8; 99-8
– palatine artery 108-11; 109-8
– – nerve 92-3, 6; 108-11; 109-8; **110**-3
– petrosal nerve 92-10; 93-2; 110; **112**-10; 232-3; 350-1; 351-2
– splanchnic nerve 55-7, 8; 348-4, 8; 353-6; 354-7; 355-11
**Levator** ani muscle 128-5; 129-5; 133-11, 134-1; 171-5; 355-7
– labii superioris muscle , aleaque nasi 95-3

**Levator** palpebrae superioris muscle **103**-1; **104**-1; **105**-8, 12; 106-7, 12; 232-11; 350-11; 363-12; **395**-12; **396**-2; 397-12; **401**-2, 5, 10; 403-1; 404-1; 405-12; **406**-1, 10; 408-12
– scapulae muscle 39-4; 51-10; 53-11; 165-4; 169-12
– veli palatini muscle 457-6
*Lien* 120-3
*Ligamentum anococcygeum* 134-12
– arteriosum 17-1; 18-11; 19-1; 35-1; 166-2
– *coronarium hepatis* 3-3; 4-12; 125-10
– *cricothyreoideum* 118-5
– *denticulatum* 184-11; 185-4; 186-3; 187-1; 198-1; 199-6
– *falciforme hepatis* 4-11; 124-10
– *fundiforme penis* 130-12
– *iliolumbale* 125-8; 348-5
– *inguinale* 127-8; 142-11
– *interfoveolare* 127-8
– *longitudinale anterius* 56-3; 58-12; 184-3
– – *posterius* 184-3; 186-6
– *mallei* 438-5, 6; **439**-2, 10; 441-1; **442**-1; 448-12; 449-9, 12
– *metacarpeum transversum superficiale* 82-1
– *ovarii proprium* 131-10
– *palpebrale mediale* 391-2; 393-10; 394-9; 408-2
– *patellae* 142-6; 153-1
– *pectinate* (or *iris*) 356-10; 369-1; 370-3; 383-3
– *sacrospinale* 171-3; 132-5; 133-1
– *sacrotuberale* 133-1; 148-7
– *sphenomandibulare* 100-8; 101-8
– *spirale cochleae* 410-8
– *teres hepatis* 4-10; 120-11; 124-10
– – *uteri* 50-5; 125-7; 129-7, 10; 131-3; 171-9
– *transversus scapulae* 61-1; 62-2, 11
– *umbilicale laterale* 50-4; 127-6
– – *medianum* 124-7; 125-7; 127-5; 171-7
**Limbus** fossae ovalis 24-12; 26-11; 27-12 28-10
– *laminae spiralis osseae* 410-2
– *palpebralis* 386-6; 388-6; 390-3, 7; 407-1, 2
**Limen** insula 272-1
**Linea** alba 127-7
– *arcuata* 50-4; 127-6
– *cephalica* 90-2
– *mensalis* 90-2
– *vitalis* 90-2
*Lingua* 102-4; 107-3; 116-2; 350-8
**Lingual** artery 7-12; 41-10; 42-9; 94-6; 99-7; 102-8; **107**-6, 7; 115-3, 9; **118**-1, 8, 9
– nerve 46-1; 92-6; 100-7; 101-7; **102**-6; 107-3; 109-8; 110-7; 111-9; 118-1, 10; 350-2, 7; 351-7, 8
– vein 45-3; 118-1, 2
*Lingula cerebelli* 228; 274-2; 276-8; 291-12; 293-1; 295-2; 296-1
**Liver**, ligamentum teres of 4-10; 120-11
–, lobe of 120-11, 12
**Lobes** of mammary gland 472-5; 473-10
*Lobulus auriculae* 459-5; 462-6
– *biventer* 292-2; 294-3
– *centralis* 274-2; 293-1
– *glandulae mammariae* 473-9
– *paracentralis* 210; 248-12; 251-12
– *parietalis* 208; 249-3; 253-7
– *quadrangularis* 291-1, 3
– *semilunaris* 291-3, 4; 292-3
*Lobus anterior* (hypophysis) 226-7; 248-6; 274-8; 275-8
– *caudatus* **120**-12
– *frontalis cerebri* 208; 209; 234-1; 256-3; 258-11; 280-1; 285-10; 286-10
– *glandula mammaria* 472-5; 473-10
– *hepatis* 120-11, 12
– *occipitalis (cerebri)* 251-3; 256-9; 257-8; 258-7
– *parietalis (cerebri)* 208; 256-12; 258-9; 279-2
– *posterior glandula pituitaria* 226; 248-6; 274-8; 275-10

*Lobus temporalis (cerebri)* 209; 241-10; 256-7; 258-3; 279-3; 284-3; 285-3; 286-4; 288-4
**Locus** coeruleus 289-2, 9; 329-1
**Long** thoracic nerve 37-5; 44-6; 59-5; 60-5; 169-5, 12
**Longissimus** capitis muscle 51-10; 52-9; 53-11
– thoracis muscle 53-9
**Longitudinal** cerebral fissure 219-1; 240-12; **247**-12; 253-6, 12; **255**-12; 258-12; 259-4, 12; 260-12; 261-12; 262-11; 265-12; 272-12; 277-1; 278-11; 279-12; **280**-1; 286-12; 287-1; 288-12
– fasciculus, inferior cerebral 298
– –, medial 274-7; 296-10; **318**; 324-3; 325-2; 326-10; 327-10; 328-12; 329-1; 330-1; 331-12; 332-12; 335-9; 338-3
– –, superior cerebral 297
– fasciculi of pons 274-7; 279-5; 329-8; 330-7
– ligaments 184-3; 186-6
– stria of supracallosal gyrus 258-2; 259-2; 283-1; 323-11, 12
**Longus** capitis muscle 58-11
**Longus** colli muscle 58-7
**Lumbar** arteries 7-2; 126-1, 2, 6; 127-1
– enlargement of spinal cord 180-8; 183-4
– ganglion 125-9; 180-4; 355-8
– lymph nodes 125-2, 8; 127-2, 10; 170-3, 9; 171-1
– – trunks 125-3, 9
– nerve 181-8; 182-8; 190-2; 348-5; 355-2, 3, 4
– –, dorsal rami 53-7
– plexus (of nerves) **119**-1; 126-2; 355
– triangle 53-5, 8; 148-12
– trunk, lymphatic 162-6; 170-9
– vein, ascending 55-6; 56-6; 125-2; 126-1, 6; 127-1
**Lumbosacral** plexus (of nerves) 119-4; 126-2
**Lumbosacral** trunk 119; 126-3; 132-12; 348-7; 355-4
**Lumbrical** muscles (hand) 87-10; 88-2, 11; 89-10
**Lumen** of auditory tube 446-8
– *pharyngis* 108-8
**Lung** 36-3, 10; 57-2, 4, 8, 9, 10; 352-5; 353-1
–, apex of 34-1, 11; 35-11
–, inferior lobe 34-4, 8; 35-4, 8, 10
–, middle lobe 34-10; 35-3
–, superior lobe 34-2, 11; 35-2, 11
**Lunula** (half-moon) 477-7; 478-8; 480-3; 481-3
**Lymph** node 127-8
– –, axillary 168-2; 169-2, 4
– –, buccal 165-9
– –, bronchopulmonary 34-3; 35-9; 166-3, 9
– –, central 169-6
– –, cervical 163-3, 9; 164-3, 4, 7; 165-4, 7, 8; 169-10, 12
– –, cubital 168-5
– –, iliac 125-8; 127-8, 9; 170-4, 8; 171-9, 10
– –, inguinal 50-7, 8; 127-8; 170-4, 5, 7; 171-3; 173-2, 8
– –, jugulodigastric 165-2
– –, juguloomohyoid 165-8
– –, lumbar 125-2, 8; 127-2, 10; 170-3, 9; 171-1
– –, mediastinal 166-4, 8, 10; 167-4
– –, mesenteric 172-2, 8, 11
– –, occipital 163-10; 165-3
– –, parotid 165-2
– –, pectoral 50-10; 169-6
– –, popliteal 174-1, 2
– –, retroauricular 163-10; 165-2
– –, sacral 170-9; 171-11
– –, submandibular 163-3; 164-9; 165-8
– –, submental 163-2; 164-9; 165-9
– –, subscapular 169-5
– –, tibial 175-10
– –, tracheal 166-12; 167-10
– –, tracheobronchial 35-2; 166-10; 167-1, 3, 9

**Lymph** nodules, conjunctival 363-10
– vessels, mammary 168-8
– –, superficial femoral 173-6
**Lymphatic** duct, right 162-11

**LYMPHATIC SYSTEM 161–175**
**Abdomen and pelvis 170–172**
**Axilla and neck 168; 169**
**Flow pattern 161**
**Head and neck 163–165**
**Iliac region 173**
**Leg 174; 175**
**Mediastinum 162; 166; 167**
**Mesentery 172**
**Thoracic duct 162**

**Lymphatic** trunk, intestinal 162-6
– –, jugular 162-11, 12; 169-10
– –, lumbar 125-3, 9; 162-6
– –, subclavian 162-11, 12; 169-8
– vessels, renal 125-10

## M

**Macula** cribrosa 414-5, 11; 417-8; 426-1, 2
– lutea 360-8; 373-8
**Macular** vessels 360-1, 8
**Main** bronchus, membranous wall 352-4
**Malleolar** artery 152-6, 7; 153-7; 157-2, 10, 12
– folds **438**-5, 11; **439**-12; 440-5, 11; 441-4, 11; 442-5, 11; 449-12; 450-2; 451-3, 9; 454-1, 10
– prominence 454-2
**Malleolus,** lateral 150-6; 151-6; 155-10; 175-6
–, medial 151-7; 155-1
**Malleus**, ligaments of 114-11; 430-2, 6, 8; 431-6, 8, 9, 10; 432-5, 7, 9, 12; 433; 436-8, 9, 10; **438**-5, 6; **439**-2; 440-8, 11; 441-1, 6; 442-1, 10, 12; 448-12; 449-1, 9, 12; 450-2, 3; 451-6

**MAMMARY GLAND 471–474**

**Mammillary body** 221; 223-9; **226**-3; **247**-10; **248**-6; 255-2, 8; 257-5; 272-11; **273**-3; 274-9; 283-7; 323-7; 343
– –, nuclei of (hypothalamus) 279-8; 283-5; 288-6
– –, peduncle 272-11
**Mammillothalamic** fasciculus 225-9; 257-7; 279-1
– tract 288-8; 323-7
**Mandible** 100-12; 102-5; 107-5; 108-5; 109-4; 115-2
**Mandibular** nerve 92-8; **100**; **101**; **102**-12; 103-5; 106-6; **110**-10; 112-1; 232-2; 247-2; 350-1; 351-1; 457-3
**Manubrium** of malleus **430**-6; **431**-6; **432**-7; 436-8; **439**-2; 440-8; 441-6; 442-10; 449-1; 450-3; 451-6; 454-2
– of sternum 38-5; 54-12
*Margo acutis* 25-7
– *infraorbitalis* 395-9; 397-7
– *pupillaris iridis* 368-1; 370-2, 8; 371-5; 377-9
– *supraorbitalis* 264-3; 396-10
**Massa** intermedia - - - - see **Interthalamic adhesion**
**Masseter** muscle 95-5; **98**-7; **99**-2, 7; 100-8
**Masseteric** nerve **99**-6; 100-12; 101-10; 102-12
**Masticator** nerve 350-8; 351-9
**Mastoid** air cells 112-9; **425**-4; 427-9; 428-11; 429-10; 448-5
– antrum 425-1; 427-11; **428**-11; 429-11, 438-10; 443-10
– branch, occipital artery 43-3; 44-1 51-10; **52**-10; 94-3
– process 99-8; 114-8; **115**-10, 11; 116-1; 350-3; 427-9; **428**-7; 458-6
**Maxilla** 107-3; 391-4; 393-8; 395-7; 396-8
–, frontal process of 393-8; 394-8
**Maxillary** artery 7-12; 94-5; 100-8; **101**-8; 102; 109-9; 110-8; 243; 350-9
– lymph nodes 163-1

**Maxillary** nerve 92-12; 103-4, 5; 104-5; 106-5; 110-11; **111**-12; **112**-1; 114-1; 232-2; 238-9; 247-2; 350-12; 351-10
– sinus **112**-3; 392-7; 394-6; 395-6; 396-6; 403-5
*Meatus acusticus externus* 100-10; **101**-10; 102-11; 428-8, 9; **448**-1, 2, 3; 449-9; 450-10; 454-3, 9; 459-4; 464-7
– – *internus* 411-5; 421-6, 8; **422**-8; 424-6
– *nasi inferior* 392-4
**Medial** circumflex femoral artery 7-3; 143-1; **144**-12; **148**-6
– cord of brachial plexus (of nerves) 61-2; 71-12
– geniculate body 273-11; 276-3; 290-10; 321; 322; 326-2
– lemniscus 324-10; **325**-10; 326-9; 327-10; 328-8; 329-10; 330-3; 331-4; **332**-6; 334-7; 336-7; 341-7
– longitudinal fasciculus 274-7; 296-10; **318**; 324-3; **325**-2; 326-10; 327-10; 328-12; 329-1; 330-1; **331**-12; **332**-12; 335-9; 338-3
– malleolar artery 152-7; 157-2, 12
– palpebral ligament 391-2; 393-10; 394-9; 408-2
– plantar artery 7-5; 159-11; 160-9
– – nerve 158-11; 159-11; 160-9, 12
– pterygoid nerve 110-8
– rectus muscle 318; 398-3; 399-2; 400-9
– retinal artery 360-4
– umbilical fold 127-5; 128-10
**Median** antebrachial vein 67-5; 68-10
– aperture, 4th ventricle (Magendi) 197-5; 199-8; 218-5; 276-6
– artery 77-9
– cubital vein 65; 67-5; 68-11
– nerve 37-7; **61**-4; 71-7, 10; **72**-5, 11; **75**-5, 11, 12; **76**-9, 12; **77**-5, 9, 12; **78**-1, 5; **79**-10; **87**-6, 7; 90-5; 169-3
– –, muscular branches 76-1; 77-9; 90-5
**Median** nerve, palmar branch 68-7; 75-5; 76-5; 82-6; 87-7; 90-5, 12
– sulcus (impression) 218-5
– –, rhomboid fossa 337-12
– umbilical fold 127-5
– – ligament 124-7; 125-7; 127-5; 171-7
**Mediastinal** lymph nodes 166-1, 4, 8, 10; 167-4
– pleura 36-3, 10
**Medulla** oblongata 180-1; 183-1; 223-7; 232-6; 239-11; **247**-5; 248-7; 272-5; **274**-7; 276-6; 277-7; **290**-8; 295-5; 320; 367
– –, anterior median fissure 331-6; 338-6; 340-7
– –, arcuate nucleus 331-7; 332-5; 338-7
– –, lateral funiculus of 272-7
– –, nucleus gracilis 231-6; 338-11; 339-11; 341-10; 342-11
– –, – –, tubercle of 289-5; 290-5; 338-1
– –, olivary nucleus **279**-7; 304; 331-4, 8; **332**-3, 8; 333-7; 334-7; 335-7; 336-8; 337-4, 8; 341-3
– –, – –, medial accessory 332-5; 337-5; 338-4
– –, pyramid **247**-5; 272-6; 290-7; **332**-7; 337-6; 338-5; 339-6
– *spinalis* **180**-8; 198-1; 241-6; 247-6; 248-7; 272-6; 274-6; 279-6; 290-6
– –, *pars cervicalis* 182-1; 183-11
– –, *pars lumbalis* 182-4; 183-7
– –, *pars thoracica* 182-3; 183-9
– –, *substantia intermedia centralis* 191-1; 192-8; 193-8; 194-4; 338-1
**Medullary** lamina 278-3
– –, internal of thalamus 283-9
– substance (cerebellum) 295-3; 296-8; 343
– – (cerebral) 250; 252; 254; 380-10
– velum, inferior 293-10; 294-10; 295-8; 334-11
– –, superior **223**-8; **248**-7; 274-2; 276-8; 289-1, 10; 293-11; 294-10; 295-10, 11; 296-1; 329-1
**Meibomian** glands ---- see Tarsal glands
*Membrana interossea* 81-7; 86-12

*Membrana reticularis* (vestibularis) 410-10
– *spiralis (cochlea)* 410-8
– *stapedis* 443-12; 445-11
– *thyreohyoidea* 118-4
– *tympani* 438-4; 439-9; 440-7; **441**-6; 442-6; 443-7; **448**-12; 449-7
– – *pars flaccida* 451-1; 454-11
– – *pars tensa* 451-8; 454-4
– – *secundaria* 447-6
**Membrane,** tympanic, umbo of 438-4; 440-8; **449**-8; **454**-4
– vestibular 410-10

**MEMBRANOUS LABYRINTH** **409**; **410**; **412**; **413**; **439**

**Meningeal** artery, anterior 103-10; 105-11; **106**-11; 107-12; 232-12
– –, middle 7-12; **94**-5; 101-8; 102-8; **103**-5; 110-8; 199-2; **232**-1, 2, 3; **233**-11
– –, –, petrosal branch 232-3
– –, posterior 115-1; 116-12
– nerve 186-8, 9
– veins, middle 233-11

**MENINGES** **187**; **190**; **232–240**

**Mental** artery 94-7; **98**-5; 99-5; **100**-5; 101-5
– nerve 92-4; **98**-5; 99-5; 100-5; 101-5; 111-4; 350-8; 351-8
**Mesencephalic** nucleus of trigeminal nerve 229-1; 231-2; 326-10
– tract of trigeminal nerve 328-1; 329-1

**MESENCEPHALON** **273**; **274**; **276**; **324–326**

**Mesencephalon**, lateral sulcus of 273-11; 325-10
**Mesenteric** artery, inferior 1-4; 7-2; 123-3; 126-2; 127-3; 128-11; 132-11
– –, superior 4-2; 7-1; 55-5; 121-3; 122-1; 123-1; 126-12; 170-2; 355-2, 9
– ganglion, inferior 125-3; 355-3
– –, superior 125-2; 355-2, 9
– lymph nodes 172-2, 8, 11
**Mesenteric** plexus, inferior 125-3, 6; 355-3, 9
– –, superior 125-2; 355-10
– vein, inferior 4-3; 123-3; 124-9; 127-2
– –, superior 4-3; 121-9; 122-12; 123-12; 124-3
**Mesocolon,** sigmoid 125-5; 127-3; 170-4
–, transverse 122-1; 123-1, 11
**Metacarpal** artery, dorsal 85-7; 86-6; 89-2
– –, palmar 88-3; 90-3, 9
– bone 89-3
**Metatarsal** artery, dorsal 7-5; 153-6; 157-6
– –, plantar 158-6; 159-6; 160-5

**MIDBRAIN** **272–274**; **276**; **289**; **290**

**Middle** cardiac vein 18-7; 20-6; 35-6
– cerebellar peduncle 276-4; 279-8; 289-9; 290-2; 293-2; 327-2; 328-9; 330-8; 333-2; 335-10
– cerebral artery 200-2; 204; 234-8; 241-10
– collateral artery 74-4

**MIDDLE EAR** **425–454**
**Ossicles 430–437**
**Walls, lateral 439–442; 451**
**Walls, medial 427–429; 443–445; 447; 449; 450**

**Middle** frontal gyrus 207; 208; 249-9; 253-11; 285-1
– genicular artery 137-3; 154-9
– meningeal artery 7-12; **94**-5; 101-8; 102-8; **103**-5; 110-8; 199-2; **232**-1, 2, 3; **233**-11
– – veins 233-11
– palatine nerve - - - - see **Lesser** palatine nerve
– rectal (hemorrhoidal) artery 128-4; 129-5; 132-5; 171-3, 4
sacral artery 7-2; 123-9; 126-6; 128-12; 129-12; **132**-10; 171-2
– – vein 126-6; 171-2
– superior alveolar nerve 92-3; 112-5
– suprarenal artery 126-1

**Middle** temporal artery 94-2; 99-10; 100-10; 101-11; 102-12
*Modiolus* 417-3; 423-1; 424-2, 5
**Motor** cortex 217
**Mucous** glands 457-6
**Multifidus** muscle 53-10
***MUSCULUS, MUSCULI***
*Musculus abductor digiti minimi,* (foot) 159-1; 160-1
– – – –, (hand) 88-4
– – *hallucis* 159-11; 160-12
– – *pollicis brevis* 87-7; 88-9; 89-8
– – – *longus* 80-7; 81-7; 86-11; 89-8
– *adductor brevis* 144-1
– – *longus* 142-2
– – *magnus* 144-3; 147-3, 4; 148-6
– – *pollicis* 86-8; 87-10; 88-9, 12; 89-9
– *anconeus* 73-6; 74-6; 80-10; 81-1
– *antitragicus* 463-6
– *arrector pili* 468-9
– *aryepiglotticus* 116-2
– *arytenoideus* 116-3; 117-3
– *auricularis* 95-8; 11; 99-9; 464-5, 11
– *biceps brachii* **71**-5; **72**-2; 73-8; 74-8; 75-1, 12; 76-12; 77-2; 12; 78-1; 79-11
– –, *caput longum* 169-4
– – *femoris* 145-9; 146-5, 6; 147-5, 8; 149-1, 5; 150-12; 154-2, 12
– *brachialis* 72-5; 73-7; 74-7; **75**-11; **76**-11; **77**-11; 78-2; 80-7
– *brachioradialis* 72-5; 75-1, 5; 76-2, 5; 77-4, 5; 78-3; 79-7; 80-7, 11; 81-11
– *bronchoesophageus* 35-1
– *buccinator* **98**-4; 99-5; 100-4; **101**-5; 102-4; 350-8
– *bulbospongiosus* 133-7; 134-7
– *ciliaris* 356-1; 368-1, 10; 369-2; 370-10
– *coccygeus* 128-2; 132-5; 355-7
– *constrictor pharyngis, inferior* 115-8; 352-1
– – –, *medii* 107-7; 115-9
– – –, *superior* 115-12; 116-1
– *coracobrachialis* 72-2
*Musculus cricoarytenoideus, posterior* 116-3; 117-4
– *cricothyreoideus* 118-7; 352-1
– *deltoideus* 41-5; 42-5; 43-4; 44-3; 45-7; 51-9; 53-2; 60-1; 61-2; 62-1, 8; 71-1; 72-1; **73**-11; **74**-11
– *depressor anguli oris* 95-4; 98-5
– *digastricus* 42-10; 109-4; 114-6
– –, *venter anterior* 41-10; 43-11; 45-12; 46-12; **99**-6; 100-5; **102**-5; 165-8
– –, *venter posterior* **99**-7; 100-7; **102**-8; 115-2, 9; 116-10
– *erector spinae* 53
– *extensor carpi radialis* 73-6; 74-6
– – – –, *brevis* and *longus* **80**-7, 11; 81-7, 9, 11; **85**-11, 12; 89-4, 7
– – – *ulnaris* 80-5, 10; 81-5; 86-1, 12
– – *digiti minimi* 80-5; 85-1
– – *digitorum* 80-8; 81-5; 85-1; 157-10
– – –, *brevis* 153-7; 157-7
– – –, *longus* 153-7, 10, 11; 157-7, 10, 12; 175-7, 10
– – *hallucis, brevis* 157-10
– – –, *longus* 153-7; 157-5, 6, 12
– – *pollicis, brevis* and *longus* 80-6; 81-5, 7; 85-10; 86-9, 11; 89-8
– *flexor carpi radialis* 75-9; 76-6, 9; 77-6; 87-6; 88-7; 89-7
– – – *ulnaris* 75-8; 76-7; 77-6, 7; 78-8; 87-6; 88-5
– – – –, *caput humerale* 73-5
– – *digitorum brevis* (foot) 90-7; 159-1, 5
– – – *longus* (foot) 90-7; 151-8; 152-9; 159-9
– – – *minimi brevis* 160-4
– – – *profundus* 77-7, 8; 78-7
– – – *superficialis* 75-7; **76**-8; 77-3, 6
– – *hallucis brevis* 159-8; 160-8
– – – *longus* 151-5; 152-5, 7; 159-8; 160-7, 9
– – *pollicis brevis* 87-8; 88-8
– – – *longus* 75-4; 76-4; 77-5; 88-8; 90-3, 5
– *flexores antebrachii* 72-7; 77-10; 78-4
– *frontalis* 280-12

*Musculus gastrocnemius* 145-5, 7; 146-6; 149-6; **150**-1, 9, 11; 154-4, 8; 174-7
– *gemelli* 147-1; 148-5, 7
– *genioglossus* **107**-3; 109-4; 110-4; 118-1
– *geniohyoideus* **107**-6; 109-4; 110-4; 118-8
– *gluteus maximus* 53-7; 133-1; 134-1, 10; 145-11; **146**-11; 147-1, 11; 148-4, 10
– – *medius* 147-1; 148-2
– – *minimus* 148-2
– *gracilis* 142-2; 143-4; 144-3; 145-5; 146-9; 149-11
– *helicis major* and *minor* 463-1, 2
– *hyoglossus* 45-1; 46-11; **102**-8; **107**-7, 8; 118-2, 8, 10
– *iliacus* 127-10; 355-8
– *iliocostalis thoracis* 53-10
– *iliopsoas* 143-11; 144-11
– *infraspinatus* 53-3; 62-2, 5
– *intercostalis* 55-9; 56-1; 184-8, 9
– *interfoveolaris* 127-8
– *interosseus dorsalis* 85-7; 86-9; 88-11; 89-10
– – *palmaris* 88-2
– *ischiocavernosus* 133-8; 134-7
– *latissimus dorsi* 51-7; 53-4, 8; 59-4; 60-5; 61-8; 169-4
– *levator ani* 128-5; 129-5; 133-11; 134-1; 171-5; 355-7
– – *labii superioris alaeque nasi* 95-3
– – *palpebrae superioris* **103**-1; **104**-1; **105**-8, 12; 106-7, 12; 232-11; 350-11; 363-12; **395**-12; **396**-2; 397-12; **401**-2, 5, 10; 403-1; 404-1; 405-12; **406**-1; 408-12
– – *scapulae* 39-4; 51-10; 53-11; 165-4; 169-12
– – *veli palatini* 116-12; 457-6
– *longissimus capitis* 51-10; 52-9; 53-11
– – *thoracis* 53-9
– *longus colli* 58-7;
– *lumbricalis* (hand) 87-10; 88-2, 11; 89-10
– *masseter* 95-5; 98-7; 99-2, 7; 100-8
– *multifidus* 53-10
*Musculus mylohyoideus* 42-10; 43-11; 45-12; 46-12; **102**-6; 107-6; 109-4; **110**-4; 350-7
– *obliquus auriculae* 464-12
– – *capitis inferior* 52-9
– – – *superior* 52-9
– – *externus abdominis* 50-2; 53-5, 8; 59-10; 60-7; 148-1
– – *inferior* **106**-4; 364; 366; 393-5; 394-5; **395**-8; 396-8; 397-3, 5, 7; 398-4; 399-10; 400-4; 403-6; 406-7; 407-8; 408-7
– – *superior* 103-9; 104-11; 105-8, 11; 106-7, 12; 364; 366; **396**-1; 397-11, 398-11; 399-4; 400-10; **401**-6, 10, 12; 403-1, 6; 404-1; 405-10; 407-1; 408-1
– *obturator externus* 148-6
– – *internus* 132-6; 147-1; 148-5
– *occipitofrontalis* 39-2; 51-1; 52-1; 95-9; **98**-2, 9; 99-1; 100-1
– *omohyoideus* 43-4; 45-4; 46-10; 61-1
– –, *venter inferior* 40-4; **41**-4; **42**-4; 45-8; 60-1; 165-6
– –, – *superior* **41**-9; 43-9; 44-11; 165-8
– *opponens pollicis* 88-8; 89-8
– *orbicularis oculi* **95**-3, 4; 100-1, 5; 392-1; 393-5; 394-5
– – –, *pars palpebralis* 363-2, 6
– – *oris* 99-4
– *orbitalis (fissurae orbitalis superioris)* 405-1
– *palatoglossus* 107-8; 118-1
– *palatopharyngeus* 116-1
– *palmaris brevis* 82-4
– – *longus* 75-9; 76-6; 77-6
– *papillaris* 26-8; 33-4
– – *anterior* 23-3; 24-8; **25**-8; 28-4; 29-3; 31-2, 10
– – *parvi* **25**-7; 26-5; 28-8; 29-7; 31-5, 7
– – *posterior* 23-5; 24-4; 27-4, 8; 31-5, 7
– – *septalis* 27-8; 28-8
– *pectinatus* 27-10; 28-1, 9
– *pectineus* 142-1; 143-1

*Musculus pectoralis major* 41-7; 42-6; 43-7; **44**-8; 45-5, 7; 46-5; 57-10; 59-12; 60-3, 11; 61-3; 71-2; 72-1
– *pectoralis minor* 42-4; 43-6; **44**-7; 57-11; 60-4; 61-2
– *peroneus brevis* 150-6; 152-5; 153-7
– – *longus* 150-5; 152-5; 153-11
– *pharyngoepiglotticus* 116-2
– *piriformis* 140-2; 147-1; 148-2
– *plantaris* 150-10; 151-1; 152-1; 154-3
– *popliteus* 152-11
– *procerus* 95-2
– *pronator quadratus* 77-5; 88-6
– – *teres* 75-10; 76-2, 10; 77-3; 78-5
– *psoas major* **126**-10; 127-2, 9; 348-4
– *pterygoideus, lateralis* **101**-1; 102-1
– –, *medial* 100-7; **101**-7; 102-8; 109-8; 110-7; 112-7
– *pyramidalis* 50-4
– *quadratus femoris* 147-2; 148-7
– – *lumborum* 70-1; 127-11; 353-7; 355-2, 9
– – *plantae* 159-10; 160-2
– *rectus abdominis* 50-3, 5; 54-6, 8; 126-4; 127-6
– – –, vagina of 50-3; 54-7; 127-6
– – *capitis posterior major* 52-11
– – *femoris* 142-10; 143-9; 144-8, 10
– – *inferior* 106-2, 5; 350-10; 364-366; **395**-4; **396**-5; 398-5; 399-1; 400-7; 403-5; 404-5; 405-8; 406-4, 8; 407-7
– – *lateralis* 103-4; 104-2; 105-4; 106-1, 5; 113-3; 356-2, 3; 364–367; 359-3; 368-2; 384-2, 9; **395**-2; 396-2, 9; 397-2; 398-10; 399-8; 400-2; 401-4, 8; 402-2, 8; 403-5, 7; 404-8; 405-4; 407-9
– – *medialis* 105-9; 106-8; 356-9, 10; 364–367; 384-8; **396**-4; 397-10; 398-4; 399-2; 400-9; **401**-2; 402-1, 5; 403-2; 404-2; 405-9; 407-2
– – *superior* 103-1; 104-1; 105-1, 8; 106-1, 7; 232-11; 364–366; **395**-1; 396-1; 397-1; 398-1; 399-5; 400-10, 12; **401**-5, 8; 403-1; 404-1, 11; 405-11; 406-2; 407-12
*Musculus rhomboideus* 51-8; 52-4, 7; 53-3
– *salpingopharyngeus* 116-1
– *sartorius* 142-5, 9; 143-5, 10; 144-4; 145-5
– *scalenus anterior* 42-8; **44**-9; 57-1; 58-10; 60-12; 169-6, 9; **354**-1, 11
– – *medius* 58-10; 165-6; 169-12
– – *posterior* 58-10; 165-5
– *semimembranosus* 145-5; 146-7; **147**-7; 149-11; 150-12; 154-9, 11
– *semispinalis capitis* 51-10; 52-1, 9, 11
– *semitendinosus* 145-4; 146-7; **147**-8; 149-12; 150-12; 154-12
– *serratus anterior* 59-11; 60-7
– – *posterior inferior* 53-9
– *soleus* 150-1, 5; 151-1, 11; 152-1, 11; 154-5, 6
– *sphincter ani externus* 133-8; 134-11
– – *pupillae* 356-1
– *splenius capitis* 43-3; 51-2, 10; 52-2; 10; 95-8; 165-4
– – *cervicis* 169-12
– *stapedius* 112-9; 429-1; 444-9
– *sternocleidomastoideus* 39-9; 40-1, 9; **41**-3; **42**-1, 7; 43-1; 45-3, 6, 9; 46-2; 51-2; 60-11; 95-7; 98-7; 99-8; 165-3
– *sternohyoideus* 41-8; 44-11; 46-10
– *sternothyreoideus* 41-8; 44-10; 46-10
– *styloglossus* 102-8; 107-8; 118-2
– *stylohyoideus* 42-9; 45-10; 99-7; 100-7; 102-8; 114-7
– *stylopharyngeus* 115-10
– *subclavius* 43-4; 57-1
– *subscapularis* 61-9; 169-4
– *supinator* 75-2; 76-1; 79-3; 81-10
– *supraspinatus* 62-1, 10
– *tarsalis* 363-11
– *temporalis* 99-1; 100-1; 101-11; 102-12; 280-2; 384-9; 402-2
– *temporoparietalis* 95-1; 98-12; 99-10
– *tensor fasciae latae* 142-11

*Musculus tensor tympani* 112-11; 439-9; 442-9, 10; 443-2; 444-1; 445-2; 446-10; 448-11; 449-2
– – –, *semicanalis* 427-3; 428-2; 445-3; 446-1
– – *veli palatini* 110-7; 116-1; 457-4
– *teres major* 51-8; 53-3; 59-3; 61-8; 62-4; 72-11; 73-1; 74-1
– – *minor* 53-3; 62-5; 74-12
– *tibialis anterior* 153-2, 5; 157-12; 175-1, 5
– – *posterior* 150-7; 151-7, 8; 152-7, 11
– *tragicus* 463-3
– *transversus abdominis* 50-3; 126-4; 127-8
– *transversus auriculae* 464-3
– – *menti* 95-5
– – *perinei superficialis* 133-8; 134-8
– – *thoracis* 50-2; 54-11
– *trapezius* 39-4; 42-4; 45-4; **51**-2, 9; 52-4; 95-8; 108-8; 165-5; 350-3
– *triceps* 53-3; 61-6; 62-6; 72-8, 9; 73-2, 7, 8, 9; 74-2, 3, 4, 8; 80-12
– *uvulae* 116-1
– *vastus lateralis* 142-8; 144-8; 146-4
– – *medialis* 142-7; 143-7
– *zygomaticus* 95-3, 4; 98-4; 99-4
**Musculocutaneous** nerve 37-7; 61-3; 71-12; **72**-2; 169-3
**Musculophrenic** artery 54-2, 10
– vein 54-2
**Mylohyoid** muscle 42-10; 43-11; **45**-12; **46**-12; 101-8; 107-6; 109-4; 110-4; 350-7
– nerve **42**-11; **43**-10; 44-11; 92-6; 100-6; 101-6, 8; **102**-6, 8; 109-8; 110-6
**Myocardium** 24-5; 26-7; 27-4

## N

**NAILS 477–481**

**Nasal** artery, dorsal 98-3; 99-2; 100-2; 105-10
– bone 391-3
**Nasal** cavity 384-5; 402-7; 403-4; 404-3
– concha 108-1, 2, 11; 109-2; 264-4; 392-3, 4; 404-4
– septal artery, posterior 107-11; 109-3
– septum 107-1; 108-2; 11; 264-4; 402-6; 403-4; 404-3
**Nasociliary** nerve 92-1; **103**-9; 104-5; 105-8; 350-12; 351-11
**Nasofrontal** vein 232-12
**Nasolacrimal** duct 392-4; 393-6; 394-7
**Nasopalatine** nerve 107-11; 108-3; 109-3; 110-3

**NECK REGION 37–46, 115–118**

**NERVES and VESSELS**
**Abdominal cavity 120–126**
**– wall 50; 54**
**Axilla 44; 59–61**
**Back, occipital region 51–53**
**Cranial cavity 232–239; 301–306**
**Female genitalia and pelvis 129; 131–134**
**Head 91–103**
**Inferior extremity 135–160**
**Larynx 116–118**
**Male genitalia and pelvis 128; 130; 132; 133**
**Nasal cavity 92; 107–110**
**Neck 37–46, 58**
**Occipital region 51–53**
**Oral cavity 92; 102; 107–110**
**Orbital cavity 103–106**
**Pharynx 115; 116**
**Superior extremity 61; 62; 65–90**
**Thoracic wall 54–57; 59; 60**

**NERVES, AUTONOMIC**
**(General Diagram) 345**
**of Abdomen 348; 349; 355**
**of Head 350; 351**
**of Neck 348; 349; 352**
**of Thorax 348; 349; 352–354**

**Nerve**, lumbosacral trunk 119-9; 126-3; 132-12; 355-4
–, of pterygoid canal 92-1; 93-3; 109-9; 110-1; 112-6; 350-1; 351-10

Nerve, to subclavius muscle 37-8; 169-10
–, sympathetic trunk 44-12; 55; **115**-3, 5; 116-3; 126-2; 350-5; 351-5; **352**-12; **354**-4, 9; **355**-9

## *NERVUS* or *NERVI*

– *abducens* **103**-4, 7; **104**-4, 6; **105**-4, 6; **106**-5, 6; 114-3; 232-5; 236-8; 238-10; 239-2; 241-8; 247-5; 272-2; 333-5; 350-12
– *accessorius* **39**-4; 40-4; 41-4; 42-3; 43-1; 44-2; **51**-10; **52**-4, 8; 114-4; 115-10, 11; 116-1, 11; 183-1; 232-5, 7; 239-3; 241-7; 247-7; 272-5; 350-3; 351-3
– *alveolaris inferior* 92-6, 7; **99**-5; **100**-6, 7; **101**-5, 8; 102-8; 109-8; 110-7; **111**-9; 350-8; 351-8, 9
– – *superior* 92-3; 101-2; 102-2; **111**-12; 112-4, 5, 6; 350-8, 9; 351-9
– *anococcygeus* 119-6; **133**-12; 134-12
– *auricularis magnus* 37-11; **39**-3; 9, 10; **40**-4; 51-1; 53-11, 12; 95-7; 98-8
– *auriculotemporalis* 92-8; **95**-12; 98-9; 99-8; 100-10, 11; 101-9; 102-9, 11; 110-9
– *axillaris* 37-8; 53-2; 59-3; 61-7; **62**-6; 69-11; 72-11; **74**-12
– *buccalis* **98**-5; 99-5; 100-3, 4; 101-4; 102-3
– *canalis pterygoidei* 92-1; 93-3; **109**-9; 110-1; **112**-6; 350-1; 351-10
– *cardiacus* 348-1, 2, 10
– – *cervicalis (sympathici)* **44**-8, 10; **57**-2; 115-4, 5; 352-1
– *caroticotympanicus* 93-1; 112-6
– *caroticus internus* 112-8; **115**-1; 116-1; **350**-2; 351-8
– *cervicalis* 42-2, 3; 43-3, 4; 181-11; 199-5; 342-4; 348-1; 350-3, 4; 351-3, 4
– – *fila radicularia dorsalia* 187-10; 188-1; 290-6
– – – – *ventralia* 188-1; 290-7; 342-4
– – *radix ventralis* 199-6; 290-7; 342-4
*Nervus cervicalis ramus dorsalis* 52-9; 53-1, 12
– – – *ventralis* 42-2, 4; 350-4; 351-5; 352-11
– *ciliaris* 369-3, 6; 370-9, 12; 383-9, 10
– – *brevis* 105-4
– – *longus* 105-8
– *clunium* 53-7; 119-7; 133-2, 11; 134-2, 10; 137-2, 11; **140**-10, 11, 12; 145-1; 146-1, 11
– *coccygeus* 132-5; 181-6; 190-6; 348-5; 355-6
– *cutaneus antebrachii lateralis* 67-4; **68**-1, 4; 71-5; 72-5; 73-7; 74-7; 82-7
– – – *medialis* 37-7; 61-6; 67-7; **68**-11; 71-11
– – – *posterior* 67-5; **69**-7; 70-5, 12; 73-7; 74-7; 83-11; 89-5
– – – *radialis* - - - - see *Nervus cutaneus antebrachii lateralis*
– – *brachii lateralis (superior)* 53-2; 62-6; **69**-1; 73-10
– – – *medialis* 37-6; 61-6; **67**-10; 68-11; 69-3; 70-12; 71-11; 169-4
– – – *posterior* 53-2; **69**-9; 70-12; 73-9; 74-1
– – *dorsalis* (foot) 139-7; 141-6; 155-8, 10
– – *femoris lateralis* 50-8; 119-10; 125-9; 126-3, 7; 127-9; **138**-11; 140-3; 142-11; 348-5, 8
– – – *posterior* 119-7; 133-4; 134-3; **140**-7; **141**-11, 12; 145-2; 146-5; 147-11; 148-7
– – *rami cutanei cruris mediales* **139**-7, 9; 141-9; **143**-3, 4; 144-7; **155**-12
– – *surae lateralis* 141-1; 145-7; 146-6; 147-6; 149-3
– – – *medialis* 141-8, 9; 145-7; 146-6; 147-6; 149-6; 155-12
– *digitales dorsales manus* **83**-7; 84-1; 85-10; 89-1; 178
– – – *pedis* 155-6; 156-12; 157-6; 178
– – – *pollicis* 89-9
– – *palmares communes* 87-9

*Nervus digitales palmares proprii* 82-3; 84-8; 85-7; **87**-1, 3, 4, 8, 11; 88-12; 89-1; 90-1, 9, 11
– *plantares communes* 158-6; 159-5
– – – *proprii* 156-6; 158-5, 8; 159-6
– *dorsalis clitoridis* 134-4
– – *penis* 130-11; 133-4
– – *scapulae* 37-9; 51-10; 52-4, 7
– *ethmoidales anterior* 92-2; 105-9; 106-9; 107-12
– *ethmoidalis anterior ramus nasalis* 95-3; 98-3; **99**-3; 100-2; 102-2; 107-1; 108-1; 109-1
– – *posterior* 105-8; 106-9
– *facialis* 91; 92-8; 10, 11; **93**-7; 95-5, 6, 7; 98; **99**-8; 100-9; 101-9; 102-9; 110-10; **112**-9, 10; 114-3, 6; 232-4; 239-3; 241-3; 247-9; 272-4; 279-7; 290-8; 350-2; 351-2; 439-3, 7; 441-5; 442-5; 444-9, 12; **445**-8; 447-9
– – *ganglion geniculi* 92-11; **112**-10; 114-2; 438-1; 439-8
– – *geniculum* 438-1; 443-1; 445-12
– – *genu* 330-1; 333-1
(– –) *nervus auricularis posterior* 39-1; 42-1; 93-8; **95**-8; **99**-9; 100-9; 102-9
– – *plexus parotideus* 98-8
– – *radix* 330-10; 335-6
– – *ramus buccalis* **95**-4, 5; 98-7
– – *r. colli* 40-11; 41-11; 95-6; 98-6
– – *r. digastricus* 99-8; 102-9; 114-6
– – *r. marginalis mandibulae* 95-5; 98-6
– – *r. stylohyoideus* 114-7
– – *r. temporalis* 95-7; 98-9
– – *r. zygomaticus* 95-7; 98-9
– *femoralis* 119-9; 125-8; **126**-5, 7; 127-8; 142-11, 12; **143**-11; **144**-11; 170-7; 348-5, 7
– – *ramus cutaneus anterior* 50-7; 138-3
– *frontalis* 92-2; **103**-8; 350-12; 351-11, 12
– – *ramus lateralis* 92-2; **95**-2; 98-1, 2; 99-2; 100-1; **101**-1; 102-1; **103**-1; 104-12; 350-11, 12; 351-10; 404-12
*Nervus frontalis r. medialis* 92-2; 95-2; 98-2; 99-2; 100-1; **101**-1; 102-1; **103**-11; 104-12; 350-10, 11
– *genitofemoralis* 119-10; 125-8; 126-11; 127-9; 171-10; 348-8
– – *ramus femoralis* 50-8; 119-10; 126-7; 138-10; 348-5
– – *r. genitalis* 119-10; 126-4, 7; 130-10; 132-9; 348-5
– *glossopharyngeus* 91; 92-8; **93**-6; 107-8; **108**-7; 114-4; 115-3, 10, 11; 116-11; **117**-1, 11; 166-11; 181-12; 239-3; 241-3; 247-7; 272-5; **350**-3; 351-3
– –, *ganglion* of 92-9; 93-5; 112-8; 115-2; 350-2
– – *rami linguales* 108-7; 117-11
– – *r. pharyngeus* 115-9
– *gluteus inferior* 119-8, 9; 147-11; 148-10, 11
– – *superior* 119-9; 148-11
– *hypoglossus* 37-12; 42-9; 43-11; 44-11; 45-1; **46**-12; **102**-6, 7; 107-6; 115-10; 116-1, 11; **118**-2; 181-12; 183-12; 241-8; 247-7; 272-5; **350**-2, 3, 7; 351-3, 7
– – *radix* 232-7; 332-8; 336-7, 8; 337-7
– *iliohypogastricus* 50-8; 53-8; 55-7; **119**-11; 125-9; **126**-11; 127-11; 138-1; 140-1; 148-8; 348-8
– *ilioinguinalis* 50-5; 8; 119-10; 125-9; 126-3, 10; 127-12; 130-1; 138-1; 170-6; 348-8
– *infraorbitalis* **92**-3; 98-3; 99-4; 100-2; 101-2, 3; 102-1, 2; 106-5; 107-5; 110-2; 111-2; **112**-2, 3; **113**-4, 5; 350-9; 351-9; 392-7; 403-6; 404-7; 405-6
– *infratrochlearis* 92-2; **95**-2; 98-3; 99-3; 100-2; 101-2; 102-2; **105**-9; 106-12
– *intercostalis* 37-5, 6; 47-4; 50-2, 9, 10; 55-8; **56**-3; 180-3; 184-9; 348-5, 8, 10; **352**-7, 8, 9, 10; 353-7, 8; 354-2, 7; 355-1, 2, 12
– – *ramus cutaneus anterior* 45-7; 60-10; 138-1

*Nervus intercostalis ramus cutaneus laterales* 59-6, 12; 60-5, 6, 9
– *intercostobrachialis* 37-6; **44**-5; 50-11; 53-3; **59**-1, 3; **60**-4; 67-10; 169-4, 6
– *intermedius* 112-10; 114-3; 232-5; 247-8; 272-4; 279-7; 439-8
– *interosseus antebrachii, anterior* 77-8
– – –, *posterior* 81-5; 86-1
– *ischiadicus* 145-10; 147-9; 148-1
– *jugularis* 115-2
– *labiales posteriores* 134-7
– *lacrimalis* 92-1; **103**-8; 104-2; 105-3; 113-1; 390-9; 404-11
– *laryngeus inferior* 117-4
– – *recurrens* 36-2, 12; 44-9; 46-3, 6; 55-1, 11, 12; 57-1, 2, 11; **116**-5, 7; **117**-6, 7; 166-2; **352**-1, 2; 354-1, 10
– – *superior* 43-9; **115**-3, 9, 10; 116-2, 9; 117-10; 118-3
– – – *r. cardiacus* 115-8
– – – *r. externus* **115**-4, 9; 350-6; 351-7
– – – *r. internus* 115-9; 117-9; 118-3; 350-7; 351-7
– *lingualis* 46-1; 92-6; 100-7; 101-7; **102**-6; 107-3; 109-8; 110-7; 111-9; 118-1, 10; 350-2, 7; 351-7, 8
– *lumbalis* 181-8; 348-5; 355-2, 4
– – *radix dorsalis* 182-8
– – *ramus ventralis* 355-2, 3
– *lumbalium rami dorsales* 53-7
– *mandibularis* 92-8; **102**-12; 103-5; 106-6; **110**-10; 111-10; 112-1; 232-2; 247-2; 350-1; 351-11; 457-3
– *massetericus* **99**-6; 100-12; 101-10; 102-12
– *masticatorius* 350-8; 351-9
– *maxillaris* 92-12; 103-4, 5; 104-5; 106-5; **110**-11; **111**-12; **112**-1; 114-1; 232-2; 238-9; 247-2; 350-12; 351-10
– *meatus acustici externus* 100-9; 102-9
– *medianus* 37-7; **61**-4; 71-7, 10; **72**-5, 11; **75**-5, 11, 12; **76**-9, 12; **77**-5, 9, 12; **78**-1, 5; **79**-10; **87**-6, 7; 90-5, 9; 169-3
*Nervus medianus, rami musculares* 76-1; 77-9; 90-5
– – *r. palmaris* 68-7; 75-5; 76-5; 82-6; 87-7; 90-5, 12
– *meningeus* 186-8, 9
– *mentalis* 92-4; **98**-5; 99-5; **100**-5; 101-5; 111-4; 350-8; 351-8
– *musculocutaneus* 37-7; 61-3; 71-12; **72**-2; 169-3
– *m. tensoris tympani* 110-9
– *mylohyoideus* 42-11; 43-10; 44-11; 92-6; 100-6; 101-6, 8; **102**-6, 8; 109-8; 110-6
– *nasales laterales, posteriores inferiores* 110-2
– – – – *superiores* 108-12
– *nasociliaris* 92-1; **103**-9; 104-5; 105-8; 350-12; 351-11
– *nasopalatinus* 107-11; 108-3; 109-3; 110-3
– *obturatorius* 119-9; 126-3; 132-9; 143-1, 12; **144**-1, 12; 171-9; 348-7
– –, *rami cutanei* 138-4; 140-8; 143-2; 144-3
– *occipitalis major* 39-3; **40**-1; **41**-3; **44**-2; 51-1, 11; 52-1; 53-12; 95-9, 11; 98-9; 99-9
– – *minor* 37-11; **39**-3; **40**-3; **41**-2; **42**-1; **44**-1; 51-1, 10; 53-11; 95-8; 98-8; 99-8
– *oculomotorius* **103**-7; **104**-6; **105**-7; **106**-6; 114-2; 223-8; **232**-2; 236-8; 238-10; 239-10; **241**-2; 242-7; **247**-10; 248-6; 274-9; 277-8; 321; 322; **324**-6; 350-1; 351-12; 367; 384-11; 405-5
– *olfactorius* 107-1; 108-12; 197-9
– *ophthalmicus* 92-12; **103**-7, 8; **104**-5; **105**-7; **106**-6; 110-12; 111-12; 112-1; 114-1; 232-1; 238-9; 247-2; 350-12; 351-10, 12
– *opticus* **105**-2, 7; **106**-1, 7; 232-1, 11; 239-12; **241**-1; 242-8; 247-1; 248-4, 5; 257-4; **273**-7; 275-1;

**362**; 367; 384-11; 385-4, 8; 404-4; 405-9; 406-2; 407-7
*Nervus opticus, vagina externa* **106**-1; **356**-7; **362**-1; 368-6; 384-1; 402-2; 404-5; 405-9; 406-2
– *opticus, vagina interna* **362**-2
– *palatinus* 92-3; 108-6; 109-3, 7; 110-3; 350-9; 351-10
– *pectoralis lateralis* 44-6
– *perinealis* 133-1; 134-1, 9
– *peroneus (fibularis) communis* 119-8; 145-8; 146-5; **147**-5; **149**-2, 5; 150-1; 151-1; **153**-1
– – (–) *profundus* 153-5, 11; 155-4; 157-11
– – (–) *superficialis* 139-7; 153-7, 11; 155-11
– *petrosus major* 92-11; 109-9; 110-10; **112**-10; 114-1; **232**-2; 350-1; 351-1; **438**-2; 439-9; 443-2; 444-1; 445-1
– – *minor* 92-10; 93-2; **112**-10; 232-3; 350-1; 351-2
– – *profundus* 92-12; 109-10; 112-1
– *phrenicus* 36-2; 37-9; 42-8; **43**-8; **44**-2; 46-9; 55-1; **57**-1, 3, 4, 5, 8, 11; 58-4, 10; 60-12; 125-10; 166-2, 10; 184-7; 348-10; 352-12; 353-4
– *phrenicus accessorius* 58-9; 169-10
– *plantaris lateralis* 158-11; 159-2, 11; 160-1, 3, 12
– – *medialis* 158-3; 160-9
– *pterygoideus lateralis* 102-1
– – *medialis* 110-8
– *pterygopalatinus* 110-2; 112-2
– *pudendus* 132-5; 133-1, 10; 134-1; 147-11
– *radialis* 37-8; 53-2; 61-6; 71-11; **72**-11; 73-2; **74**-2; 75-1; **76**-1, 2; **77**-1; 78-3; **79**-1; 169-2
– –, *ramus profundus* 75-1; 76-1; 77-1; 79-3, 6; 80-9; 81-10
– –, *r. superficialis* 68-5; 70-7; 75-1; 76-1, 5; 77-5; 79-9; 80-7; 81-7; **83**-10; 89-6
– *rectales inferiores* 119-7; 132-4; **133**-1
*Nervus saccularis* 412-7; 413-8
– *sacralis* 53-7; **132**-3, 4; 181-7; 348-5; 355-4, 6
– –, *ramus dorsalis* 53-6, 7
– –, *r. ventralis* 132-1; 355-4, 5
– *saphenous* 138-5; **139**-1; 141-7; 11; **143**-3, 4; 144-7; **155**-12
– *scrotalis* 133-6, 7
– *spinalis* **47**-5; 176-2; 181-1; 184-2; 186-9; 188-3, 10; 189-9; 190-1
– – *radix dorsalis* 176-2; 184-1, 11; 186-10; **189**-11; 191-2; 193-1
– – – *ventralis* 176-2; 184-1, 11; 186-8; **189**-8; 191-8
– – *ramus dorsalis* 176-3, 10; 185-3; 186-9; **189**-3
– – *r. ventralis* 176-3, 10; 185-4; 186-9; **189**-3
– *splanchnicus lumbalis* 125-4
– – *major* **55**-6, 8; 56-8; 126-12; 184-8; 348-4, 9; **352**-7; 353-7; 354-8; 355-12
– – *minor* 55-7, 8; 348-4, 8; 353-6; 354-7; 355-11
– *statoacusticus* - - - - see *Nervus vestibulocochlearis*
– *subclavius* 37-9; 169-10
– *sublingualis* 92-4; 118-12
– *suboccipitalis* 52-11; 53-11
– *subscapularis* 37-8; 53-3; 61-12
– *supraclavicularis* 37-9; 39-6; 40-6; 50-11; 53-1; 67-12; 169-1
– *suprascapularis* 37-8; 44-2; 61-2; 62-11; 169-2
– *supratrochlearis* 92-2; **95**-2; 98-2; 99-2; 100-2; 101-2; 102-2; 103-11; 104-12; 350-10; 351-10
– *suralis* **141**-4; 145-7
– *temporalis profundus* 101-12; 102-1, 12
– *tensoris veli palatini* 110-8
– – *tympani* 110-9
– *thoracicus, ramus dorsalis* 52-6; 53-1, 8, 10
– – *longus* 37-5; 44-6; **59**-5; **60**-5; 169-5, 12

*Nervus thoracodorsalis* 37-8; 44-6; **59**-5; **60**-4; 61-7
– *tibialis* 119-7; 145-4; 146-5; **147**-7; 149-2; 150-1, 7; **151**-1, 7, 9; 152-2, 12; 174-2
– *transversus colli* 37-10; 39-9; 40-9
– *trigeminus* **91**; **92**-12; 98; 102; **103**-7; **104**-6; 105-6; **106**-6; 110-10; 111-11; 112-12; **232**-4; 239-2; 241-2; **247**-9; 290-9; **350**-1; 351-1
– – *ganglion trigeminale (ganglion semilunare)* **103**-5; 104-6; 110-10; **111**-11; 114-3; **247**-3; 328-5; 350-1; 351-1; 457-12
– *trigeminus nucleus motorius* 229-10; 230-2; 328-1
– –, – *sensorius superior* 229-2; 231-2; 328-1
– – – *tractus mesencephalici* 229-1; 231-2; 326-10
– – – – *spinalis* 229-4; 230-10; **331**-2, 9; 332-2; 333-2; 334-8; 335-1; 336-2; 337-9; **338**-3, 11; 339-10; **340**-2, 10; 341-2; 342-2
– –, *radix motoria (portio minor)* **110**-11 **112**-1; 247-2; 290-9; 350-1; 351-1
– –, – *sensoria (portio major)* 110-11; 290-9
– –, *tractus mesencephalicus* 328-1; 329-1
– –, – *spinalis* 328-5; 333-2; 334-3; 335-3, 9; 336-9; 337-9; 338-10; 339-9; 340-2; **341**-3
– *trochlearis* **103**-7, 9; **104**-6; **105**-6, 8; 230-2; **232**-2; 236-8; 238-10; 242-7; 247-3; 272-4; 276-3; 289-1; 290-1; 327-1; 350-12; 351-12
– – *decussatio* 327-12
– *tympanicus* 92-10; 93-12; **112**-8; **350**-2; 351-2; 443-5; 444-6; 445-4; 447-2
– *ulnaris* 37-7; **61**-4; 71-7, 11; 72-9; 73-5; 74-5; 75-7, 12; 76-7; 77-7, 12; **78**-7, 9; 80-1; 81-1; 82-5; 90-7, 9; 169-3
– – *ramus palmaris [manus]* 68-7; 75-6; 87-6; 88-5
*Nervus ulnaris, r. dorsalis [manus]* 70-5; 75-7; 76-7; 77-7; 80-5; 81-5; 83-1
– –, *r. profundus* 87-5; 88-4, 11
– –, *r. superficialis* 87-4; 88-4
– *utriculi* 412-11; 413-4
– *utriculoampullaris* 412-8; 439-6
– *vagus* 36-2, 11; 42-7; 43-9; **44**-10, 12; 55-11, 12; 57-1, 11; 102-7; 114-4; 115-5, 7, 11; **116**-1, 3, 5, 7, 9, 11; 125-12; 181-12; **232**-7; 239-12; 241-3; 247-7; 272-5; **350**-4; **351**-5; **352**-2, 12; **353**-12; **354**-1, 10, 11
– –, *chordae esophageae* 184-4
– –, *fila radicularis* 332-3; 9; 337-9
– – *ganglion inferius* 110-9; **115**-2, 10; 116-11; 350-3; 351-3
– – – *superius* 110-9; 115-11; 336-4
– – *nucleus dorsalis* 229-8; 230-5; 332-1; 336-1, 10; 337-12; 338-2
– – *plexus esophageus truncus vagalis* 352-4; 353-3; 354-3, 8
– – *ramus auricularis* 93-7, 11; 95-7; 98-9; 99-9; 100-9; 101-9; **102**-10; **115**-10; 116-11
– – *r. bronchialis* 55-1; 352-3, 4; 353-2; 354-1, 10
– – *ramus cardiacus* 44-10; 57-1; 115-7, 8; 116-4; 350-4; 351-10; 352-1
– – *r. esophageus* 55-2; 353-1
– – *r. pharyngeal* 115-10
– – *r. trachealis* 352-3
– *vestibulocochlearis* 110-10; 114-4; **232**-4; 241-3; 247-8; 272-4; 290-8; 335-4, 8; **411**-7; 439-8
– –, *pars cochlearis* 410-5; 411-6; **412**-9; **413**-8; 439-8; 448-9
– –, *pars vestibularis* 411-7; **412**-8; **413**-8; 439-7
– *zygomaticus* 92-2; **95**-2; 98-1, 3; 99-1, 2; 106-4; 112-2; 113-5; 350-9; 351-10
– – *ramus communicans* 113-2, 6; 350-10
**Network** – see **Anastomoses of arteries**
**Neurohypophysis** 226
**Neuron,** primary motor 315

**Nipple** (breast) 168, 471-474
**Nodulus** vermis 274-6; 292-1; 293-5; 294-3; 295-7
***Nodus lymphaticus,* or *Nodi lymphatici,*** or **Node, Nodes**
*Nodus fasciculi atrioventricularis* 12; 32-1
– *lymphatici apicales* 169-2
– – *axillaris* 168-2; 169-4
– – *bronchopulmonales* 34-3; 35-9; 166-3, 9
– – *buccalis* 165-9
– – *buccinatores* 163-1
– – *centrales* 169-6
– – *cervicales profundi inferiores* 163; 164-4; 165-7, 8; 169-10
– – – – *superiores* 163-3; 164-3; 165-8; 169-12; 470-6
– – – – *supraclaviculares* 164-7
– – – *superficiales* 163-4, 9; 164; 165-4; 169-12
– – *conjunctivales* 363-10
– – *cubitales* 168-5
– – *gastrici* 125-12; 170-1
– – *iliacus externi* 125-8; 127-8; 170-8
– – – *internus* 127-9; 170-4; 171-10
– – *infraclaviculares* 169-8
– – *inguinales profundi* 127-8; 170-7; 171-3
– – – *superficiales* 50-7, 8; 170-4, 5; 173-2, 8
– – *jugulodigastricus* 165-2
– – *juguloomohyoideus* 165-8
*Nodi lymphatici lumbales* 123-2; 125-8; 127-2, 10; 170-3, 9; 171-1
– – *maxillares* 163-1
– – *mediastinales* 166-1, 4, 8, 10; 167-4
– – *mesentericus* 172-2, 8, 11
– – *obturatorius* 127-8; 171-8
– – *occipitales* 163-10; 165-3
– – *parasternalis* 50-2
– – *parotideus* 165-1
– – *pectorales* 50-10; 169-6
– – *popliteus* 174-1, 2
– – *preauriculares* 163-11
– – *rectalis* 171-3, 4
– – *retroauriculares* 163-10; 165-2
*Nodi lymphatici sacrales* 171-11
– – *subinguinalis profundus* 170-6
– – *submandibulares* 163-3; 164-9; 165-8
– – *submentales* 163-2; 164-9; 165-9
– – *subscapulares* 169-5
– – *supraclavicularis* 169-1
– – *supramandibulares* 163-2
– – *suprarenales* 170-10
– – *tibialis anterior* 175-10
– – *tracheales* 166-12; 167-10
– – *tracheobronchialis, superior* 35-2; 166-2, 9; 167-1, 3, 9
– *sinoatrialis* 12
**Notch** – see ***Incisura***
–, cerebellar anterior 292-12
–, – posterior 292-6; 293-6; 294-6; 296-6
–, interarytenoid 117-9
–, intertragic 458-7; 459-4; 460-6
**Notch,** tympanic 450-1; 451-12
***Nucleus*** or ***Nuclei***
*Nucleus accessorius (autonomicus)* (Ed.-Westphal) 229-11; 230-1; 326-2
– *ambiguus* **229**-7; 230-6; **331**-1; 332-4; 336-2, 9, 10; **337**-3; 339-3; 340-9
– *anterior thalami* 283-2
– *arcuatus* 331-7; 332-5; 338-7
– *basalis tractus optici* 301 b
– *caudalis centralis* 229-12; 230-1
– *caudatus* 219-10; 222; 224-2; 225-1; **259**-8, 10; 260-11; 262-10; 265-2; **271**-8; 283-2
– –, *caput* **259**-10; 260-1; 261-1; 262-11; 265-11; **271**-1; 276-11; 278-1; 279-10; **280**-1, 11; 281-1, 11; 285-2; 286-10; 287-2
– –, *cauda* **276**-9; 278-3; 279-3; **280**-3; 281-4
– –, *corpus* 259-8; 288-2
– *cochlearis, dorsalis* 229-3; 304; 332-2; 334-9
– –, *ventralis* 229-3; 331-9; 334-8; 335-3
– *colliculi inferioris* 304; 325-12
– *corporis geniculati lateralis* 278-3; 281-5; 284-9
– – *mamillaris* 223-8; 279-8; 283-5; 288-6

*Nucleus corporis trapezoidei, dorsalis* 333-8
– – –, *ventralis* 330-9
– *cuneatus* 336-10; 337-10; 338-11; 339-10; 341-10
– *dentatus* **295**-2; **296**-2; 333-1; 334-2; 335-10; 343
– *dorsalis* 192-2
– –, *nervi vagi* **229**-8; **230**-5; **332**-1; 336-1, 10; 337-12; 338-2
– *dorsolateralis* 229-11; 230-12; 326-2
– *dorsomedialis (hypothalamus)* 226-1
– *emboliformis* 296-8; 334-1
– *fastigii* 296-1; 335-12
– *globosus* 296-7; 335-1
– gracilis 231-6; 338-11; 339-11; 341-10; 342-11
– –, tubercle of 289-5; 290-5; 338-1
– *hypothalamicus, lateralis* 224-4
– – *posterior* 223-6; 225-6
– of hypothalamus 223–226
– *infundibularis* 226-5
– *intercalatus* 225-5; 332-12
– *interpeduncularis* 301 b; 324-4
– *lateralis thalami* 283-2
– *lemnisci lateralis* 328-2; 329-11
– *lentiformis* 278-9; **279**-2; **280**-10; 281-1; 284-11; 285-2; 286-10; 287-8; **288**-3; 321; 322
– *lentis* 380-1
– *mamillaris (parvi cellularis)* 225-8
– – *(magni cellularis)* 225-7
– *mediales thalami* 283-3; 300-5
– *motorius nervi trigeminis* 229-10; 230-2; 328-1
– *nervus abducentis* 229-9; 230-3; 318; 330-1; 333-8
– – *cranialium* **229**–231
– – *facialis* 229-9; 230-3; 330-10; 335-2, 7
– – *hypoglossi* 229-6; 230-5; 336-10
– – *oculomotorii* 301 b; **302**; 324-2
– – *trochlearis* 229-11; 230-1; 302; 325-2; 327-1
– *olivaris* 279-7; **331**-8; **332**-3, 8; 334-7; 335-7; 336-8; **337**-8; 341-3
*Nucleus olivaris accessorius dorsalis* 332-3
– – – *medialis* 332-5; 337-5; 338-4
– *paramedianus* 225-2
– *paraventricularis* 223-3; 224-6; 226-1
– *pontis* 327-3; 328-8; 329-4; 330-4; 333-5
– *premamillaris* 226-2
– *preopticus* 223-1
– *ruber* (red) 273-1; 281-5; 301 b; 324-5; 326-3; 343
– *salivatorius inferior* 229-8; 230-4; 337-9
– – *superior* 229-9; 230-4
– *sensorius superior nervi trigemini* 229-2; 231-2; 328-1
– of spinal tract 337-9
– *spinalis nervus accessorii* 229-7; 230-7; 339-2; 340-2
– *subthalamicus* 225-3; 279-1; 281-4
– *supraopticus* 223-2; 224-6, 10; 226-10
– *tegmenti* 329-2
– *thalami* 224-2; 225-2; 278-8; 283-2, 3, 8
– *tractus mesencephalici nervus trigeminus* 229-1; 231-2; 326-10
– – *solitarii* (VII) 229-2; 231-2; 332-2; 334-9; 336-10; 337-1
– – – IX, X 229-2, 5; 231-3, 5
– – *spinalis nervus trigeminus* 229-4; 231-4; 330-10; **331**-2, 9; 332-2; 333-2; 334-8; 335-1; 336-2; 337-9; **338**-3, 11; 339-10; **340**-2, 10; 341-2; 342-2
– of trapezoid body 330-9
– *tuberales* 223-7; 224-6, 7; 226-4
– *tuberomamillaris* 226-2
– *ventromedialis* 226-11; 229-11; 230-12
– *vestibularis inferior* 229-4
– – *lateralis* 229-3; 331-2, 10; 335-2
– – *medialis* 229-2; 331-1; 332-11; 333-9; 334-3; 335-2
– – *superior* 229-3; 330-11; 335-2, 9

## O

**Obex** 182-1; 248-8; 289-7
**Oblique** abdominal muscle, external 50-2; 53-5, 8; 59-10; 60-7; 148-1

**Oblique** arytenoid muscle 116-3
– muscle, inferior 106-4; 364; 366; 393-5; 394-5; 395-8; 396-8; **397**-5, 7; 398-4; 399-10; 400-4; 403-6; 406-7; 407-8; 408-7
– –, superior 103-9; 104-11; 105-8, 11; 106-7, 12; 364; 366; **396**-1; **401**-6, 12; 403-1, 6; 404-1; 405-10
– vein of left atrium 18-4
**Obliquus** auriculae muscle 464-12
– capitis inferior muscle 52-9
– – superior muscle 52-9
**Obturator** artery 7-2; 127-8; 128-11; **132**-7, 9; 143-1; 144-1; 171-9
– fossa 127-4
– lymph nodes 127-8; 171-8
– muscle, externus 148-6
– –, internus 132-6; 147-1; 148-5
– nerve **119**-9; 126-3; **132**-9; 143-1, 12; **144**-1, 12; 171-9; 348-7
– –, cutaneous branches 138-4; **140**-8; 143-2; **144**-1, 12
– vein 128-11; 171-9
**Occipital** artery 39-3; 40-3; 41-3; 43-2, 3; **44**-12; 51-1, 10, 11; 52-2, 10; 53-12; **94**-3, 5; 95-9; 99-7, 9; 100-8; 101-8; 102-9; 116-1
– –, auricular branch 39-2; 94-3
– –, mastoid branch 43-3; 44-1; 51-10; **52**-10; 94-3
– –, meningeal branch 232-5
– –, occipital branch 51-10; 52-9; 94-3; 98-10; 232-5
– bone 115-12; 180-11; 236-2; 448-8
– condyle 455-4
– diploic vein 196-8
– gyrus 249-4; 253-7; 255-11; 259-5; 280-5; 285-5
– lobe, cerebrum 251-3; 256-9; 257-8; 258-7
– lymph nodes 163-10; 165-3
– nerve, greater 39-3; **40**-3; **41**-3; **44**-2; 51-1, 11; 52-1; 53-12; 95-9, 11; 98-9; 99-9
**Occipital** nerve, lesser 37-11; **39**-3; **40**-3; **41**-2; **42**-1, **44**-1; 51-1, 10; 53-11; 95-8; 98-8; 99-8
– pole (cerebrum) 206; 247-5; 248-9; 249-4; 253-7; 255-6
– protuberance, external 52-12
– sinus 197-4; 233-3, 4
– sulcus, transverse 249-4
– vein 39-3; 40-3; 41-3; 51-1, 11; 52-1; 53-12; 95-9
Occipitofrontalis muscle, 39-2; 51-1; 52-1; 95-9; **98**-2, 9; **99**-1; 100-1
Occipitotemporal gyrus, lateral (fusiform) 209; 210; 220-8; 247-9; 251-5; 255-4
– –, medial (lingual) 209; 210; 248-9; 251-5; 255-5
– sulcus 251-5; 255-7
**Ocular** axis 356-7 C

## OCULAR MUSCLES **103–106**; **364–366**; **395–408**

**Oculomotor** centers 301
– nerve **103**-7; **104**-6; **105**-7; **106**-6; 114-2; 223-8; **232**-2; 236-8; 238-10; 239-10; **241**-2; 242-7; **247**-10; 248-6; 272-3 C; 274-9; 277-8; 321; 322; **324**-6; 350-1; 351-1, 12; 367; 384-11; 405-4
– nucleus 302; 324-2
– –, accessory (autonomic) nucleus (Ed.-Westphal) 229-11; 230-1; 326-2
– –, central caudal nucleus 229-12; 230-1
– –, dorsolateral nucleus 229-11; 326-2
– –, ventromedial nucleus 229-11
– rootlets 324-5
**Olecranon** 69-5; 70-1; 73-6; 78-10
**Olfactory** bulb 197-9; 241-1; 247-1; 257-4; 272-12; 305; 323-9; 367
– gyrus 305
– nerve 107-1; 108-12; 197-9
– pathway 306
– stria 247-2; 272-1
– sulcus 247-12; 255-1; 272-12; 285-6

**Olfactory** tract 241-1; 247-1; 257-4; 272-12; 285-7; 323-9; 343; 367
– trigone 255-1; 272-11; 273-5; 305
**Olivary** nucleus **279**-7; **331**-8; **332**-3, 8; 334-7; 335-7; 336-8; 337-4; 341-3
– – dorsal accessory 332-3
– –, inferior 332-8; 337-8
– – medial accessory 332-5; 337-5; 338-4
**Olive** 247-5; 272-7; 290-8
**Olivocerebellar** fibers 336-5
– tract 331-3; 332-9; 336-8; 337-9
– –, cells of 336-8
**Olivospinal** tract 336-5; 340-4; 341-8; 342-8
**Omental** artery 120-4
– vein 120-4
*Omentum majus* 120-6
**Omohyoid** muscle 43-4; 45-4; 46-10; 61-1
– –, inferior belly 40-4; 41-4; 42-4; 45-8; 60-1; 165-6
– –, superior belly 41-9; 43-9; 44-11; 165-8
*Operculum frontoparietale* 249-12
**Ophthalmic** artery 103-8, 9; 104-6, 12; **105**-7; 106-7, 8; 200-2; 232-10; **236**-1; 243
– –, sympathetic plexus on 104-5
– nerve 92-12; **103**-7, 8; **104**-5; **105**-7; **106**-6; 110-12; 111-12; 112-1; 114-1; 232-1; 238-9; 247-2; 350-12; 351-10, 12
– vein, superior 232-10
**Opponens** pollicis muscle 88-8; 89-8
**Optic** canal 103-8; 106-7; 402-10
– chiasma 218-9; 226-9; 241-1; **247**-1; **248**-5; 255-12; 272-11; **273**-6; 274-9; 277-2; 286-6; 320–322; 343; 367; 384-12; 385-7; 401-6
– disc 356-7 C; 358-6; 360-2; 373-2; 384-3; 403-1
– nerve **103**-8; **104**-7; **105**-2, 7; **106**-1, 7; 110-12; 112-1; 113-3; 223-9; 226-9; 232-1, 11; 233; 236-10; 238-1; 239-12; **241**-1; 242-8; **247**-1; 248-4, 5; 257-4; **273**-7; 275-1; 350-12; 351-12; **362**; **367**; **368**-7; **369**-6; 384-11; 385-4, 8; 401-6; 402-1; 404-4; 405-9; 406-2; 407-7
**Optic** nerve, external sheath **106**-1; **356**-7; **362**-1; 368-6; 384-1; 402-2; 404-5; 405-9; 406-2
– –, internal sheath **362**-2
– –, intervaginal space 356-6; 362-2; 402-5; 403-11; 406-5
– pathways 301 a, b; 321; 322
– radiations 282; 301 a; 321; 322
– recess (third ventricle) 218-9; 233-10; 226-10; 248-5; 263-9; 274-9; 276-1
– tract 222-4; 224-8; 225-9; 272-10; **273**-8; 279-4; 283-8; 286-5; 287-6; 288-6; **290**-10; 320–322; **385**-5, 8
**Ora** serrata 356-2 C; 359-2 C; 368-2; 372-3, 9; 376-9; 382-11; 402-7
**Orbicularis** oculi muscle 95-3, 4; 100-1, 5; 392-1; 393-5; 394-5
– – –, palpebral portion 363-2, 6
– oris muscle 99-4
**Orbiculus** ciliaris 356-10 C; 372-1; 376-8; 377-8; 382-7; 383-2; 384-8
**Orbit**, adipose body of 103-11; 391-8; 410-12; 402-2; 403-2; 404-3; 406-5; 407-8; 408-2
**Orbital** cavity, roof of 263-9
– fissure, inferior 113-4; 395-6; 396-4; 404-8
– –, superior 405-2
– gyri of frontal lobe 247-11; 255-11; 285-5
– muscle, (smooth) superior orbital fissure 405-1
– septum 350-10; 363-12; 391-1, 8, 12; 406-11
– sulci 247-11; 255-1
*Organum spirale* 410-8
**Orifice**, urethral external 134-5
*Os coccygeum* 128-4; 181-6
– *frontale* 113-12; 395-11; 396-12; 404-12; 405-1
– –, *pars orbitalis* 280-1; 403-12
– –, *processus zygomaticus* 397-1
– *hyoideum* 102-6; 118-7

*Os hyoideum, cornu majus* 107-7; 117-10
– *metacarpale* 89-3
– *nasale* 391-3
– *occipitale* 115-12; 180-11; 236-2; 448-8
– *parietale* 237-10
– *petrosum* 263-6 C
– *pisiforme* 87-5; 90-8
– *pubis* 128-10; 129-8
– *sacrum* 181-5
– *sphenoidale* 107-11; 395-3; 396-3; 456-3
– *temporale* 110-10; 115-1; 236-5; 439-1, 10; 448-1; 455-3; 456-9; 457-9
– –, *pars petrosa* 236-5; 264-8; 448-10; 455-3; 457-9
– –, *processus mastoideus* 114-8
– *zygomaticum* 100-1; 101-1; 102-2; 391-7; 397-5; 403-8; 408-7
*Osseous* labyrinth 411
– spiral lamina 410-3; 413-12; 416-7, 8; 417-2, 4; 423-2, 4; 424-10; 426-2

## OSSICLES (Auditory) 430–437

*Ossis palatini lamina horizontalis* 455-2
– *sphenoidalis ala major* 113-2; 384-2, 8; 385-2, 9; 401-4; 402-3; 404-8, 9; 405-3; 455-11
*Ostium atrioventriculare* 24-1; 25-7; 26-1; 28-2, 9
– *pharyngeum tubae auditivae* 107-12; 116-12
– *sinus coronarii* 20-5; 26-10
– *tympanicum, tubae auditivae* 428-2; 429-2; 438-4; 439-9; 441-10; **442**-8; **443**-5; 444-2; 451-7
– *urethrae externum* 134-5
**Otic** ganglion 92-2; 110-9; 350-1; 351-1
**Ovarian** artery 124-1; 125-3, 9; 129-7, 11; 131-3, 9; 171-11
– ligament 131-10
– vein 125-3, 9; 129-7, 11; 171-11
*Ovarium* 125-8; 129-8, 11; 131-1, 9
**Ovary** 129-8, 11; 131-1, 9
– vessels of 129-7, 11

# P

*Pachymenix* - - - - see *Dura mater*
**Pacinian** corpuscles (lamellated) 178
**Palate,** soft (uvula) 107-9; 108-7; 109-8
**Palatine** artery, ascending 94-5; 102-8; 108-7; 109-8; 115-3; 117-1, 4
– –, –, tonsillar branch 108-7; 117-1, 4
– –, descending 94-8; 109-2
– –, greater 108-5; 109-6
– –, lesser 108-11; 109-8
– bone, horizontal lamina 455-2
– nerves 92-3; 108-6; 109-3, 7; **110**-3; 350-9; 351-10
– tonsil 108-6; 116-10; 117-1
**Palatoglossus** muscle 107-8; 118-1
**Palatopharyngeal** arch 116-10
**Palatopharyngeus** muscle 116-1
**Palmar** aponeurosis 82-7
– arch, deep 7-9; 88-8; 90-8
– –, superficial 7-9; 87-8; 90-4
– digital nerves 82-3; 84-8; 85-7; **87**-1; 3, 4, 8, 11; 88-12; 90-11, 12; 178
– interosseous muscle 88-2
– lines 90-2
– metacarpal artery 88-3; 90-3, 8
Palmaris muscle, brevis 82-4
– –, longus 75-9; 76-6; 77-6
*Palpebra inferior* 113-8; 384-8; **386**-7; 387-6; 393-4; **394**-4
– *superior* 113-9; 386-1; 387-10; **390**-11; 393-1; **394**-1
**Palpebral** arch 95-2, 3
– artery, medial 98-2
– commissure 386-7; 407-9
– ligament, medial 391-2
– raphe, lateral 391-9
– sulcus 386-5, 11; 387-1, 5
**Pampiniform** plexus (of veins) 130-9
**Pancreas** 120-4; 121-3, 8; 123-1
**Pancreaticoduodenal** artery, inferior 121-2; 123-12
– –, superior 121-9
– veins 124-9
**Papilla,** hair 468-7

**Papilla** *lacrimalis* 388-2, 8; 392-3, 12; 393-1, 4; 407-3, 4
– *mammae* 168-9; 471-8; 472-8; 473-10; 474-8
– *nervi optici* - - - - see *Discus n. optici*
– *pili* 468-7
– *vallatae* 108-6; 116-2; 117-12
**Papillary** muscle 26-8; 33-4
– –, anterior 23-3; 24-8; **25**-8; 28-4; 29-3; 31-2, 10
– –, posterior 23-5; 24-4; **27**-4, 8; 31-5, 7
– –, small **25**-7; 26-5; 28-8; 29-7
**Paracentral** lobule 210-12; 248-12; 251-12
**Parahippocampal** gyrus 209; 210; 220-4; **247**-9; **251**-7; 255-4; 261-9; 266-2; 267-3; 268-4; 269-3; 270-1, 12; 288-7; 323-5
– –, uncus of 247-10; 251-7; 255-2; 257-5; 261-10; 266-1; 268-2
**Paramedian** nucleus 225-2
**Parasternal** lymph node 50-2
**Parasympathetic** outflow 345
**Paraterminal** gyrus 210; 223-10; 248-4; 274-10; 286-7
**Parathyroid** gland 116-4
**Paraumbilical** vein 50-8; 124-8
**Paraventricular** nucleus 223-3; 224-6; 226-1
*Paries membranaceus bronchus principalis* 352-4
– – *tracheae* 35-1; 116-5; 167-1
– *pharyngis* 107-8
**Parietal** bone 237-10
– lobe (cerebrum) 208; 256-12; 258-9; 279-2
– lobule 208; 249-3; 253-7
– pericardium 17-2, 6, 9; 25-11
– pleura 57-7
**Parietooccipital** sulcus 207–209; 242-2; 248-10; 249-3; **251**-2; **253**-6; 255-6; 257-10; 320-322
**Parolfactory** sulcus 248-4; 251-8; 274-10
**Parotid** duct 95-4
– fascia 95-7
– gland 39-12; 45-1; 46-1; 95-7, 8
– lymph node 165-1
*Pars ampullaris tubae uterinae* 125-8
– *basilaris pontis* 329-4; 330-4
– *centralis ventriculus lateralis* 219-2; 235-2; 259-10; 260-2; 262-2; 265-9; 279-11; 283-2
– *ciliaris retinae* 356-2; 368-1, 10; 372-6; 376-9; 377-1; 402-4
– *diaphragmatica pericardii (planum inclinatum)* 36-6; 184-5
– *dorsalis pontis* 329-2; 330-2
– *intermedia hypophyseos* 275-9
– *membranacea septi interatrialis* 27-1
– – – *interventricularis* 23-9; 32-1; 33-1
– *muscularis septi interventricularis* 31-1; 33-8
– *occipitalis (radiationis corporis callosi)* 321; 322
– *olfactoria (commissurae anterioris)* 323-9
– *optica retina* 356-3 C, 8; 368-4; 372-3, 12; 373-1; 376-9; 384-8; 402-4
– *petrosa ossis temporalis* 236-5; 264-8; 448-10; **455**-3; 457-9
– – – –, *processus mastoideus* 114-8
– *squamosa ossis temporalis* 451-1; 458-2
– *sternocostalis pericardii* 36-4
– *triangularis (gyri frontalis inferioris)* 249-9
– *tympanica ossis temporalis* 458-3
**Parumbilical** veins 50-8; 124-8
**Patella** 139-9, 11
**Patellar** ligament 142-6; 153-1
**Pathways,** auditory 304
–, optic 301a, b
–, visual 301a, b
**Pectinate** ligament (of iris) **356**-10; 369-1; 370-3; 371-4; 383-3
– muscles 27-10; 28-1, 9
**Pectineus** muscle 142-1; 143-1
**Pectoral** fascia 473-6
– lymph nodes 50-10; 169-6
– nerve, lateral 44-6

## PECTORAL REGION 50; 58–60

**Pectoralis** muscle, major 41-7; 42-6; 43-7; **44**-8; 45-5, 7; 46-5; 57-10; 59-12; **60**-3, 11; 61-3; 71-2; 72-1

**Pectoralis** muscle, minor 42-4; 43-6; **44**-7; 57-11; **60**-4; 61-2
**Pedunculus** cerebellaris, inferior (restiform body) 209-8; **289**-8; 290-8; 330-10; 331-10; **332**-10; 337-10; 343
– –, *medius* (brachium pontis) 276-4; 279-8; **289**-9; 290-2; 293-2; 330-8; 327-2; 328-9; 333-2; 335-10
– –, *superior* (brachium conjunctivum) 276-4; **289**-9, 10; 290-2; 293-2; 294-2; 295-1; 296-10; 327-2; 328-11; 329-11; 333-1; 334-2; 335-2
– *cerebri* 242-7; 247-10; **272**-8; 273-9; **274**-8; 276-9; 283-8; 290-10; **324**-7; **325**-4; 343; 384-12
– *corporis mamillaris* 272-11
– *flocculi* 276-4; 293-2; 294-10


## PELVIC REGION 127–134


**Penis,** bulb of, artery to 133-5
– corpus cavernosum 128-6
– – spongiosum 133-6
–, dorsal artery of 128-8; 130-11
–, – nerve of 130-11; 133-4
–, fundiform ligament of 130-12
–, superficial fascia of 130-8
**Perforated** substance 241-9; 247-10; 248-6; **255**-11; **272**-2, 8; 273-4, 8; 305; 323; 325
**Perforating** artery 7-3, 4; 144-2, 9; 145-8, 10; 147-3, 4, 5; 154-1
**Pericardiacophrenic** artery 36-2; 54-11; **57**-3; 166-2; 148-7
– vein 36-2; 57-3, 9; 166-2; 184-7
**Pericardial** recess 17-2, 10
– sinus transverse 18-10; 19-10; 36-10
**Pericardium** 18-4, 10; 19-1, 10, 11; 25-1; 34-12; 35-3, 7; **36**-4, 6; 57-6; 167-8; 353-3
–, diaphragmatic portion of 184-5
–, oblique sinus of 18-C; 36-3
– *parietale* 17-2, 6, 9; 25-11; 36-4
– *viscerale* 25-11
**Perichorioidal** space (eye) 356-2, 5, 8
**Perineal** artery 133-8
– nerves 133-1; 134-1, 9


## PERINEUM 127–134


**Periorbita** 350-10, 11; 395-12; 396-7; 403-9; 405-8
**Peritoneum** 125-10; 127-2, 5
**Peroneal** artery (fibular) 137-5; 151-2; 152-1; 153-7; 154-6; 157-11
– nerve common (fibular) 119-8; 145-8; 146-5; **147**-5; **149**-2, 5; 150-1; 151-1; **153**-11
– –, deep (fibular) 153-11; 155-4; 157-11
– –, superficial (fibular) 139-7; 153-7, 11; 155-11
**Peroneus** muscle, brevis 150-6; 152-5; 153-7
– –, longus 150-5; 152-5; 153-11
– tertius muscle, tendon of 153-7
**Pes** hippocampi 220-8; **261**-8; 266-8; 267-8; **268**-12; 269-5, 6; 272-2; 278-4; 279-8; 288-8; 323-6
**Petrooccipital** fissure 236-2
**Petrosal** bone 263-6 C
– nerve, deep 92-12; 109-10; 112-1
– –, greater 92-11; 93-2; 109-9; 110-10; **112**-10; 114-1; **232**-2; 350-1; 351-1; **438**-2; 439-9; 443-2; 444-1; 445-1
– –, lesser 92-10; 93-2; 110-10; **112**-10; 232-3; **350**-1; **351**-2
– sinus superior 232-4, 8; 233-6
**Pharyngeal** artery, ascending 94-5; **115**-2, 3, 10
– constrictor muscle, inferior 115-8; 352-1
– – –, middle 107-7; 115-9
– – –, superior 115-12; 116-1
– plexus (of nerves) 115-8
– recess 457-7
– tonsil (adenoids) 116-12
– vein 115-12
– wall 107-8
**Pharyngobasilaris** fascia 116-12
**Pharyngoepiglottic** fold 116-10
– muscle 116-2
**Pharynx,** lumen 108-8

**Phrenic** artery, inferior 120-2; 121-1; 125-1; 10, 12; **126**-11; 170-10
– nerve 36-2; 37-9; **42**-8; 43-8; **44**-2; 46-9; 55-1; **57**-1, 3, 4, 5, 8, 11; 58-4, 10; 60-12; 125-10; 166-2, 10; 184-7; 348-10; 352-12; 353-4
– –, accessory 58-9; 169-10
– veins, left inferior 124-1; 125-1, 10; 170-10
**Pia** mater 185-10; 191-6; 235-9; 239-5; 283-12; 284-3
– –, *spinalis* 185-10; 186-4
**Pigmented** layer of retina 356-2, 2 C, 4, 8
**Pineal** body 223-2; 242-2; 248-12; **261**-5; 271-5; 274-2; **276**-10; 281-7
– recess 248-1; 263-3; 274-2; 289-12; 290-1
**Piriform** recess 116-9; 117-8
**Piriformis** muscle 140-2; 147-1; 148-2
**Pisiform** bone 87-5; 90-8
**Pituitary** gland, anterior lobe 248-5; 274-9; 275-9
– –, hypophysis 226; 232-10; 238-2; 239-11; 247-11; 248-6
– –, intermediate part 275-9
– –, posterior lobe 248-6; 274-8; 275-10
– tracts 226
**Plantar** aponeurosis 158-1
– arch 160-3
– artery, lateral 159-1; 160-1
– metatarsal artery 158-6; 159-6; 160-5
– nerve, lateral 158-11; 159-2, 11; 160-1, 3, 12
– –, medial 7-5; 158-11; 159-11; 160-9, 12
**Plantaris** muscle 150-10; 151-1; 152-1; 154-3
**Platysma** 39-9; 40-11; 43-11; 95-5; 98-7
*Pleura costalis* 184-4
– *diaphragmatica* 36-8; 57-7; 184-8
– *mediastinalis* 36-3, 10
– *parietalis* 57-7; 58-7
*Plexus chorioideus (ventr. lateralis)* 219-10; 220-1; 235-2; 259-8; **260**-1, 8; 262-3; **265**-3; 272-2; 278-4; 280-8; 283-9; 284-1; 288-6, 11
*Plexus chorioideus (vent. quartus)* 197-5; 223-8; 235-8; 241-5; 274-6; **276**-5; **279**-6; 295-2; 334-1, 8; 336-12
– – *(vent. tertius)* 197-1; **219**-11; 223-1; 225-9; **274**-1; **283**-9; 288-10

## PLEXUS of NERVES:

**Aortic** 36-2; 184-4; 348-3, 9; 353-6; 354-1; 355-2
**Brachial** 37-4; 41-6; 42-4; 43-5; 44-2, 5; 46-3; **58**-2; 59-2; 60-1, 12; 165-6; 166-2; 348-10; 352-11
–, lateral cord 61-3; 71-12
–, medial cord 61-2; 71-12
**Cardiac** 57-9; 354-1
**Carotid** 116-3
–, communis 115-5
–, internal 93-3, 4; 109-10; 112-11; 232-2; 438-3
**Celiac** 125-1; 355-10
**Cervical** 37-2; 41-3
**Coccygeal** **119**-5; 355-6
**Dental,** inferior 100-5; 111-6
–, superior 111-12; 112-4; 350-9; 351-9
**Esophageal** (n. vagus) 353-3; 354-3
**Gastric** 125-1; 354-6
**Hypogastric**, superior 125-4; 127-9
**Iliac** 355-8
**Lumbar** 119-1; 126-2; 355
**Lumbosacral** 119-4
**Mesenteric,** inferior 125-3; 355-9
–, superior 125-2; 355-10
**Pharyngeal** 115-8
**Pudendal** **119**-5; 132-5; 355-5
**Pulmonary** 352-4
**Renal** 125-2; 355-10
**Sacral** **119**-4; 132-2; 355-5
**Subclavian** 348-2
**Plexus** of superior thyroid artery 348-1
**Tympanic** 112; 350-2; 444-6; 445-5
**Vertebral** 348-1

## PLEXUS of VEINS:

**Basilar** 232-8
**Carotid,** internal 456-9; 457-9
**Pampiniform** 130-9
**Pterygoid** 100-11
**Rectal** 124-5
**Suboccipital** 52-2
**Thyreoideus impar** 46-3
**Uterine** 129
**Vaginal** 129-5
**Vertebral,** internal 184-2; 186-3, 8
**Vesical** 128-8

## Plica or Plicae

– *aryepiglottica* 116-10
– *ciliares* 376-1; 377-10; 382-6
– *fimbriata* 118-12
– *iridis* 371-11; 382-4
– *mallearis, anterior* **438**-5; **439**-12; 440-11; 441-11; 442-11; 449-12; 450-2; 451-9; 454-1
– –, *posterior* **438**-11; 440-5; 441-4; 442-5; 451-3; 454-10
– *mesenterica inferior* 127-2
– *pharyngoepiglottica* 116-10
– *rectouterina* 129-2; 171-4
– *salpingopharyngea* 116-10
– *semilunaris conjunctiva* 388-5; 392-12; 393-2
– *umbilicalis, lateralis* 127-4; 128-10
– –, *medialis* 127-5; 128-10
– –, *mediana* 127-5
– *ureteris* 127-3
*Polus frontalis* 206; **247**-12; **248**-4; 249-9; 251-8; **253**-12; 255-12; 367
– *lentis* 356-6, 12, 12 C; 370-11; 379-6, 11; 383-2, 8
– *occipitalis* 206; **247**-3, 5; 248-9; 249-4; **253**-7; 255-6
– *temporalis* 206; 247-11; 249-8; 251-8; 255-10; 266-12; 367
**Pons** 183-12; 223-7; 247-10; 248-6; **272**-8; 274-8; 277-3; 290-9; 294-1; 321; 322; 325-5; **329**-2, 4; **330**-2, 4
–, basilar portion 329-4; 330-4
**Pons**, basilar sulcus of 272-8; 330-5
–, dorsal portion 329-2; 330-2
–, longitudinal fasciculi of 274-7; 279-5; 320; 329-8; 330-7
**Pontine** cistern 197-7
– fibers, transverse 272-8; 320; 325-5; 328-8; **329**-3, 7; **330**-8; 333-9
– nucleus 327-3; 328-8; **329**-4; **330**-4; 333-5
**Popliteal** artery 7-7; 137-2, 4; **145**-5; 146-7; 147-7; **149**-2; 151-11, 12; 152-12; **154**-3; 174-8
– lymph nodes 174-1, 2
– vein 145-5; 146-7; 147-7; **149**-3; 150-1; 151-1; 174-2
**Popliteus** muscle 152-11
*Pori sudoriferi* 475-2

## PORTAL VEIN (circulation) 2

**Portal** vein 4-10; 5-2; 120-9; 121-9; 124-10
*Portio major* - - - - see *Radix sensoria*
– *minor* - - - - see *Radix motoria*
*Porus acusticus, externus* 448-1
– –, *internus* 411-5
**Postcentral** gyrus 207; 208; **249**-1; 253-4
– sulcus 208; **249**-2; 253-4
**Posteriolateral** sulcus of spinal cord 182-9; 187-11; **189**-1; 191-10; 289-7; 290-7
**Posterior** auricular artery 39-2; 42-1; 51-1; 94-4, 5; 95-7; 98-9; **99**-8; 100-8; 101-9; 102-9
– – nerve (facial nerve) 39-1; 42-1; 93-8; **95**-8; **96**; 99-9; 100-9; **102**-9
– – vein 39-1; 40-1; 46-10; 51-11; 52-1
– cerebellar notch 292-12; 293-6; 294-6; 296-6
– cerebral artery 200-3; **241**-2, 8; **242**-3, 7; 284-8
– ciliary artery 358-6; 359-3, 6; 369-7, 9
– circumflex humeral artery 53-2; 59-1; 61-3; **62**-3; 74-1, 11; 169-3
– – – vein 53-2; 59-1; 69-1
– commissure 223-2; 248-1; 274-1
– communicating artery 200-2; 241-2; 242-8

**Posterior** cord of brachial plexus 61-7; 71-11
– cricoarytenoid muscle 116-3; 117-4
– ethmoidal artery 105-8; 106-9; 107-12; 108-12
– funiculus 191-1; 192-12; 313; 316; 341-1
– horn, apex 191-2; 192-2
– inferior cerebellar artery 200-4; 241-6; 242-6
– intercostal artery 55-2
– intermediate sulcus of spinal cord 191-11; 289-7; 290-5
– interosseus artery 77-4; 80-7, 8; 81-4
– limiting membrane (cornea) 356-12
– lobe, pituitary gland 226; 248-6
– longitudinal ligament 184-3; 186-6
– median sulcus 182-8; 187-12; 191-12; 194-12; 289-7; 338-12; 339-12
– mediastinal lymph nodes 167-4
– meningeal artery 115-1; 116-12
– palatine nerve - - - - see **Lesser** palatine nerve
– spinal artery 186-10; 200-4; 242-6
– superior alveolar artery 94-9; 101-4; 350-9
– – – nerve 351-9
– vein of left ventricle 18-8
**Preauricular** lymph nodes 163-11
**Precentral** gyrus 207; 208; 249-1; 253-2
– sulcus 249-1; 251-12; 253-2
**Precuneus** 210; 248-11; 251-1
**Premammillary** nuclei 226-2
**Preoptic** area 226-11
– nucleus 223-1
**Prepyloric** vein 124-10
**Primary** motor neuron - - - - see **Final common pathway**
**Princeps** pollicis artery 86-7; 88-10; 90-4
**Procerus** muscle 95-2
*Processus anterior (malleus)* 430-2; 431-8; 436-9; 451-10
– *articularis superior vertebrae* 184-11
– *ciliares* 368-10; 372-10; **376**-2; **377**-10; **382**-5, 12; 383-2; 384-8; 402-4
*Processus cochleariformis* 427-2; 428-2; 429-2; 442-10; 444-1; 445-3; 449-2
– *coracoideus* 61-2
– *coronoideus mandibulae* 100-12
– *frontalis maxillae* 391-4; 393-8; **394**-8
– *lateralis mallei* 430-8; 431-8; 432-5; 436-9; 450-2; 454-2
– *lenticularis incudis* **434**-6; 438-12; 439-3; **440**-6; 441-5; 442-7; 450-7
– *mastoideus* 99-8; 114-8; 115-10, 11; 116-1; 350-3; 427-9; **428**-7; 458-6
– *spinosus axis* 52-3
– *styloideus radius* 90-5
– – *temporal bone* 92-8; 115-10; 425-8; 428-5; 458-5
– – *ulnae* 90-7
**Profunda** brachii artery 7-11; 53-2; 71-9; 72-10; 73-3; 74-2
– – vein 53-2
**Prominence,** laryngeal (Adam's apple) 45-2; 46-9;
*Prominentia canalis facialis* 427-13; 428-13; 438-10; 443-11; 444-12; 447-10
– – *semicircularis lateralis* 428-11; 438-10; 443-10
– *mallearis* 454-2
– *spiralis* 410-9
**Promontory** (middle ear) 128-1; **428**-4; **429**-5; **443**-5; **444**-5; 445-4; **447**-1; 449-2; 450-5; 454-8
– sulcus 427-5; 428-4
**Pronator** quadratus muscle 77-5; 88-6
– teres muscle 75-10; 76-2, 10; 77-3; 78-5
**Proper** digital artery (foot) 156-6; 158-5, 6; 159-6
– – – (hand) 82-2; 84-6; 87-1, 11; 88-12; 89-1, 2; **90**-1, 3, 4, 9, 11, 12
– – nerve, plantar 156-6; 158-5, 8; 159-6
– – –, palmar 89-1; 90-1
– hepatic artery 4-10; 120-12
Prostate 128-5
*Protuberantia laryngica* 45-2; 46-9
– *occipitalis externa* 52-12

**Psoas** muscle, major 126-10; 127-2; 348-4
– –, minor 126-11
**Pterygoid** canal, artery of 109-9
– –, nerve of 92-1; **109**-9; 110-1; **112**-6; 350-1; 351-10
– muscle, lateral **101**-1; 102-1
– –, medial 100-7; **101**-7; 102-8; 109-8; 110-7; 112-7
– nerve, lateral 102-1
– –, medial 110-8
– venous plexus 100-11
**Pterygopalatine** fossa 112-6
– ganglion 92-2; 109-9; **110**-2; **112**-6; 350-1, 10; 351-10
– nerves 110-2; 112-2
**Pubic** bone 128-10; 129-8
– symphysis 124-7; 132-7
**Pudendal** artery, external 50-7; 130-2; 138-2
– –, internal **128**-5; **129**-5; **132**-5; 133-1, 5, 10; 134-1, 4, 10; 147-11; 148-7; 171-3
– –, –, inferior rectal artery 133-11
– –, –, posterior labial branches 134-8
– –, –, – scrotal branch 118-6
– nerve **132**-5; 133-1, 10; 134-1; 147-11
– plexus (of nerves) **119**-5; 132-5; 355-5
– vein, internal 124-5; **128**-5; **129**-5; 133-10; 134-1, 4, 10; 147-11; 148-7
– –, external 50-7
*Pulmo* 36-3, 10; 57-2, 4, 8, 9, 10; 352-5; 353-1
– *lobus inferior* 34-4, 8; 35-4, 8, 10
– – *medius* 34-10; 35-3
– – *superior* 34-2, 11; 35-2, 11
**Pulmonary** artery 3-1, 11; 17-1; **18**-2, 10; **19**-1, 10; 25-1, 12; 34-2, 3, 9, 10; 35-3, 9, 10; 36-2; 166-2, 9; 167-3, 9
– plexus (nerve) 352-4
– semilunar valves 20-10; 25-1, 10
– trunk, artery 5-3; 17-2, 10; 18-10; **19**-1; 20-12; **21**-1; 22-12; 25-12; 34-9; 36-2
**Pulmonary** veins 3-1, 10; 18-3, 9; 22-1, 10; 34-3, 9, 10; 35-2, 3, 9; **36**-3, 9; 166-2, 3, 9; **167**-4, 8, 9; 352-6; 353-2
*Pulvinar thalami* 222-3; **271**-4; 273-11; **276**-2; 290-1; 321; 322
**Punctum** lacrimale 388-2; 390-4; 392-3, 12; 393-1, 4
**Pupil** 358-12; 377-2; 386-2; 398-2
**Putamen** 224-3; 225-2
–, lentiform nucleus 222; 278-2; 279-8; **280**-9; 281-8; 282; 286-2; **287**-3; 288-6
**Pylorus** 354-6
**Pyramidal** decussation 183-11; 247-6; 272-6; **279**-6; 339-5; **340**-5; 342-6
– eminence 427-8; **428**-12; 443-7; **445**-9; **447**-8; 450-9
– tracts 299; 312
**Pyramidalis** muscle 50-4
**Pyramis** 247-6; 272-6; 290-7; 332-7; 337-6; **338**-5; 339-6
– vermis 274-5; 292-7; 294-6
– vestibuli (ear) 426-12

## Q

**Quadrangular** intermuscular space 74-1
– lobule 291-3
**Quadratus** femoris muscle 147-2; 148-7
– lumborum muscle 70-1; 127-11; 353-7; 355-2, 9
– plantae muscle 159-10; 160-2
**Quadrigeminal plate** - - - - - see **Tectal lamina**

## R

**Radial** artery 7-10; 68-5; **75**-1, 5; 76-1, 5; 77-5; 78-5; 79-8; **85**-10, 11; **86**-10; **87**-6; **88**-7; **89**-6, 7; **90**-5
– –, dorsal carpal branches 85-11; 86-9; 89-4
– –, palmar carpal branches 88-7

**Radial** artery, superficial palmar branches 75-6; 76-6; 77-5; 87-7; 88-7; 89-7; 90-5
– collateral artery 80-12; **81**-12
– nerve 37-8; 53-2; 61-6; 71-11; **72**-11; 73-2; **74**-2; 75-1; **76**-1; **77**-1; 78-3; **79**-1; 169-2
– –, deep branch 75-1; 76-1; 77-1; 79-3, 6; 80-9; 81-10
– –, superficial branch 68-5; 70-7; 75-1; 76-1, 5; 77-5; 79-9; 80-7; 81-7; **83**-10; 89-6
– recurrent artery 75-2; 76-1; 77-1; 79-7
*Radiatio corporis callosi* 279-11; 285-1; 287-2; 288-1; 321; 322
– *optica* 282; 301a; 321; 322
– *tegmenti* 326-2
**Radiations,** coronal 222
–, thalamic **222**; 321; 322
*Radii lentis* 378-2; 379-1; 381; 383-5
*Radix motoria (trigemini) (portis minor)* 110-11; 112-1; 247-2; 290-9; 350-1; 351-1
– *nervi oculomotorii* 324-5
– *partis vestibularis* 331-11; 332-10
– *sensoria ganglion trigeminale (portio major)* 110-11; 290-9
– *superior ansae cervicalis* 42-9
*Ramus alveolaris superioris anterior* 92-3; **111**-12; 112-4; 350-9; 351-9
– – – *medius* 92-3; **111**-12; 112-5
– – – *posterioris* 92-3; 102-2; **111**-12; 112-6; 350-8, 9; 351-9
– *auricularis* 116-11
– communicans 44-12; 47-5; 98-3; 152-5; 352-1, 11; 354-4; 355-1, 8
– of mandible 115-2
– *thyreohyoideus ansae cervicalis* 42-9
**Raphe,** lateral palpebral 391-9; 408-9
– of medulla 331-5; 332-12; 337-2
– of pons 329-3; 330-4; 331-5; 332-12; 337-2
*Recessus cochlearis* 417-6; 426-5
– *costomediastinalis* 57-5
– *ellipticus* 417-1; 418-1; 419-11; 426-8
*Recessus epitympanicus* 439-2; **440**-12; **441**-12; 442-12; 448-12; 449-10, 12; 451-11
– *fasciculi optici* 263-9
– *hypotympanicus* 448-7; 449-3
– *infundibuli* 218-8; 226-5; 248-5; 263-9; 274-8
– *lateralis ventriculi quarti* 218-7; 276-4; 289-4; 293-8; 334-8
– *membranae tympani* 440-6, 9; 441-4, 10; 449-9
– *opticus (ventriculi tertii)* 218-9; 223-10; 226-10; 248-5; 274-9; 276-1
– *pericardei* 17-2, 10
– *pharyngeus* 457-7
– *pinealis* 248-1; 263-3; 274-2; **289**-12; 290-1
– *piriformis* 116-9; 117-8
– *sphericus* 417-5; 418-2; 419-11; 426-1
– *suprapinealis* 263-2; 274-1
– *triangularis* 218-10; 323-11
**Rectal** artery, (hemorrhoidal) inferior 128-5; 129-5; 133-11; 134-10
– –, (–) middle 128-4; 129-2, 4, 5; 132-5; 171-3, 4
– –, (–) superior 123-6; 128-6; 129-1; 171-2
– lymph node 171-3, 4
– veins, (hemorrhoidal) inferior 124-5; 128-5; 129-5
– –, (–) middle 128-4; 129-2, 4; 171-2, 4
– –, (–) superior 128-2; 129-1
– venous plexus 124-5
**Rectouterine** fold 129-2; 171-4
**Rectovesical** pouch 171-4
**Rectum** 123-6; 126-6; 128-4; 129-2; 171-2; 355-6
**Rectus** abdominus muscle 50-5; 54-6, 8; 126-4; 127-6
– – –, sheath of, 50-3; 54-7; 127-6
– capitis muscle, posterior major 52-11
– femoris muscle 142-10; 143-9; 144-8, 10
– muscle, inferior 106-2, 5; 350-10; 364–366; **395**-4; 396-5; 398-5; 399-1; 400-7; 403-5; 404-5; 405-8; 406-4, 8; 407-7

**Rectus** muscle, lateral 103-4; 104-2; 105-4; 106-1, 5; 113-3; 356-2, 3; 359-3; 364-367; 368-2; 384-2, 9; **395**-2; 396-2, 9; 397-2; 398-10; 399-8; 400-2; **401**-4, 8; 402-2, 8; 403-5, 7; 404-8; 405-4; 407-9
– –, medial 105-9; 106-8; 356-9, 10; 364–367; 384-8; **396**-4; 397-10; 398-3; 399-2; 400-9; **401**-2; 402-1, 5; 403-2; 404-2; 405-9; 407-2
– –, superior 103-1; 104-1; 105-1, 8; 106-1, 7; 232-11; 364–366; **395**-1; 396; 397-1; 398-1; 399-5; 400-12; **401**-5, 8; 403-1; 404-1, 11; 405-11; 406-2; 407-12
**Recurrent** interrosseus artery 74-6; 79-5; 80-2; 81-3
– laryngeal nerve 44-9; 46-3, 6; 55-1, 11, 12; 57-1, 2, 11; **116**-5, 7; **117**-6, 7; 166-2, 5, 7; **352**-1, 2; 354-1, 10
– radial artery 75-2; 76-1; 77-1; 79-7
– ulnar artery 74-5; 76-9; 77-10; 78-7; 80-1
**Red** nucleus 221; 273-1; **281**-5; 301b; **324**-5; 326-3; 343
**Referred** pain 347
**Reflex** arcs, monosynaptic 307
– –, polysynaptic 307
– pathways, spinal intersegmental 308
*Regio perinealis* - - - see *Perineum*
– *urogenitalis* - - - - see *Perineum*
*Ren* 123-3; **127**-2; 180-4
**Renal** adipose capsule 125-9
– artery 4-2; 7-1; 125-2; 126-11; 170-2; 355-10
– ganglion 125-2
– lymph vessels 125-2
– plexus (of nerves) 125-2; 355-10
– vein 4-2; 124-1; 125-2; 126-11
**Restiform** body - - - - see **Cerebellar peduncle, inferior**
*Rete* - - - - see **Anastomoses** of arteries
**Reticular** formation 191-10; **317a**; 327-1; 328-2; 329-2; 330-2; 331-4; 332-9, 11; 333-6; 334-7; 335-7; 336-1; 337-11; 338-8; 339-9
**Reticular** substance - - - - see **Reticular formation**
– zone 225-9
**Retina** 359-5 C; 368-9; 373-9; 376-8; 402-8
–, central vessels 106-1; 356-6; 359-7; 362-8; 368-6
–, ciliary part 356-2; 368-1, 10; 372-6; 376-9; 377-1; 402-4
–, fovea centralis 356-6; 368-6; 373-7; 374; 375
–, pars optica 356-3 C, 8; 368-4; 372-3, 12; 373-1; 376-9; 384-8; 402-4
–, pigmented layer of 356-2 C, 2, 4, 8
–, vessels of 359-8; 360-1, 2, 4, 6; 368-8; 373-2
*Retinaculum extensorum* (wrist) 80-6; 81-6; 85-1; 86-10; 89-7
– *flexorum* (wrist) 82-5; 87-7; 88-7
– – (ankle) 150-7; 151-7; 158-11; 159-11
– *musculi extensorum inferius* 153-5; 155-11; 175-5
–, superior peroneal 150-6; 151-6
**Retinal** vein 356-2; 360-2, 3, 5, 6

**RETINAL VESSELS 358–360; 373–375**

**Retroauricular** lymph nodes 163-10; 165-2
**Retromandibular** vein 40-11; 41-9; 42-11; 43-1; 45-11; 46-11; **95**-6; 98-7; 99-6; 100-7, 8

**RHOMBENCEPHALON 229–231; 276; 289; 290**

**Rhomboid** fossa 181-12; 235-8; 274-7; 276-5; **289**-4; 290-4; 296-1; 330-12; 337-12
**Rhomboideus** muscle 51-8; 52-4, 7; 53-3
**Rib** 38-6; 46-5; 47-3; 54-1; **55**-7; 57-3; **58**-4; 180-8; 184-9; 355-1, 10, 11
**Right** lobe of liver 120-11
– lymphatic duct 162-11
– ventricle (heart) 17-8; 18-6; 21-8; 22-5; 25-1, 7; 26-7; 31-2, 5; 34-7; 35-7

**Rima** palpebrarum 390-4, 8; 408-4
**Ring,** femoral 128-8; 171-3
–, inguinal, deep 127-8
–, –, superficial 130-1
**Rootless,** abducens nerve 330-1
–, accessory nerve 290-7; 332-3, 9; 341-9
–, cervical nerve 290-6
–, glossopharyngeal 279-7; 331-8
–, hypoglossal nerve 332-8; 336-7, 8
–, oculomotor nerve 324-3; 326-6
*Rostrum corporis callosi* 248-4; 251-8; 257-4; 274-11; 285-8
**Round** ligament of uterus 125-7; 171-9
**Rubrospinal** tract 327-2; 328-2; 333-3; 334-3; 336-3; 341-3; 342-3

## S

**Saccular** nerve 412-7; 413-8
**Sacculus** 409-2; 412-6; 413-7
*Saccus endolymphaticus* 409-12
– *lacrimalis* 392-2; 393-9; 394-9; 408-2
**Sacral** artery, lateral 132-12
– –, middle 7-2; 123-9; 126-6; 128-12; 129-12; **132**-10; 171-2
– canal 128-1
– ganglion 132-2; 348-5; 355-7
– lymph nodes 170-9; 171-11
– nerve 132-3, 4; 181-7; 348-5; 355-4, 6
– –, dorsal ramus 53-6, 7
– –, ventral ramus 132-1; 355-4, 5
– plexus (of nerves) **119**-4; 132-2; 355-5
– spinal ganglion 180-7; 182-5
– veins, middle 126-6; 171-2
**Sacrospinalis** muscle - - - - see **Erector spinae** muscle
**Sacrospinous** ligament 132-5; 133-1; 171-3
**Sacrotuberous** ligament 133-1; 148-7
**Sacrum** 181-5
**Sagittal** sinus, superior 232-6, 12; **233**-1; **234**-2, 6, 10, 12; 235-1; 237-1; 245; 246; 280-7
– –, inferior 232-12; **233**-2, 10; 245; 246; 280-7
**Sagittal** suture 196-12
**Salivatory** nucleus, inferior (IX) 229-8; 230-4
– –, superior, (VII) 229-9; 230-4
**Salpingopharyngeal** fold 116-10
– muscle 116-1
**Saphenous** hiatus 50-7; 138-1; 173-2
– nerve 138-5; **139**-1; 141-7, 11; **143**-3, 4; 144-7; **155**-12
– vein, accessory 174-1
– –, great 50-7; **138**-2, 5; **139**-1, 6; 140-7; 141-11; 142-1; 144-12; **155**-1, 12; 170-5, 7; **173**-5; 174-7, 11
– –, small **140**-6; **141**-1, 6, 8; 146-6; 147-7; 149-3; 150-1; **155**-9; 174-1, 6
**Sartorius** muscle 142-5, 9; 143-5, 10; 144-4; 145-5
**Scala** tympani 409-5; 410-6; 413-9; 416-8; 417-2; 423-9; 424-9
– vestibuli 409-4; 410-1; 413-10; 416-8; 417-2; 423-10; 426-2
**Scalenus** muscle, anterior 42-8; **44**-9; 57-1; 58-10; 60-12; 165-6; 169-9; **354**-1, 11
– –, medius 58-10; 165-6; 169-12
– –, posterior 58-10; 165-5
**Scapha** 458-10; 459-9; 460-11
**Scapula**, spine of 62-1
**Scapular** artery, circumflex 53-3; 59-4; 61-7; 62-5
– –, descending 38-9; 44-2; 60-1
– nerve, dorsal 52-4, 7
*Scapus pili* 468-2
**Schlemm's** canal – see *Sinus venosus sclerae*
**Sciatic** nerve 145-10; 147-9; 148-1
**Sclera** 356-2, 7; 359-5; 368-5, 10; 369-4; 372-4; 373-9; 376-8; 402-8; 403-5
**Scrotal** nerve 133-6, 7
**Sebaceous** gland 465-8; 468-9
**Secondary** spiral lamina 417-5; 424-9
– tympanic membrane 447-6
**Sella** turcica 263-8; 264-4

**Semicanal** of auditory tube 427-4; 445-3; 446-4
*Semicanalis musculus tensoris tympani* 427-3; 428-2; **445**-3; 446-1
**Semicircular** canal, anterior **411**-2; 413-5; 414-1; 415-12; 416-1; **417**-12; 418-12; 419-1; 420-11; 423-2; 426-10; 439-4
– –, –, ampulla of 414-1; 415-1; 416-1; **418**-12; **419**-12; 425-11; 426-11
– –, lateral **411**-3; 413-2; 414-3; 415-9; 416-3; **417**-10; 419-2; 420-10; 423-9; 425-11; 426-9; 439-4; 444-11; 445-12
– –, –, ampulla of 415-1; 416-2; **418**-10; **420**-12; 426-9
– –, –, prominence of 428-11; 438-10; 443-10
– –, posterior 409-8; **411**-4; 414-3; 415-8; 416-3; **417**-8; **418**-8; 419-8; 420-8; 423-8; 439-4
– –, –, ampulla of 414-5; 415-7; 416-5; 417-7; **418**-7; **419**-6; 420-7
– duct, anterior 412-1; 413-7; 439-4
– –, –, ampulla of 409-12; 412-12; 413-7; 439-6
– –, lateral 409-8; 412-4; 413-2; 445-11
– –, –, ampulla of 412-2; 413-2
– –, posterior 409-7; 412-3
– –, –, ampulla of 409-7; 412-5
**Semilunar** gyrus 305
– lobule 291-3, 4; 292-3
– valve 20-1; 23-2, 9
**Semimembranosus** muscle 145-5; 146-7; **147**-7; 149-11; 150-12; 154-9, 11
**Seminal** vesicals 127-4; 128-5
**Semispinalis** capitis muscle 51-10; 52-1, 9, 11
**Semitendinosus** muscle 145-4; 146-7; 147-8; 149-12; 150-12; 154-12
**Septomarginal** trabecula 25-6; 26-6; 29-7
*Septum atriorum* - - - - see *Septum interatriale*
– *canalis musculotubarii* 427-3; 428-2; 442-10; **443**-4; 444-2; **445**-3; 446-2; 450-3
*Septum interatriale* 24-12; 26-12; 27-12
– *intermusculare* 71-7; 73-7; 75-11; 78-11
– *interventriclare* 23-8; 24-4; 25-4; 26-7; **27**-7; 31-1; 32-1; 33-1; 33-8
– *medianum posterius (medulla spinalis)* 189-12; 192-12; 193-12
– *nasi* 107-1; 108-2, 11; 264-4; 402-6; 403-4; 404-3
– *orbitale* 350-10; 363-12; 391-1, 8, 12; 406-11
– pellucidum 223-11; **248**-2; 251-8; 257-1; 259-1; **260**-11; 261-11; 262-1; 264-11; 265-1; 271-1; 274-11; 276-12; 278-11; 279-1; 280-2; 281-1; 285-11; 286-2; 287-10; 288-1; 323-10
– –, cavity of 260-1; **261**-1; 262-1; 265-1; 271-1; 278-11; 285-1
– –, vein of 265-1
– *subarachnoidale* 185-10
**Serratus** anterior muscle 59-11; 60-7
– posterior muscles 53-9, 10
**Sheath** of rectus abdominis 50-3; 54-7; 127-6
**Sigmoid** artery 123-4; 127-3
– colon 122-5; 123-4, 5; 125-5; 127-3; 170-4
– mesocolon 125-5; 127-3; 170-4
– sinus 116-11; 246
– veins 4-4; 123-4; 124-5; 127-3
**Sinoatrial node** 12
*Sinus aortae* 23-2
– *cavernosus* 232-10; 233-7; 238-5
–, confluence of 233-4; 237-3; 246
– *coronarius cordis* 18-8; 20-6, 8; 26-9; 28-9; 35-6
– *ethmoidal air cells* 384-5; 402-7; 403-2; 404-3; 405-9
– *frontales* 264-9; 280-12
– *intercavernosus* 232-1, 8
– *lactiferus* 50-11; 473-1
– *maxillaris* **112**-3; 392-7; 394-6; 395-6; **396**-6; 403-5
– *obliquus pericardii* 36-3
– *occipitalis* 233-3, 4

*Sinus* **paranasal** - - - - see **Maxillary**; **ethmoidal air cells**
– *petrosus* 232-4, 8; 233-6, 7
– *rectus* 197-4; 232-7; 233-3; 246
– *sagittalis inferior* 232-7, 12; **233**-2, 10; 245; 246; 280-7
– – *superior* 197-1, 3, 4, 10; 199-12; 232-6, 12; **233**-1; **234**-6, 12; 235-1; 237-1; 245; 246; 280-7
– *sigmoideus* 116-11; 246
– *sphenoidalis* 107-11; **108**-11; 109-10; 238-3; 275-3; 384-1; 402-12
– *sphenoparietalis* 232-10; 233-7
– *transversus* 114-5; 115-11; 116-11; 199-4; **232**-4, 8; **233**-2; 235-4; 237-4; 245; 246
– – *pericardii* 18-10; 19-10; 36-10
– *venarum cavarum* 18-4
– *venosus sclerae* (Schlemm) 356-1; 359-1; 368-1

## SKIN 466–481

**Small** saphenous vein **140**-6; **141**-1, 6, 8; 146-6; 147-7; 149-3; 150-1; **155**-9; 174-1, 6
**Soft** palate, (uvula) 107-9; 108-7; 109-8
**Soleus** muscle 150-1, 5; 151-1, 11; 152-1, 11; 154-5, 6
**Solitary** tract 331-11; 332-1; 336-10; 337-1
– –, nucleus of 229-2, 5; 231-3, 5; 332-2; 334-9; 336-11; 337-1
*Spatium intervaginale (n. opticus)* 356-6; 362-2; 402-5; 403-11; 406-5
– *perichorioideale* (eye) 356-2, 5, 8
– *perilymphaticum* (vestibulum) 409-7
**Spermatic** cord 128-7; 130-2, 11; 170-6
**Sphenoid** bone 107-11; 395-3; 396-3; 456-3
– –, body of 238-6; 275-7
– –, greater wing **113**-2; 264-3; 384-2, 8; 385-2, 9; 401-4; 402-3; 404-8, 9; 405-3; 455-11
– –, lesser wing 236-9; 264-9; 384-10
– –, spine of 455-8
**Sphenoidal** sinus 107-11; 108-11; 109-10; 238-3; 275-3; 384-1; **402**-12
**Sphenomandibular** ligament 100-8; 101-8
**Sphenopalatine** artery 94-10; 102-2; 108-11; 109-9
**Sphenoparietal** sinus 232-10; 233-7
**Sphenozygomatic** suture 113-2
**Sphincter** ani muscle, external 133-8; 134-11
– pupilla muscle 356-1
**Spina** helicis 458-1; 460-3; 461-9; 462-9
– *ossis sphenoidalis* 455-8
– *scapulae* 62-1 -
– *tympanica* 450-2, 11; 451-2, 10
**Spinal** arachnoid 184-1; 185-11; 187-8
– artery 184-1; 186-4, 8, 10; 200-4; 241-7; 242-6

## SPINAL CORD 179–194

– – **180**-8; 241-6; 247-6; 248-7; 272-6
– –, anterior median fissure 183-1; 187-12; 188-11; 189-6; 190-1; **191**-6; **192**-7; 193-7; 194-7
– –, – white commissure 191-8; 192-7
– –, cervical portion 182-1; 183-11
– –, columns of, anterior 189-5, 7; 191-4; 192-8; 232-8; 338-8; 339-5; 340-8; 341-8; 342-4
– –, – of, lateral 192-2
– –, – of, posterior 189-2; 191-2; 192-1; 193-2; 194-1; 338-2; 340-10
– – funiculi, anterior 191-8; 192-5; 340-6
– – –, lateral 191-9; 192-3
– – –, posterior 191-1, 11; 192-12; 340-12; 341-1
– –, lumbar portion 180-8; 182-4; 183-7
– –, posterior median septum 189-12; 192-12; 193-12
– –, substantia intermedia centralis 191-1; 192-8; 193-8; 194-4
– –, thoracic portion 182-3; 183-9
– – tract, ascending 310; 313; 314
– – –, descending 311; 314
– – –, fasciculus proprius 310
– – –, proprioceptive 316

Spinal Cord tract, spinobulbar 316
– ganglion 47-5; 180-1; 181-1, 4; 182-5; **184**-1, 10, 12; 185-3; 186-9; 187-5; **188**-2; **189**-3; 190-1; 198-1 313
– –, dorsal 176-2
– –, sacral 180-7; 182-5

**SPINAL NERVES 47; 176; 180; 185–189**

– – **47**-5; **176**-2; 181-1; **184**-1, 2; 186-9; 188-3, 10; 189-9; 190-2
– –, branches 176
– –, intercostal nerve (ventral ramus) **47**
– – rami, dorsal 176-10; 189-3
– – –, ventral 176-10
– – roots, dorsal **176**-2, 3; 184-11; 186-10; **189**-11; 191-2; 193-1; 198-2
– – –, ventral 176-2, 3, 10, 12; 184-11; 186-8; **189**-8; 191-8
– nucleus of accessory nerve 229-7; 230-7; 339-2; 340-2

**SPINAL TRACTS 308–316**

– –, trigeminal nerve 328-5; 333-2; 334-3; 335-3, 9; 336-9; 337-9; 338-10; **339**-9; **340**-2; 341-3; 342-2
– vein 184-1
**Spine** of scapula 62-1
**Spinocerebellar** tract, anterior 328-1, 12; 329-11; 333-12; 334-5; 335-3; 336-3; 338-4; **340**-4; 341-3; 342-3
– –, posterior 334-3; 335-2; 336-3; 338-3; **340**-3; 341-3; 342-3
**Spinothalamic tract** 333-3; 334-7; 336-9; 342-8
– –, lateral 313; 341-9
– –, ventral 313
**Spiral** ganglion of cochlea 334-5; 410-3
– lamina, hamulus of 417-4; 423-1
– –, osseous **410**-3; 413-12; 416-7, 8; 417-2, 4; **423**-2, 4; **424**-10; 426-2
– ligament of cochlea 410-8
– membrane (cochlea) 410-8
– organ (of Corti) (cochlea) 410-8
**Splanchnic** ganglion 125-3; 348-9
**Splanchnic** nerve, greater **55**-6, 8; 56-8; 126-12; 176-9 C; 184-8; 348-4, 9; **352**-7; 353-7; 354-8; 355-12
– –, lesser **55**-7, 8; 348-4, 8; 353-6; 354-7; 355-11
– –, lumbar 125-4
**Spleen** 120-3
**Splenic** artery 4-2; 7-1; 120-2; 121-2; 170-2
– vein 4-2; 121-2; 123-1; 124-1
*Splenium corporis callosi* **248**-11; **251**-2; 255-5; **257**-11; **258**-7; 259-3; 260-6; 270-12; **274**-2; 280-8; 282; 321; 322; 323-2
**Splenius** capitis muscle 43-3; 51-2, 10; 52-2, 10; 95-8; 165-4
– cervicis muscle 169-12
**Stapedius** muscle 112-9; 429-1; 435-2; 444-9
– –, tendon of 429-1; 443-6; 445-10; 450-9
**Stapes** 114-4; 409-6; **435**-**437**; **443**-1; 444-12; 445-1, 8; 449-8; 450-7; 454-9
–, base of 435-7; 436-6; 437-9
–, crura of **435**-3, 9; 436-4, 7; 443-1, 12; 445-1
–, head of 112-9; 435-1; **437**-2; 439-3; 443-1; 444-12; 445-8
–, membrane of 443-12; 445-11
**Statoacoustic** nerve - - - - see **Vestibulo-cochlear** nerve
**Stellate** ganglion 348-2; 352-11
**Sternocleidomastoid** artery 42-12; 94-5
– muscle 39-9; **40**-1, 9; **41**-3; 42-1, 7; 43-1; 45-3, 6, 9; 46-2; 51-2; 60-11; 95-7; 98-7; 99-8; 165-3
**Sternocostal** surface of heart 25-6
**Sternohyoid** muscle 41-8; 44-11; 46-10
**Sternothyroid** muscle 41-8; 44-10; 46-10
**Stomach** 120-9; 354-5
**Straight** sinus 197-4; 232-7; 233-3
*Stratum griseum colliculi superoris* 281-5; 324-11; 326-1
– *pigmenti retinae* 356-2 C, 2, 4, 8
**Stria** of Gennari 303

*Stria longitudinalis* 258-2; 259-2; 283-1; 323-11, 12
– *mallearis* 454-2
– medullaris 218-5; 331-11; 454-2
– –, *thalami* 271-8; 276-11
*Striae medullares ventriculus quartus* 289-8; 290-4
– *olfactoria* 247-2; 272-1
– terminalis 260-2; 262-2; 271-2; 276-1
**Striate** body 285-2
– cortex 303
**Styloglossus** muscle 102-8; 107-8; 118-2
**Stylohyoid** muscle 42-9; 45-10; 99-7; 100-7; 102-8; 114-7
**Styloid** process, radius 90-5
– –, temporal 92-8; 115-10; 425-8; 428-5; 458-5
– –, ulnar 90-7
**Stylomastoid** artery 94-4; 100-8; 101-9
– foramen 112-8; 114-7; 429-8
**Stylopharyngeus** muscle 115-10
**Subarachnoid** septum 185-10
– space 184-2; 186-11; **197**-2; **198**-11; **199**-1, 4; 235-1, 2; 264-12; 284-2, 3, 9, 362-8
**Subclavian** artery 3-11; 7-12; 17-12; 18-12; 34-1; 35-12; 36-1; 38-4; 41-6; 42-4; 43-8; 44-9; **46**-3, 7; **55**-1, 11; **58**-3; **60**-12; 116-4, 9; 167-10; 354-1, 11
– nerve 37-9; 169-10
– plexus 348-2
– trunk, lymphatic 162-11, 12; 169-8
– vein 42-4; 46-5, 7; 56-1; 57-11; 116-5, 8; 162-1, 11
**Subclavius** muscle 43-4; 57-1
**Subcostal** artery 7-11; 55-7; 56-7
– nerve 55-6; 119-11
– vein 55-7; 56-7
**Subdural** space 184-2; 186-1; 197-5; 198-11
**Subinguinal** lymph nodes 170-6
**Sublingual** artery 102-6; **107**-6; 118-1, 9, 11
– gland 102-5; 118-1; 350-7
– nerve 92-4; 118-12
**Sublingual** vein 46-1; 118-1
**Submandibular** duct 102-6
– ganglion 92-6; 102-7; 351-7
– gland 41-10; 42-11; 43-9; 45-11; 101-6; **102**-7; 350-7
– lymph nodes 163-3; 164-9; 165-8
**Submental** artery 42-11; 43-10; 44-11; 94-7; 100-5; **101**-6; 102-6
– lymph nodes 163-2; 164-9; 165-9
– vein 42-11; 45-1, 11; 99-5; 100-6
**Suboccipital** nerve 52-11; 53-11
– venous plexus 52-2
**Subparietal** sulcus 248-10; 251-12
**Subscapular** artery 7-11; 61-6
– lymph nodes 169-5
– nerve 37-8; 53-3; 61-12
– vein 59-1
**Subscapularis** muscle 61-9; 169-4
**Substantia** gelatinosa 191-2; 193-3; 313
– *grisea centralis mesencephali* 273-12; 324-2; 325-1; 329-1
– *intermedia centralis* 191-1; 192-7; 193-5; 194-7; 338-1
– *medullaris (cerebri)* 250; 252; 254; 280-10
– *medullaris hemispherii cerebelli* 295-3; 296-8; 343
– nigra 255-3; 273-2; 279-4; 284-8; **301 b**; 320; 324-8; 325-8; 326-8
– *perforata* 241-9; 247-10; 248-6; **255**-11; **272**-2, 8; 273-4, 8; 305; 323-9
– *reticularis* - - - - *Formatio reticularis* **317 a**; 331-4; 332-9, 11; 336-1; 337-11
**Subthalamic** nucleus of hypothalamus 225-3; 279-1; 281-4
**Sudoriferous** gland 468-9; 469-6
– pores 475-2

## Sulcus or Sulci

*Sulcus anthelicis transversus* 461-1; 462-1
– *basilaris pontis* 272-8; 330-5
– *calcarinus* 209; 248-9; **251**-3; 252; 255-7; 257-9; 259-6; 260-6; 266-5; 282; 301 a; 312; 322; 323-3

*Sulcus centralis* 207; 208; 248-12; **249**-1; 250; 251-1; 252; **253**-4, 10
–, cerebral hemisphere 207-210
– *cinguli* 248-2, 12; **251**-1, 9, 11; 252; 253-6; 257-11
– *circularis insulae* 256-2; 258-2
– *collateralis* 220-6; **251**-6; 255-8; 268-6
– *collateralis* - - - - see *Fissura collateralis*
– *coronarius* 18-5
– *corporis callosi* 248-11; 251-11; 283-11
– cutis (grooves) 475-1
– *deltoideopectoralis* 50-1
– *frontalis* 208; 253-1, 11
– *hippocampi* 220-2; 255-8; 266-3; **268**-4; **269**-4
– *hypothalamicus* 226-1; 242-12; **248**-5; 263-C; **274**-1
– *intermedius posterior* 191-11; 289-7; 290-5
– *interventricularis anterior* 11-1; 21-7; 25-3
– – posterior 18-7; 22-6
– *intraparietalis* 207; 208; 249-3; 253-5, 8
– *lateralis* **249**-5, 8; 250; 253-9; 279-9; 281-2, 9; 285-3; 286-9; 287-9; 288-3, 9
– – *anterior* 183-1; 188-10; **191**-5; 290-7
– – *mesencephali* 273-11; 325-10
– – *posterior* 182-9; 187-11; 189-1; **191**-10; 289-7; 290-7
– limitans 289-3
– *medianus fossae rhomboideae* 337-12
– – *posterior* 182-8; 187-12; **191**-12; 194-12; 232-12; 289-7; 338-12; 339-12
– *nervi oculomotorii* 272-10
– – *petrosi majoris* 426-1
– *occipitalis transversus* 249-4
– *occipitotemporalis* 251-5; 255-7
– *olfactorius* **247**-12; 255-1; 272-12; 285-6
– *orbitales* 255-1
– *palpebralis* 386-5; 11, 387-1, 5
– *parietooccipitalis* 207-209; 210-2; 242-2; 248-10; 249-13; **251**-3; 252; 253-6; 255-6; 257-10; 320–322
*Sulcus parolfactorius* **248**-4; 251-8; 274-10
– *postcentralis* 208; **249**-2; 253-4
– *precentralis* 208; **249**-1; 251-12; 253-2
– *primarius* 228; 291-2
– *promotorii* 427-5; 428-4
– *subparietalis* 248-10; 251-2
– *temporalis inferior* 247-9; 249-7; 255-2, 9
– – *superior* 249-5, 8; 253-8
– – *transversus* 258-3
– *terminalis* 18-5
– *tympanicus* 428-5; 449-7
*Supercilium* 387-12; 407-1
**Superficial** cardiac plexus 36-2
– cervical artery **38**-3; 41-8; 42-8; 43-3; **44**-2; 50-11; 52-8; 169-10
– – lymph nodes 163-4, 9; 165-4; 169-12
– – vein 45-9; **46**-9; 50-11; 169-10
– circumflex iliac artery 50-4, 8; 138-10
– – – vein 50-4, 8; 138-10
– epigastric artery 50-8; 138-11
– – vein 50-8; 138-11; 173-1
– inguinal ring 130-1
– palmar arch 7-9; 87-8; 90-4
– peroneal nerve (fibular) 139-7; 153-7, 11; 155-11
temporal artery **94**-1, 11; 95-1, 11; **98**-1, 10, 11; 99-1, 8, 11; 100-1, 9, 11; 101-11; 102-10, 11
– – –, frontal branch **94**-11; 95-1; **98**-1; 99-1; 100-1
– – –, parietal branch **94**-1; **98**-11; 99-11; 100-11; 101-11; 102-11
– transverse metacarpal ligament 82-1
**Superior** alveolar nerve, anterior 92-3; **111**-12; **112**-4; 350-9; 351-9
– – –, middle 92-3; 111-12; **112**-5
– – –, posterior 92-3; 101-2; 102-2; **111**-12; **112**-1, 4, 5, 6; 350-8, 9; 351-9
– articular process of vertebra 184-11
– brachial cutaneous nerve 53-2
– cerebellar artery 200-3; **241**-2, 8; **242**-7; 278-5
– – peduncle **276**-4; **289**-9, 10; 290-2; 293-2; 294-2; 295-1; 296-10;

327-2; 328-11; 329-11; 333; 334-2; 335-2

**Superior** cerebral vein 197-1, 10, 11; 233-1; 234-1, 7, 10, 12; 235-10; 237-2

– cervical sympathetic ganglion **44**-11; 109-8; 110-8; **115**-2; 116-2; 301a; 348-11; **350**-2, 3; 351-2, 3

– colliculus 229-12; 255-4; **271**-5; **276**-10; 278-7; 281-7; 289-1; 290-1, 2; 295-1

– –, gray matter of 281-5; 324-11; 326-1

– deep cervical lymph nodes 163-3; 164-3; 169-12

– dental plexus 111-12

– epigastric artery 50-2; **54**-9; 138-11

– – veins 50-2; 54-3; 138-11

– ganglion of glossopharyngeal nerve 334-8

– –, vagus nerve 110-9; 115-11; 336-4

– genicular artery 137-3; 144-5; 145-5; 149-3; 151-11; 153-1, 12; **154**-2, 9

– gluteal artery 7-2; 127-3; 132-1; **147**-12; 148-11

– – nerve 119-9; 148-11

– intercostal artery 38-7; 55-11

– labial artery 94-8

– laryngeal artery 41-9; 42-9; 43-9; 116-2; 117-10; 118-3

– – nerve 43-9; **115**-3, 8, 9, 10; 116-2, 9

– – –, external branch 115-4, 9; 350-6; 351-7

– – –, internal branch 115-9; **117**-9; 118-3; **350**-7; 351-7

– – vein 116-2

– longitudinal fasciculus 297

– medullary velum **248**-7; 276-8; 289-10; 295; 296-1; 329-1

– mesenteric artery 1-4; 4-2; 7-1; 5-5; 121-3; **122**-1, 123-1; 126-12; 170-2; 355-2

– – ganglion 152-2; 355-9

– – vein 124-3

– oblique muscle 103-9; 104-11; 105-8, 11; 106-7, 12; 364; 366; **396**-1; **401**-6, 12; 403-1, 6; 404-1; 405-10

**Superior** oblique muscle, tendon of 105-12; 106-1; 396-1; 397-11; 398-11; 399-4; 400-10; **401**-1, 10; 400-10; **401**-1, 10; 407-1; 408-1

– – –, trochlea of 106-12; 396-12; **401**-1

– orbital fissure 405-2

– rectal (hemorrhoidal) artery 123-6; 128-2; 129-2; 171-2

– – vein 4-6; 123-6; **128**-2; **129**-2; 171-2

– rectus muscle 398-1; 399-5; 400-10; 12

– sagittal sinus 197-1, 3, 4, 10; 199-12; 232-6, 12; **233**-1; **234**-6, 12; 235-1; 237-1; 245; 246; 280-7

– – –, lateral lacuna of 234-2, 10

– salivatory nucleus, facial nerve nuclei 229-9; 230-4

– thyroid artery 41-9; 42-9; 43-9; **44**-10; 46-9; 94-6; 102-7; 115-4, 9; 118-3, 9

– – vein 42-9; 44-10; 45-3; 46-9

– ulnar collateral artery 71-8; 72-8; 75-12; 77-12; 78-11

– vena cava 3-11; 5-3; 17-10; 18-2; 19-11; 21-11; 22-1; 26-12; 34-10; 35-1; 36-10; **46**-6; 56-11; **57**-9; 162-11; 167-1; 352-3

**Supinator** muscle 75-2; 76-1; 79-3; 81-10

**Supracallosal** gyrus, longitudinal stria of **258**-1, 2; 259-1, 2; **283**-1; 323-11, 12

**Supraclavicular** lymph node 169-1

– – –, deep cervical 164-7

– nerves 37-9; 39-6; **40**-4, 6; 50-11; 53-1; 67-12; 169-1

**Supramandibular** lymph nodes 163-2

**Supramarginal** gyrus 207; 249-2; 253-8

**Supraoptic** nucleus 223-2; 224-6; 226-10

**Supraorbital** artery 95-2; 98-2; 99-2; 103-1; 104-12; 105-12; 404-1

– margin 264-3; 396-10

– notch 408-1

**Suprapineal** recess 263-2; 274-1

**Suprarenal** artery, middle 70-1; 125-2, 10; 126-11

– gland 125-2, 10

– lymph nodes 170-10

**Suprarenal** vein 125-2, 10
**Suprascapular** artery 38-4; 41-6; 43-4; 44-3; 60-12; 61-1; 62-11
– nerve 37-8; 44-2; 61-2; 62-11; 169-2
**Supraspinatus** muscle 62-1, 10
**Supratrochlear** artery 95-2; 98-2; 99-2; 101-2; 105-12
– nerve 92-10; **95**-2; 98-2; 99-2; 100-2; 101-2; 102-2; 103-11; 104-12; 350-10; 351-10
– vein 95-2
**Supraventricular** crest 25-2
**Supravesical** fossa 127-4
**Sural** arteries 137-4; 149-3; 154-3; 150-1, 11
– cutaneous nerve, lateral 141-1; 145-7; 146-6; 147-6; 149-3
– – –, medial 141-8, 9; 145-7; 146-6; 147-6; 149-6; 155-12
– nerve **141**-4; 145-7
– veins 150-1, 11
*Sutura sagittalis* 196-12
– *sphenozygomatica* 113-2
**Sympathetic** ganglion 47-6; **55**-8; 56-6; 176-10 C; **184**-9
– –, cervicothoracic (stellate) 352-11
– –, inferior cervical 115-6; **116**-8; 348-10; 352-11; 354-11
– –, middle cervical **44**-8; 58-10; **115**-5; **116**-8; 348-1, 10; 352-1, 12; 354-12
– – sacral 132-2; 355-7
– –, superior cervical **44**-11; 109-8; 110-8; **115**-2; **116**-1; 301a; 348-11; **350**-2, 3; 351-2, 3
– –, thoracic **352**-7, 8, 9, 11; **353**-8, 9, 10, 11; 354-9, 10; 355-10
– outflow 345
– trunk 44-12; 55-10; 58-10; 115-3, 5; 116-3; 125-3; 126-2; 127-1; **148**-8; **348**-10; 350-5; 351-5; **352**-12; 354-4, 9; 355-9
– –, lumbar 125-3
Symphysis pubis 124-7; 132-7

## T

**Tapetum** 266-7; 320
**Tarsal** artery 157-3, 9
– gland (Meibomian) **363**-9; 388-6; **389**-2, 3, 5; 407
– –, excretory duct 389-3
– muscle 363-11
*Tarsus inferior* 389-6; **390**-6; **391**-6; 406-8; 407-6; 408-7
– *superior* 363-10; 389-12; **390**-1; **391**-1; 406-9; 408-11
**Tectal** lamina (quadrigemina) 223-2; 248-10; 261-5; **274**-2; **276**-8; 324-2; 325-11
**Tectospinal** tract 324-9
**Tegmen** tympani 427-2
– *(vent. quartus)* 276-7; 293-11
**Tegmental** decussation 324-3
– nucleus 329-2
– radiations 326-2
**Tegmentum** 273-1; 324-10; 325-3
– *pedunculi cerebri* 326-3
*Tela chorioidea (ventriculus quartus)* 197-1; 248-7; 336-12
– – (– *tertius*) **219**-11; 242-8; 248-1; 262-7; 265-3; **283**-9

**TELENCEPHALON 206–217; 221; 222; 249–262; 265–271**

**Temporal** artery, deep **94**-10; **101**-11, 12 102-1, 12
– –, middle **94**-2; 99-10; 100-10; **101**-11; 102-12
– –, superficial **94**-1, 11; **95**-1, 11; 98-1; 10, 11; 99-1, 8, 11; 100-1, 9, 11; 101-11; 102-10, 11
– bone 110-10; 115-1; 439-1; 448-1; 456-9
– –, mastoid process of 114-8
– –, petrous portion 236-5; 264-8; **427**-3; 448-10; **455**-3; 457-9
– –, squamous portion 451-1; 458-2
– –, tympanic portion 458-3
– fascia 99-12; 100-12

**Temporal** gyrus 206–210; 235-3; **249**-6, 7, 8; 251-5; 255-4; 258-3; 269-1
– lobe, cerebrum 209; **241**-10; 256-7; 258-3; 279-3; 284-3; 285-3; 286-4; 288-4
– muscle **99**-1; **100**-1; 101-11; **102**-12; 280-2; 384-9; 402-2
– sulci 247-9; **249**-5, 7, 8; 253-8; 255-2, 9; 258-3
– vein, middle 99-1; 100-11, 12
– –, superficial 95-12; 100-9
**Temporoparietal** muscle 95-1; 98-12; 99-10
**Temporopontine** tract 299-4; 300-6; 326-3; 327-3
*Tendo calcaneus* 150-6; 151-6; 152-6
– *musculi stapedi* 427-7; 443-6; **445**-10 450-9
– – *tensoris tympani* 438-5; 439-2; 441-10; **442**-9, 10; 443-1; 445-12; 448-12; 449-1; 450-3
**Tendon** sheath of flexor muscles 90-3, 8, 10
– sheaths, foot 160
– –, hand 88; 89; 90
**Tenia** chorioidea 260-10; 276-1; **283**-2, 9; **284**-1, 6
– fornicis 260-8; 283-11
– *(ventriculus quartus)* 289-5, 8; 337-11
**Tensor** fasciae latae muscle 142-11
– tympani muscle 112-11; 432-6; 438-5; 439-2, 9; 441-10; **442**-10; 443-1, 2; 444-1; **445**-2, 12; 446-10; 448-11; 449-1, 2; 450-3
– – –, semicanal of 427-3; 428-2; 445-3; 446-1
– – nerve 110-9
– veli palatini muscle 110-7; 116-1; 457-4
**Tentorium** cerebelli 199-3; 232-6, 8; 233-2, 5; **235**-3; **237**-4
**Teres** major muscle 51-8; 53-3; 59-3; 61-8; **62**-4; 72-11; 73-1; **74**-1
– minor muscle 53-3; 62-5; 74-12
**Terminal** sulcus 18-5
**Terminal** vein - - - - see **Internal** fronto-parietal vein
– ventricle 198-2
**Testicular** artery 7-2; **126**-7, 11; 127-8, 9; 128-1; **130**-8
– vein 124-1; **126**-7; 11; 127-8, 9; 128-1
**Thalamic** nuclei 224-2; 225-2; 278-8; 283-2, 3, 8; 300-5
– radiations 222
– vein 205
**Thalamoolivary** tract 324-2; 325-1; 329-11; 331-3; 337-3
**Thalamostriate** vein 219-2; 245; 246; **262**-1; **265**-3; 271-2; 283-2; 288-2
**Thalamus** 219-8; 221; 223-1; 248-1; 257-8; **271**-4; 274-1; 280-9; **281**-8; 282; **283**; 284-9; 320
–, anterior tubercle of 261-10; **271**-1; 276-1
–, pulvinar of 271-4; 273-11; 276-2; 290-1
–, stria medullaris of 271-8; 276-11
**Third** ventricle **218**-12; 219-3; 235-8; 261-2; 263-12; 264-2; 271-11; **274**-1; **276**-11; 278-1, 7; 279-10; 280-8; **283**-9; 286-7; 287-6; 288-7; 289-11; 320
– –, chorioid plexus 197-1; **219**-11; 223-1; 235-9; **274**-1; **283**-9; 288-10
– –, ependyma 283-3
– –, tela chorioidia **219**-11; 242-8; 248-1; 262-7; 265-3; **283**-9
**Thoracic** aorta, descending 3-1; 7-1; 18-10; 46-5; **55**-3; 184-4; 353-6; **354**-3
– artery, internal 7-11; **38**-5; 43-7; 44-9; 45-6; 50-2; **54**-1, 11; 55-1; 57-2; 58-8; 60-10
– –, –, intercostal branches 54-10
– –, –, perforating branch 40-7; 44-8; 45-7; 54-11; 166-11
– –, lateral 7-11; **44**-6; 50-10, 11; 59-12; 60-4, 10; 169-5
– –, supreme 7-1; 169-7
– duct 55-3; **56**-1; 127-10; **162**-1, 3, 12; 169-9; 184-5

**Thoracic** ganglion 56-11; 116-8; 348-2, 10; **352**-7, 8, 9, 11; **353**-8, 9, 10, 11; 354-9, 10; 355-10
– nerve, dorsal ramus 52-6; 53-1, 8, 10
– –, long 169-5, 12
– vein, internal 18-1; 34-10; 36-11; 40-7; 45-6; 46-5, 7; 50-2; **54**-2; 58-8; 60-10; 166-11
– –, lateral 44-6, 7; 50-10, 11; **59**-12; **60**-4; 168-12; 169-5
**Thoracoacromial** artery 41-5; 42-6; 43-6; **44**-3; 46-7; **60**-1; 69-12
– vein 7-1; 42-6; 43-6; 45-5; 69-12
**Thoracodorsal** artery 50-10; **59**-4; **60**-4; 61-8
– nerve 37-8; 44-6; 59-5; 60-4; 61-7
– veins 59-4; 60-4
**Thoracoepigastric** vein 44-6; 50-10; 59-1, 7; **60**-6; 168-6

## THORAX 50–60

**Thymic** vein 36-12; 46-6
**Thyrocervical** trunk, artery 7-12; 38-4; 43-8; 44-9; 58-9; 60-12; 116-4, 8
**Thyrohyoid** membrane 118-4
**Thyroid** artery, inferior 38-4; 43-8; 44-9; **115**-5, 6, 7; **116**-8; **117**-5, 7; 118-5
– –, superior 41-8, 9; 42-9; 43-9; **44**-10; 46-9; 94-6; 102-7; 115-4, 9; 118-3, 9
– cartilage 117-8, 10; 118-4
– gland 42-8; 43-8; 44-9; **46**-9; 57-1; **115**-7; 116-4; **117**-5; 167-12; 354-12
– –, isthmus of 45-3; 118-6
– vein, inferior 44-8; 46-3
– –, superior 44-10; 46-2, 9
– venous plexus 46-3
**Thyroidea** ima vein 36-12; 44-8; **45**-6; 46-6; 56-12; 166-11
**Tibia** 157-12
–, condyles of 137-4
**Tibial** artery, anterior 7-7; 137-5; 152-12; **153**-8, 10; 154-6; 157-11; 175-7, 9
– –, – recurrent 137-5; 153-1
**Tibial** artery, posterior 7-7; 137-5; 150-7; 151-7, 10; **152**-7, 11; 154-6; **158**-11; 159-11; 160-12
– –, – recurrent 152-1; 154-5
– lymph node, anterior 175-10
– muscle, anterior 153-2, 5; 157-12; 175-1, 5
– –, posterior 150-7; **151**-7, 8; 152-7, 11
– nerve 119-7; 145-4; 146-5; **147**-7, 9; 149-2, 4; 150-1, 7; 151-1, 7, 9; **152**-1, 2, 12; 174-2
– tuberosity 137-8; 175-1
– vein 150-7, 11; 175-8, 9
Tongue **102**-4; 107-3; **108**-5, 6; 117-1, 12; 350-8
*Tonsilla cerebelli* 247-5; **292**-2; 294-5; 295-7; 334-2
– *palatina* 108-6; 117-1; 116-10
– *pharyngea* 116-12
**Torus** tubarius 116-10
**Trabeculae** carneae 24-7; 26-1; 27-5; 27-8; 32-C; 33-8
– septomarginalis 25-6; 26-6; 29-7
**Trachea** 34-12; 36-12; 44-9; 46-3; **55**-12; 56-12; 57-12; 117-6; 118-6; 354-12
–, bifurcation of 35-1; 167-1
–, membranous wall of 35-1; 116-5; **167**-1
**Tracheal** cartilages 352-1
– glands, membranous wall 116-5
– lymph nodes 35-2; 166-12; 167-10
**Tracheobronchial** lymph node 35-2; 166-2, 9; 167-1, 3, 9

## TRACTS, or TRACTUS

## TRACTS, ASCENDING and DESCENDING 308–316; 318; 319

## TRACTS and NUCLEI of CEREBRUM 320–323

**Tracts,** auditory 304
–, cortical projection 299
–, hypophysis 226
–, hypothalamus 226
–, pyramidal 299; 312
*Tractus cerebellorubralis* 393

*Tractus corticonuclearis* 326-4; 327-5; 328-5; 333-7
– *corticopontinus* 326-3, 5; **327**-3; 328-7; 333-6
– *corticospinalis* **299**; **312**; 320; 326-4; 327-5; 328-5; **333**-7; 334-6; 335-5; **336**-6; 341-5
– – *anterior* 311; 312; 315-12
– – *lateralis* 311; 340-9
– *mamillothalamicus* 288-8; 323-7
– *mesencephalicus nervus trigeminus* 328-1; 329-1
– *olfactorius* 241-1; 247-1; 257-4; 272-12; 285-7; 323-9; 343; 367
– *olivocerebellaris* 331-3; 332-9; 336-8; 337-9
– *olivospinalis* 336-5; 340-4; 341-8; 342-8
– *opticus* 224-8; 225-9; 272-10; **273**-8; 279-4; 283-8; 286-5; 287-6; 288-6; 290-10; **301a**; 320; 321-322; 385-5, 8
– *reticulospinalis* 301b
– *rubrospinalis* 327-2; 328-2; **333**-3; 334-3; 336-3; 341-3; **342**-3
– *solitarius* 331-11; **332**-1; 336-10; **337**-1
– *spinalis n. trigeminus* 328-5; 333-2; 334-3; 335-3, 9; 336-9; 337-9; **338**-10; 339-9; **340**-2; 341-3; 342-2
– *spinocerebellaris anterior* 328-1; 12; 329-11; 333-12; 334-5; 335-3; 336-3; 338-4; **340**-4; 341-3; 342-3
– – *posterior* 334-3; 335-2; 336-3; 338-3; **340**-3; 341-3; 342-3
– *spinothalamicus* 333-3; 334-7; 336-9; 342-8
– – *lateralis* 313; 341-9
– – *ventralis* 313
– *spiralis foraminosus* 421-8; 424-8
– *tectospinalis* 324-9
– *tegmentalis centralis* 327-2; 328-12; 333-3; 334-5; 335-5; 336-5
– *temporopontinus* 299-4; 300; 326-3; 327-3
*Tractus thalamoolivaris* 324-2; 325-1; 329-11; 331-3; 337-3
– *vestibulospinalis* 335-7
**Tragicus** muscle 463-3
**Tragus** 448-3; 459-3; 465-8
**Transversalis** fascia 56-7; 125-3
**Transverse** arytenoid muscle 116-3
– abdominal muscle 50-3; 127-8
– cervical artery 41-8
– – –, ascending branch 60-12
– – –, deep branch 41-4; 51-9; 52-8
– – –, descending branch 42-4; 43-4
– – –, superficial **41**-4; 42-4; 43-3; 44-2; 46-9; 52-8
– – nerve 37-10; 39-9; 40-9
– – vein 40-6; **45**-9; 46-9; 51-9
– colon 122-12; 123-12
– facial artery 94-5; 95-5; **98**-9; 101-10
– fasciculus 82
– fissure of cerebrum 260-8; 262-5
– mesocolon 122-1; 123-1, 11
– pericardial sinus 18-10; 19-10; 36-10
– scapular ligament 61-1; 62-2, 11
– sinus 114-5; 115-11; 116-11; 199-4; **232**-4, 8; **233**-2; 235-4; 237-4; 245; 246
– temporal gyrus (Heschl) 206; 258-9; 269-1
**Transversus** abdominis muscle 50-3; 126-4
– auriculae muscle 464-3
– menti muscle 95-5
– perinei muscle, superficial 133-8; 134-8
– thoracis muscle 50-2; 54-11
**Trapezius** muscle 39-4; 42-4; 45-4; **51**-2, 9; 52-4; 95-8; 99-8; 165-5; 350-3
**Trapezoid** body 330-3, 9; 333-8
– –, filaments 335-7
**Triangular** fossa (ear) 459-1; 460-1
– recess 218-10
**Triceps** muscle 53-3; 61-6; 62-6; 72-8, 9; **73**-2, 7, 8, 9; **74**-2, 3, 4, 8; **80**-12
**Tricuspid** valve **25**-3, 4, 7; 26-5, 6, 8; 27-9; 28-3; 29-8; 12
**Trigeminal** ganglion (semilunar ganglion) **103**-5; 104-6; 110-10; **111**-11;

114-3; **247**-3; 328-5; 350-1; 351-1; 457-12
**Trigeminal** impression 427-3; 428-2; 429-3; 457-12

**TRIGEMINAL NERVE** 92; 95; 98; 110–114

Trigeminal nerve **91**; 92-12; **103**-7; **104**-6; **105**-6; **106**-6; **107**-7; 109-10; 110-11; 111-11; 112-12; 114-2; **232**-4; 233-6; 236-8; 239-2; 241-2; **247**-9; 272-4; 277-8; 290-9; 326-2; **350**-1; 351-1
– –, main sensory nucleus of 221-2; 231-2; 328-1
– –, mesencephalic nucleus of 229-1; 231-1; 326-10
– –, – tract 328-1; 329-1
– –, motor nucleus of 229-10; 230-2; 328-1
– –, – root **110**-11; **112**-1; 247-2; 290-9; 350-1
– –, sensory root 110-11; 290-9
– –, spinal tract 328-5; 329-5; 333-2; 334-3; 335-3, 9; 336-9; **337**-9; 338-10; 339-9; **340**-2; 341-3; 342-2
– –, – –, nucleus of 229-4; **231**-5; 330-10; **331**-2, 9; 332-2; 333-2; 334-8; 335-1; 336-2; 337-9; **338**-3, 11; 339-10; **340**-2, 10; 341-2; 342-2
– –, trigeminal ganglion (semilunar) **103**-5; 104-6; **110**-10; **111**-11; 114-3; 247-3; 328-5; 350-1; 351-1; 457-12
*Trigonum collaterale* 263; **265**-8; 267-8; 268-10;
– *fibrosum* 20-3, 9
– *habenulae* 261-2; 274-1; **276**-11
– *lemnisci* 290-1
– *lumbale* 53-5, 8; 148-12
– *nervi hypoglossi* 289-8
– – *vagi* 289-7; 331-12
– *olfactorium* 255-1; 272-11; 273-5; 305
*Trochlea musculus obliqui superioris* 106-12; 396-12; 401-1
**Trochlear** nerve **103**-7, 9; **104**-6; **105**-6, 8; 230-2; **232**-2; 238-10; 242-7; **247**-3; 272-4; **276**-3; 289-1; 290-1; 327-1, 12; 350-12; 351-12
– –, nucleus of 229-11; 230-1; 302; 325-2; 327-1
*Truncus brachiocephalicus* (art.) 3-12; **7**-11; 17-11; 18-1; 34-12; 35-1; 36-1; **38**-5; 46-7; 55-12; 56-12; **57**-11; **58**-6; 116-5; 167-1; 352-2
– *bronchomediastinalis* (lymph) 169-8
– *celiacus* 55-5; **120**-1; **121**-12; 125-1; 126-12; 170-2; 355-2
– *cisterna chyli* (lymph) 125-2; 162-5
– *corporis callosi* **248**-2; 251-12; 257-1; **258**-1; 265-1, 6; 274-12; 279-1; 283-2
– *costocervicalis* 38-9; 55-11
– *fasciculi atrioventricularis* 20-7; 32-1
– *intestinalis* (lymphatic) 125-2; 162-6; 170-10
– *jugularis* (lymphatic) 162-11, 12; 169-10
– *lumbalis* (lymphatic) 125-3, 9; 162-6; 170-9
– *lumbosacralis* (nerve) 119-9; 126-3; 132-12; 348-7; **355**-4
– *lymphaticus* 162-11
– *nervus trigeminus* 112-12
– *plexus brachialis* 58-3
– *pulmonalis* 5-3; 17-2; 18-10; 19-1; 20-12; **21**-1; 22-12; **25**-12; 34-9; 36-2
– *subclavius* (lymphatic) 162-11, 12; 169-8
– *sympathicus* (nerve) 44-12; 55-10; 58-10; **115**-3, 5; 116-3; 125-3, 10; 126-2; 127-1; **184**-8; **348**-10; 350 5; 351-5; 352-12; **354**-4, 9; **355**-9
– *thyreocervicalis* 7-12; 38-4; 43-8; **44**-9; 58-9; **60**-12; 116-4, 8
– *vagalis* 352-4; 353-3; 354-3, 8

**TRUNK** **47–53**

**Trunk**, sympathetic cervical ganglion, inferior 115-6; **352**-11; 354-11
–, – – –, middle **44**-9; 115-5; **352**-1, 12; 354-12
–, – – –, superior **44**-11; 109-8; 110-8; **115**-2; 301 a; 350-2, 3; 351-2, 3
***Tuba*** or ***Tubae***
*Tuba auditiva* 110-9; 112-6; 350-2; 438-4; **439**-9; 440-9; 441-10; 442-8; 443-4; 444-2; 446-8; **456**-2; **457**-3
– – *cartilago* 109-9; 439-11; 456-1
– – *lamina lateralis cartilaginous* 455-2; 457-2
– – – *membranace* 457-5
– – *ostium pharyngeum* 107-9; 116-12
– – – *tympanicum* 428-2; 429-2; 438-4; **439**-9; **441**-10; 442-8; 443-4; **444**-2; 451-8
– – *semicanalis* 427-4; 445-3; 446-4
– – tunica mucosa 439-9; 446-5
– uterina 129-8, 10; 131-3, 9
**Tuber** cinereum **223**-9; **247**-2; 255-9; 272-12; 273-7; 274-9; 343
– vermis 228; 274-4; **291**-6; 292-5
**Tuberal** nuclei 223-7; 224-6, 7; 226-4
**Tubercle** of cuneate nucleus 289-5; 290-5 338-1
– of nucleus gracilis 289-5; 290-5; 338-1
*Tuberculum anterius thalami* 261-10; 271-1; 276-1
– *auriculae* 459-10
– *corniculatum* 116-9
– *intercondylare mediale et laterale* 137-9
– *intervenosum* 26-11
– supratragicum 459-3
**Tuberomammillary** nucleus 226-2
*Tuberositas tibiae* 137-8; 175-1
*Tunica conjunctiva bulbi* **356**-1, 10; 386-5; **388**-8; 392-9; 397-9; 398-8
– *conjunctiva palpebrae* 363-8; **388**-7; 390-1; **392**-8
– *mucosa linguae* 117-1
– – *oris* 46-12; 102-4; 108-3; 110-3, 4
– – *septi nasi* 107-8
**Tympanic** air cells 427-5; 428-4
**Tympanic** artery 101-8; **102**-9; 110-9; 115-12; **232**-2
– cavity 112-6, 8; 413-1; **438**-8; **439**-12; **443**-10; **444**-8; **445**-4; 449-3, 9
– –, labyrinthine wall 427-6; 447-4
– membrane 438-4; 439-9; 440-7; 441-6; 442-6; 443-7; **448**-12; 449-7; **452**; **454**
– –, fibrocartilaginous ring 441-7; 442-7; 449-6; 450-8; **451**-6; **454**-6
– –, pars flaccida 451-1; 454-11
– –, pars tensa 451-8; 454-4
– –, recess of 440-6, 9; 441-4, 10; 449-9
– membrane, umbo of 438-4; 440-8; 449-8; **454**-3
– nerve 92-10; 93-12; **112**-8; 350-2; 351-2; **443**-5; **444**-6; 445-4; 447-2
– plexus 112; 351-2; **444**-6; **445**-5
– ring 454-7
– spine 450-2, 11; 451-2, 10
– sulcus 428-5; 449-7

## U

**Ulnar** artery 7-10; **75**-7, 11; **76**-1, 7; **77**-7; **78**-6; 82-5; 87-6; 88-5; 90-7, 8
– –, deep palmar branch 7-9; 87-5; 88-3, 5
– –, dorsal carpal branch 86-2; 87-5; 88-3, 5
– collateral artery, inferior **71**-7; 72-7; 73-5; 74-4; 75-11; 77-11; 78-12; 81-1
– – –, superior **71**-7, 8; 72-8; 75-12; 77-12; **78**-11
– – veins 71-7
– nerve 37-7; **61**-4; 71-7, 11; 72-9; 73-5; 74-5; 75-7, 12; 76-7; 77-7, 12; **78**-7, 9; 80-1; 81-1; 82-5; 90-7; 169-3
– –, deep branch 87-5; 88-4, 11; 90-8
– –, dorsal branch 68-7; 75-6; **76**-7
– –, dorsal cutaneous branch 70-5; 75-7; 77-7; 80-5; 81-5; **83**-1

**Ulnar** nerve, hypothenar muscle branch 90-8
– –, palmar cutaneous branch 90-9, 11
– –, superficial branch 87-4; 88-4
– recurrent artery 74-5; 76-9; 77-10; 78-7; 80-1
**Umbilical** artery 3–6, 11; 5-1; **127**; **128**-11; **129**-11; 132-10
– cord 3-7
– fold, lateral 127-4; 128-10
– –, medial 127-5; 128-10
– –, median 127-5;
– ligament, lateral 50-4; 127-6
– –, median 171-7; 124-7; 125-7
– plica, medial 128-10
– ring 3-7; 5-1
– vein 3-7; 5-11; 124-8
**Umbo** of tympanic membrane 438-4; 440-8; 449-8; 454-3
**Uncinate** fasciculus 297
*Uncus gyri hippocampalis* 305
– – *parahippocampalis* 209; 210; **247**-10; **251**-7; **255**-2; 257-5; 261-10; 266-1; 268-2; 269-3
*Unguis* 477-481
**Ureter** **125**-3, 9; 126-6; 127-2, 3, 10; **128**-11; **129**-2, 11; 170-3; 171-5, 11
**Urethral** orifice, external 134-5
**Urinary** bladder 125-7; 126-6; **127**-4; 128-11; **129**-9; 171-7
– –, venous plexus 128-8
**Urogenital** diaphragm 128-5; 129-6; 134-8
**Uterine** artery 5-9; **129**-1, 4, 8; 131-3, 9, 10; 171-3
– tube 129-8, 10
– –, ampulla of 125-8
– –, infundibulum of 129-10; 131-3, 9
– –, isthmus of 125-7; 171-6
– vein 5-9; 129-4; 171-3
– venous plexus 129
**Uterus** 129-11; 171-6
–, body of 131-2
–, cervix of 131-3
–, fundus of 125-7; 131-12
**Uterus**, round ligament of 50-5; 125-7; 129-7, 10; 131-3; 171-9
**Utricular** nerve 412-11; 413-4
**Utriculoampullary** nerve 412-8; 439-6
**Utriculus** 409-1; 412-11; 413-7
**Uvula** muscle 116-1
–, of soft palate 107-9; 108-7; 109-9
–, of vermis 228; 274-5; 292-7; 293-6; 294-7

## V

**Vagina** 129-5; 131-4
– *bulbi* 402-3; 403-11; 406-1, 12; **407**-5
– *externa nervi optici* **106**-1; **356**-7; **362**-1; **368**-6; 384-1; 402-2; 404-5; 405-9; **406**-2
– *fibrosae digitorum manus* 87-2
– *interna nervi optici* 362-2
– *musculus recti abdominis* 50-3; 54-7; 127-6
– *synovialis communis mm. flexorum* 90-7, 8, 10
– – *digitalis pedis* 106-5
– – *tendinis* 89-10
– – *tendinum digitorum* 89-5; 90-1
– *tendinis m. flexoris pollicis longi* 90-3
**Vaginal** artery 129-4; 131-4; 171-3
– venous plexus 129-5
**Vagus** nerve 36-2, 11; 42-7; 43-9; **44**-10, 12; 46-3, 5, 8; 55-11, 12; 57-1, 11; 60-11; 91; 93-5; 102-7; 112-8, 114-4; 115-5, 7, 11; **116**-2, 10; 125-12; 166-1, 3, 5, 7, 9, 11; 181-12; **232**-7; 241-3; 247-7; 272-5; **350**-4; **351**-4; **352**-2, 12; **353**-12; **354**-1, 10, 11
– –, auricular branch 93-7, 11; 95-7; 98-9; 99-9; 100-9; 101-9; **102**-10; **115**-10; 116-11
– –, bronchial branch 55-1; 352-3, 4; 353-2; 354-1, 10
– –, cardiac branch 44-10; 57-1; 115-7, 8; 116-4; 350-4; 351-5; 352-1
– –, dorsal motor nucleus 229-8; 230-5; 332-1; 336-1, 10; 337-12; 338-2

**Vagus** nerve, dorsal esophageal branch 55-2; 353-1
– –, – cord 184-4
– –, – plexus 353-3; 354-3
– –, – trunks 134-4; 352-4; 353-3; 354-3, 8
– –, ganglion, inferior (nodose) 110-9; 115-2, 10; 116-11; 350-3; 351-3
– –, –, superior 110-9; 115-11; 336-4
– –, pharyngeal branch 115-10
– –, rootlets 332-3, 9; 337-9
– –, tracheal branch 352-3
– –, trigone 289-7; 331-12
**Vallate** papilla 108-6; 116-2; 117-12
**Vallecula** cerebelli 293-5, 7
*Vallecula epiglottica* 117-2
*Vallum unguis* 478-9; 479-2, 6; 480-6; 481-8
*Valva or Valvae*
*Valva aorta* 20-1; 33-C
– *atrioventricularis* 20-C; 32-C; 33-3
– *tricuspidalis* **25**-3, 4, 7; 26-5, 6, 8; 27-9; 28-3; 29-8, 12
– *trunci pulmonalis* 20-10; 25-1, 10
*Valvula sinus coronarii* 20-6; **26**-9; 28-9
– *venae cavae inferioris* 26-9
– *venosa* 6
**Vas** deferens - - - - see **Ductus deferens**
**Vasa** - - - - see **Arteria** and **Vena**
*Vasa centralis retinae* 106-1; 356-6; 359-7; 362-8; 368-6
– *conjunctivalia* 359-1
– *lymphatica mammaria* 168-8
– – *renis* 125-2
– – *superficialis femoris* 173-6
– *macularia* 360-1, 8
– *retinae* 359-8; 368-8; 373-2; 375-C
**Vastus** muscle, lateral 142-8; 144-8; 146-4
– –, medial 142-7; 143-7
**Vein** of round ligaments of liver 124-10
**Veins** - - - - see **Vena, Venae**
–, **venous plexus** - - - - see **Plexus of veins**
*Velum medullare inferior* 293-10; 294-10; **295**-8; 334-11
*Velum medullare superior* 248-7; **274**-2; **276**-8; 289-1, 10; 293-10, 11; 294-10, 11; 295-8, 10, 11; 296-1; 329-1; 334-11
***Vena*** *or* ***Venae***
*Vena angularis* 95-2
– *appendicis vermiformis [appendicularis]* 4-7; 124-8
– *auricularis posterior* 39-1; **40**-1; 46-10; 51-11; 52-1
– *axillaris* 43-7; **44**-3; 45-5; 59-1; 60-1, 4; 166-2; 168-12
– *azygos* 3-1; 18-2; 35-1; **55**-2, 7, 11; **56**-2, 9, 11; 124-12; 167-2; 184-6; 353-12
– *basalis* 205
– *basilica* **65**-2; 67-6, 7; 68-10, 11; 70-5; 71-9; 83-1; 168-5
– *basivertebrales* 186-8
– *brachialis* 59-2; 61-4; 71-11
– *brachiocephalica* 18-1, 12; 34-10; 36-11, 12; **42**-7; **43**-7; **44**-8; **46**-6, 7; 56-11, 12; 57-9, 11; 58-7; 60-11; 116-5, 7; 162-12
– *bulbi vestibuli* 134-4
**Vena cava**, foramen (diaphragm) 353-4
– –, inferior 1-9; 3-4; 4-8; 5-3; 18-5; 22-2; 26-9, 11; 35-6; 36-8; 56-6; 120-12; 121-11; **124**-10, 11; **125**-11; **126**-11; **127**-10; 167-5; 170-9, 11; 184-6; 353-4
– –, superior 3-1; 5-3; 17-10; 18-2; 19-11; 21-11; 22-2; 26-12; 34-10; 35-1; 36-10; **46**-6; 56-11; **57**-9; 58-7; 116-5; 162-11; 167-1; **352**-3
– *cephalica* **41**-6; **42**-6; **43**-6; **44**-3, 7; **45**-5, 7; **46**-5; 50-1, 10; 60-1; 65-11; 67-3; 68-1, 5; 69-8; 70-7, 12; 71-4, 12; 83-7, 11; 168-1, 5
– *cerebri* 232-8; 233-1, 5; **234**-1, 7, 10; 235-10; 237-2; 240-7; **245**; **246**
– –, *interna* 205; 242-2; 265-9
– –, *magna* (Galen) 197-3; **232**-7; 233-2; 242-2; 246; **262**-5; **265**-7

**Vena** *cerebri, superior* 197-1, 10, 11; 233-1; **234**-1, 7, 10, 12; 235-10; 237-2; 240-7
– *cervicalis profunda* 52-4; 58-9
– – *superficicialis* 40-6; 45-9; **46**-9; 50-8, 11; 51-9; 169-10
– *chorioidea* 265-9
– *circumflexa humeri* 53-2; 59-1; 69-1; 71-1
– – *ilium profunda* 125-8; 126-5; 128-10
– – – *superficialis* 50-4, 8; 138-10
– – *scapulae* 53-3; 59-4
– *colica* 4-3, 8; 122-1, 9, 11; 123-2, 11; 124-3, 8, 9
– *collateralia ulnaris* 71-7
– *cordis anterior* 19-9; 34-8
– – *magna* 17-3; 18-9; 19-3; 20-9; 25-3
– – *media* 18-7; 20-6; 35-6
– – *minimae* 19-8; 28-10
– – *parva* 20-5; 35-6
– *coronaria ventriculi* 124-10
– *costoaxillaris* 59-12; 60-5
– *cremasterica* 130-2
– *cystica* 4-10; 120-12; 124-10
– *digitales dorsales pedis* 155-6
– *diploica* 196-5, 6, 8; 197-12
– *dorsalis penis* 128-8; 130-7, 12
– *epigastrica inferior* **50**-5; **54**-5, 6; 122-7; 123-7; 124-4, 8; 125-8; 126-5; **127**-7; 128-10; 171-9
– – *superficialis* 50-8; 138-11; 173-1
– – *superior* 50-2; 54-3; 138-11
– *epiploica* 120-4
– *episcleralia* 359-6
– *esophageae* 124-1; 184-4
– *facialis* 40-10; 41-9, 11; 42-11; 45-1, 2, 10, 11; 46-1, 2, 10, 11; **95**-4, 5, 6; 98-6; 99-6; 100-5, 6
– – *profunda* 99-4; 100-2
– *femoralis* 127-8; **138**-12; 142-1; 143-2; 144-2, 3, 12; 170-7; 173-3
– *frontoparietalis interna* 205
– *gastrica* 4-9; 120-4; 124-2, 10
– *gastroepiploica* 4-9; 120-3, 4; 121-1, 10, 11; 124-2, 9
– *genus* 141-12

**Vena** *glutea* 148-10, 11
– *hemiazygos* **55**-2; **56**-2, 4; 124-12; 184-3
– – *accessoria* 56-2
– *hemorrhoidalis* - - - - see *Vena rectalis*
– *hepaticae* 3-9; 124-11; 125-11; 170-11; 184-6
– *ileae* 4-4; 124-4
– *ileocolica* 4-8; 124-8
– *iliaca communis* 126-2; **128**-12; 129-11; 132-10; 170-3
– *iliaca externa* 124-7; 126-5; **128**-11; 129-10; 142-12; 171-9
– – *interna* 124-7; 126-5; 128-1; **129**-1
– *intercapitulares* 83-3
– *intercostalis* 50-2; 54-1; 55-10; 56-2, 8; 184-9; 186-9; 353-7
– *jejunalis* 4-4; 122-3; 123-9; 124-4
– *jugularis anterior* 40-9; 42-5; **45**-3, 12; 169-9
– – *externa* 39-9; 40-4, 9; 41-7; 42-5; 43-4; 44-7; **45**-2, 3, 9, 10; 46-10; 51-2; 56-1; 95-7; 100-9; 169-9
– – *interna* 41-3; 43-4; 44-7, 12; **45**-3, 9; **46**-3; 56-1; 57-11; 115-4; 162-12; 164-7; 165-7; 350-2
– –, *inferior bulbu* 42-7; **46**-3; 115-5; 116-4
– –, *superior bulbus* 115-10; 116-1; 448-8
– *lacrimalis* 232-11*s*; 350-10
– *laryngea superior* 116-2
– *lienalis* 4-2; 121-2; 123-1; 124-1
– *ligamentum teretis hepatis* 124-10
– *lingualis* 45-3, 9; 118-1, 2
– *lumbalia* 125-3; 126-1, 6
– – *ascendens* 55-6; 56-6; 125-2; 126-1; 127-1
– *mediana antebrachii* 67-5; 68-10
– – *cubiti* 65; 67-5; 68-11
– *meningea media* 233-11
– *mesenterica inferior* 4-3; **123**-3; **124**-3, 9; 127-2
– – *superior* 4-3; 121-9; **122**-12; 123-12
– *musculophrenica* 54-2
– *nasofrontalis* 232-12
– *obliqua atrii sinistri* (vein of Marshall) 18-4

**Vena** *obturatoria* 128-11; 171-9
– *occipitalis* 39-3; 40-3; 41-3; 51-1, 11; 52-1; 53-12; 95-9
– *ophthalmica superior* 232-10
– *ovarica* 124-1; 125-3, 9; 129-7, 11; 171-11
– *pancreaticoduodenales* 4-8; 124-9
– *paraumbilicalis* 50-8; 124-8
– *pericardiacophrenica* 36-2; 57-9; 166-2; 184-7
– *pharyngea* 115-12
– *phrenica* 124-1; 125-1, 10; 170-10
– *poplitea* 141-1; 145-5; 146-7; 147-7; **149**-3; 150-1; 151-1; 174-2
– *portae* 3-6; 4-10; 5-2; 120-9; 121-9; 124-10
– *posterior ventriculi sinistri* 18-8
– *prepylorica* 4-9; 120-9; 124-10
– *profunda brachii* 53-2
– – *femoris* 144-2
– – *linguae* 118-2
– *pudenda externa* 50-7; 130-2; 138-2
– – *interna* 124-5; 128-5; 129-5; 133-10; **134**-1, 4, 10; 147-11; 148-7
– *pulmonalis* 3-1, 10; **18**-3, 9; 22-1, 10; 34-3, 9, 10; **35**-3, 9; **36**-3, 9; 166-2, 3, 9; 167-9; 352-6; 353-2
– *rectalis* 123-6; 124-5; 128-2, 4, 5; 129-1, 2, 4, 5; 171-2, 4
– *renalis* 4-2; 124-1; 125-2; 126-11
– *retromandibularis* 40-11; 41-9; 42-11; 43-1; 45-11; 46-11; **95**-6; 98-7; 99-6; 100-7, 8
– *sacralis media* 126-6; 171-2
– *saphena accessoria* 174-1
– – *magna* 50-7; **138**-2, 5; **139**-1, 6; 140-7; 141-11; 142-1; 144-12; 155-1, 12; 170-5, 7; 173-5; 174-7, 11
– – *parva* 140-6; 141-1, 6, 8; 146-6; 147-7; 149-3; 150-1; 155-9; 174-1, 6
– *septi pellucidi* 265-1
– *sigmoideae* 4-4; 123-4; 124-5; 127-3
– *subclavia* 42-4; **46**-5, 7; 56-1; 57-11; 116-5, 8; 162-1, 11
**Vena** *subcostalia* 55-7; 56-7
– *sublingualis* 46-1; 118-1
– *submentalis* 42-11; 45-1, 11; 99-5; 100-6
– *subscapularis* 59-1
– *suprarenalis* 125-2
– *supratrochlearis* 95-2
– *surales* 150-1, 11
– *temporalis interna* 205
– – *media* 99-1; 100-11, 12
– – *superficialis* 95-12; 100-9
– *terminalis* - - - - see *Vena fronto-parietalis interna*
– *testicularis* 124-1; 126-7, 11; 127-8, 9; 128-1
– *thalamostriata* 219-2; 245; 246; 262-1; 265-3; 271-2; 283-2; 288-2
– *thoracica interna* 18-1; **34**-10; 36-11; 40-7; 45-6; 46-5, 7; 50-2; 54-1; **58**-8; **60**-10; 166-11
– – *lateralis* 40-7; 44-6; 45-6; 50-11; **59**-12; **60**-4; 168-12; 169-5
– *thoracoacromialis* 42-6; 43-6; 45-5; 69-12
– *thoracodorsalia* 59-4; 60-4
– *thoracoepigastrica* 44-6; 50-10; 59-1, 7; **60**-6; 168-6
– *thymica* 36-12; 46-6
– *thyreoidea ima* 36-12; 44-8; 45-6; **46**-6; 56-12; 166-11
– – *inferior* 44-8; 46-3
– – *superior* 42-9; 44-10; 45-3; 46-2, 9
– *tibialis* 150-11; 175-8
– *transversa colli* 40-6; **45**-9; 46-9; 51-9
– *umbilicalis* 3-7; 5-11; 124-8
– *uterina* 5-9; 129-4; 171-3
– *vertebralis* 18-1; 44-7; 52-2; 58-9
– *vesicalis* 127-3; 128-1, 11; 129-6
– *vorticosa* 232-11; 358-3, 9; 359-4; 369-9
– *vesicoumbilicalis* 124-7, 8
**VENOGRAMS 245–246**
**Venous** angle 46-7
– network (foot) 141-5; 155-7
– – (of hand) 83-2, 7
– plexus, basilar 235-8
– –, internal carotid 456-9; 457-9

**Venous** plexus, internal pudendal 134-4
– –, – vertebral 184-2; 186-3, 8
– –, pterygoid 100-11
– –, pampiniform 130-9
– –, rectal 124-5
– –, suboccipital 52-2
– –, thyroid 46-3
– –, urinary bladder 128-8
– –, vaginal 129-5
– sinus - - - - see **Sinus**

## VENOUS SINUS of DURA

**233–235; 237; 238**

– valves 6
**Ventral** root (spinal nerve) 184-1; 198-1
**Ventricle,** left (heart) 3-10; **17**-4; 18-8; 21-5; 22-8; **27**; 31-7, 10; 34-5
–, right (heart) **17**-8; 18-6; 21-8; 22-5; **25**-1, 7; 26-7; **27**; 31-2, 5; 34-7; 35-7
– (of brain) 218-220; 263-264
**VENTRICULOGRAM 263; 264**
*Ventriculus* 120-9; 354-5
– *cordis dexter* **17**-8; 18-6; 21-8; 22-5; **25**-1, 7; 26-7; **27**; 31-2, 5; 34-7; 35-7
– – *sinister* 3-10; **17**-4; 18-8; 21-5; 22-8; **27**; 31-7, 10; 34-5
– *lateralis* **218**; 219; 224; **262**; 263; 264; 269
– –, *cornu anterius* **218**-10; 259-11; **260**-1; 261-1; 262-1; **263**; 265-11; 277-11; 278-1; 280-11; 281-11; 285-10; 286-11; 287-10
– –, – *inferior* **218**-4; 220-12; 259-7; **260**-3; **261**-2; 262-3, 8; **263**; 265-8; 266-11; 267-12; 269-6; 272-2; 279-8; 284-3; 287-8; 288-5
*Ventriculi lateralis, cornu posterius* 259-6; **260**-5; **261**-3, 7; 262-7; **263**; 265-9; 266-7; 267-7; 278-4; 280-3; 323-3
– –, *pars centralis* **218**-12; 219-2; 235-2; 259-10; **260**-2; 262-2; 265-9; 279-11; 283-2
*Ventriculi lateralis, plexus chorioideus* **219**-10; 235-2; 259-8; **260**-1, 8; **262**-3; **265**-3; 272-2; 278-4; 280-8; **283**-9; **284**-1; 288-6, 11
– *quartus* **218**-5; **248**-7; 263-4; **274**-2; 295-10; 320; 328-12; 329-1; 330-12; 333-12; 334-1; 336-12
– – *apertura lateralis* (Luschka) 199-8; 276-5
– – – *mediana* (Magendi) 197-5; 199-8; 218-5; **276**-6
– – *plexus chorioideus* 197-5; 223-8; 235-8; 241-5; 247-7; 274-6; **276**-5; **279**-6; 295-2; 334-1, 8; 336-12
– – *striae medullares* 289-8; 290-4
– – *tegmen* 276-7; 293-11
– – tela chorioidea 197-1; 248-7; 336-12
– – tenia 289-5, 8; 337-11
– terminalis 198-2
– tertius **218**-12; 219-3; 235-8; **261**-2; 263-12; 264-2; **271**-11; **274**-1; **276**-11; **278**-1, 7; 279-10; **280**-8; **283**-9; 286-7; 287-6; 288-7; 289-11; 320
– – ependyma 283-3
– – plexus chorioideus 197-1; **219**-11; 223-1; 235-9; **274**-1; **283**-9; 288-10
– – *tela chorioidea* **219**-11; 242-8; 248-1; 262-7; 265-3; **283**-9
**Ventromedial nucleus** 226-11; 229-11
*Venulae maculares* 360-12
*Venula retinae* 356-2; 360-2, 3, 5, 6
**Vermiform** appendix 122-6
**Vermis** (cerebelli) 247-6; 248-8, 9; 260-6; 261-6; 271-7; 274-3, 5; 281-6; **292**-11; **293**-5; 296-6; 333-12
–, cortex 334-12; 335-12
–, folium 228; 274-4; 291-7; 292-5
–, medullary substance 248-8; 274-5
–, tuber 228; 274-4; **291**-6; 292-5
–, uvula 228; 274-5; 292-7; 293-6; **294**-7
*Vertebra cervicalis* 58-12
**Vertebral** arch 181-2, 4, 5; 184-10; 354-4
– artery 7-1; **38**-2; 43-8; 44-9; 52-1, 9, 10; 53-11; **58**-1, 9; 60-12;

199-5, 7; 200-4; 232-7; 239-7; **241**-7; 242-6
**Vertebral** artery, meningeal branches 232-6
– column 352-7
– plexus 348-1
– vein 18-1; 44-7; 52-2; 58-9
– venous plexus, internal 184-2; 186-3, 8
*Vesica fellea* 3-4; 120-11
– *urinaria* 125-7; 126-6; 127-4; 128-11; 129-9; 171-1
**Vesical** artery **127**-3, 8; **128**-1, 4, 9, 11; **129**-6; 131-4, 8; 132-6; 171-8
– vein 127-3; 128-1, 11; 129-6
**Vesicoumbilical** vein 124-7, 8
*Vesicula seminalis* 127-4; 128-5
**Vesicular** appendix 131-9
**VESSELS** - - - - see **ARTERIES, VEINS, VASA** and **LYMPHATICS**
**Vestibular** aqueduct 417-1; 419-1; 426-12; 439-6
– cecum 409-5; 413-1
– ganglion, cells of 335-4
– membrane (vestibular wall, cochlear duct) 410-10
– nerve, root fibers 331-11; 332-10
– nucleus, inferior 229-4
– –, lateral **229**-4; **331**-2, 10; 335-2
– –, medial **229**-2; **331**-1; 332-11; 333-9; 334-3; 335-2
– –, superior **229**-3; **330**-11; 335-2, 9
**Vestibule** 414-5; **415**-2; 419-7; 420-6; 426-8
–, perilymphatic space 409-7
**Vestibulocochlear** nerve 110-10; 114-4; **232**-4; 241-3; **247**-8; 272-4; **290**-8; 335-4, 8; 411-7; **439**-8
– –, cochlear portion 410-5; 411-6; 412-9; 413-8; 439-8; 448-9
– –, vestibular portion 412-8; 413-8; 439-7
**Vestibulospinal** tract 335-7
**Virchow's** Node 169-9
**Visceral** pericardium 25-11
**Visual** cortex 303
– fields 301
– pathways 301a, b
**Volar** arch - - - - see **Palmar** arch
**Vorticose** vein 232-11; 358-3, 9; 359-4; 369-9

## Z

*Zona reticulata* 225-9
**Zonular** ciliaris 368-1; 372-2; 376-2; 383-5
– fibers 356-11 C; 377-1; 383-4
**Zygomatic** arch 101-11; 102-12
– bone 100-1; 101-1; 102-2; 391-7; 397-5; 403-8; 408-7
– muscle 95-3; 4; 98-4; 99-4
– nerve 92-2; **95**-2; 98-1, 3; 99-1, 2; 106-4; 112-2; 113-5; 350-9; 351-10
**Zygomaticolacrimal** communication 113-2, 6; 350-10
**Zygomaticoorbital** artery 94-10; 95-1; 98-2; 99-8; 101-10
– foramen 113-7

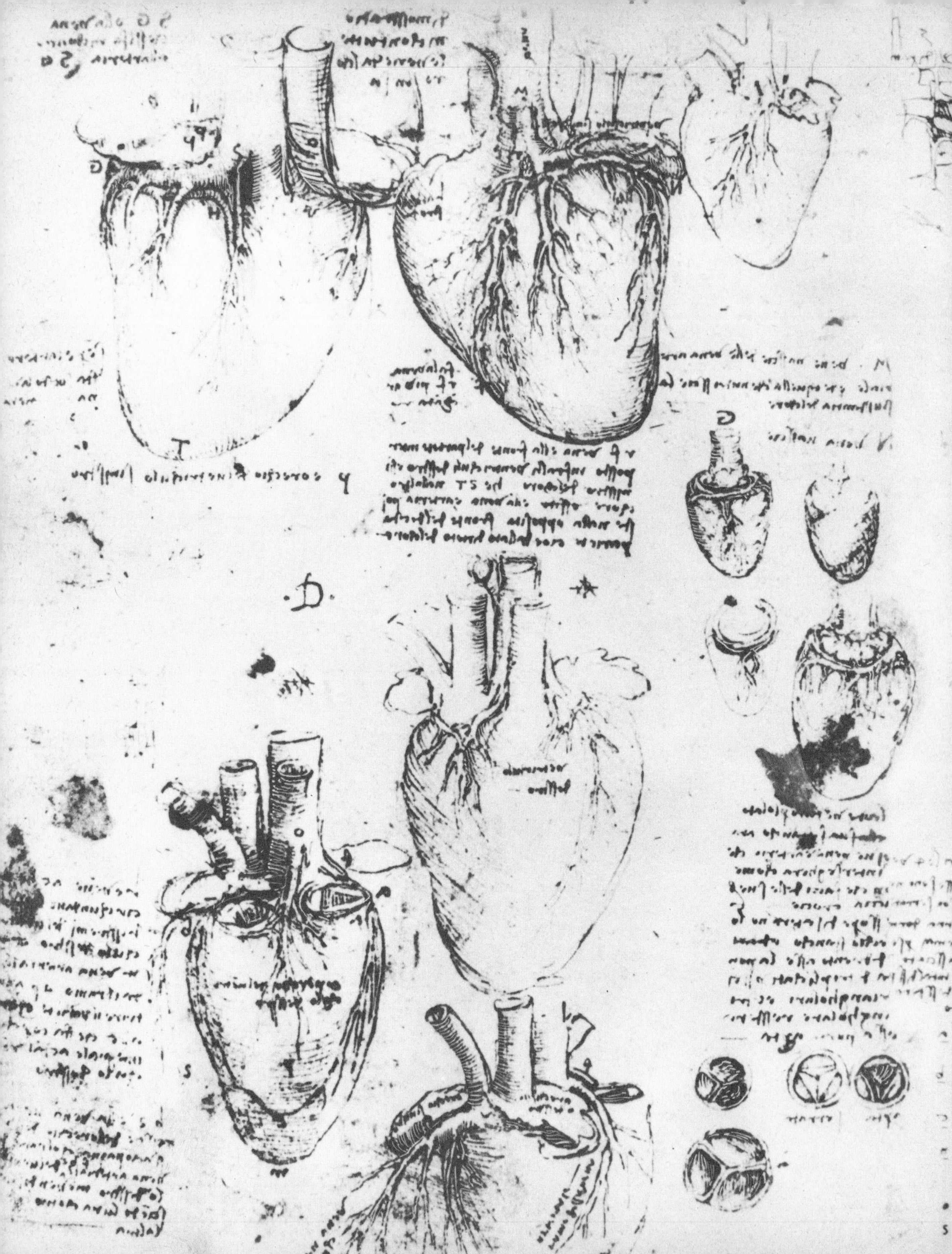